Marshall's Marine Sourcebook

Also by Roger Marshall

Designed to Cruise
Yacht Design Details
A Sailor's Guide to Production Sailboats
Designed to Win
Race to Win

Marshall's Marine Sourcebook

Roger Marshall

St. Martin's Press
New York

Library of Congress Cataloging-in-Publication Data

Marshall, Roger.

Marshall's marine sourcebook: where to find absolutely everything nautical / Roger Marshall.
    p.   cm.
ISBN 0-312-09871-5 (pbk.)
1. Sailboats--United States--Purchasing. 2. Motorboats--United States--Purchasing. 3. Ship chandlers--United States. I. Title. II. Title: Marine sourcebook.
VM321.M29 1994
623.8'223--dc20   93-21623
                                                                              CIP

First Edition: June 1994

10 9 8 7 6 5 4 3 2 1

Contents

Introduction

How many times have you been to a boat show or to a marina store, wanting to purchase a piece of equipment for your boat, only to find yourself unsure? How do you know if you are seeing the best of what is on the market? How do you know what works well and what does not? How do you decide what is best for your particular boat?

This book helps you answer these questions. Each section is devoted to a particular kind of marine product. The first part of a section tells you what to look for when selecting that product. The second part gives you the names, addresses, and phone and fax numbers of suppliers. If you read part one of a section first, you'll know what questions to ask when you talk with the supplier. Remember when calling or meeting a supplier to mention that you saw their company's name in *Marshall's Marine Sourcebook*. This helps encourage suppliers to keep us abreast of changes in their products, so that we can inform you.

If you are a supplier of gear or services and I left you out, I'm sorry. I checked magazines, boat show directories, and numerous other sources to make up these lists. But a particular entry would be included only if I could verify that the company was still in business and the product was still available. I am sure that in the process some companies and products were missed. If you drop me a note with your brochure or catalog, I will make sure your company is included in the newsletter, *Marshall's Monthly Review*, in subsequent editions of *Marshall's Marine Sourcebook*, and in *Marshall's Marine Sourcebook, Electronic Edition*.

Marshall's Monthly Review is a monthly newsletter with the latest information on new products, independent testing of new products, new faces, new addresses, and new developments in the marine industry. It is distributed in an electronic edition, for Windows, MacIntosh, Unix, and PowerPC computers, and in a print edition, in water-resistant, looseleaf format with a handy reference binder for storage, printed on on DuPont Tyvek sheets for marine durability.

Marshall's Marine Sourcebook, Electronic Edition contains this entire book, plus manufacturers' catalogs, marine reference charts and tables, and multimedia presentations, in a CDROM format.

The electronic edition of *Marshall's Marine Sourcebook,* and *Marshall's Monthly Review* both use the latest in computer technology, to enable you:

- to read, annotate, and mark the monthly newsletters;
- to print out part or all of a newsletter;
- to search through one, several, or all editions for a name, product, subject, source, or word and to review the results of searches on screen or on print-

ed reports;

- to automatically scan each issue for items of special concern;
- to build personalized research files on areas of your own personal interests or needs;
- to access manufacturers' catalogs and to order literature or equipment by fax or electronic mail; and
- to see and hear multimedia reports and demonstrations.

Computer network users may arrange electronic distribution of *Marshall's Monthly Review* and may order *Marshall's Marine Sourcebook, Electronic Edition* using their Prodigy, Compuserve, America On-Line, Internet, Bitnet, GEnie, MCI Mail, Delphi, or SprintNet connections. For general information, contact the editor by electronic mail at *news@marshall.org*. For subscriptions by email, contact *subs@marshall.org*. For further information about this book, the sources and products in it, or electronic access to *Marshall's Monthly Review*, email *news@marshall.org* or write to:

Roger Marshall
Marshall Organization
44 Fort Wetherill Road
Jamestown, R.I. 02835.

Acknowledgments

I used to keep file cabinets full of catalogs with products I might specify when designing a boat, but I found that most were out of date when I needed them. So I tossed the catalogs, giving my garbage collector a hernia, and I kept manufacturers names and addresses in a computer file. This file is the basis for this book.

I also asked many professionals in the boating industry for their files. They responded wonderfully. For instance, when I called Dean Clarke for help with the fishing gear section, he responded with a long list of fishing gear makers, plus an excellent introduction to the fishing gear section. So not only does this book contain a great introduction to fishing equipment, it also has what is probably the most complete listing of fishing gear manufacturers ever put together. Thanks Dean.

Other experts have also been free with their time. Tom Whidden (president of North Sails) and Dick Rath (vice president of IM/Lewmar) took considerable time out of their busy schedules to help provide the best information possible. David Sipperly, an expert diver and top-notch diving instructor, gave me information about one of the fastest growing sports. Louis Siegel, vice president of sales and marketing at Marine Development Corporation, wrote the introduction to the section on marine air conditioning. In addition, I had help from the following people: Steve Hollister,

computer expert and developer of the Nautilus naval architecture software, designer Chuck Neville, boat-builder Steve White, Scott Alexander, Stephanie Bernardo-Johns, Jonathon Young, Will Keene, the irrepressible Jeff Foster, Missy Johnson, and Steven Justus. To all of them I owe an great debt of gratitude, and, in the case of Jeff Foster, lunch.

And there were others. When I had questions as to whether a company was still in business, Bill Larson of Exmar could often tell me immediately. Joe Smullin of Soundown looked over my insulation story and commented on it. Ron Barr of the Armchair Sailor bookstore and Oscar, at Robert Hale, helped put together the list of major book sellers. John and Lisa Merrifield of Merrifield-Roberts, Inc. sent their current suppliers list. Jim Mattingly of Shipyard Supply, loaned me a huge pile of current catalogs and offered advice on many facets of this book. Jeff McDonough, harried editor of our local newspaper, helped considerably with design and layout of the pages. Mike DiLorenzo, Ben Dodge, and Robin Herbison at Brown University, formatted the book using a state of the art computer language known as SGML. My wife Mary edited the introductions and proofed the addresses. To all of them I offer sincere thanks.

Roger Marshall
Jamestown, RI

Air Conditioning Systems

By Louis Siegel

Louis Siegel is the vice president of Sales/ Marketing at Marine Development Corporation. He is a long-time sailor and has cruised extensively.

This introduction provides a practical, easy-to-understand guide to help you select an air conditioning system for your boat. Remember, though, that all boats are different, as are personal tastes and needs, so you should consult with a qualified boat air conditioning dealer to specify the right system for you. Also, be aware that federal law prohibits the intentional venting of refrigerant gas into the environment. This means that anyone installing or servicing a boat air conditioner must have special equipment to recover the refrigerant gas for recycling.

An often-asked question is why a boat air conditioning system is more expensive than a household system. One reason is that the marine market is smaller, and a smaller volume of production is less efficient and more costly. But there is another, more significant factor. The engineering and construction of a marine air conditioning system are very different from those of a household system. Water flow, air flow, noise levels, the corrosive effects of salt water, and boat movement must all be considered. After all, heeling and pounding are not the usual concerns regarding a household air conditioner (except maybe in parts of California!). The marine air conditioner, then, must operate in conditions that are decidedly more hostile than those to which a house air conditioning system is exposed.

THE BASICS ABOUT BOAT AIR CONDITIONERS

A direct-expansion, seawater-cooled air conditioning system removes heat and moisture from the cabin. The heat is absorbed by refrigerant gas that flows through sealed tubes, and it is then transferred to seawater, which is pumped through the system and discharged overboard. When the refrigerant flow is reversed, the opposite occurs. Heat is extracted from the seawater and is used to warm the air flowing into the living area.

There are two basic types of marine air conditioning systems: the self-contained type and the remote condensing unit. In a self-contained system, all of the major air conditioning components are mounted on a single chassis, which is installed inside the cabin. In a remote condensing unit system, the compressor, condenser, and other mechanical components are installed in the engine room, and the cooling/heating unit (consisting of the evaporator and fan) is mounted in the compartment, with copper refrigerant lines running to the engine room. Self-contained air conditioners are normally the easiest to retrofit on an existing boat, so we will focus primarily on them here. Much of this discussion, however, applies equally to both types of systems.

MAJOR COMPONENTS

The self-contained air conditioning system includes several different subsystems: the self-contained air conditioning unit, the seawater cooling system, the air distribution system, the electrical wiring system, and the control/switch assembly.

The Self-Contained Air Conditioning Unit

The air conditioning unit is normally installed in an out-of-the-way location in the living area — under a settee or V-berth, or in a closet or hanging locker. It is never mounted in an engine compartment, where it could circulate poisonous or noxious gases through the system into the living area. Cabin air is pulled into the self-contained unit through a return-air grill, and discharge air is carried through flexible or built-in ducts to one or more discharge grills, normally located on a bulkhead high in the compartment. The refrigerant loop is precharged and sealed at the factory, and no additional charging is needed during installation under normal conditions. A typical self-contained air conditioning unit is shown in Figure 1.

Figure 1: A self-contained air conditioner manufactured by Marine Development Corporation.

The Seawater Cooling System

The seawater cooling system consists of a thru-hull fitting, water shut-off valve or seacock, strainer, seawater pump, water hose, and overboard discharge fitting. If more than one system is using a single seawater pump, a water manifold and pump relay are also needed.

The thru-hull intake fitting may be either a scoop or non-scoop type. The choice depends mostly on how fast the boat goes through the water. A displacement hull can usually use a non-scoop type, but on planing hulls, where the air conditioner may be running while the boat is operating at high speed, you need a scoop-type thru-hull to avoid the venturi effect of water rushing over the opening. Note that the scoop should face toward the bow, forcing water into the system. In any case, the thru-hull should be as close to the keel as possible, and clear of other obstructions that could affect water flow.

Two types of seawater pumps may be used with a boat air conditioning system. Normally, we recommend use of a magnetically-driven centrifugal pump for quiet, efficient operation. Centrifugal pumps are not self-priming and must be mounted below the water line. For shallow-draft boats, on which it is impractical to mount the pump below the water line, a self-priming pump must be used.

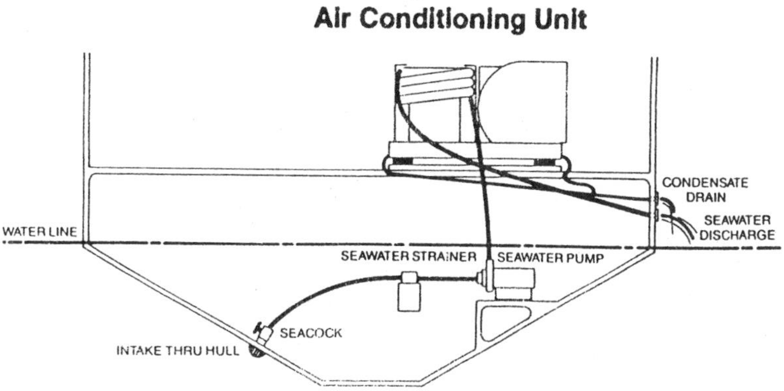

A seawater strainer must be placed in the seawater line between the seacock and the pump. Seawater lines should be at least single-braided neoprene. Any good-quality automotive-type heater hose works well. Non-reinforced plastic hoses should never be used.

Whenever you are using a centrifugal-type seawater pump, it is vitally important that the seawater plumbing system be self-draining to avoid air-locks. This means that seawater must be routed continuously uphill from the inlet thru-hull to a single high point, which is normally the condensing unit outlet.

A typical seawater plumbing system is shown in Figure 2. The overboard discharge fitting should be about three inches above the water line, in a location that you can easily see from on deck. You should always check for a brisk water flow from the overboard discharge every time you turn on the air conditioning system.

Air Conditioning Unit

Figure 2: A typical plumbing installation. Note that the seawater is piped continuously "uphill" from the pump through the system without loops or dips which could cause an airlock.

The Air Distribution System

Good air flow is a primary consideration in a marine air conditioning system. Improper air flow means that the system is operating at a lower efficiency, robbing you of cooling and dehumidifying power. A combination of plenums and built-in or flexible ducts are used to carry air from the blower on the unit to one or more discharge grills. If a wooden channel or built-in duct is used to carry discharge air, it should be insulated to avoid condensation. A return-air grill is situated near the air conditioning unit, permitting the cabin air to be drawn into the unit for cooling or heating. A lint screen or air filter is placed in the return air path, or it is mounted directly on the unit in front of the evaporator coils. Figure 3 on page 4 shows a typical installation beneath a settee. Note the use of a plenum to direct discharge air to different grills.

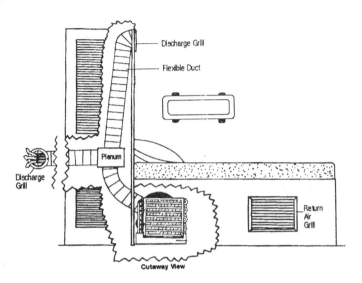

Air conditioning system are usually controlled from a switch cr panel mounted on a bulkhead. The control unit may be manual with rotary knobs or it may be an advanced digital control unit with microprocessor. The latter types have a wide array of programmable features allowing you to fine-tune settings to your tastes. A typical modern computer control panel is shown in Table 1 on page 5.

Figure 3: A typical installation. Note the use of a plenum to split the airflow for discharge in two different places. Note also that the return air grill does not have to be in front of the air conditioning unit, as long as there is an unobstructed flow of air across the coils.

The Electrical Wiring System

Most boat air conditioning systems operate on 115V or 230V, 60 Hz, single-phase alternating current (AC). A 230V, 60 Hz or 115V, 60 Hz system can sometimes be operated at 200V or 100V (respectively) in a 50 Hz environment. In such environments, rated capacity must be decreased by 17%. A transformer should be used in these applications to maintain the lower voltage in areas where voltage fluctuations may exceed operating ranges specified by the compressor manufacturer. Full-rated capacity in a 230V, 50 Hz environment can be attained by specifying a 220V/240V, 50 Hz unit. It is always a good idea to ask the manufacturer to provide you with performance data for units in your specific operating ranges.

CHECKLIST OF QUESTIONS

Having looked at the major parts of a marine air conditioning systems, we conclude with a list of questions to ask when selecting an air conditioner.

How much air conditioning capacity do I need?
To answer this question, divide your boat into three categories: (1) below-deck cabins where the hull slopes inward toward the keel and there are minimal port lights and hatches, (2) mid-deck areas situated partly below and partly above the deck, and (3) above-deck compartments. Measure the area of each compartment in square feet. If one end of the compartment is narrower

Table1. Use the worksheet below to list the components you will need for your boat. Then take a copy of the worksheet to your dealer to make final equipment selections.

SYSTEM #1   SYSTEM #2

Air Conditioning Unit Air Conditioning Unit
Capacity _____ BTU Capacity _____ BTU

Return Air Grill   Return Air Grill
Min. Area ____ Sq In Min. Area ____ Sq In

Discharge Air Grills   Discharge Air Grills
1. _____ Sq In   1. _____ Sq In
2. _____ Sq In   2. _____ Sq In
3. _____ Sq In   3. _____ Sq In

Insulated Duct   Insulated Duct
Diameter _____ in Diameter _____ in
Length _____ ft Length _____ ft

Seawater Pump
Capacity _____ GPM
(Should be sufficient for both air conditioning units)

System Electrical Requirements
Voltage _____ VAC
Frequency _____ Hz
Wiring _____ gauge
Breakers _____ amps

Note that this chart assumes that your boat has average headroom of about 6-1/2 feet, that you have an average amount of furniture, and that you and sail in temperate climates. If any of these assumptions do not apply to you, consult with your dealer to determine the optimum capacity.

Table 2. Determining the Right Capacity

Capacity (BTU/hr)	Below-Deck Cabins (sq.ft.)	Mid-Deck Cabins (sq.ft.)	Above-Deck Cabins (sq.ft.)
7,000	117	78	58
10,000	167	111	83
12,000	200	150	100
16,000	267	178	133

than the other, take your measurement in the middle for an average. Once you have measured all of the living spaces, use the table in Table 2 to determine the total capacity needed for your boat.

How many units do I need?
It depends on the layout of your boat. If you have an aft stateroom, it may be desirable to put a separate unit there, and a larger unit in the salon and forward areas. Remember that you can use a plenum to split the air flow from a single unit and route it to two different locations. Check with your dealer for specific guidance.

Where should I locate the units?

Self-contained units are designed for built-in installation low in a hanging locker, under a settee or V-berth, or any other convenient location, with discharge air ducted to one or more discharge grills located as high as possible in the compartment. You should survey the boat for possible locations and take careful measurements to make sure the unit will fit there, using the dimensions found on the product specification sheet. The air conditioning unit must be mounted in a space large enough to provide clearance on all sides for air circulation. Some units have a detachable electrical box, which can be remotely mounted to save space if there is not sufficient clearance. It is not necessary that the coil be placed directly behind the return-air grill, but an unobstructed path must be provided for the air to get to the coil.

What seawater components do I need?

It is normally recommended that you use one pump of adequate capacity for all of the air conditioning units on board. If more than one unit is run from the same pump, you also need a pump relay. Your dealer can give you more guidance in this area. Use the table in Table 3 to determine the proper size pump for your system.

Table 4. Recommended Wiring and Breaker Sizes

Capacity (BTU/hr)	Voltage (VAC)	Wire Size	Breaker Size (amps)
7,000	115	#14	15
	230	#14	10
10,000	115	#12	15
	230	#14	15
12,000	115	#12	20
	230	#14	15
16,000	115	#10	30
	230	#12	20

Table 3. Component Specification Guidelines

Capacity (BTU/hr)	Min. Pump Capacity (GPH)	Duct Size (in)	Return Grill (sq.in.)	Discharge Grill (sq.in.)
7,000	250	5	80	50
10,000	250	6	100	60
12,000	500	6	120	70
16,000	500	7	140	80

What ducts and grills should I use?

There is a wide selection of grill sizes and shapes, as well as materials. Check with your dealer to select grills that match your boat's interior. The table in Table 3 gives recommended grill areas and duct sizes.

What are the electrical requirements?
Table 4 on page 6 provides recommended circuit breaker sizes and electrical wiring for your system. Remember that you must allow for an amperage surge that occurs when the compressor cycles on.

How much noise will the system make?
All units make some noise and self-contained units will be heard the most since they are located in the living and sleeping areas. But in most cases, the noise level is not objectionable. Tens of thousands of self-contained boat air conditioning systems are sold every year, and most people find them acceptably quiet. You can obtain additional sound deadening, however, by using insulating foam and baffles in the compartments where the air conditioning units are mounted.

Manufacturers of Air Conditioning Systems

American Air Co.
10537 Steel Trace Ct.
Charlotte, NC 28278
Tel: (704) 357-9987
Fax: (704) 588-9877
Sea Breeze systems from 9,000 BTU to 60,000 BTU

Aqua Air Mfg.
Mfg. Division of James D. Nall Co., Inc.
1050 E. 9th St.
Hialeah, FL 33010
Tel: (305) 884-8363
Fax: (305) 883-8549
Aqua Air marine air conditioning systems

Eastern Industrial Machine Mfg., Inc.
3361 S.E. Slater St.
Stuart, FL 34997
Tel: (407) 288-4291
Fax: (407) 288-6808
Over 97 models in stock from 4,000 BTU to 500 tons

Glacier Bay, Inc.
4053 Harlan St. #113
Emeryville, CA 94608
Tel: (510) 654-9333
Fax: (510) 658-3996
Refrigeration and air conditioning in one system

Lunaire Marine
P.O. Box 3246
4 Quality St.
Williamsport, PA 17701
Tel: (800) 772-6777
 or (717) 326-1747
Fax: (717) 326-7304
Lunaire systems

King Marine Air of Florida
8420 Ulmerton Rd.
Largo, FL 34641
Tel: (813) 532-0048
Fax: (813) 531-7130
Manufacturers of King-Air air conditioning systems

Marine Development Corp.
P.O. Box 15299
Richmond, VA 23227-0699
Tel: (804) 746-1313
Fax: (804) 746-7248
Manufacturers of Cruisair air conditioning systems

Figure 4: The SMX computer based control system by Marine Development Corp. can be retrofitted to replace the traditional three knob switch assembly.

Marine Air Systems
2000 N. Andrews Ave. Ext.
Pompano Beach, FL 33069
Tel: (305) 973-2477
Fax: (305) 979-4414
Grunert systems

Marine Products, Inc.
1822 Erle Rd.
Mechanicsville, VA 23111
Tel: (804) 783-8000
Fax: (804) 746-7248
Zephyr and Carry-on portables

Mermaid Mfg. Co.
1171 N. Tamiami Trail
Fort Myers, FL 33903
Tel: (800) 330-3553
  or (813) 656-3553
Fax: (813) 656-4297
*Low price units for owner
installation*

Ocean Options, Inc.
50 Fort St.
Fairhaven, MA 02719
Tel: (508) 922-3644
Fax: (508) 999-5338
Air conditioning systems

Rich Beers Marine, Inc.
P.O. Box 14034
210 S.W. 7th Ave.
Ft. Lauderdale, FL 33302
Tel: (305) 764-6192
Fax: (305) 764-7259
*Technicold air conditioning
systems*

Sea Frost
C.F. Horton & Co, Inc.
Rt. 4
Barrington, NH 03825
Tel: (800) 435-6708
  or (603) 868-5720
Fax: (603) 868-1040
*Sea Frost air conditioning and
refrigeration systems*

Westerbeke Corp.
Avon Industrial Pk.
Box 181
Avon, MA 02322
Tel: (508) 588-7700
Fax: (508) 559-9323
Rotary Aire systems

Alternative Power Systems

On most boats, power is generated by either running an alternator off the main engine or using a separate generator. Both of these systems use fuel and create noise and heat in addition to power. Solar cells, while they are not yet powerful enough to run the entire boat, are gradually becoming more commonplace. For instance, Hunter Marine installs a solar cell as a stock item on some of its boats. If you are thinking of installing solar cells or a wind generator, you should first check the type and size of your battery. It makes no sense to generate power and have no place to store it. If you have to invest in new batteries, get the deep-cycle type and make sure they are as large as you can fit in the space allotted.

If you are interested in installing solar cells, here are a few tips. Solar cells should be located where they are not likely to be walked on or have winch handles dropped on them. That usually means the cabin top or transom. Other possible spots are on the afterdeck, if space is available, or on top of hatches. Don't expect a tremendous amount of power from solar cells either. Usually they will generate only enough power to keep the battery topped up. For instance, a high efficiency module measuring 37 x 13 inches will generate about 780 milliamps at 14 volts at peak power. That's enough to charge the battery, but not enough to run a motor or even an average computer.

Wind generators, on the other hand, generate a large amount of power. Some will cut in at 7 1/2 knots and produce up to 500 watts when the wind is blowing at 30 knots. However, a unit of this size will have fairly large blades which will need to be shielded from the crew. The disavantage of wind generators is the whirling blades, which need to be high and which reduce stability, the blade noise, and the inconsistent power output (it varies with the wind strength).

A quieter and safer way to generate power is to use a propeller that drives backwards, turning a generator or alternator inside the boat. In the first BOC round-the-world race, Philippe Poupon had a large, propeller-powered generator that looked like an outboard motor. When he needed power, he lowered the unit into the water. While it gave him plenty of power, it also cost him over a knot in boatspeed. This is a drawback if speed is important to you. Another drawback is potential damage to or loss of the unit. Some units with towed spinners attached by long towlines have been eaten by fish! If you can work around these problems, though, you can easily generate plenty of power while underway.

Manufacturers of Alternative Power Systems

Atlantic Orient
P.O. Box 1097
Norwich, VT 05055
Tel: (802) 649-5446
Fax: (802) 649-5404
Rutland wind generators

Balmar Products, Inc.
902 N.W. Ballard Way
Seattle, WA 98107
Tel: (206) 789-4970
Fax: (206) 784-0878
Balmar wind generators

Bugger Products, Inc.
P.O. Box 259
Key Largo, FL 33037
Tel: (305) 451-4495
Fax: (305) 451-1971
Wind Bugger wind generators

Cruising Equipment Co.
6315 Seaview Ave. N.W.
Seattle, WA 98107
Tel: (206) 782-8100
Solar cells

Everfair Enterprises, Inc.
2520 N.W. 16th Ln. #5
Pompano Beach, FL 33064
Fourwinds wind generators

Hoxan America
One Centennial Plaza
Piscataway, NJ 08854
Tel: (908) 980-0707
Solar cells

Hamilton Ferris II Co.
P.O. Box 126
Ashland, MA 01721
Tel: (508) 881-4602
Fax: (508) 881-3846
Water, wind, solar generators

Heart Interface
811 - 1st Ave. S.
Kent, WA 98032
Tel: (206) 859-0640
Fax: (206) 859-3579
Inverters

Kyocera
8611 Balboa Ave.
San Diego, CA 92123
Tel: (619) 576-2647
Solar cells

Jack Rabbit Marine, Inc.
425 Fairfield Ave.
Stamford, CT 06902
Tel: (203) 961-8133
Fax: (203) 358-9250
*Wind generators, solar cells,
inverters*

JSI
P.O. Box 20926
St. Petersburg, FL 33742
Tel: (800) 234-3220
Uni-Solar battery charger

Offshore Marine Systems
836 Ritchie Highway, No. 19C
Severna Park, MD 21146
Tel: (800) 826-3336
 or (301) 544-4311
Solar electric generators

Real Goods
966 Mazzoni St.
Ukiah, CA 95482-3471
Tel: (800) 762-7325
*Solar panels, solar cookers,
and solar lights*

Remote Technologies
5 Veesom St., Suite 201
Marblehead, MA 01945

Tel: (800) 531-4044
*Solarex, uni-solar panels,
Fourwinds wind generators*

Siemens Solar Industries
4650 Adohr Ln.
P.O. Box 6032
Camarillo, CA 93011
Tel: (800) 272-6765
 or (805) 462-6800
Fax: (805) 388-6395
Solar cells

Solec International
12533 Chadron Ave.
Hawthorne, CA 90250
Tel: (310) 970-0065
Solar cells

Solemate Solar Products
11648 Manor Rd.
Glenarm, MD 21057
*Arctec solar control and
monitoring instruments*

Solarex Corp.
630 Solarex Ct.
Frederick, MD 21701
Tel: (301) 698-4200
Solar cells

SunWatt Corp.
RFD Box 751
Addison, ME 04606
Tel: (207) 497-2204
Solar cells

United Solar Systems
1100 W. Maple Ave.
Troy, MI 48084
Tel: (800) 843-3892
 or (313) 362-4170
Fax: (313) 362-4442
Solar battery chargers

Anchors and Anchor-Handling Gear

What do you look for in the perfect anchor? Before you answer, let me tell you that this is a trick question. There isn't a perfect anchor unless you define the type of boat using the anchor, the holding ground, the amount of rode and chain, and the length of time you are going to be at anchor. For instance, if you are going to anchor in coral, you do not want to use a plow anchor with a nylon rode. Instead, you probably want to set a fisherman anchor with chain to ensure that the coral does not chafe the anchor line.

The type of boat affects the size of the anchor. A boat with a lot of top hamper will have a lot of windage, so the anchor for this boat needs to be larger than for a low-profile, high-performance boat. Similarly, a sailboat with a tall mast, bimini top, and dodger will probably require a slightly larger anchor than a yacht with a short rig and no awnings or dodger. Length of stay also affects anchor size. For a short stay a light anchor can be used, but if the boat is to be left unattended for any length of time, the largest and heaviest anchor is called for.

The holding ground plays a very important part in the anchoring scenario. As a general rule, in mud or sand, anchors that dig in are the best. Plow anchors, Danforths, CQR and the Bruce anchor are all dig-in types. A fisherman anchor can also dig-in, but the palms on each fluke are usually so small that the anchor will not stay in

a sandy or muddy bottom very long. This anchor is better used on a rocky or coral bottom where it can snag a crevice and stay put.

After selecting an anchor, you will also need anchor line, some chain, or an anchor line weight. Plus, if you anchor in an area where the anchor is likely to foul you might want a buoy line and a buoy to help get the hook off the bottom. The amount of rode and chain that you pay out is affected by many things. They are:

- *The depth of water.* A good rule is to pay out five to seven times the depth of water.
- *The proximity of dangers.* Obviously, if a jetty or pier is nearby, you will not want to pay out as much line as you would if you were in unobstructed waters.
- *The rise and fall of tide.* You should pay out less anchor cable if the rise and fall of tide are relatively small, as they are in Florida, and more if they are larger, as in Maine.
- *The weather.* In a strong wind you should pay out more scope than if the weather is calm.
- *The boat's windage.* A boat with high windage necessitates more scope.
- *The direction of the tidal stream.* Although you should always proceed up stream when anchoring, you should note any hazards in the opposite direction and

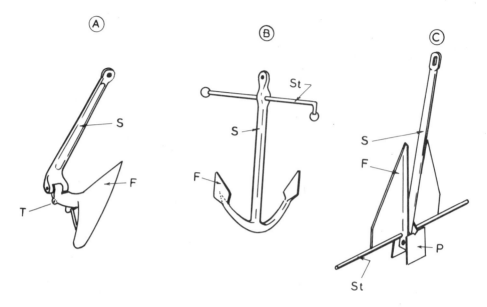

Figure 1: The parts of an anchor. F is the fluke, P is the palm, S is the shank, St is the stock, and T is the tripping line attachment point.

take them into account when paying out anchor line.

- *The hardness of the bottom.* A hard bottom requires more scope than a very soft bottom in order to keep the pull of the anchor chain as near to horizontal as possible. One way to make sure the anchor pull is as near to horizontal as possible is to insert a few feet of chain between the anchor and the nylon anchor line. (An anchor line should always be nylon because of its stretchiness.) If you cannot insert chain, use an anchor weight to lower the catenary of the anchor line.
- *The type of anchorage.* You will need to pay out more scope if you are anchored in an open roadstead than if you are anchored in a small cove.

Another item that every deep-sea sailor should carry is a sea anchor or a drogue. According to *The Oxford Companion to Ships and the Sea*, a sea anchor is used to keep the vessel's bow into the wind during severe conditions. It may consist of gear, such as a pair of spinnaker poles or a hatch cover, tied to a long line. In essence, it is any item that is used to control the drift of a boat when the water is too deep to anchor. A drogue is used for a slightly different purpose. When a sailing vessel is running downwind at high speed, there is a possibility that control of the boat may be lost. The drogue is used to slow the vessel down. In shape, the drogue looks like a canvas bucket on the end of the anchor line. Quite often, long warps towed behind the boat will serve the same purpose.

Manufacturers of Anchors and Anchor-Handling Gear

Anchors

A & B Industries
1261 Anderson Dr.
Suite C
San Rafael, CA 94901
Tel: (415) 258-9300
Fax: (415) 258-9461
*ABI plow, Sea Hold
lightweight anchors, and
rollers*

Avon Seagull Marine
1851 McGaw Ave.
Irvine, CA 92714
Tel: (714) 250-0880
CQR Simpson-Lawrence

Canor Plarex
P.O. Box 33765
Seattle, WA 98133
Tel: (206) 621-9209
Fax: (206) 340-8845
Folding anchor

Creative Marine
P.O. Box 2120
Natchez, MS 39121
Tel: (800) 824-0355
The Max anchor

Crosby Co.
183 Pratt St.
Buffalo, NY 14240
Tel: (716) 852-3522
Fax: (716) 852-3526
Signature anchors

Down Under Marine
P.O. Box 3216
Clearwater, FL 34630-8216
Tel: (813) 585-0023
Fax: (813) 584-3112
Flook Flying anchor

Hans C-Anchor, Inc.
P.O. Box 66756
St. Petersburg, FL 33736
Tel: (813) 867-4645
Fax: (813) 867-6797

**Hathaway, Reiser &
Raymond**
184 Selleck St.
Stamford, CT 06902
Tel: (203) 324-9581
Fax: (203) 348-3057
Sea anchors and drogues

Imtra
30 Barnet Blvd.
New Bedford, MA 02745
Tel: (508) 995-7000
Bruce anchor, East coast

Paul E. Luke
Box 816
E. Boothbay, ME 04544
Tel: (207) 633-4971
Fax: (207) 633-3388
Luke Yachtsman anchor

Mooring, Inc.
Box 60204
Houston, TX 77205
Tel: (713) 443-8229
Bruce Anchor, West coast

Nav-X Corp.
1386 West McNab Rd.
Ft. Lauderdale, FL 33309
Tel: (800) 825-NAVX
 or (305) 978-9988
Fax: (305) 974-5378
Fortress, Guardian anchors

Old Ark, Inc.
Lukkaniementie 1E30
00200 Helsinki
FINLAND
Tel: (+358) 0-670044
Arkarolina anchor

Para-Tech Engineering Co.
10770 Rockville "B"
Santee, CA 92071
Tel: (619) 448-1189
Fax: (619) 448-3059
Sea anchor

Rule Industries
70 Blanchard Rd.
Burlington, MA 01803
Tel: (617) 272-7400
Fax: (617) 272-0920
Danforth anchors

Shewmon, Inc.
1000 Harbor Lake Dr.
Safety Harbor, FL 34695
Tel: (813) 447-0091
Sea anchor

**Simpson Lawrence USA,
Inc.**
3004 29th Ave. E.
Bradenton, FL 34208
Tel: (813) 746-7161
Fax: (813) 746-7166
Delta anchors

Spartan Marine
Robinhood Marine Center
Robinhood, Maine 04530
Tel: (207) 371-2542
Fax: (207) 371-2024
Plowmaster anchors

Viscom International, Inc.
507 Hopmeadow St.
Simsbury, CT 06070
Tel: (203) 658-2201
Fax: (203) 651-8406
FOB anchors

Bow Rollers and Deck Pipes

Buck Algonquin Marine Hardware
370 N. Main St.
Smyrna, DE 19977
Tel: (302) 659-6900
Fax: (302) 659-6909
Chocks, deck pipes

Moonlite Marine
776 W. 17th St.
Costa Mesa, CA 92627
Tel: (714) 645-0130
Stern rollers

Mooring, Inc.
Box 60204
Houston, TX 77205
Tel: (713) 443-8229
Rollers

R.C. Plath
5300 S.E. Johnson Creek Blvd.
Portland, OR 97222
Tel: (503) 777-2441
Fax: (503) 777-2450
Rollers

Tops-In-Quality
P.O. Box 148
Marysville, MI 48040
Tel: (313) 364-7150
Fax: (313) 364-7925
Rollers and bowsprit rollers

Windline Marine
4201 Redwood Ave.
Los Angeles, CA 90066
Tel: (310) 306-8558
Fax: (310) 823-8888
Rollers, brackets

Anchor Chain and Line Weights

Acco Chain & Lifting Device Co.
76 Acco Dr.
P.O. Box 792
York, PA 17405
Tel: (717) 741-4863
Fax: (717) 741-8568
Up to 1 inch proof coil galvanized chain

Ada Liesure Products
P.O. Box 284
Ada, MI 49301
Tel: (616) 676-0274
Anchor rode-rider weights

ANP, Inc.
P.O. Box 1667
Houston, TX 77251
Tel: (713) 499-6168
Fax: (713) 499-0370
Stainless steel chain

E & B Marine Supply
201 Meadow Rd.
Edison, NJ 08818
Tel: (800) 533-5007
Galvanized chain

IM/Lewmar Marine, Inc.
P.O. Box 308
New Whitfield St.
Guilford, CT 06437
Tel: (203) 458-6200
Fax: (203) 453-5669
Galvanized chain, gypsies, and hawse pipes

Jamestown Distributors
28 Narragansett Ave.
P.O. Box 348
Jamestown, RI 02835
Tel: (800) 423-0030
  or (401) 423-2520
Fax: (800) 423-0542
  or (401) 423-0542
Up to 3/4 inch galvanized chain, links, swivels, and shackles

Jamestown Distributors
Hwy 17 & 21
Gardens Corner
Rt 1 Box 375
Seabrook, SC 29940
Tel: (800) 423-0030
  or (803) 846-9500
Fax: (800) 423-0542
  or (803) 846-9005
Up to 3/4 inch galvanized chain, links, swivels, and shackles

Rule Industries
70 Blanchard Rd.
Burlington, MA 01803
Tel: (617) 272-7400
Fax: (617) 272-0920
Galvanized and vinyl-covered chain

Simpson Lawrence USA., Inc.
3004 29th Ave. East
Bradenton, FL 34208
Tel: (813) 746-7161
Fax: (813) 746-7166
BBB, and Hi-test chain

Vetus - Den Ouden, Inc.
P.O. Box 8712
Baltimore, MD 21240-0712
Tel: Orders only: (800)
GO-VETUS
  or (410) 712-0740
Fax: (410) 712-0985

Chain Stoppers

Deep 7 Co.
14260 Innerarity Pt. Rd.
Pensacola, FL 32507
Tel: (904) 492-0250
Fax: (904) 492-4484
Chain stoppers

IM/Lewmar Marine, Inc.
P.O. Box 308
New Whitfield Street
Guilford, CT 06437
Tel: (203) 458-6200
Fax: (203) 453-5669
Chain stoppers to Lloyds specs

Figure 2: Different types of anchor. A is a stockless anchor, B is a Bruce anchor, C is a mushroom anchor for permanent moorings, D is a Danforth lightweight, E a grapnel for use in rocky areas, F is a Fisherman anchor with G and H showing different styles of flukes. P is a plough or SQR anchor and N is a Stock-in-head style anchor.

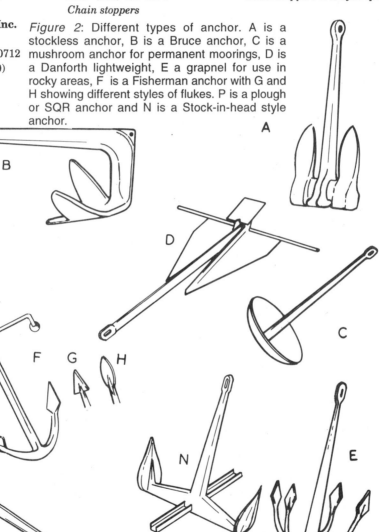

Associations and Societies

A number of associations and societies serve the marine industry. Some put out standards for boat construction. For instance, if you reside in the USA and intend to build or sell boats in England or France, it would probably be beneficial to obtain a copy of the Construction Standards for Small Craft manual put out by the International Council of Marine Industry Associations (ICOMIA). On the other hand, if you live in Europe and plan to send boats to the US, you might want to get the American Boat & Yacht Council's (ABYC) manual Safety Standards for Small Craft. While it is not mandatory to construct boats in conformity with these standards, doing so indicaties to buyers the quality of a boat. When breaking into another marketplace, it often helps to have boats built to a nationally recognized standard. Probably the most widely recognized association producing such a standard is Lloyd's Register of Shipping. Boats built to Lloyd's 100 A1 are instantly acknowledged to be quality boats. In recent years, especially in America, the American Bureau of Shipping's rules for small craft have also become accepted.

The marine industry also has associations for designers and naval architects. Professional's in this field should be members of either the Society of Naval Architects and Marine Engineers or The Royal Institution of Naval Architects. Both affliliations are recognized worldwide.

US Sailing (formerly USYRU) is the national sailing association in America and serves as the central organization for American sailing. In Britain, its counterparts are the Royal Yachting Association and The International Yacht Racing Union. While US Sailing runs olympic, offshore, and one-design class events in America, these events are spread among different agencies in Britain. For instance, offshore sailing is the province of the Royal Ocean Racing Club (RORC).

Figure 1: Membership in fishing or conservation associations can ensure that the trophy sized fish you catch are credited to you. (Photo by Dean Clarke)

Addresses of Associations and Societies

Boating Associations

**American Power Boat
Association**
17640 E. Nine Mile Rd.
East Detroit, MI 48021
Tel: (313) 773-9700
Fax: (313) 773-6490

**Electric Boat Association of
America**
P.O. Box 11197
Naples, FL 33941
Tel: (813) 774-3773

Fishing Associations

**Alaska Marine
Conservation Council**
430 W. 7th Ave. Rm. 215
Anchorage, AK 99501
Tel: (503) 223-2125

American Fisheries Society
5410 Grosvenor Ln.
Suite 110
Bethesda, MD 20814-2199
Tel: (301) 897-8616

American Littoral Society
Sandy Hook
Highlands, NJ 07732
Tel: (201) 291-0055

**American Oceans
Campaign**
535 Pennsylvania Ave. S.E.
Washington, D.C. 20003
Tel: (202) 544-3526

**Aquarium for Wildlife
Conservation**
602 Surf Ave. & W. 8th St.
Brooklyn, NY 11224
Tel: (718) 265-3400

**The Atlantic Center for the
Environment**
39 South Main St.
Ipswich, MA 01938
Tel: (508) 356-0038

**Atlantic States Marine
Fisheries Commission**
1776 Massachusetts Ave. NW
Suite 600
Washington, D.C. 20036
Tel: (202) 452-8700

**Bass Anglers Sportsman
Society (B.A.S.S.)**
P.O. Box 17900
Montgomery, AL 36117
Tel: (205) 272-9530

The Billfish Foundation
2419 E. Commercial Blvd.
Ft. Lauderdale, FL 33308
Tel: (800) 438-8247

**Center for Marine
Conservation**
1725 DeSales St. N.W. #500
Washington, D.C. 20036
Tel: (202) 429-5609

Clean Water Network
1350 New York Ave. N.W.
#300
Washington, D.C. 20005
Tel: (202) 624-9357

Coast Alliance
235 Pennsylvania Ave. S.E.
Washington, D.C. 20003
Tel: (202) 546-5609

Coastal Resources Center
926 J St.
Suite 801
Sacramento, CA 95814
Tel: (916) 444-2161

The Coastal Society
P.O. Box 2081
Gloucester, MA 01930-2081
Tel: (508) 281-9209

**Conservation Law
Foundation**
62 Summer St.
Boston, MA 02110
Tel: (617) 350-0990

Council on Ocean Law
The Decatur House
1600 H St. N.W.
Washington, D.C. 20006
Tel: (202) 347-3766

Earthtrust
25 Kaneohe Bay Dr.
Suite 205
Kailua, HI 96734
Tel: (808) 254-2866

**Environmental Defense
Fund**
5655 College Ave.
Oakland, CA 94618
Tel: (510) 658-8901

Federation Of Flyfishers
200 Yellowstone Ave.
P.O. Box 1088
West Yellowstone, MT 59758
Tel: (406) 646-9541

Fisheries Defense Fund
230 Park Ave.
New York, NY 10169
Tel: (212) 867-3730

Fish Unlimited
P.O. Box 1073
Shelter Island, NY 11965
Tel: (516) 749-2185

**Fishermen Involved in
Saving Habitat (FISH)**
P.O. Box 221
Depoe Bay, OR 97341
Tel: (503 765-2229

**Florida Conservation
Assocation**
905 East Park Ave.
Tallahassee, FL 32301
Tel: (904) 224-3474

**Florida Keys Land and Sea
Trust**
P.O. Box 536
Marathon, FL 33050
Tel: (305) 743-3900

Florida League of Anglers
P.O. Box 1109
Sanibel, FL 33957

Friends of the Earth
4512 University Way N.E.
Seattle, WA 98105
Tel: (206) 633-1661

**Future Fisherman
Foundation**
1250 Grove Ave.
Suite 300
Barrington, IL 60010
Tel: (708) 381-4061

Greenpeace
1436 U St. N.W.
Washington, D.C. 20037
Tel: (202) 319-2528

**Gulf Coast Conservation
Association**
4801 Woodway,
Suite 220-W
Houston, TX 77056
Tel: (713) 626-4222

**International Association
of Fish and Widlife
Agencies**
444 N. Capitol St. N.W.
Washington, D.C. 20001
Tel: (202) 624-7890

**International Game Fish
Association**
1301 East Atlantic Blvd.
Pompano Beach, FL 33060
Tel: (305) 941-FISH

**International
Oceanographic Foundation**
4600 Rickenbacker Causeway
Miami, FL 33149
Tel: (305) 361-4888

**IUCN Species Survival
Commission**
Shark Specialist Group
9300 S.W. 99th St.
Miami, FL 33176
Tel: (305) 274-0628

**Jersey Coast Anglers
Association**
22 Cruiser Ct.
Toms River, NJ 08753
Tel: (908) 270-9102

Sport Fishing Institute
1010 Massachusetts Ave. N.W.
Washington, D.C. 20001
Tel: (202) 898-0770

**United Anglers of
California**
5200 Huntington Ave. #300
Richmond, CA 98404
Tel: (510) 525-0367

Mote Marine Lab.
1600 Thompson Pkwy.
Sarastoa, FL 34236
Tel: (813) 388-4441

**National Academy of
Sciences**
2101 Constitution Ave.
Washington, D.C. 20418
Tel: (202) 334-2714

**National Association of
Underwater Instructors
(NAUI)**
Environmental Programs and
Projects
159 Buckingham Rd.
Tenafly, NJ 07670
Tel: (201) 569-1605

National Audubon Society
550 S. Bay Ave.
Islip, NY 11751
Tel: (516) 859-3032

**National Coalition for
Marine Conservation**
5105 Paulsen St.
Suite 243
Savannah, GA 31405
Tel: (912) 354-0441

Natural Resource Defense Counsil
40 W. 20th St.
New York, NY 10011
Tel: (212) 727-4424

New York Sportfishing Federation
401 East Shore Rd.
Lindenhurst, NY 11757

North American Fishing Club
P.O. Box 3403
Minnetonka, MN 55343
Tel: (612) 936-0555

Pacific States Marine Commission
42 82nd Dr. #100
Gladstone, OR 97627
Tel: (503) 326-7033

People for Puget Sound
1326 5th Ave.
Suite 450
Seattle, WA 98101
Tel: (206) 382-7007

Project ReefKeeper
16345 West Dixie Hwy.
Miami, FL 33160
Tel: (305) 361-4495

Safari Club International
4800 W. Gates Pass Rd.
Tucson, AZ 85745
Tel: (602) 620-7890

Sierra Club Marine Committee
5101 Westbard Ave.
Bethesda, MD 20816
Tel: (301) 229-4967

Sierra Club National Marine Committee
1414 Hilltop Dr.
Tallahassee, FL 32303
Tel: (904) 385-7862

The Sounds Conservancy
P.O. Box 266
43 Main St.
Essex, CT 06426
Tel: (203) 767-1933

South Carolina Conservation League
P.O. Box 1765
Charleston, SC 29402
Tel: (803) 723-8035

Sportfishing Promotion Council
1250 Grove Ave.
Suite 300
Barrington, IL 60010
Tel: (708) 381-9518

Sportsmen Conservationists of Texas
807 Brazos
Suite 311
Austin, TX 78701
Tel: (512) 472-2267

Trout Unlimited
800 Follin Ln. S.E.
Suite 250
Vienna, VA 22180
Tel: (703) 281-1100

World Wildlife Fund
1250 24th St. N.W.
Washington, D.C. 20037
Tel: (202) 778-96040

Industry Associations

American Boat Builders and Repairers Association, Inc.
P.O. Box 1236
Stamford, CT
Tel: (203) 967-4745
Fax: (203) 967-4618

Association des Professionels Belges du Nautisme (NAUTIBEL)
St. Hubertusiaan 38
B-2232 Schilde
BELGIUM
Tel: (+32) 3 658 8687
Fax: (+32) 3 658 0437

Allied Boating Association of Canada
5468 Dundas St. West
Suite 324
Islington, Ontario M9B 6E3
CANADA

The Danish Boating Industry Association (DANBOAT)
Borsen
DK-1217 Copenhagen K
DENMARK
Tel: (+45) 33 912 323
Fax: (+45) 33 325 216

The Finnish Boat and Motor Boat Association (FINNBOAT)
Mariankatu 26B 19
SF-00170 Helsinki 17
FINLAND
Tel: (+358) 0 135 1010
Fax: (+358) 0 135 5261

**Federation des Industries
Nautiques**
Port de la Bourdonnais
75007 Paris
FRANCE
Tel: (+33) 1 455 510 49
Fax: (+33) 1 475 394 75

**British Marine Industries
Federation**
Boating Industry House
Vale Rd. Oatlands
Weybridge, Surrey KT13 9NS
ENGLAND
Tel: (+44) 932 854511
Fax: (+44) 932 852874

**Bundeswirtschaftsvereingung
Freizeit-Schiffahrt e. V.**
Postfach 25 03 70
Agrippina-Werft (Haus
Caponiere)
D-5000 Cologne
GERMANY
Tel: (+49) 221 313079
Fax: (+49) 221 325417

**Deutscher Boots-und
Schiffbauer-Verband e.V.**
Messehaus
Jungiusstrasse
D-2000 Hamburg
GERMANY
Tel: (+49) 40 35 2817
Fax: (+49) 40 35 692180

**Greek Marine
Manufacturers Association
(SEKAPLAS)**
7 N. Kokkinou St.
Ano Patissia
111-41 Athens
GREECE
Tel: (+30) 1 292-8300
Fax: (+30) 1 292-8300

**Irish Federation of Marine
Industries (IFMI)**
Confederation House
Kildare St.
Dublin 2
IRELAND
Tel: (+353) 1 779 801
Fax: (+353) 1 777 823

**Unione Nazionale Cantieri
e Industrie
(CONSORNAUTICA)**
Piazzale Kennedy 1
16129 Genoa
ITALY
Tel: (+39) 010 589 371
Fax: (+39) 010 553 1104

**Japan Boating Industry
Association**
5-1, 2-Chome
Ginza
Chou-Ku
Tokyo
JAPAN
Tel: (+81) 3 567-6707
Fax: (+81) 3 567-0635

**Nederlandse Vereniging
Van Ondernemingen In De
Bedrijfstak Watercreatie
(HISWA)**
Jan Nieuwenhuizenplein 12
1135 WV Edam
NETHERLANDS
Tel: (+31) 2993 726 20
Fax: (+31) 2993 715 28

NORBOAT
Huitfeldts gt. 15
N-0253 Oslo
NORWAY
Tel: (+47) 2 43 04 20
Fax: (+47) 2 55 15 60

**Associacion de Industrias
Nauticas (ADIN)**
Muell de Reloj
Calle Varadero No. 5, 1, 1a
08003 Barcelona
SPAIN
Tel: (+34) 3 310 79 48
Fax: (+34) 3 315 42 59

**Batbranschens
Riksforbund (BRF)**
Ljusstoparbacken 20
S-117 45 Stockholm
SWEDEN
Tel: (+46) 8 744 02 20
Fax: (+46) 8 744 18 29

**Schweizerischer
Bootbauer-Verband**
P.O. Box 74
CH 8117 Fallanden-Zurich
SWITZERLAND
Tel: (+41) 1 8250388
Fax: (+41) 1 8252256

**Taiwan Yacht Industry
Association**
Universal Business Center
14th Floor
665 Tunhua South Rd.
Tapei
TAIWAN, ROC
Tel: (+886) 2 703 8481
Fax: (+886) 2 754 1744

**National Marine
Manufacturers Association
(NMMA)**
401 North Michigan Ave.
Chicago, IL 60611
Tel: (312) 836-04747
Fax: (312) 329-9815

National Marine
Manufacturers Association
(NMMA)
600 Third Ave.
New York, NY 10016
Tel: (212) 922-1212
Fax: (212) 922-9607

One Design Class Associations

Note: The information
contained in this section was
made available by Sailing
World Magazine.

18 Sq. Meter Assn.
1460 West 17th St.
Hastings, MN 55033
Tel: (612) 437-6852

**American Shark
Association**
4880 County Rd. 11
Rushville, NY 14544
Tel: (716) 554-6778

American Y Flyer Y.R.A.
7349 Scarborough Blvd.
Indianapolis, IN 46256
Tel: (317) 849-7588

Atlantic Class Association
255 Milbank Ave.
Greenwich, CT 06830
Tel: (203) 661-4926

B-25 Class Association
359 Sheridan St.
Corona, CA 91720
Tel: (714) 534-3369

Banshee Class Association
10 Lawrence Ave.
Annapolis, MD 21403
Tel: (301) 280-0396

BBoats
359 Sheridan St.
Corona, CA 91720
Tel: (714) 279-0781

Buccaneer A. Class Assn.
31 Old Trolley Way
Rowayton, CT 06853
Tel: (203) 853-7563

Bullseye Assn.
31 Atlantic Ave.
Rockport, MA 01966
Tel: (508) 546-6955

**Byte International Class
Assn.**
65 Allan Pt.
Dorval, Quebec H9S 2Z3
CANADA
Tel: (514) 631-8326
Fax: (514) 631-1772

**Cape Cod Frosty Class
Assn.**
P.O. Box 652
Cataumet, MA 02534
Tel: (508) 563-3073
Fax: (508) 563-3080

**Cape Cod Knockabout
Class Assn.**
265 Grange Park
Bridgewater, MA 02324
Tel: (508) 697-7880

Capri 14.2 National Assn.
10250 N 92nd #210
Scottsdale, AZ 85258
Tel: (602) 391-1991

Capri 18 Class Assn.
c/o Catalina Yachts
P.O. Box 989
Woodland Hills, CA 91367
Tel: (818) 884-7700

Capri 22 National Assn.
3337 W. Overbrook Dr.
Peoria, IL 61604
Tel: (309) 685-0780

Capri 30 National Assn.
c/o Catalina Yachts
P.O. Box 989
Woodland Hills, CA 91367
Tel: (818) 884-7700
Fax: (818) 884-3810

Catalina 22 National Assn.
P.O. Box 30368
Phoenix, AZ 85046-0368
Tel: (602) 971-4511

Catalina 25 National Assn.
5011 Revere Ave.
NW Massillon, OH 44647
Tel: (216) 837-1067

Catalina 27 National Assn.
21 Rector Ave.
Annapolis, MD 21403
Tel: (410) 268-1228

Catalina 30 National Assn.
9141 Mahalo Dr.
Huntington Beach, CA 92646
Tel: (714) 964-1615

Catalina 34 National Assn.
10970 Seville Ct.
Garden Grove, CA 92640
Tel: (714) 537-9436

Catalina 36 National Assn.
10710 Montgomery Dr.
Manassas, VA 22111
Tel: (703) 368-8429

Catalina 38 National Assn.
P.O. Box 2892
Seal Beach, CA 90740
Tel: (714) 551-4212

Comet Class Yacht Racing Assn.
4 Cedar Trail
Fayson Lakes, NJ 07405
Tel: (201) 838-7175

Coronado 15 National Assn.
5157 El Roble
Long Beach, CA 90815
Tel: (310) 498-2690

Day Sailer Assn.
1936 Danebo
Eugene, OR 97402
Tel: (503) 689-2190

DC 10 Class Assn.
Box 498
Woodshole, MA 02543

Designer's Choice Class Assn.
Box 783
Moosup, CT 06354
Tel: (800) 428-7305

Dragon Assn.
2244 Kilbirnie Dr.
Germantown, TN 38139
Tel: (901) 756-6942

El Toro International YRA
39673 Catamaran Ct.
Fremont, CA 94538
Tel: (510) 656-1276

Ensign Class Assn.
736 Scotland St.
Dunedin, FL 34698
Tel: (813) 734-1837

Enterprise Assn.
265 Willow St.
New Haven, CT 06511-2427
Tel: (203) 562-5775

Express 27 National Class Assn.
3350 Brittan Ave. #1
San Carlos, CA 94070
Tel: (415) 592-4572

Express 37 Class Assn.
21 Peninsula Rd.
Belvedere, CA 94920
Tel: (415) 435-4887

FJ U.S.
12725 Florida Ln.
Apple Valley, MN 55124
Tel: (612) 432-3628

Flying Dutchman Class Assn.
215 Redcliffe Rd.
Greenville, SC 29615
Tel: (803) 288-9071

Flying Scot Sailing Assn.
3008 Millwood Ave.
Columbia, SC 29205
Tel: (800) 445-8629

FORCE 5 Class Assn.
238 Horizon Dr.
Edison, NJ 08817
Tel: (908) 248-8563

Frers 33 National Class Assn.
130 E 77th St.
New York, NY 10021

G.P. 14 Class Assn.
1734 Green St.
Philadelphia, PA 19130

Geary 18 International Y.R.A.
P.O. Box 101
North Bend, OR 97459
Tel: (503) 756-3547

H Class Assn.
P.O. Box 1
Cataumet, MA 02534
Tel: (508) 748-0334

Hampton One-Design Assn.
3385 Kings Neck Dr.
Virginia Beach, VA 23452
Tel: (804) 463-6895

Hawkfarm One-Design Class Assn.
115 C Southampton Ln.
Santa Cruz, CA 95062-3472
Tel: (408) 429-8449

Highlander Class Assn.
1674-A S. Elm St.
W. Carrolton, OH 45449
Tel: (513) 866-7785

Hobie 33 Class Assn.
1713 N. Cliff St.
Alexandria, VA 22301
Tel: (703) 549-0271

I.O.D.World Class Assn.
c/o Sailing World
5 John Clarke Rd.
Newport, RI 02840
Tel: (401) 847-1588
Fax: (401) 848-5048

Ideal 18 Class Assn.
100 Pattonwood Dr.
Rochester, NY 14617
Tel: (716) 342-1040
Fax: (716) 266-4722

Impulse 21 Class Assn.
10610 Metric Dr.
Suite 145
Dallas, TX 75243
Tel: (214) 340-3111
Fax: (214) 340-3112

Impulse 26 Class Assn.
10610 Metric Dr.
Suite 145
Dallas, TX 75243
Tel: (214) 340-3111
Fax: (214) 340-3112

Inland Lake Yachting Assn.
P.O. Box 311
Fontana, WI 53125
Tel: (414) 275-6921

**International C Class
Catamaran Assn.**
48 Osborne Ave.
Norwalk, CT 06855

International DN Ice YRA
3497 E Erie Ave.
Lorain, OH 44052
Tel: (216) 288-2510
Fax: (216) 949-2979

**International & U.S.
Sunfish Class Assn.**
P.O. Box 128
Drayton Plains, MI
48330-0128
Tel: (313) 673-2750

**International 110 Class
Assn.**
49 Vautrinot Ave.
Hull, MA 02045
Tel: (617) 925-3432

**International 210 Class
Assn.**
38 Fearing Rd.
Hingham, MA 02043
Tel: (617) 749-3259

**International 30 Class
Assn.**
2262 Bay St.
San Francisco, CA 94123
Tel: (415) 929-1223

International 470 Assn.
158 Colburn Rd.
Westwood, MA 02090
Tel: (617) 329-4499

**International 5.5 Metre
Assn.**
1600 S. Bayfront
Balboa Island, CA 92662
Tel: (714) 640-8510

**International 505 Class
Y.R.A.**
64 Indian Trail
Westbrook, CT 06498
Tel: (203) 669-8000

**International Abbott 33
Class Assn.**
4232 Elmway Dr.
Toledo, OH 43614
Tel: (419) 382-6118
Fax: (419) 473-3765

**International Blue Jay
Class Assn.**
937 S. Lagoon Ln.
Mantoloking, NJ 08738
Tel: (908) 295-0238
Fax: (908) 561-5004

**International Contender
Assn.**
P.O. Box 831
Summerland, CA 93067
Tel: (805) 969-3527
Fax: (805) 565-1936

**International Etchells
Assn.**
HCR 33
Box 30, Rt. 102A
Bass Harbor, ME 04653
Tel: (207) 244-7203
Fax: (207) 244-9897

International H-Boat Assn.
c/o Finn Yacht U.S.A.
P.O. Box 231
Barnstable, MA 02630
Tel: (617) 775-1017

**International Laser Class
Assn.**
8466 N Lockwood Ridge Rd.
#328
Sarasota, FL 34243
Tel: (813) 359-1384

**International Lightning
Class Assn.**
808 High St.
Worthington, OH 43085
Tel: (614) 885-0475

**International MC Class
Sailboat Racing Assn.**
2059 Wyndham Hill Dr. N.E.
#101
Grand Rapids, MI 49505
Tel: (616) 364-7856

**International Mobjack
Assn.**
3431 Northridge Rd.
Richmond, VA 23235
Tel: (804) 320-4025

**International Moth Class
Assn. U.S.A.**
705 S. Shore Rd.
Palermo, NJ 08223
Tel: (609) 390-3522

**International NACRA Class
Assn.**
1810 E. Borchard St.
Santa Ana, CA 92705
Tel: (714) 835-6416
Fax: (714) 541-6643

International Naples Sabot Assn.
690 Senate St.
Costa Mesa, CA 92627-2509
Tel: (714) 645-1245

International Nonsuch Assn.
317 Bay Ave.
Huntington, NY 11743

International Penguin Dinghy Class Assn.
Rt. 3, Box 129
Cashton, WI
Tel: (608) 625-2042

International Star Class Y.R.A.
1545 Waukegan Rd.
Glenview, IL 60002
Tel: (708) 729-0630
Fax: (708) 729-0718

International Tornado Assn.
11331 Lazy Lake Dr.
Baton Rouge, LA 70818
Tel: (504) 261-1894

Interlake Sailing Class Assn.
500 Glendale Cir.
Ann Arbor, MI 48103

Isotope Class Assn. 8240
Morrow Millard Chapel Hill,
NC 27514
Tel: (919) 563-1604

J/22 Class Assn.
P.O. Box 843
Franklin, TN 37064
Tel: (615) 791-1780
Fax: (615) 791-1788

J/24 Class Assn.
612 Third St.
Suite 4A
Annapolis, MD 21403
Tel: (410) 626-0240

J/27 Class Assn.
2329 Highway #34
Manasquan, NJ 08736
Tel: (908) 528-9496
Fax: (908) 528-5123

J/29 Class Assn.
95 Penn Hill Dr.
Schnecksville, PA 18078

J/30 Class Assn.
P.O. Box 247
Riverside, NJ 08075
Tel: (609) 786-8958

J/35 Class Assn.
c/o MBA
P.O. Box 1126
Marblehead, MA 01945-5126

J/44 Class Assn.
30 Walnut St.
Newport, RI 02840
Tel: (401) 841-5356

Javelin Assn.
30 Central St.
Essex Junction, VT
05452-3137
Tel: (802) 878-3928

Jet 14 Class Assn.
26 Pontiac Dr.
Wayne, NJ 07470
Tel: (201) 839-0487

JY 15 Class Assn.
38 Bayside Ave.
Noank, CT 06340
Tel: (203) 536-6567
Fax: (203) 536-9848

Laser II Class Assn.
8466 N Lockwood Ridge Rd.
#328
Sarasota, FL 34243
Tel: (813) 359-1384

Lido 14 International Class Assn.
7435 Ashford Pl.
San Diego, CA 92111

M-20 Sailing Assn.
2881 S.E. Merritt Terr.
Port St. Lucie, FL 34952
Tel: (407) 335-7337

Mercury Class Y.R.A.
54 Lakewood Ave.
San Francisco, CA 94127
Tel: (415) 398-2300

Millimeter Y.R.A.
29 Oak Creek Ln.
San Carlos, CA 94070
Tel: (800) 755-1311

Mistral Class Assn.
7222 Parkway Dr.
Dorsey, MD 21076
Tel: (410) 643-1248

North American Redwing Dinghy Assn.
33 Nicholls St.
Lockport, NY 14094
Tel: (716) 433-7002
Fax: (716) 433-7005

North American Yngling Assn.
P.O. Box 4047
Spencer, IA 51301
Tel: (712) 337-0133

Narrasketuck One-Design
81 Jean Rd.
W. Islip, NY 11795
Tel: (516) 669-3331

**National A Scow Class
Assn.**
P.O. Box 311
Fontana, WI 53125
Tel: (414) 275-6932

**National C Scow Class
Assn.**
P.O. Box 311
Fontana, WI 53125
Tel: (414) 275-6932

**National M Scow Class
Assn.**
P.O. Box 311
Fontana, WI 53125
Tel: (414) 275-6932

National Butterfly Assn.
4503 N. Orange Blossom Trail.
Orlando, FL 32804
Tel: (407) 843-9518

**National Class E-Scow
Assn.**
122 Laurel Ave.
Toms River, NJ 08753
Tel: (908) 240-2704

**National Dolphin Senior
Class Assn.**
2253 Jamestown Ln.
Carrollton, TX 75006
Tel: (214) 406-0094

**National Interclub
Frostbite Dinghy Assn.**
286 Bunker Hill St.
Charlestown, MA 02129
Tel: (617) 639-1490

National Rebel Class Assn.
3690 Saunt Rd.
Jackson, MI
Tel: (708) 298-8936

**National Shields Class
Assn.**
87 Manepashemet St.
Marblehead, MA 01945
Tel: (617) 258-3954

National Triton Assn.
300 Spencer Ave.
E. Greenwich, RI 02818
Tel: (401) 884-1094

National X Boat Class Assn.
P.O. Box 311
Fontana, WI 53125
Tel: (414) 275-6932

**New England Beetle Cat
Assn.**
23 Stratford Rd.
Seekonk, MA 02771

New York 36 Class Assn.
655 Cahoone Rd.
Greene, RI 02827
Tel: (401) 333-1200 Ext. 2456

OK Dinghy U.S. Assn.
14555 Brownsville Hwy. N.E.
Poulsbo, WA 98370
Tel: (206) 697-2179

Olson 25 Class Assn.
6144 Wood Dr.
Oakland, CA 94611
Tel: (510) 946-1529

Olson 30 Class Assn.
196 Nathan Court
Soquel, CA 95073

Optimist Pram Assn.
9 Oscar Hills Rd.
The Landing
Tarpon Springs, FL 34689
Tel: (813) 937-0166

Pacific Cat Class Assn.
447 North Newport Blvd.
Newport Beach, CA 92663
Tel: (714) 645-4520

**Pearson 30 Chesapeake
Bay Assn.**
2 Brice Rd.
Annapolis, MD 21401
Tel: (301) 757-0655

**Penguin Class Dinghy
Assn.**
1215 West George
Chicago, IL 60657

**Phantom Class Racing
Assn.**
Box 783
Moosup, CT 06354
Tel: (800) 428-7305

Point Jude Owners Assn.
P.O. Box 547
Rye, NY 10580
Tel: (914) 967-1656

Prindle Class Assn.
10965 Rochester Ave., No.303
Los Angeles, CA 90024
Tel: (310) 473-4004

Rhodes 18 Class Assn.
Box 245
Barnstable, MA 02630
Tel: (508) 362-2296
Fax: (508) 362-2236

Rhodes 19 Class Assn.
1100 Poydras St.
Suite 2150
New Orleans, LA 70163

Rhodes 22 Assn.
25 Hawthorne Ave.
Princeton, NJ 08540

Rhodes Bantam Class Assn.
806 Hanshaw Rd.
Ithaca, NY 14850
Tel: (607) 257-7683

S2 7.9 Class Assn.
533 Avalon Terr. S.E.
Grand Rapids, MI 49503
Tel: (616) 458-1437
Fax: (616) 458-1451

San Juan 21 Class Assn.
312 Tanbark Ct.
Kernersville, NC 27284
Tel: (919) 996-2165

San Juan 24 N.A.C.A.
P.O. Box 70163
Seattle, WA 98107
Tel: (206) 624-0900
Fax: (206) 386-7500

Santan 20 Assn.
P.O. Box 1844
Newport Beach, CA 92663
Tel: (714) 631-3141

Schock 35 Class Assn.
23125 Temescal Canyon Rd.
Corona, CA 91719
Tel: (714) 277-3377

Snipe Class International Racing Assn.
4096 Chestnut Dr.
Flowery Branch, GA 30542
Tel: (404) 287-8405

Sonar Class Assn.
2 Possum Ln.
Rowayton, CT 06854
Tel: (203) 853-3888

SR 17 Class Assn.
1150 19th St. N.
St. Petersburg, FL 33713
Tel: (813) 822-7663

SR Max Class Assn.
1150 19th St. N.
St. Petersburg, FL 33713
Tel: (813) 822-7663

Starwind/Spindrift 19 Assn.
P.O. Box 21262
Columbus, OH 43221-0262
Tel: (614) 457-3152

Supercat Race Assn.
118 Hickory St.
Mahtomedi, MN 55115
Tel: (612) 426-3922
Fax: (612) 426-7935

Tanzer 16 Class Assn.
P.O. Box 26003
Raleigh, NC 27611
Tel: (919) 859-0177

Tanzer 22 Class Assn.
P.O. Box 22
Ste. Anne De Bellevu, Quebec
H9X 3L4
CANADA
Tel: (514) 457-3929

Tartan Ten Class Assn.
35 Lakecrest Ln.
Gross Pointe, MI 48236
Tel: (313) 885-6912

Thistle Class Assn.
1811 Cavell Ave.
Highland Park, IL 60035-2282
Tel: (708) 831-3304

Thunderbird Class Assn.
P.O. Box 1033
Mercer Island, WA 98040-1033
Tel: (206) 455-0429

U.S. A Div. Catamaran Assn.
320 First Ave. S.
Teirra Verde, FL 33715

U.S. Albacore Assn.
13701 Beauwick Ct.
Silver Springs, Md 20906
Tel: (301) 871-1145

U.S. International 14 Assn.
P.O. Box 30831
Seattle, WA 98103
Tel: (206) 784-9810

U.S. International 420 Class Assn.
66 Elmwood Ave.
Rye, NY 10580
Tel: (914) 967-8387

U.S. International Canoe Class Assn.
385 Leland Ave.
Palo Alto, CA 94306-1128
Tel: (415) 327-3717
Fax: (408) 942-5659

U.S. International Finn Class Assn.
6425 Bellac St.
Corpus Christi, TX 78414
Tel: (512) 993-4659

U.S. International Fireball Assn.
P.O. Box 3973
Walnut Creek, CA 94598
Tel: (415) 939-4069

U.S. International Tempest Assn.
P.O. Box 483
Newport, RI 02840
Tel: (401) 846-8393

U.S. Mariner Class Assn.
140 Redwood Dr.
East Hills, NY 11576
Tel: (516) 621-7180

U.S. Mirror Class Assn.
5305 Marian Dr.
Lyndhurst, OH 44124
Tel: (216) 461-7231

U.S. Manta Assn.
15618 E. Ave. Q7
Palmdale, CA 93591
Tel: (805) 264-4270

U.S. One-Design 14 Class Assn.
P.O. Box 176
Armonk, NY 10504
Tel: (914) 273-5240
Fax: (914) 273-5243

U.S. One-Design Class Assn.
P.O. Box 176
Armonk, NY 10504
Tel: (914) 273-5240
Fax: (914) 273-5243

U.S. Optimist Dinghy Assn.
6500 Riviera Dr.
Coral Gables, FL 33146
Tel: (305) 667-2412

U.S. Sabot National Assn.
13555 Figi Way H 1181
Marina Del Ray, CA 90292

U.S. Soling Assn.
5375 Mariner's Cove Dr.
No 114
Madison, WI 53704
Tel: (608) 241-1115

U.S. Tornado Assn.
11331 Lazy Lake Dr.
Baton Rouge, LA 70818
Tel: (504) 261-1894

U.S. Wayfarer Assn.
4765 Crescent Pt.
Waterford, MI 48327
Tel: (313) 682-0782

Udell Class Assn.
141 W. Jackson, Rm. 1325
Chicago, IL 60631
Tel: (312) 427-7422
Fax: (312) 347-1260

US1 Class Assn.
111 Lemon Ln.
Casselberry, FL 32718
Tel: (407) 331-4375

West Wight Potter Assn.
40915 Cantare Pl.
Fremont, CA 94539
Tel: (510) 656-2984

Windmill Class Assn.
417 Golf Dr.
Birmingham, AL 35226-2316
Tel: (205) 823-7023

Windsurfer Class Assn.
621 Stone Canyon Rd.
Los Angeles, CA 90077
Tel: (213) 608-1651

Wylie Wabbit Class Assn.
c/o North Coast Yachts
2100 Clement Ave.
Alameda, CA 94501
Tel: (415) 523-8330

Professional Societies

National Association of Marine Surveyors (NAMS)
P.O. Box 9306
Chesapeake, VA 22321
Tel: (800) 822-6267

The Royal Institution of Naval Architects
10 Upper Belgrave St.
London SW1X 8BQ
ENGLAND
Tel: (+44) 1 235 4622
Fax: (+44) 1 245 6959

Society of Accredited Marine Surveyors
4238 Lakeside Dr.
Jacksonville, FL 32210
Tel: (800) 344-9077

Society of Naval Architects & Marine Engineers
601 Pavonia Ave.
Jersey City, NJ 07306
Tel: (201) 798-4800
Fax: (201) 798-4975

Yacht Architects and Brokers Association, Inc.
584 Bellerive Dr.
Suite 3D
Annapolis, MD
Tel: (301) 974-4472

Safety Organizations

National Fire Protection Association
Batterymarch Park
Quincy, MA 02269
Tel: (617) 770-3000

Underwriter's Laboratories, Inc.
333 Pfingsten Rd.
Northbrook, IL 60062

Underwriter's Laboratories, Inc.
P.O. Box 13995
12 Lab Dr.
Research Triangle Pk, NC 27709
Tel: (919) 549-1565
Fax: (919) 549-1842

U.S. Coast Guard, Navigation Safety & Waterway Services
2100 Second St. S.W.
Washington, DC 20593-0001
Tel: (202) 267-0984

United States Marine Safety Association
1900 Arch St.
Philadelphia, PA 19103-1498
Tel: (215) 564-3484

Sailing Associations

International Yacht Racing Union
60 Knightsbridge
London SW1X 7JX
ENGLAND

The Royal Ocean Racing Club
20 St. James's Place
London SW1A 1NN
ENGLAND
Tel: (+44) 71 493 2248
Fax: (+44) 71 493 5252

Canadian Yachting Association
1600 James Naismith Dr.
Gloucester, Ontario K1B 5N4
CANADA
Tel: (613) 748-5687
Fax: (613) 748-5688

U.S. Sailing
Box 209
Newport, RI 02840
Tel: (401) 849-5200
Fax: (401) 849-5208

Societies Issuing Standards

American Boat & Yacht Council
405 Headquarters Dr.
Suite 3
Millersville, MD 21108
Tel: (301) 923-3932
Fax: (301) 923-3988
Publishes a handbook of standards for the marine industry

American Bureau of Shipping
2 World Trade Center
106th Floor
New York, NY 10048
Tel: (212) 368-9100

American Bureau of Shipping Marine Services
16855 Northchase Dr.
Houston, TX 77060-6008

International Council of Marine Industries Association
Meadlake Pl.
Thorpe Lea Rd.
Egham, Surrey TW20 8HE
ENGLAND
Tel: (+44) 784 473377
Fax: (+44) 784-439678

International Maritime Organization
Publications Section
4 Albert Embankment
London SE1 7SR
ENGLAND
Tel: (+44) 71-735 7611
Fax: (+44) 71-587 3210
Publishes conventions, codes, recommendations, and guidelines for the promotion of maritime safety and prevention of marine pollution

Lloyd's Register of Shipping
71 Fenchurch St.
London EC3M 4BS
ENGLAND
Tel: (+44) 1 709 9186
Fax: (+44) 1 488786

Lloyd's Register of Shipping
17 Battery Pl.
New York, NY 10004
Tel: (212) 425-8050
Fax: (212) 363-9610

Autopilots

Selecting an autopilot can be critical to your enjoyment of your boat. The wrong unit can spoil your entire sailing trip when it breaks down often or uses too much power. A client of mine once estimated that the autopilot on his boat works only 35% of the time it is needed. If this is happening to you, you should seriously consider a critical assessment of your autopilot needs.

CHECKLIST OF QUESTIONS

If you are in the market for an autopilot, there are certain key questions you should ask. They are:

What are the features of the unit you are considering buying?
For easiest steering, the autopilot should interface with Loran, GPS, electronic charts (such as those produced by KVN Technologies), and wind instruments. It should also be able to steer the boat, turn it at a given waypoint, and sound a warning if the boat is standing into danger.

What does the unit cost relative to the features you get?
Try to access whether you are getting value for your dollar.

Is the unit large enough to handle the type of sea conditions you usually encounter when you go sailing?
It is false economy to purchase a system that will steer the boat only in a flat calm.

What is the power consumption of the unit?
Picking an autopilot with a high power consumption may drain your batteries quickly. This would mean that you would have to run the engine more often or buy larger batteries. Both mean higher costs.

What service facilities are available?
Even though the autopilot you select is listed as the most reliable in the world, it can still get dowsed with seawater, or develop an electrical glitch. If you are going to sail around the world, you want an autopilot that can be serviced in almost any major port. Otherwise you will have to put your trip on hold while new parts are shipped to you.

Is the autopilot watertight?
Few are. Only autopilots with a screw-down case and rubber gaskets are truly watertight. Most others are water-resistant. Water-resistant units can operate when spray is flying, but they cannot be submerged, as would happen if a green wave came into the cockpit.

What is the force output of the autopilot?
The unit should have just enough force to turn the rudder. If there is not enough force, the unit will have to struggle to steer the boat. If there is too much force, the unit will do its job, but it will consume much more power than is really needed.

Does the steering system have the ability to get you home if the autopilot dies?
This means that the boat's primary steering system should be entirely separate from the autopilot steering system. In hydraulic systems, this is often difficult.

How is the linkage between the helm and the unit constructed?
The very best linkage is the one that connects the autopilot to the rudder stock by a short quadrant or lever arm independent of the normal steering quadrant or quadrants. Then, if the autopilot goes out of commission, the steering system can still operate. Some autopilots have a chain drive between the rudder stock and the unit. The chain should be positioned in such a way that it cannot slip off the gears at either end of the system. If slippage is possible, guards should be fitted. Another type of linkage has rubber belts between the autopilot and the helm station. With this type, it is prudent to carry a spare belt, just as you should for your engine.

What is the load on the helm when the system is not in use?
Ideally, there should be no load when the autopilot is turned off. This can be checked only by taking the boat out to sea and turning on the autopilot.

LOCATING THE CONTROL UNIT

Where you intend to fit your autopilot may dictate the style and size that you can use. For instance, if there is no room around the rudderstock to fit the black box, you may have to use a unit that attaches directly to the steering wheel, such as the Autohelm 4000. This unit is easy to attach or remove and will steer a moderate sized boat.

Hydraulic steering systems for larger vessels can easily have an autopilot incorporated into them. The Cetrek Wagner is simply connected by a hydraulic line. When the autopilot is in use, the hydraulic fluid passes through it. When not in use, the hydraulic fluid bypasses the autopilot.

The control unit should also be located where it will stay cool and dry. The usual position is in a locker near the rudder stock or in the lazarette.

THE COMPASS

The compass is another integral part of the autopilot that needs to be tip-top. Most modern autpilots use fluxgate electronic compasses that take many readings per second and average the output. If you use an integrated electronics package, the compass reading can also be displayed separately. In an integrated package, it is easy to add in compass deviation and variation so that your course is absolutely correct.

REMOTE CONTROLS

While many sailors scoff at the idea of remote controls, they do have their place. For instance, who wants to stand behind a steering wheel in heavy, driving rain? With a remote, you can stand in the cabin and steer the boat. Or if you are sportfishing, you can steer the boat and still watch the lures being trolled astern. Remote controls enable the helmsman to move around the cockpit while underway and disengage the autopilot in an emergency. Usually, the remote is connected to the autopilot by a long cable, but other systems are emerging.

Manufacturers of Autopilots

Advanced Control Applications
163 W. Cerritos Ave.
Anaheim, CA 92805
Tel: (714) 535-4101
Fax: (714) 535-0723

Alpha Marine Systems
996 Hanson Ct.
Milpitas, CA 95035
Tel: (408) 945-1155

Anschuetz of America
One Madison St.
East Rutherford, NJ 07073
Tel: (201) 779-8474
Fax: (201) 779-3336

Autohelm
A Raytheon Company
46 River Rd.
Hudson, NH 03051
Tel: (603) 881-5838
Fax: (603) 881-4756

Benmar Marine Electronics
3320 W. MacArthur Blvd.
Santa Ana, CA 92704
Tel: (714) 540-5120
Fax: (714) 641-2614

IM/Brookes & Gatehouse
7855 126th Ave. N.
Largo, FL 34643
Tel: (813) 536-1400
Fax: (813) 536-1717

Castle Navigation
1261-J N. Lakeview Ave.
Anaheim, CA 92807
Tel: (714) 961-0585

Cetrek/Wagner, Inc.
300 Oak St.
260 Corporate Park
Pembroke, MA 02359
Tel: (800) 323-8735
 or (617) 826-7497
Fax: (617) 826-2495

Cetrek/Wagner USA
12700 N.E. 124th St.
Suite 5117
Kirkland, WA 98034
Tel: (206) 823-1372
Fax: (206) 823-0362

ComNav Marine Systems
1420 Frances St.
Vancouver, British Columbia
V5L 1Y9
CANADA
Tel: (604) 254-0212
Fax: (604) 255-3523

Coursemaster-Hydrive USA
232 Richardson St.
Greenpoint, NY 11222
Tel: (718) 383-4968
Fax: (718) 383-1864

CPT, Inc.
4336 N.E. 11th Ave.
Ft. Lauderdale, FL 33334
Tel: (305) 564-1445

Davis Instruments
3465 Diablo Ave.
Hayward, CA 94545
Tel: (510) 732-9229
Fax: (510) 732-9188

Encron
2900 T Ave. #G
Anacortes, WA 98221
Tel: (206) 455-4666

Figure 1: The Cetrek Seastar 770 hand-held control unit makes it easy to control your autopilot.

Euro Marine Trading
64 Halsey St. #27
Newport, RI 02840
Tel: (800) 222-7712
Fax: (401) 849-3230
NKE electronics, Topline autopilot

First Mate
41 Kindred St.
Stuart, FL 34994
Tel: (407) 286-4480
Fax: (407) 286-4481

Garmin
9875 Widmer Rd.
Lenexa, KS 66215
Tel: (800) 800-1020
  or (913) 599-1515
Fax: (913) 599-2103

Metal Marine Pilot
2119 W. Mildred St.
Tacoma, WA 98466
Tel: (206) 564-5902

Micrologic
9610 Desoto Ave.
Chatsworth, CA 91311
Tel: (818) 998-1216
Fax: (818) 709-3658

Moonlight Marine
776 W. 17th St.
Costa Mesa, CA 92627
Tel: (714) 645-0130

Navico
7411 114th Ave.
Suite 310
Largo, FL 34643
Tel: (813) 546-4300
Fax: (813) 546-5539

Octopus Precision Products
3396 Marine Dr.
W. Vancouver, British Columbia V7V 1M9
CANADA
Tel: (604) 925-1514
Fax: (604) 922-8340
Autopilot drive systems

C. Plath, North America
222 Severn Ave.
Annapolis, MD 21403
Tel: (410) 263-6700
Fax: (410) 268-8713

Radio Holland U.S.A.
8943 Gulf Freeway
Houston, TX 77017
Tel: (713) 943-3325
Fax: (713) 943-3802

Robertson Marine Electronics
400 Oser Ave.
Hauppauge, NY 11788
Tel: (800) 645-3738
  or (516) 273-3737
Fax: (516) 273-3270

Tiller Master
1592 S. Anaheim Blvd. #D
Anaheim, CA 92805
Tel: (714) 533-7371

Vetus - Den Ouden, Inc.
P.O. Box 8712
Baltimore, MD 21240-0712
Tel: Orders only: (800)
GO-VETUS
  or (410) 712-0740
Fax: (410) 712-0985

WH Autopilots
655 N.E. Northlake Pl.
Seattle, WA 98105
Tel: (206) 633-1830

Figure 2: The Autohelm 4000 can be clipped to a yacht's wheel for easy installation.

Binoculars and Telescopes

Good binoculars are a precious tool. They can help you find buoys, landmarks, and other features barely distinguishable to the naked eye. Good binoculars are expensive, but well worth it. Your boat and life could be at stake, so why settle for a pair of dime-store glasses that barely allow you to see beyond the end of the boat?

The first thing to look for when selecting binoculars or a telescope is the numbers on the end. They might read 7x50 or 6x40. The first number refers to the magnifying power of the instrument. In other words, a binocular that is 7x50 will make an object 7 times larger, making it seem 7 times nearer. Most binoculars have a magnifying power ranging from 5 to 10. The lower values are better on boats because a boat bounces around a lot. A high-powered set of glasses is likely to be hard to hold on the target.

The second number on binoculars refers to the diameter of the front lens. In general, larger lenses are better, because they gather more light and make the glasses more usable in low-light conditions. For sailors, 50 mm lenses are ideal.

A third number appears on more expensive binoculars. It refers to the field of view — that is, the area that can be viewed at a certain distance, usually 1,000 feet. This number will be in the 300 to 500 range. If your boat is small and gets bounced around a lot, you might look for a very wide field of view so that you can keep the image in sight as long as possible.

Another feature of good marine glasses is their ruggedness. Usually marine binoculars are protected with a rubber coat, or a polyurethane shell to cushion the inevitable knocks and bangs. Expensive marine glasses are also nitrogen purged, — that is, filled with nitrogen to prevent the growth of molds and fungii and to prevent oxidation. This is one reason why marine binoculars are so expensive.

Finally, but of major importance, comes the coating and optical quality. The most expensive glasses allow up to 95% of the available light to reach the eyes because they have superior coatings and optics. Less expensive versions may only allow 75% of the available light to get to the eye.

Suppliers of Binoculars and Telescopes

Avon Seagull Marine
1851 McCaw Ave.
Irvine, CA 9Z714
Tel: (714) 250-0880
Fax: (714) 250-0740

Bushnell, Division of Bausch & Lomb
300 N. Lone Hill Ave.
San Dimas, CA 91773
Tel: (714) 592-8000
Fax: (714) 599-8938

Celestron
2835 Columbia St.
Torrance, CA 90503
Tel: (213) 328-9560

Fujinon
10 High Point Dr.
Wayne, NJ 07470
Tel: (201) 633-5600
Fax: (201) 633-5216
Binoculars

Figure 1: KVH Industries' Data-Scope digital compass range finder.

KVH Industries
110 Enterprise Ctr.
Middletown, RI 02840
Tel: (401) 847-3327
Fax: (401) 849-0045
KVH Datascope

Leica Camera, Inc.
156 Ludlow Ave.
Northvale, NJ 07647
Tel: (201) 767-7500
Fax: (201) 767-8666
Binoculars

New Atlantis Marine
126 East 16 St.
Costa Mesa, CA 92627
Tel: (714) 548-9617
Fax: (714) 548-9619
Binoculars

Nikon
623 Stewart Ave.
Garden City, NY 11530
Tel: (516) 222-0200
Fax: (516) 222-0265

Optolyth-USA
18805 NE Melvista Ln
Hillsboro, OR 97123
Tel: (800) 447-6881

Pentax
35 Inverness Dr. E.
Englewood, CO 80112

Selsi Company, Inc.
40 Veterans Blvd.
Carlstadt, NJ 07072
Tel: (201) 935-0388
Fax: (201) 935-5851
Binoculars

Swarovski Optik
1 Wholesale Way
Cranston, RI 02920
Tel: (800) 426-3089
Binoculars

Swift Instruments
952 Dorchester Ave.
Boston, MA 02125
Tel: (617) 436-2960
Fax: (617) 436-3232
Binoculars

Steiner Optics/Pioneer Research, Inc.
216 Haddon Ave.
Westmont, NJ 08108
Tel: (800) 257-7742
 or (609) 854-2424
Fax: (609) 858-8695
Binoculars

Tamaya Technics
4-4, Ginza 4-Chome
Chuo-Ku, Tokyo 104
JAPAN
Tel: 03-3561-8711
Binoculars

Unitron
170 Wilbur Pl. P.O. Box 469
Bohemia, NY 11716
Tel: (516) 589-6666
Fax: (516) 589-6975
Binoculars, spotting scopes, telescopes, field glasses

Vetus - Den Ouden, Inc.
P.O. Box 8712
Baltimore, MD 21240-0712
Tel: (Orders only:) (800) GO-VETUS
 or (410) 712-0740
Fax: (410) 712-0985
Binoculars

Carl Zeiss Optical
1015 Commerce St.
Petersburg, VA 23803
Tel: (804) 861-0033
Fax: (804) 862-3734
Binoculars

Night Vision Scopes

Fujinon
10 High Point Dr.
Wayne, NJ 07470
Tel: (201) 633-5600
Fax: (201) 633-5216
Starscope

ITT Electro-Optical Products
7635 Plantation Rd.
Roanoke, VA 24019
Tel: (703) 563-0371
Night Mariner binocular

Star-Tron Technology
R.I.D.C. Industrial Pk.
526 Alpha Dr.
Pittsburgh, PA 15238
Tel: (800) 842-7170
Fax: (412) 963-1552

Swarovski Optik
1 Wholesale Way
Cranston, Rl 02920
Tel: (800) 426-3089

Vetus - Den Ouden, Inc.
P.O. Box 8712
Baltimore, MD 21240-0712
Tel: Orders only: (800)
GO-VETUS
 or (410) 712-0740
Fax: (410) 712-0985

Figure 2: This night vision scope from Star-Tron Technology makes it easy to spot potential dangers in conditions of little or no light.

Boat Builders: Custom

By Steve White

Steve White is the president of Brooklin Boat Yard, Inc. in Brooklin, Maine. This yard has built several large yachts, among the most recent is a design of the author's for Pip and Judy Wick. Steve is a graduate of Colby College, and took over Brooklin Boat Yard from his father, naval architect Joel White.

Why would anyone have a custom boat built today? Aren't there hundreds of manufacturers with thousands of designs available off the shelf? There are, but it is surprising how many voids exist in the production boat-building world. You can't always find a production boat that is exactly what you want.

Generally, the person who is considering a custom yacht is quite knowledgeable. He or she has owned several boats before, and has a mental picture of the ideal yacht. The pride of ownership of a custom boat can be substantial, and the joy of creating something new and special is what it is all about. If owner, designer, and builder all share these emotions, the process is pleasurable and the rewards lasting.

SELECTING A BUILDER

So you have decided to have a custom yacht built. You have selected a designer and are well along with the design concept. The requirements you have given the designer have been incorporated inside a hull of sufficient volume to fit everything you want. It is bigger than you thought. The sail plan is defined, the deck plan conceived, and the interior exactly right. Well, almost exactly.

Now it is time to select a builder. Undoubtedly, the designer has some suggestions and perhaps you have someone in mind. At this point, you should have selected a hull and deck material, and your choice of builder should reflect this selection. Any design can be well executed in any of the major construction methods: steel, aluminum, wood, or fiberglass. But some designs suit a particular material better than others. Although it seems obvious to select a builder who has experience with your material of choice, I know of several instances where this has not been the case. At best the result is an excellent product that may cost the owner a little more than necessary as the builder learned about the personality of the materials. At worst the result is a structural failure.

Send your plans to several builders and ask for bids. When you have narrowed it down to two or three, go and visit the yard personally. It is better for you to go to the yard than for the builder to come to you. At the yard, the builder can often show you examples of his latest work. You will also get a feeling for what the yard is like. No brochure can give this feeling. If you don't have a positive feeling about a yard, go somewhere else.

When you are down to couple of builders, it is time to ask some questions. Are they experienced with custom building? It is very different from production building or even semi-custom work. I define custom as a one-off boat, which includes building the hull and deck for the first time. Semi-custom uses a hull from an existing mold. How long ago did they launched their last custom project? Do they have a project now underway? Ask if you can speak to a recent customer about his or her satisfaction with the yard. Talk to that customer when a representative of the yard is not around; you'll get a more candid view. Ask the builder how long it will take to build your boat. Do they have the manpower now or will they be hiring new people? Most importantly, check into the financial situation of the yard. Call Dunn & Bradstreet. Find out who owns the company and the land the company is on. How long have they been in business? Is your boat going to provide the money to keep the yard afloat or is the yard a going concern?

CUSTOM DESIGN PLANS

The builder will also ask specific questions. The most important will be about the plans. How complete will they be? The more complete the designer's plans are, the more accurate the builder's bid will be. Ideally, the plans should be completely finished before the builder calculates construction costs, but this almost never happens. Designers blame overeager yards that will quote a price based on a sketch on a napkin. Builders complain that designers never finish the plans quickly enough, or that they make too many changes during construction. The owner, however, is also at fault if he has given the go-ahead prematurely. It is the owner's responsibility to ensure that the plans are complete and represent all that he wants. To ignore this responsibility usually costs an owner a lot of money. I have built boats from plans that were virtually never changed, and in other cases we have kidded about mounting our fax machine inside the boat under construction so we could keep on working. It is easy to guess which boat was the more efficiently built.

CONSTRUCTION CONTRACTS

When you decide upon a builder, you will be given a contract. These are basically of three kinds: contract price, cost plus, and fixed fee. Each has its pros and cons.

The contract price type of contract makes the customer feel the most secure because he is told exactly what the bottom line will be. But to draw up a fair one, the builder needs a very complete set of drawings and specifications. If you can't provide that, the builder will have to add in extra to protect his profit margin. This can make the contract price quite costly for the customer.

The cost plus type of contract can also end up costly for the owner. Stories of astronomical prices and unfinished boats abound. Basically, with a cost plus contract, the owner and builder agree on a flat labor rate and a percentage markup on materials. There is no limit on the work hours spent.

Figure 1: Brooklin Boatyard have built many fine yachts. Among them is Lucayo, seen here at her launching. Designed by the author for Pip and Judy Wick.

The disadvantage to this is that there is no built-in incentive for the builder to hurry and finish the job. In fact, if there are no other projects on the horizon, the builder is encouraged to take his time. The more hours he works, the more money he makes. This type of contract is most appropriate for unusual projects where there is no data base to make accurate cost estimates. Radical projects or ground-breaking designs cannot be estimated with much accuracy. In such cases, a builder may insist upon a cost plus contract to protect himself. Needless to say, you must be able to trust your builder completely before signing such a contract.

The fixed fee contract is probably the most equitable to both the builder and the owner. In this arrangement, the builder makes his best possible estimate of the total work hours needed to complete the project, and these hours are multiplied by the builder's cost per hour.

Then materials are estimated at cost plus a percentage markup. Finally, the builder calculates a fixed fee for profit and overhead. This fixed fee is usually between 8 and 20% of the cost of total labor and materials depending upon the size of the boat. The fixed fee is a number that doesn't change even if the total number of hours required is adjusted. It is usually paid to the builder in thirds: one third upon turning the hull right-side-up, one third when the deck is on, and the final third upon acceptance of the boat by the owner. By holding the final third, the owner is assured that all the minor details and problems are attended to after the boat is launched. Payment of the final third usually coincides with the transfer of insurance exclusively to the owner. The beauty of this method is that if the builder completes the job in fewer hours than estimated, his profit margin goes up, and the owner pays for fewer man-hours. On the other hand, if the job exceeds the estimated hours, the builder still gets paid, but only at his cost. His profit margin goes down. So the builder has an incentive to finish the job and get on with other profitable work. Another built-in plus for this system is that it is to the builder's advantage to avoid unrealistic low-ball bids just to get the work. So, as an owner, you will be assured that the estimated cost will be quite accurate.

OTHER CONSIDERATIONS

There are several other factors to consider when having a custom boat built.

Subcontractors

Ask about performance assurances by the subcontractors. Usually a subcontractor makes his own guarantees, but it should be the builder's responsibility to guarantee that you will ultimately be satisfied, at no extra cost to you.

Insurance

The builder should carry "builder's risk" insurance on your boat. This will repay you for money spent on labor and materials if, for example, the builder's shop burns down. The builder's fire insurance will pay for his shop, but not for your unfinished boat. Usually, this insurance is billed directly to you and the builder reports monthly to the insurance company as to what the value of your boat is.

Taxes and Registration

This is somewhat out of the custom builder's realm. Talk to him about what is customary in his state or country. Then talk to an accountant and a lawyer.

Billing

How much is the down payment on deposit? How often will you be billed? Will the bills be in equal amounts (some percentage of the estimated price), or will it be progress billing? I recommend getting detailed bills at least once a month. The bills should include the number of hours worked and the progress of the project. Read the bills carefully, ask questions about anything you don't understand, and then pay the bill on time.

Building a custom boat is a demanding task for everyone involved. Modern electrical, mechanical, plumbing, and sailing systems require a high degree of sophistication and craftsmanship to install. When your boat is finished, you take it out on the ocean. In the case of a sailboat, you tip it 25 degrees and pound it up and down, sometimes for days at a time. It is a very demanding environment. But custom builders are a very demanding breed. They produce craft that are up to the rigors they must face. Once you have successfully commissioned a custom yacht, you will be hooked. That is why there are an awful lot of repeat customers out there.

Builders of Custom Boats

Domestic Builders

Able Marine Companies
P.O. Box 8055
Bar Harbor Airport Rd.
Trenton, ME 04605
Tel: (207) 667-6235
Fax: (207) 667-3986

Admiral Marine Works, Inc.
919 Haines St.
Port Townsend, WA 98368
Tel: (206) 385-4670
Fax: (206) 385-4256
Luxury yachts to 160 ft LOA.

Advanced Ocean Systems
2551 State Rd. 84
Ft. Lauderdale, FL
33312-4802
Tel: (305) 792-4128
 or (305) 791-9332
Fax: (305) 791-9306

Alden Yachts
1909 Alden Landing
Portsmouth, RI 02871
Tel: (401) 683-4200
*Custom and semi-custom
yachts*

**Alex Willis Boat
Construction**
P.O. Box 266
Harkers Island, NC 28531
Tel: (919) 728-6054
Sport-fishing and work boats

Art DeFever Yachts
2740 Shelter Island Dr.
San Diego, CA 92106
Tel: (619) 222-2414

Asay Boats & Millwork
1001 Boardwalk
Ashbury Pk., NJ 07712
Tel: (908) 776-5424
*Fiberglass and wooden skiffs
and work boats*

Atlantic Boats, Inc. of NC
1415 W. New Bern Rd.
Kinston, NC 28501
Tel: (919) 523-3520
*Commercial or pleasure
fishing boats*

Atlantic Marine, Inc.
8500 Heckscher Dr.
Jacksonville, FL 32226
Tel: (904) 251-3111
Fax: (904) 251-3500
Steel commercial boats

Barbour Boat Works, Inc.
P.O. Box 1069
New Bern, NC 28563
Tel: (919) 637-2500
Fax: (919) 637-4295
*Commercial fishing boats in
steel or aluminum*

Beals Boatshop
P.O. Box 274
Millbridge, ME 04658
Tel: (207) 546-7932
Lobster and pleasure boats

Barattucci Yachts, Inc.
23622 Calabassas Rd.
Calabassas, CA 92302
Tel: (818) 888-5260
Fax: (818) 883-9704

**Belkov Yacht Carpentry
Co.**
311 3rd St.
Annapolis, MD 21403
Tel: (410) 269-1777
Fax: (410) 269-8477
*Work boats and sport-fishing
boats*

Black Dog Boat Works
River Landing Rd.
Denton, MD 21629
Tel: (410) 479-3355
Fax: (410) 267-9668
Work and pleasure boats

**Brooke Yachts
International**
65 East 55th St.
New York, NY 10022
Tel: (212) 980-0055
Fax: (212) 832-3876
US office of Brooke Yachts

Brooklin Boatyard, Inc.
Brooklin, ME 04616
Tel: (207) 359-2236
Fax: (207) 359-8871

Broward Marine, Inc.
2051 N.W. 11th St.
Miami, FL 33125
Tel: (305) 522-1701
*Luxury power boats to 150 ft
LOA*

Broward Marine, Inc.
1601 S.W. 20th St.
Ft. Lauderdale, FL 33315
Tel: (305) 522-1701
Fax: (305) 522-1884
Luxury power boats

Burger Boat Company
1811 Spring St.
Manitowoc, WI 54220
Tel: (414) 684-1600
Fax: (414) 684-6555
Luxury power boats

Caliari Yacht USA
2065 N.E. 121 Rd.
Miami, Fl 33181
Tel: (305) 891-7742
Fax: (305) 891-4804
Large luxury power yachts

Christensen Motor Yacht Corp.
4400 Columbia Way
Vancouver, WA 98661
Tel: (206) 695-7671
Fax: (206) 695-6038
Luxury yachts to 150 ft LOA

Christensen Motor Yachts
2160 S.E. 17th St.
Ft. Lauderdale, FL 33316
Tel: (305) 523-5906
Fax: (305) 763-1053
Large power yachts

Cooper Yachts
20030 Stewart Crescent
Maple Ridge
British Columbia V2X 7E6
CANADA
Tel: (604) 465-9171
Fax: (604) 465-5122
Large power yachts

Concordia Custom Yachts
300 Gulf Rd.
S. Dartmouth, MA 02748
Tel: (508) 992-9733
Fax: (508) 996-5765

Cranberry Island Boatyard
Dog Point Rd.
Cranberry Island, ME 04625
Tel: (207) 244-7316
Custom finished lobster boat and pleasure craft

Crescent Beach Boatbuilders Ltd.
1200 Westlake Ave. N.
Suite 414
Seattle, WA 98109
Tel: (206) 298-3630
Fax: (206) 284-0487
Large power yachts

Crockers Boat Yard
P.O. Box 268
Ashland Ave.
Manchester, MA 01944
Tel: (508) 526-1971
Fax: (508) 526-7625

Custom Fiberglass Products
8136 Leo Kidd Ave.
Port Richey, FL 34668
Tel: (813) 847-5798

D & C Marine Boatbuilders
145 Dewolf Ave.
Bristol, RI 02809
Tel: (401) 253-4176
Pleasure and sport boats

Dark Ages Boatworks
23 1/2 Water St.
P.O. Box 33
Thomaston, ME 04861
Tel: (207) 354-6436

Deerfoot Samples Shipyard
P.O. Box 462
120 Commercial St.
Boothbay Harbor, ME 04583
Tel: (207) 633-3171
Fax: (207) 633-3824

Delta Marine
1608 S. 96th
Seattle, WA 98108
Tel: (206) 763-2383

Dencho Marine
1517 W. 15th St.
Long Beach, CA 90813
Tel: (213) 432-3487
Fax: (213) 495-0082

Derecktor Shipyards
311 E. Boston Post Rd.
Mamaroneck, NY 10543
Tel: (914) 698-5020
Fax: (914) 698-4641
All types of workboats, luxury yachts and powerboats

deVries Scheepsbouw, b.v.
Feadship America
801 Seabreeze Ave.
Ft. Lauderdale, FL 33316
Tel: (305) 761-1830

Diaship
1535 S.E. 17th St.
Suite 201
Ft. Lauderdale, FL 33316
Tel: (305) 761-1699
Fax: (305) 761-1788

Duffy & Duffy
Box 383
Brooklin, ME 04616
Tel: (207) 359-4658
Fax: (207) 359-8948
Lobster-boat-style runabouts, yachts, and work boats

East Bay Boatworks
Fulford St.
Harkers Island, NC 28531

Ellis Boat Co., Inc.
Box 20
Seawall Rd.
Manset, ME 04656
Tel: (207) 244-9221
Fax: (207) 244-9222
Lobster-boat-style cruising
yachts

Euroship Intl.
1300S. E. 17th St.
Suite 201
Ft. Lauderdale, FL 33316
Tel: (305) 763-8666
Fax: (305) 763-3979

Evans Boat Construction &
Repair, Inc.
Route 413
Crisfield, MD 21817
Tel: (410) 986-3396
Bay and coastal fishing vessels

Even Keel Marine
44 Spring St.
Yarmouth, ME 04096
Tel: (207) 846-4878
Lobster and pleasure boat
builder

Feadship America
801 Seabreeze Ave.
Bahia Mar
Ft. Lauderdale, FL 33316
Tel: (305) 761-1830
Fax: (305) 761-3412

Flagship Marine
Corporation
2375 Tamiami Trail N.
Suite 308
Naples, FL 33904
Tel: (813) 263-3524
Fax: (813) 262-7511

Flye Point Marine
P.O. Box 217
Brooklin, ME 04616
Tel: (207) 359-4641
Fax: (207) 359-2372
Semi-custom pleasure and
lobster boats

Foley Boatbuilding, Inc.
Cutts Island
Kittery Point, ME 03905
Tel: (207) 439-3601
Fax: (207) 439-8889
Semi-custom fiberglass lobster
and pleasure boats

Forsberg's Boat Works, Inc.
1692 West End Dr.
Pt. Pleasant, NJ 08742
Tel: (908) 892-4246
Fiberglass and wooden garvies

Gannon & Benjamin, Inc.
Marine Railway
P.O. Box 1095
Beach Rd.
Vineyard Haven, MA 02568
Tel: (508) 693-4658
Fax: (508) 693-1818
Wooden skiffs and workboats

General Marine, Inc.
Airport Industrial Park
Biddeford, ME 04005
Tel: (207) 284-7517
Custom tuna, lobster, and
pleasure boats

Gladding-Hearn
Shipbuilding Corporation
1 Riverside Ave.
Somerset, MA 02725
Tel: (508) 676-8596
Fax: (508) 672-1873
Steel and aluminum work and
pleasure boats

Glebe Point Boat Co.
Glebe Point, Box 133
Burgess, VA 22432
Tel: (804) 453-3467

Eric Geotz Custom
Sailboats, Inc.
15 Broad Common Rd.
Bristol, RI 02809
Tel: (401) 253-2670
Fax: (401) 253-3640

Giverson's Boats
P.O. Box 617
Pleasantville, NJ 08232
Tel: (609) 645-3697
Sport-fishing boats

Goudy & Stevens
P.O. Box 245
East Boothbay, ME 04544
Tel: (207) 633-3521
Steel and aluminum fishing
and work boats

Gougeon Brothers, Inc.
P.O. Box X908
Bay City, MI 48708
Tel: (517) 684-7286
Fax: (517) 684-1374

Greene Marine, Inc.
343 Gilman Rd.
Yarmouth, ME 04096
Tel: (207) 846-3184

Feadship America, Inc.
801 Seabreeze Ave.
Bahia Mar
Ft. Lauderdale, FL 33316
Tel: (305) 761-1830
Fax: (305) 761-3412

Flagship Marine Corp.
2375 Tamiami Trail N.
Suite 308
Naples, FL 33940
Tel: (813) 263-FLAG
Fax: (813) 262-7511

H & H Marine
Box 113A
RFD 1
Milbridge, ME 04658
Tel: (207) 546-7477
Lobster-boat-style work boats

Hans Pedersen & Sons, Inc.
165 West Front St.
Keyport, NJ 07755
Tel: (908) 264-0971
Fax: (908) 264-0926
Lobster and pleasure skiffs

Harley Boat Co.
300 S. First Ave.
Bartow, FL 33830
Tel: (813) 533-2800
Fax: (813) 533-0787
Semi-production sport and motor yachts

Harter Marine, Inc.
18 North Rd.
Lake Ronkonkoma, NY 11779
Tel: (516) 981-9674
Fax: (516) 981-9674
Steel and aluminum work and fishing boats

Hatteras Custom Yacht Services
Division of Genmar
P.O. Box 2690
High Point, NC 27261
Tel: (919) 889-6621

Henriques Boat Works
198 Hilton Ave.
Bayville, NJ 08721
Tel: (908) 269-1180
Fax: (908) 269-1606
Sport-fishing boats and lobster-style work boats

The Hinckley Company
P.O. Box 699
Shore Road
Southwest Harbor, ME 04679
Tel: (207) 244-5531
Fax: (207) 244-9833

Hitachi Zosen Corp.
150 E. 52nd St., 20th Fl.
New York, NY 10022
Tel: (212) 355-5650

Hodgdon Yachts, Inc.
P.O. Box 505
East Boothbay, ME 04544
Tel: (207) 633-4194
Molded wood fishing and work boat builder

Holland's Boat Shop
Mill Lane
Belfast, ME 04915
Tel: (207) 338-3155
Yacht-quality lobster-style pleasure and work boats

Howdy Bailey Custom Boats
Marine Metals, Inc.
Cobbs Marina
4523 Dunning Rd.
Norfolk, VA 23518
Tel: (804) 480-0058
Fax: (804) 480-1330

Huckins Yacht Corp.
3482 Lakeshore Rd.
Jacksonville, FL 32210
Tel: (904) 389-1125
Fax: (904) 388-2281
Power yachts

Infinity Yachts
2698 S.W. 23rd Ave.
Ft. Lauderdale, FL 33312
Tel: (305) 581-3313
Fax: (305) 797-8986

J. Ervin Jones
Murray Hill Rd.
P.O. Box 134
East Boothbay, ME 04544
Fishing and pleasure boats

J.O. Brown & Son, Inc.
Sea Side Ln.
North Haven, ME 04853
Tel: (207) 867-4621
Wooden fishing skiffs

Jarvis Newman Boats
P.O. Box 707
Shore Rd.
Southwest Harbor, ME 04679
Tel: (207) 244-3860
Lobster-style work boats

John M. Williams Co., Inc.
Hall Quarry
Mount Desert, ME 04660
Tel: (207) 244-7854
Fax: (207) 244-9912
Work, fishing, and pleasure boats

John's Bay Boat Co.
P.O. Box 58
McFarland's Cove Rd.
S. Bristol, ME 04568
Tel: (207) 644-8261
Fishing and pleasure boats

The Joiner Shop, Inc.
Rte 102
West Tremont, ME 04690
Tel: (207) 244-9632
Fishing and pleasure boats

Jones-Goodall, Inc.
1690 Marine View Dr.
Tacoma, WA 98422
Tel: (206) 272-1212
Fax: (206) 272-1092
Large fiiberglass yachts

Knight & Carver Marine
3650 Hancock St.
San Diego, CA 92109
Tel: (619) 222-6488
Fax: (619) 295-0213
Custom yacht builder

Lazzara Yachts
5300 West Tyson Ave.
Tampa, FL 33611
Tel: (813) 835-5300
Fax: (813) 835-0964

Libby's Boat Shop
P.O. Box 154
Beals Island, ME 04611
Tel: (207) 497-5487
Lobster, sport-fishing and pleasure boats

Mark Lindsay Boatbuilders
30 Blackburn Industrial Park
Gloucester, MA 01930
Tel: (508) 283-4141
Fax: (508) 283-5099

Little Harbor Custom Yachts
One Little Harbor Landing
Portsmouth, RI 02871
Tel: (401) 683-5600
Fax: (401) 683-3009
Large production and custom cruising sailboats

Lydia Yachts of Stuart
272 N. Flagler St.
Stuart, FL 33994
Tel: (407) 692-0002
Fax: (407) 288-4896

Lyman-Morse Boatbuilding Co., Inc.
49 Knox Street
Thomaston, ME 04861
Tel: (207) 354-6904
Fax: (207) 354-8176
Power and sailboats

Maine-Way Boat Works
RR2
Box 629 (Rt. 137)
Belfast, ME 04915
Tel: (207) 342-5611
Fax: (207) 342-4000
A custom finish shop

Marine Systems Boatbuilders, Inc.
Long Hill Rd.
Southwest Harbor, ME 04656
Tel: (207) 244-5696
Lobster, fishing, and pleasure boat builder

Figure 2: Puffin, one of the more traditional projects built by Merrifield-Roberts. M-R have also built America's Cup yachts, Maxi racing yachts, and recently, a 100 ft.LOA crusing yacht.

Merrifield-Roberts, Inc.
71 Broad Common Rd.
Bristol, RI 02809
Tel: (401) 253-0315
Fax: (401) 253-1720
America's Cup yachts, pleasure yachts, and powerboats

Monterey Bay Marine
P.O. Box 8
Capitola, CA 95010
Tel: (408) 722-6276
Fax: (408) 724-6008

Monterey Marine
6800 S.W. Jack James Dr.
Stuart, FL 34997
Tel: (407) 286-2835
Fax: (407) 288-4993
Large sport-fishing yachts

Montgomery Boat Yard
29 Ferry St.
Gloucester, MA 01930
Tel: (508) 281-6524
Wood and fiberglass lobster and work boats

Mount Desert Island Boatworks, Inc.
P.O. Box 60
Southwest Harbor, ME 04679
Tel: (207) 244-0000
Fax: (207) 244-0009
Commercial or pleasure lobster-style boats

Narragansett Shipwrights
215 3rd St.
Newport, RI 02840
Tel: (401) 846-3312
Molded yacht and sport-fishing boats

Nauset Marine, Inc.
Rte. 6A, Box 357
Orleans, MA 02653
Tel: (508) 255-0777
Builders of Lobster-boat-style work boats

New England Boatworks, Inc.
One Lagoon Rd.
Portsmouth, RI 02871
Tel: (401) 683-6110
Fax: (401) 683-6988
Pleasure yachts and boats

Norship International
1600 S.E. 17th St.
Suite 309
Ft. Lauderdale, FL 33316
Tel: (305) 763-8700
Fax: (305) 763-9162
Luxury powerboats

Nordlund Boat Co., Inc.
1621 Taylor Way
Tacoma, WA 98421
Tel: (206) 627-5300

Otis Enterprises Marine Corp.
Prospect St.
Searsport, ME 04974
Tel: (207) 548-6362
Lobster and sport-fishing boats

Owens Boatyard
General Delivery
Deltaville, VA 23043
Tel: (804) 776-9686
Fishing boats

Pacific Victor Marine
P.O. Box 1491
Marysville, WA 98270
Tel: (206) 653-4844
  or (206) 658-5347
Aluminum sport-fishing boats

Padebco Custom Boats
Round Pond, ME 04564
Tel: (207) 529-5106

Palmer Johnson, Inc.
61 Michigan St.
Sturgeon Bay, WI 54235
Tel: (414) 743-4412
Fax: (414) 743-3381

Passamaquoddy Yacht Co.
P.O. Box 222
Harrington, ME 04643
Tel: (207) 483-4601
Lobster and sport-fishing boats

Payne and Franklin, Inc.
31 Hazard Rd.
North Kingstown, RI 02852

Malcolm L. Pettigrew, Inc.
P.O. Box 1160
Seal Cove Rd.
Southwest Harbor, ME 04679
Tel: (207) 244-5082
Fax: (207) 244-5084
Lobster-boat-style yachts and fishing boats

Pease Boatworks
50 Great Western Rd.
N. Harwich, MA 02645
Tel: (508) 432-8112
Yacht tenders

Pilots Cove Boats
P.O. Box 452
Somerset, MA 02726
Tel: (508) 679-3353
Fax: (508) 679-0827
Lobster and sport-fishing boats

Pilot's Point Marina
63 Pilot's Point Dr.
Westbrook, CT 06498
Tel: (203) 399-7906
Fax: (203) 399-7259

Profile Boats
RR 2, Box 2A2
Sumner, IA 50674
Tel: (319) 578-8556

Prospect Boatworks
1231 State Rd.
Prospect, KY 40059
Tel: (502) 228-0111
Fax: (502) 228-4767
Aluminum yacht and work boats

Provincial Boat & Marine Ltd.
P.O. Box 125
Kensington, Prince Edward's Island COB 1MO
CANADA
Fiberglass work and lobster boats

Rennaissance Yachts
31 Water St.
Thomaston, ME 04861
Tel: (207) 354-8773
Fax: (207) 354-8775
Large sailing yachts

RKL Boatworks
P.O. Box D52
Mt. Desert, ME 04660
Tel: (207) 244-5997
Custom lobster-boat-style yachts and launches

Rosborough Boats Ltd.
P.O. Box 188
Armdale, Nova Scotia B3L 4J9
CANADA
Tel: (902) 477-1415
Fax: (902) 479-2980
Lobster-style work and pleasure boats

Rybovich Yachts
4200 N. Dixie Hwy.
West Palm Beach, FL 33041
Tel: (407) 844-4331

Scarano Boat Building, Inc.
Port of Albany, NY 12202
Tel: (518) 463-3401
Fax: (518) 463-3403
*Custom pleasure and fishing
boats*

Seaboard Marine
6650-13 Crescent St.
Ventura, CA 93003
Tel: (805) 656-2628

Seamaster Yachts
2238 S.W. 34th St.
Fort Lauderdale, FL 33312
Tel: (305) 583-9505

**Sintes Fiberglass Designs,
Inc.**
7410 South Roadway
New Orleans, LA 70124
Tel: (504) 288-4814
*Custom frame kits, hulls, and
molds*

Smoker Craft
68143 Clunett St.
New Paris, IN 46553
Tel: (219) 831-2103

Sovereign Yachts
7814 8th Avenue S.
Seattle, WA 98108
Tel: (206) 767-6944
Fax: (206) 767-6724

Ralph W. Stanley
Southwest Harbor, ME 04679
Tel: (207) 244-3795
Lobster and pleasure boats

Steiger Craft
99 Bellport Ave.
Bellport, NY 11713
Tel: (516) 286-2136
Fax: (516) 286-2139
*Pleasure and sport-fishing
boats*

Sterling Yachts
2101 South Andrews Ave.
Suite 104
Ft. Lauderdale, FL 33316
Tel: (305) 522-0173
Fax: (305) 761-3216

Sterling Yacht Int'l
3350 S.E. Slater St.
Stuart, FL 34997
Tel: (407) 220-9685

Stiletto Boat Works
P.O. Box 122
Nokomis, FL 34274
Tel: (813) 484-0479

Stuart Yacht Builders
450 S.W. Salerno Rd.
Stuart, FL 34997
Tel: (407) 283-1947
Fax: (407) 286-9800

Sunward Yacht Corp.
8118 Market St.
Wilmington, NC 28405
Tel: (919) 686-7532
Fax: (919) 686-1332

Swiftships, Inc.
P.O. Box 1908
Morgan City, LA 70381
Tel: (504)384-17800
Fax: (504) 384-0914
*Oil rig supply and military
vessels, now in the luxury
yacht market*

Technomarine Yachts
2065 N.E. 121 Rd.
North Miami, FL 33181
Tel: (305) 891-4361
*US rep of Technomarine
Yachts, Italy*

Thomas Marine
37 Bransford St.
Patchogue, NY 11772
Tel: (516) 289-0621
Fax: (516) 447-1605
Fishing and pleasure boats

Tillotson Pearson
Rt. 136
Market St.
Warren, RI 02885
Tel: (401) 245-1200
Fax: (401) 247-2669
*Fishing and pleasure boats,
production and custom*

Treworgy Yachts
5658 N. Oceanshore Blvd.
Palm Coast, FL 32137
Tel: (904) 445-5878
Fax: (904) 446-1824
Steel and aluminum yachts

Trinity Marine Group
14055 Industrial Seaway Rd.
Gulfport, MS 39505
Tel: (800) 877-0029
  or (601) 864-0029
Fax: (601) 867-1666

Vantare International, Inc.
1715 S. Orange Blossom Trail
Apopka, FL 32703
Tel: (407) 884-5606
Fax: (407) 884-1841

Washburn & Doughty Assoc., Inc.
P.O. Box 296
Enterprise St.
East Boothbay, ME 04544
Tel: (207) 633-6517
Fax: (207) 633-7007
Steel and aluminum yachts and boats

Wayne Beal's Boat Shop
Main St.
Jonesport, ME 04649
Tel: (207) 497-2173
Pleasure or work boat lobster-style boats

Westship, Inc.
1441 S.E. 16th St.
Ft. Lauderdale, FL 33316
Tel: (305) 463-0700
Fax: (305) 764-2675

Westport Shipyard
P.O. Box 308
Westport, WA 98593
Tel: (206) 268-0117
Fax: (206) 268-0119

Westerly Marine
660 W. 17th St., 39B
Costa Mesa, CA 92627
Tel: (714) 642-0146
Fax: (714) 642-9145

W.S. Wilbur
Seawall Rd.
Manset, ME 04656
Tel: (207) 244-5000
Lobster-boat-style yachts and fishing boats

Wiggers Custom Racing Yachts
RR 2
Bowmanville, Ontarios L1C 3K3
CANADA
Tel: (416) 623-5261
Fax: (416) 623-0755
Sailing yachts

Winninghoff Boats
Warehouse Ln.
Rowley, MA 01969
Tel: (508) 948-2314
Fax: (508) 948-2315
Sport-fishing and pleasure boats, custom and semi-production

Worldcruiser Yacht Co.
1310 G. Logan Ave.
Costa Mesa, CA 92626
Tel: (714) 549-9331
Fax: (714) 347-9016

Foreign Builders

Abeking & Rasmussen
P.O. Box 1160
An der Fahre 2
D-2874 Lernwerder
GERMANY
Tel: (+49) 421 673 3532
Fax: (+49) 421 673 3114

Alloy Yachts Int. Ltd.
1 Selwood Rd.
P.O. Box 21480
Henderson, Auckland
NEW ZEALAND
Tel: (+64) 9 838-7350
Fax: (+64) 9 838-7393

Alucraft Consulting, Inc.
Hadlaubstrasse
CH-8044
Zurich
SWITZERLAND
Tel: (+41) 1 362 82 92
Fax: (+41) 1 362 82 48

Amels BV
P.O. Box 1
8754 ZN Makkum
THE NETHERLANDS
Tel: (+31) 5158 2525
Fax: (+31) 5158 2719

Aqua Star Ltd.
Ocean Yard
Bulwer Ave.
St. Sampsons, Guernsey
CHANNEL ISLANDS

Astilleros Amatique, S.A.
Zolic Zona Libre de
Industria y Commercio
Santo Thomas de Castilla,
Izibal
GUATAMALA
Tel: (+502) 9-483-136

Australian Yacht Builders Pty. Ltd.
47 Byron St.
Box 98
Bulimba
Brisbane
Queensland 4171
AUSTRALIA
Tel: (+61) 7 399-3488
Fax: (+61) 7 395-5990

Azimut S.p.A.
Viale Dei Mareschi
14-10051 Avigliana
Torino
ITALY
Tel: (+39) 11-936 7271
Fax: (+39) 11-936 7270

Baglietto Shipyard
Piazza Stefano Baglietto, 3
17019 Varazze
ITALY
Tel: (+39) 19 95901
Fax: (+39) 19 96515

Baia
Via Lucollo
45/A 80070 Baia
ITALY
Tel: (+39) 81 8687 231
Fax: (+39) 81 8687 648

Baltic Yachts
Box 2320
SF-68555 Bosund
FINLAND
Tel: (+358) 67-83070
Fax: (+358) 67-83216

Fratelli Benetti
Viale dei Mareschi
14-10051 Avigliana
Torino
ITALY
Tel: (+39) 11-936 7271
Fax: (+39) 11-936 7270
HQ of Azimut/Bennetti Groupe

Azimut/Benetti Groupe
Via Michele Coppino
104-55049 Viareggio
Lucca
ITALY
Tel: (+39) 584 38 49 22
Fax: (+39) 584 39 62 32

Baglietto
Piazza Stefano Baglietto, 3
17019 Varazza (SV)
ITALY
Tel: (+39) 19 95 901
Fax: (+39) 19 96 515
Power yachts

Blohm & Voss
Box 10 07 20
D-200 Hamburg 11
GERMANY
Tel: (+49) 40 3119 3355
Luxury yachts over 200 ft LOA

**Brooke Yachts
International Ltd.**
Heath Rd.
Lowestoft, Suffolk NR99 9LZ
ENGLAND
Tel: (+44) 502 517151
Fax: (+44) 502 514663

Camper & Nicholson Ltd.
The Green Mumby Rd.
Gosport, Hants PO12 1AH
ENGLAND
Tel: (+44) 705 580221
Fax: (+44) 705 501882

**Cantiere Naval de
Valdettaro**
Via Liberta 12
Le Grazie
Portovenere 19022
ITALY

**Cantiere Naval Santa
Margherita-Spertini**
Via Milite Ignoto N.
1-16038 Santa Margherita
Ligure
ITALY
Tel: (+39) 185 287 891
Fax: (+39) 185 281-238

**Constructiones
Industrielles et Maritimes
(CIM Shipyard)**
Z.I. du Canal de Soeurs
17300 Rochefort
FRANCE
Tel: (+33) 46 99 54 51
Fax: (+33) 46 99 78 03

Cheoy Lee Shipyards, Ltd.
863-865 Lai Chi Kok Rd.
Kowloon
HONG KONG
Tel: (+852) 786-2873

Concorde Yachts, Ltd.
167/4 Moo 4
Najomtien
Sattahip
Chonburi 20250
THAILAND
Tel: (+66) 38-237799
Fax: (+66) 38-237755
Large sailing yachts

**Constuzione e Charter
Yachts Diporto (CCYD)**
Via dell'Elettronice
21/B Loc.
Fusina
30030 Malcontenta (VE)
ITALY
Tel: (+39) 41 698-355
Fax: (+39) 41 698-295
Large luxury yachts

**Constructione Navale
Bordeaux (CNB)**
162 Quai de Brazza
33100 Bordeaux
FRANCE
Tel: (+33) 56 86 15 06
Fax: (+33) 56 40 55 94
Aluminum yachts

Codecasa
Via Amendola
55049 Viareggio
Lucca
ITALY
Tel: (+39) 584 383-221

Danyard AAlborg A/S
P.O. Box 660
DK-9100 AAlborg
DENMARK
Tel: (+45) 99 37 37 00
Fax: (+45) 99 37 37 02

Devonport Management
Royal Dockyard
Devonport Devon
ENGLAND

Diaship Inc.
Heesen Shipyard
Kanaalstraat 14
Postbus 3
5340 AA Oss
HOLLAND
Tel: (+31) 4120-32510
Fax: (+31) 4120-37385

Dixon's Moulding Enterprises
Woods Harbour
Nova Scotia BOW 2EO
CANADA
Tel: (902) 723-2558
Fax: (902) 723-2878

Farocean
Box 38
Paarden Eiland
7420 Cape Province
REPUBLIC OF SOUTH
AFRICA
Tel: (+27) 21-471714
Fax: (+27) 21-478655

Feadship
Zonnelaan 12
2012 TC Haarlem
THE NETHERLANDS
Tel: (+31) 23 290352
Fax: (+31) 23 291629
*Probably the best known name
in large powerboats*

Greene Marine
Undershore Rd.
Walhampton
Lymington, Hampshire
ENGLAND

Gunnay Construction Ltd.
Baglarbasi-Tophanelioglu Cad
28
Uskadar
81130 Istanbul
TURKEY
Tel: (+90) 1 3439990
Fax: (+90) 1 3439999

Hackvoort BV. Shipyards
Havenstraat 17-22
Monnichendam
HOLLAND
Tel: (+31) 2995-1403
Fax: (+31) 2995-1041

Heesen Shipyard
Rijnstraat 2
P.O. Box 8
5340 AA Oss
HOLLAND
Tel: (+31) 4120-32510
Fax: (+31) 4120-37385

Hitachi-Zosen
1-1 Hitotsubashi 1-Chome
Chiyoda-Ku
Tokyo
JAPAN
Tel: (+81) 3 3217-8445
Fax: (+81) 3-3213-0905

Jachtwerf Jongert BV
Dahm International Gmblt.
Bendemannstrasse 9
D-4000 Dusseldorf 1
GERMANY
Tel: (+49) 211-3555 103
Fax: (+49) 211-364 030

Kees Conelisson/Euroship
Waaldjik 11 a &b
6621 KG Dreummel
HOLLAND
Tel: (+31) 8877 2880
Fax: (+31) 8877 2908

Lurssen Yachts
Friedrich Klippert Str. 2820
Bremen
GERMANY
Tel: (+49) 421-6604 160
Fax: (+49) 421 6604 343
Large power boats

Lloyd's Ships
Box 121
Bulimba, Brisbane 4171
AUSTRALIA
Tel: (+61) 7 399-6866
Fax: (+61) 7 395-5000

Malcolm Hart Marine
1110-1124 Nepean Hwy.
Mornington, Victoria 3911
AUSTRALIA

Marinteknik Verstads
Varvsvagen 6
S-740 71 Oregrund
SWEDEN
Tel: (+46) 173-304-60
Fax: (+46) 173 309-76

Marten Marine Industries
P.O. Box 38484
Howick, Auckland
NEW ZEALAND
Tel: (+64) 9 576 3573
Fax: (+64) 9 576 2150

McQueen's Boatworks
11571 Twigg Place
Richmond, British Columbia
V5K 5C4
CANADA
Tel: (604) 235-4544
Fax: (604) 235-4516

Moonen Shipyards
P.O Box 3186
Veedam 1
5308 Aaslt
NETHERLANDS
Tel: (+31) 73 210094

Oy Nautor AB
P.O. Box 10
Pietarsaari 68601
FINLAND
Tel: (+358) 67-60111
Fax: (+358) 67-67364

Neptunus Shipyard
Veedam 1
5308 Aaslt
NETHERLANDS

Norship Europe
P.O. Box 6
Blackfield
Southampton, Hampshire SO4
1UP
ENGLAND
Tel: (+44) 703 243532
Fax: (+44) 703 893135

Oceanfast Pty., Ltd.
26 St. George's Terrace
Perth
W. Australia 6001
AUSTRALIA
Tel: (+61) 9 410-1900
Fax: (+61) 9 410-2095

Ortona Navi S.P.A.
Via Cervana 30
66026 Ortono (CH)
ITALY
Tel: (+39) 85 906-2817
Fax: (+39) 85 906-2922

Oyster Marine
Fox's Marina
Ipswich, Essex 1P2 8SA
ENGLAND
Tel: (+44) 473 688888
Fax: (+44) 473 686861
*Production and semi custom
yachts*

Pendennis Shipyard
The Docks
Falmouth, Cornwall, TR11
4NR
ENGLAND
Tel: (+44) 326-211344
Fax: (+44) 326-319253

Perini Navi
114-55048 Viareggio
Lucca
ITALY
Tel: (+39) 584 396639
Fax: (+39) 584 384207

Picchiotti Cantieri Navali
Darsena Italia
N. 42, 55049
Viareggio
ITALY
Tel: (+39) 584-45345
Fax: (+39) 584-31273

PKM
Sekzor
Tersaneleri
Bolgesi 81700
TURKEY

Porsius Group Inc.
Zuiderstraat 89
1486 ML West-Graftdijk
HOLLAND
Tel: (+31) 2981-1205
Fax: (+31) 2981-1680

President Marine
17 King Yeh Rd.
Kuan. Tein Industrial
TAIWAN

Royal Huisman Shipyard
Flevoweg 1
8325 PA
Vollenhove
HOLLAND
Tel: (+31) 5274-3131
Fax: (+31) 5274-3800
*Large luxury power and
sailing craft*

Salthouse NZ
Raine Rd.
Auckland
NEW ZEALAND

Sensation Yachts
11 Selwood Rd.
Henderson, Auckland
NEW ZEALAND
Tel: (+64) 9 837-2210
Fax: (+64) 9 836-1775

Souter Shipyard
Thetis Rd.
Cowes, Isle of Wight
ENGLAND
Tel: (+44) 983-29471

**Southern Pacific Batyard,
Ltd.**
28A Poland Rd.
Glenfield, Auckland 9
NEW ZEALAND
Tel: (+64) 9 444-9636
Fax: (+64) 9 444-9117

Sterling Yachts
P.O. Box 467
Paarden Eiland 7420
SOUTH AFRICA
Tel: (+27) 21 419 2930
Fax: (+27) 21 25 3201

Sunseeker Ltd.
27-31 Quay St.
Poole, Dorset
ENGLAND

Swede Ship
Box 704
S-572 28 Oskarshamn
SWEDEN
Tel: (+46) 491-85500
Fax: (+46) 491-15312

Tecnomarine Yachts
Via Pisana 13
55049 Viareggio
ITALY
Tel: (+39) 584-384466
Fax: (+39) 584-387630

Tencara
Via Della Chimica 5
30175
Porto Marghera
Venice
ITALY

Ultimar
AM
Seedeich
Bremerhaven
GERMANY

Valdettaro Shipyard
Via Liberta 12
19022 Le Grazie(SP)
ITALY
Tel: (+39) 187-900018
Fax: (+39) 187-901373

C. Van Lent & Zonen
Julianalaan 3
2159 La Kaag
THE NETHERLANDS
Tel: (+31) 2542-5941
Fax: (+31) 2542-4341
One of the Feadship building group

Vision Yachts
Clarence Botyard
East Cowes, Isle of Wight
ENGLAND

Walsteds Baadewerft A/S
Thuro
DK-5700 Svendborg
DENMARK
Tel: (+45) 62 205168
Fax: (+45) 62 205124

Boat Builders: Multihulls

If you are the type of sailor who likes to sail fast, have plenty of living space, and get into coves too shallow for monohulls, perhaps there is a multihull in your future. Multihulls offer conveniences not often found on monhulls. For instance, a 42 foot LOA multihull I was aboard recently offered a huge dining area over the bridge deck, 10 berths in the hulls, a galley, an engine compartment, and huge amounts of room on deck for sunbathing or just enjoying the view. Trimarans don't offer quite as much living space, but they are fast and comfortable.

So why doesn't everybody have a multihull? A major reason is because multihulls have a reputation for turning over. Let's put this problem in perspective, however. The initial part of the righting moment curve for a catamaran is much more vertical than for a monohull. That means it takes much more wind to make a multihull heel over. Whereas a monohull might be reefed in 20 knots of wind, a multihull will stand up to that breeze without reefing. But when the multihull is overpowered, the boat may turn completely over, whereas a monhull, when overpowered, returns to the upright after the wind gust passes. On the other hand, when the monohull is inverted, it usually sinks due to the weight of ballast, whereas a multihull usually stays afloat. Sailors have survived many days in an overturned multihull.

What type of multihull is best for you? That depends upon the type of sailing you want to do. If you are a go-fast, gung-ho sailor who wants only speed, you should look at the beamiest, lightest boat available. Stability is directly proportional to beam, so any increase in beam will result in an increase in stability, which in turn will give more speed, until the boat is more stable transversely than longitudinally. If, on the other hand, you want to live aboard, you should look at a large catamaran and see just how much space there is.

The major problem with living aboard a multihull is one of weight. The effect of increasing the load of stores or other gear has a much greater effect on speed and movement through the water than a similar increase in weight has on a monohull. This is because a multihull is substantially lighter than a monhull of the same length. For instance, a 40 foot monohull might weigh 20,000 lbs, so adding 1,000 lbs increases the total weight by only 5%. In contrast, a 40 foot cat might weigh 9,000 lbs, so the same 1,000 lbs would represent an 11% increase in weight. The cat, therefore, would be more adversely affected by the load.

Manufacturers of Multihulls

Sailing Multihulls

Burtis Boat Works
3 Maple Pl.
Glen Head, NY 11545
Tel: (516) 676-4201
Builders of the Cobra 35 and 45

Corsair Marine
3040 Terminal Marine, Inc.
Suite 200
National City, CA 91950
Tel: (619) 474-4661
Fax: (619) 474-6961
Builders of the F-24 and F-27

Dragonfly Sailboats, Inc.
29 Argyle Dr.
Northport, NY 11768
Tel: (516) 754-6238
Dragonfly swing-wing trimarans are available here

Edel Strat
U.S. Agent:
P.O. Box 112
Hopedale, MA 01747
Tel: (508) 478-5300

Fountaine Pajot
Zone Industrielle
17290 Aigrefeuille
FRANCE
Tel: (+33) 46 35 70 40
Fax: (+33) 46 35 50 10

Foutaine Pajot
Catamarine
43 Edgewater Rd.
Hull, MA 02045-2761
Tel: (617) 925-9668
Fax: (617) 925-3096

Fountaine Pajot
Les Voilures Sag lac
Bernard Larocque
Chicoutimi, Quebec G7H3Z4
CANADA

Endeavour International Corp.
6021 142nd Ave.
Clearwater, FL 34622
Tel: (813) 535-1269
Builders of Endeavour cats

Matrix Marine, Inc.
49 Fir St.
Mahtomedi, MN 55115
Tel: (612) 426-3922
Fax: (612) 426-7935
Builders of the Supercat 20 and 22

Mystere International
150 27th Ave.
Pt.- Calumet, Quebec J0N 1G1
CANADA
Tel: (514) 472-8042
One-design catamarans

PDQ Yachts, Inc.
1710 Charles St.
Whitby, Ontario L1N 1C2
CANADA
Tel: (416) 430-2582
Fax: (416) 430-8306
PDQ catamarans

Performance Cruising
P.O. Box 381
Mayo, MD 21106
Tel: (410) 798-5150
Fax: (410) 798-4781
Builders of the Gemini cats

Performance Catamarans, Inc.
1810 E. Borchard Ave.
Santa Ana, CA 92705
Tel: (714) 835-6416
Fax: (714) 541-6643

Prout Catamarans Ltd.
Kings Close
Charfleets Industiral Estate
Canvey Isl., Essex SS8 OGY
ENGLAND
Tel: (+44) 26 8511500
Fax: (+44) 26 8510094
U.S. Agent:
Douglas Ziesel
P.O. Box 15466
Baltimore, MD 21220
Tel: (301) 687-3409

Tremolino Boat Co.
411 East 6th St.
Chaska, MN 53318
Tel: (612) 339-6717
Builders of Newick designed trimarans

Power Multihulls

Lightnin' Fiberglass
P.O. Box 268 Kilauea
Kauai, HI 96754
Tel: (808) 828-1583
Builder of the Cougar cat

Mares International
1535 S.E. 17th St.
Ft. Lauderdale, FL 33316
Tel: (305) 523-2287
Fax: (305) 523-2236
Makers of a line of high-performance catamarans

North American Fiberglass Corp.
P.O. Drawer C
Greenville, NC 27835
Tel: (919) 758-9901
Fax: (919) 758-4387
Power catamarans

Ocean Designs, Inc.
P.O. Box 981
Biloxi, MS 39533
Tel: (601) 875-3267
Builders of the Manta power catamaran

PDQ Yachts, Inc.
1710 Charles St.
Whitby, Ontario L1N 1C2
CANANDA
Builders of the PDQ 36

Pacific Boat Sales, Inc.
P.O. Box 4010
Kailua-Kona, HI 96740
Tel: (808) 325-5000
Fax: (808) 325-7023
Builders of the Kevlacat International

Performance Cruising, Inc.
P.O. Box 381
Mayo, MD 21106
Tel: (410) 798-5150
Fax: (410) 798-4781
Builders of the Gemini cats

Priviledge Yachting
1650 S.E. 17th St.
Suite 204
Ft. Lauderdale, FL 33316
Tel: (305) 462-6706
Fax: (305) 462-6104
Importers of the French designed and built Euphorie 40 catamaran

Prout Catamarans
Kings Close
Charfleets Industiral Estate
Canvey Isl., Essex SS8 OGY
ENGLAND
Tel: (+44) 26 8511500
Fax: (+44) 26 8510094
U.S. Agent:
Douglas Ziesel
P.O. BOX 15466
Baltimore, MD 21220
Tel: (301) 687-3409

Ultress Boats
P.O. Box 7115
Hilton Head, SC 29938
Tel: (803) 757-5790
Builders of the Ultress catamaran

Windmar International, Inc.
3330 N.E. Indian River Dr.
Jensen Beach, FL 34957
Tel: (407) 334-6580
Fax: (407) 334-1510
Power and sailing catamarans

Boat Builders: Production Power

By Charles W. Neville

Charles Neville is a naval architect with over fifteen years of experience. He has designed luxury yachts of over 100 feet and consulted on the design of ships several hundred feet long. He is also one of the most prolific designers of motor catamarans in the commercial excursion market. In recent years his work has focused mainly on moderately sized long-range power cruisers and motorsailers. He also writes for many of the leading yachting magazines.

If you are looking for the perfect boat, it doesn't exist. People who are holding out for some perfect combination generally become the most disillusioned in their search. Some people use their 30 footers unmercifully, but I know of many others whose "platinum plated" 70 footers sit like unused shrine behind their homes or in the marina. Ultimately, the best boat is the one you actually use and enjoy.

The most important part of buying a boat is getting one that is right for the kind of boating you do. Buying a "world cruiser" for bass fishing is as inappropriate as planning a deep water passage in a center console runabout. How do you make the right decision?

KNOWING WHAT YOU WANT

First and most important, you need to decide what kind of boating interests you.

This decision becomes the basis for the rest of your search. Next, make a realistic evaluation of your lifestyle. How is your boating likely to fit in (not how you would like it to fit in)? How much time will work and family allow you to spend on the water? Is time spent at the dock or working on the boat as important to you as time spent underway? How many people will be boating with you on day trips or overnight? Does your husband or wife give the same answers to these questions as you do? This kind of personal inventory, if you are honest, should at least keep you from shopping 55 foot cruisers when your boating horizons encompass an eleven acre pond.

The next thing to do is to seek out others who do the kind of boating that interests you. What kind of boats do these "experienced" boaters consider reasonable for the job. If you are a bass fisherman introduce yourself to other bass fishers. Talk with people at the yacht club. Read relevant magazine articles and reviews. Armed with this wisdom of "the experts" (critically assessed, of course) you are now ready to take on the professionals: the people who talk boats for a living.

Now, there are many wonderful people out there selling boats. Some have more experience than you or I will have in a lifetime. They try to do their job honestly and provide a valuable service to the customer. But, and this is a big "but," never lose sight of the fact that their goal in this transaction is decidedly different from yours. Question things. Remember, a boat that is too good to be true probably is. Look for boats that fall into the middle ground of vessels of your chosen type. Radical departures from the norm may be excellent choices for people knowledgeable enough to understand all the tradeoffs involved, but the novice should avoid them.

SOME ASSESSMENT TOOLS

It also helps to have some tools to sort out the differences between similar boats. First, you need some tools for assessing boat size. We are all accustomed to thinking of boats by length alone. Like any other structure, however, boats get bigger or smaller in three dimensions: length, width, and depth. From the brochure, you can get the load waterline length (LWL) and the maximum beam. The third variable, the depth, can be approximated. Depth is the vertical measurement from the bottom of the hull, excluding the keel, to the side deck of a typical cruiser. Keep all the numbers in the same unit (i.e., feet or inches). Multiply these three dimensions to determine what's called the Cubic Number (CN) of a vessel. You can then compare vessel size by CN. For example:

LWL x Beam x Depth = CN

Boat # 1: 46 x 15 x 7 = 4830

Boat # 2: 50 x 17 x 8 = 6800

Dividing the CN of boat #2 by the CN of boat # 1 yields a ratio of 1.41. Although their lengths are not dramatically different, boat # 2 is almost 40% bigger than boat #1. You might therefore expect boat #2 to cost more to buy, outfit, maintain, and operate. As larger deck structures come into play, you may choose to adapt this formula to be sure you are examining the true volume.

A second consideration is how heavy a boat is compared to its length. Boats that are very light may be under-built at one extreme, or may be very expensive (with ultra-sophisticated, "high tech" materials) at the other extreme. The displacement/length ratio (D/L) can help you judge the length-to-weight relationship for a given vessel and how it compares with other boats. It tells a lot about how a boat may be expected to perform. The formula for calculating the D/L ratio is:

$$\frac{\text{Displacement in lbs/2240}}{\text{Waterline length /100}^3}$$

This ratio is considered non-dimensional. Whether you are considering a 20 footer or a 120 footer, a low D/L means a lightweight boat. By the same token, a high D/L indicates a vessel that is heavy for its length.

Planing hulls will generally fall into the 130 to 225 D/L range. Light weight is essential to operate these boats at higher speeds. A moderate-speed, semi-planing boat might be expected to be in the 225 to 300 D/L range. Heavy, full-displacement power boats are commonly in the 300-400 range and above. Heavy boats are most efficient at low speeds. High or even moderate speeds may be impractical or even impossible for very heavy boats to achieve.

Performance is also judged by the relationship between boat speed and the vessel's waterline length. The speed/length ratio (S/L), another non-dimensional number, provides an indication of how fast a boat is relative to its length. A realistic vessel speed is important when comparing S/Ls. If you can, evaluate speeds for a comparable loading condition (i.e., with tanks full). The speed/length ratio formula is:

$$\frac{\text{Vessel speed in knots}}{\sqrt{\text{Waterline length}}}$$

An S/L of less than 1.3 or 1.4 indicates that the vessel is operating at displacement speeds. Generally, that means low power can yield excellent efficiencies. Above about 1.4 but below 2.5 or 3.0 puts the vessel into a semi-displacement (or semi-planing) range. This is generally one of the most inefficient ranges. Here the yacht is fighting to get up on top of the water and become fully planing. Boats that operate solely within this semi-displacement range cannot fully plane. They aren't light enough, don't have the right shape, lack enough horsepower, or some combination of the three. They can only "keep trying" to climb on top of the water. Significant fuel consumption is usually the result. Once the S/L goes over 2.5 or 3.0 the vessel is operating at a true planing speed. Planing speeds can range up to S/L's of 8 and beyond. The higher the number, the faster the yacht is traveling in relation to its length. Here speed and horsepower go hand in hand. So

does fuel consumption.

The S/L can help you categorize the performance of a boat and separate truth from sales hype. For instance, a "trawler yacht type" vessel operating at an S/L of 2.5 is probably not a true world cruiser, and a "planing type" cruiser wallowing around at a S/L of 1.3 is just an uncomfortable displacement boat.

GETTING SPECIFIC

You now have a general idea of the kind of boat that best suit your needs, and a few simple tools that can help you evaluate different ones. It is time to get more specific. For sport fishing, you are probably looking for a relatively beamy boat capable of getting you to the fishing grounds in a hurry. A planing hull of some type will likely do the best job. The ease with which you can fish is important, too. That suggests a large cockpit and low enough freeboard so that you can lean over the side without falling. Stern doors, bait wells, or other features become appropriate as boat size increases.

If overnight trips are part of the adventure, determine the fewest berths you need most of the time. Four good berths are often bettter than six uncomfortable ones. A couple of sleeping bags on the deck may be a satisfactory alternative for occasional use. Engine performance and durability should also be high on your list of features to look for. Engines that handle both high-speed and trolling conditions are essential.

Commuters and high-speed sport boats are a special breed. Deep-V hulls are considered the norm. These boats tend to be lightweight for speed, but structures should be very well reinforced to take punishment in a seaway. In addition to strong structures, reliable mechanicals should be paramount. If you are not able to do your own mechanical work, stay away from the truly exotic high-speed boats. Offshore in a seaway is no place to figure out the finer points of turbocharger adjustment.

Boats in this category perform best in open water. Since they can achieve speeds of over eighty miles per hour, they typically use very large engines. The net outcome is a substantial bill at the fuel dock, so be realistic as to the operating costs if you really plan to use the boat.

The upper end of deep-V monohulls and some catamarans are true racing boats. Like many racing machine, these boats are not for the timid. They are probably not the best choice unless your goal is serious racing (or drug smuggling). Extremely highly strung, these machines require plenty of time and ambition to keep running at their peak. Even more importantly, at speeds that can achieve more than 100 miles an hour, these boats are downright dangerous in the hands of the inexperienced. Before you purchase one, seek out professional courses and training like those offered by the American Power Boat Association (APBA).

Selecting a boat for cruising, or for full-time living aboard, is a very personal choice. The right arrangement for one family may be totally inappropriate for another. You have to examine your own priorities. If you are living aboard, be wary of the boat that is loaded with a great many household amenities. They are terrific at dockside, but you won't want to spend an hour securing everything before heading off for a sunset cruise. Unfortunately, many liveaboards get trapped into rarely leaving the dock because securing all their stuff becomes such an unpleasant project.

Economy becomes more of an issue if your crusies will be long, as does fuel capacity. If you are spending much of your time underway, consider engine noise-control essential. The reliability of machinery should also be a major concern, with simplicity a prime objective. Make sure that you can get at every part and piece of the boat. Everything you are buying will need to be serviced sooner or later.

Finally, look for the minimum boat that will do most of what you need. As our size comparison showed, a boat that's a bit bigger can take a lot more time and money to maintain. A ten dollar part on one boat can carry a hundred dollar price tag on a boat that's "just a little bit bigger."

Manufacturers of Production Power Boats

Abbott Boats Ltd.
1458 London Rd.
Sarnia, Ontario N7S 1P7
CANADA
Tel: (519) 542-2771
Fax: (519) 542-2324
Builders of the Abbot 22

**Able Custom
Yachts/Trenton Marine,
Inc.**
P.O. Box 8055
Bar Harbor Airport Rd.
Trenton, ME 04605
Tel: (207) 667-6235
Fax: (207) 667-3986
*Builders of the Able 42 coastal
crusing yacht*

Academy Yachts
P.O. Box 1204
Melville, NY 11747
Tel: (516) 842-0257
Fax: (516) 842-8261
*Sport-fishing boats and motor
yachts*

Advantage Boats
4530 Eisenhower Circle
Anaheim, CA 92807
Tel: (714) 970-2634
*Builders of sport boats, party
cats, and runabouts*

Aero-Fino Marine
P.O. Box 1181
Pt. Pleasant, NJ 08742
Tel: (908) 295-9295
Fax: (908) 892-7236
*High performance and
sport-fishing boats*

**Aero-Tek High
Performance, Inc.**
2360 Whitfield Park Ave.
Sarasota, FL 34243
Tel: (813) 753-3582
Fax: (813) 758-7097
*Builders of limited edition
high-performance boats*

Albemarle Boats
P.O. Box 349
Hwy 17S
Edenton, NC 27932-0349
Tel: (919) 482-7423
Fax: (919) 482-8289
Builders of sport-fishing boats

Albin Marine, Inc.
P.O. Box 228
143 River Rd.
Cos Cob, CT 06807
Tel: (203) 661-4341
Fax: (203) 661-6040
*Importers of the Albin trawler
yachts*

Alexander Marine Co. Ltd.
Sturgeon Bay Yacht Harbor
306 Nautical Dr.
Sturgeon Bay, WI 54235
Tel: (414) 743-3311
Fax: (414) 743-4298
*Builders of the Classico
trawler yachts*

Alexander Yachts, Inc.
2150 S.E. 17th St.
Ft. Lauderdale, FL 33316
Tel: (305) 763-7676
Fax: (305) 763-7758
*Builders of the Classico
trawler yachts*

Allweather Boats, Inc.
2353 Mt. View Rd.
Ferndale, WA 98248
Tel: (206) 384-4686
28 foot double-ender

Alshaali Marine USA
2710 Westlake Ave. N.
Seattle, WA 98109
Tel: (206) 270-0130
Fax: (206) 285-7121

Altech Yachts, Inc.
1500 Cordova Rd.
Ft. Lauderdale, FL 33316
Tel: (305) 462-0400
Fax: (305) 462-4968
Motor yacht builders

American Offshore
Highway 59
Grove, OK 74344
Tel: (918) 786-2875
*Builders of the American
Offshore high-performance
catamaran*

American Skier Boat Co.
P.O. Box 150065
Cape Coral, FL 33915
Tel: (813) 574-4612
Fax: (813) 574-5084
Powerboats and ski boats

The Anchorage, Inc.
57 Miller St.
Warren, RI 02885
Tel: (401) 245-3300
Fax: (401) 245-3302
*Builders of Dyer cruising
powerboats*

Angler Boat Corp.
4450 N.W. 128th St.
Miami, FL 33054
Tel: (305) 681-4990
Fax: (305) 685-3845
*Builder of center-console
sport-fishing boats*

Answer Marine Corp.
9500 N.W. 36th Ave.
Miami, FL 33147
Tel: (305) 836-1033
Fax: (305) 836-1040
Sportfishing boat builders

Apache Performance
2800 N. 30th ave.
Hollywood, FL 33020
Tel: (305) 920-1455
Fax: (305) 920-1466
*High-performance powerboat
builders*

Aquasport
A Genmar Industries
Company
1651 Whitfield Ave.
Sarasota, FL 34243-3948
Tel: (813) 755-5800
Fax: (813) 751-7808
Builders of sport-fishing boats

Atlantic Yacht Corp.
P.O. Box 1318
Palatka, FL 32178-1318
Tel: (800) 325-6460
  or (904) 328-8348
Fax: (904) 329-2231
Builders of sportfishing boats

Atlas Boat Works, Inc.
P.O. Box 2011
Cape Coral, FL 33910
Tel: (813) 574-2628
*Builders of lobster-style
pleasure and work boats*

Baha Cruisers
Division of F.R.P. Industries,
Inc.
P.O. Box 478
Highway 51 N.
Mayo, FL 32066
Tel: (904) 294-2431
Fax: (904) 294-2065
*Builders of Baha cruisers and
fishing boats*

Baia of America
2541 N.W. 74th Ave.
Miami, FL 33122
Tel: (305) 522-0677
*Builder of high-performance
boats*

Baja Boats, Inc.
P.O. Box 151
1520 Isaac Beal Rd.
Bucyrus, OH 44820
Tel: (419) 562-5377
Fax: (419) 562-8458
*Builders of the Baja express
and power cruisers*

Figure 1: The deck plan of a
typical sportfishing boat.

Banana Boat Ltd.
1128 Narragansett Blvd.
Cranston, RI 02905
Tel: (401) 941-2000
Fax: (401) 941-2202
*Center-console and offshore 24
footer*

Barnegat Yacht
P.O. Box 1181
Pt. Pleasant, NJ 08742
Tel: (908) 295-9295
Fax: (908) 892-7236
*High-performance and
sport-fishing boats*

Bartel Boats
Box 719 Dock Rd.
Remsenburg, NY 11960
Tel: (516) 325-1677
Fax: (516) 325-1035
*Builders of a 22 and 34 foot
high-performance boats*

Bayliner Marine Corp.
A Brunswick Marine Company
Product Information Services
P.O. Box 3800
Mt. Olive, NJ 07828
Tel: (800) 443-9119
*Builders of the Bayliner series
of sport boats and motor yachts*

Bayliner Marine Corp.
A Brunswick Marine Company
P.O. Box 9029
Everett, WA 98206
Tel: (206) 435-5571
Fax: (206) 435-9849
*Builders of the Bayliner series
of sport boats and motor yachts*

Bay Marine
P.O. Box 595
Clearwater, FL 34617
Tel: (813) 441-2066

Beckman, Ltd.
P.O. Box 97
Wakefield, RI 02880-0097
Tel: (401) 783-1859
Builders of pleasure tugs

Bertram Yacht
3663 N.W. 21 St.
Miami, FL 33142
Tel: (305) 633-8011
Fax: (305) 635-1388
Builder of Bertram yachts

Black Fin Yacht
P.O. Box 22982
Ft. Lauderdale, FL 33335
Tel: (305) 535-6314
Fax: (305) 523-7728
Builders of the Blackfin line of sport-fishing boats

Black Thunder Powerboats, Inc.
2244 Warren Barrett Dr.
Hannibal, MO 63401
Tel: (314) 221-3311
Fax: (314) 221-2444
High-performance power boats

Black Watch Corp.
One Little Harbor Landing
Portsmouth, RI 02870
Tel: (401) 683-5600
Fax: (401) 683-3009
Builders of sport-fishing boats

Blount Industries, Inc.
461 Water St.
Warren, RI 02885
Tel: (401) 245-8300
Fax: (401) 245-8303
Steel and aluminum workboats, ferries, fishing, and pleasure craft

Blue Water Boats, Inc.
P.O. Box 70091
Eugene, OR 97401
Tel: (503) 741-1111
Fax: (503) 741-2885
Builders of Blue Water sport-fishing boats

Bluewater Marine
811 East Maple
Mora, MN 55051
Tel: (612) 679-3811
Fax: (612) 679-3820
Builders of the Bluewater cruising power yachts

Boating Corp. of America
P.O. Box 8126
365 Maple St.
Gallatin, TN 37066
Tel: (615) 452-4343
Fax: (615) 451-0352
Builders of Harbor Master motor yachts

Bonner Aero Marine Corp.
P.O. Box 8888
La Jolla, CA 92038-8888
Tel: (619) 272-7000
Builders of new technology powerboats

Boston Whaler, Inc.
1149 Hingham St.
Rockland, MA 02370
Tel: (800) WHALERS Ext. 201
 or (617) 871-1400
Fax: (617) 871-6462
Builders of the unsinkable Boston Whalers

Bounty Hunter Yachts
6473 Crater Lake Hwy.
Central Point, OR 97502
Tel: (503) 826-8877
Fax: (503) 826-9086
Sport-fishing boats

Braginton Boat Co.
Stuart Island Airway Park
Friday Harbor, WA 98250
Tel: (206) 378-5906

Broward Marine
1601 S.W. 20th St.
Ft. Lauderdale, FL 33315
Tel: (305) 522-1701
Fax: (305) 522-1884
Builders of fast luxury power yachts

Cabo Sportfishers by Cat Harbor Boats
9780 Rancho Rd.
Adelanto, CA 92301
Tel: (619) 246-8917
Fax: (619) 246-8970
Sport-fishing boats

Cadorette Marine Co.
P.O. Box 727
1991 3rd Ave.
Grand-Mere, Quebec G9T 2W6
CANADA
Tel: (819) 538-0781
Builders of the Thundercraft series of family sport and sport-fishing boats

Cape Craft
5567 Doug Taylor
St. James City, FL 33956
Tel: (813) 283-1626
Fax: (813) 283-4676
Builders of Cape Craft sport-fishing boats

Cape Dory Yachts
334 S. Bayview Ave.
Amityville, NY 11701
Tel: (516) 264-1313
Fax: (516) 264-1316

Cape Island Boats
163 Rocky Hill Rd.
Brewster, MA 02631
Tel: (508) 385-8094
*Builders of lobster and
pleasure boats*

Caravelle Boats, Inc.
111 Mathews Dr.
P.O. Box 1899
Americau, GA 31709
Tel: (912) 924-1185
*Builder of the Caravelle
Classic line of sport boats*

Carrara Boats
1501 Pomona Rd.
Corona, CA 91720
Tel: (714) 735-7000
Builder of a line of sport boats

Carri-Craft Catamarans
P.O. Box 4
328 Ripon Rd.
Berlin, WI 54923
Tel: (414) 361-4566
Fax: (414) 361-4570
*Builder of Carri-Craft
catamarans*

Carver Boat Corp.
P.O. Box 1010
790 Markham Dr.
Pulaski, WI 54162-1010
Tel: (414) 822-3214
Fax: (414) 822-8820
Builder of Carver yachts

Cat Harbor Boats, Inc.
9780 Rancho Rd.
Adelanto, CA 92301
Tel: (619) 246-8917
Fax: (619) 246-8970
Cabo 35 sport-fishing boat

Cee Bee Mfg., Inc.
11511 Bellinger St.
Lynwood, CA 90262
Tel: (310) 537-0073
*Builder of the Avenger line of
sport boats*

Celebrity Boats, Inc.
P.O. Box 394
451 E. Illinois Ave.
Benton, IL 62812
Tel: (800) 328-1422
  or (618) 439-9444
Fax: (618) 435-4063
*Builder of the Celebrity line of
sport cruisers and fishing
boats*

Century Boats
6725 Bay Line Dr.
Panama City, FL 32404
Tel: (904) 769-0311
Fax: (904) 769-0731
Sport boat builders

Chaparral Boats, Inc.
P.O. Drawer 928
Nashville, GA 31639
Tel: (912) 686-7481
Fax: (912) 686-3660
*Builders of the Chaparral line
of power cruisers*

Charter Boat Mfg.
(Eagle Boats)
200 Naco Rd.
Suite A
Ft. Pierce, FL 34946
Tel: (407) 468-2111
Fax: (407) 464-0205
Eagle sport-fishing boats

Checkmate Boats, Inc.
P.O. Box 723
3691 State Road 4 North
Bucyrus, OH 44820
Tel: (419) 562-3881
Fax: (419) 562-0632
*Builder of performance
pleasure boats*

Cheoy Lee Shipyards, Ltd.
863 Lai Chi Kok Rd.
Kowloon
HONG KONG
Tel: (852) 743-7710
*Builders of the Cheoy Lee line
of power and sailing yachts*

**Chesapeake Custom Yacht
Company**
402 Brookletts Ave.
Easton, MD 21601
Tel: (410) 822-1977
Fax: (410) 822-4692
Builders of the Dettling 48

Chris-Craft Boats
8161 15th St., East
Sarasota, FL 34243
Tel: (813) 351-4900
Fax: (813) 351-8914
*Builders of a line of sport and
power cruisers*

Cigarette Racing Team
3131 N.E. 188th St.
N. Miami Beach, FL 33180
Tel: (305) 931-4564
Fax: (305) 935-0276
*Builders of high-performance
deep-V craft*

Clark Island Boat Works
Rte. 73, P.O. Box 113
South Thomaston, ME 04858
Tel: (207) 594-4112
Lobster boat builder

Cobalt Boats
P.O. Box 29 1101 Illinois St.
Neodesha, KS 66757
Tel: (316) 325-2653
Fax: (316) 325-2361
*Builders of inboard/outboard
sport boats*

Cobia Boat Co.
P.O. Box 99
200 Cobia Dr.
Vonore, TN 37885
Tel: (407) 323-3100
Fax: (407) 323-4515
*Builders of the Cobia line of
sport boats*

Commander Boats
Hwy. 59
Grove, OK 74344
Tel: (918) 786-2875
Fax: (918) 786-6756
*Builder of American Offshore
catamarans*

Concept Boats
2159 N. W. 23rd Ave.
Miami, FL 33142
Tel: (305) 635-8712
Fax: (305) 635-9543
*Builder of the Concept
sport-fishing boats*

Contender Boats, Inc.
395 N.E. 59th St.
Miami, FL 33137
Tel: (305) 759-0690
Fax: (305) 757-0540
Builders of sport-fishing boats

Cooper Yachts Ltd.
23352 Fisherman Rd. maple
Ridge, B.C. V2X 7E6 CANADA
Tel: (604) 463-1077
*Builders of mid-sized motor
yachts*

Correct Craft, Inc.
P.O. Box 13389
6100 S. Orange Ave.
Orlando, FL 32809
Tel: (800) 346-2092
Fax: (407) 851-7844
Builders of inboard ski-boats

Covey Island Boatworks
2 River Rd.
Petite Riviere, Nova Scotia
BOJ2PO
CANADA
Tel: (902) 688-2843
*Pleasure and sportfishing
lobster-style boats*

**Crescent Beach Boat
Builders**
1200 Westlake Ave.
Suite 414
Seattle, WA 98109
Tel: (206) 298-3630
Fax: (206) 284-0487
*Custom and production power
yachts*

Crosby Yacht Yard, Inc.
72 Crosby Circle
Osterville, MA 02655
Tel: (508) 428-6958
Fax: (508) 428-0323
Sport-fishing boats and tugs

Crownline Boats, Inc.
Rt. 4, Box 339A
W. Frankfort, IL 62896
Tel: (618) 937-6426
Fax: (618) 937-2277
*Builders of bow rider, cuddy
cabin, and cruising boats*

Cruisers, Inc.
Division of Cruistar
804 Pecor St.
Oconto, WI 54153
Tel: (414) 834-2211
*Builders of family sport and
express cruisers*

Dansair
3460 Yacht Club Dr. #908
Aventura, FL 33180
Tel: (305) 936-8494
Airboats

Davis Yachts, Inc.
P.O. Box 609
Wanchese, NC 27981
Tel: (919) 473-1111
Fax: (919) 473-2603
Builders of sport-fishing boats

DeFever Yachts
2730 Shelter Island Dr.
San Diego, CA 92106
Tel: (619) 222-2414
Fax: (619) 225-0930
Importers of DeFever yachts

Delta Boats
770 Mullet Rd.
Cape Canaveral, FL 32920
Tel: (407) 783-3536
Fax: (407) 784-6407
Sport-fishing boat builder

Devlin Boat Builders
2424 Gravelly Beach Loop
N.W.
Olympia, WA 98502
Tel: (206) 866-0164
*Builders of fantail power
cruisers*

Dorado Marine, Inc.
1401 N. Myrtle Ave.
Clearwater, FL 34615
Tel: (813) 447-2171
Fax: (813) 446-5707
Sport-fishing boat builder

Doral Boats Ltd.
P.O. Box 667
1991 3rd Ave.
Grand-Mere, Quebec G9T 2W6
CANADA
Tel: (819) 538-0781
*Builders of the Doral line of
family sport cruisers*

Douglas Marine
Box 819
Douglas, MI 49406
Tel: (616) 857-4308
Fax: (616) 857-1606
*Builders of the Skater line of
high-performance catamarans*

Duffy & Duffy
H.C.R. 64, Box 383
Brooklin, ME 04616
Tel: (207) 359-4658
Fax: (207) 359-8948
*Builders of lobster, tuna, and
pleasure boats*

Dusky Marine
110 N. Bryan Rd.
Dania, Fl 33004
Tel: (305) 945-9564
Fax: (305) 925-1548
Builder of Dusky boats

Dynasty Boats
P.O. Box 310
Vinemont, AL 35179
Tel: (205) 739-4182
Fax: (205) 739-4185
Sport boat builders

Edey & Duff Ltd.
128 Aucoot Rd.
Mattapoisett, MA 02739
Tel: (508) 758-2743
Builders of sport-fishing boats

Egg Harbor Yacht Co.
P.O. Box 375
801 Philadelphia Ave.
Egg Harbor City, NJ 08215
Tel: (609) 965-2300
Fax: (609) 965-2870
Sport-fishing boat builders

ELCO/Electric Launch Co.
261 Upper North Rd.
Highland, NY 12528
Tel: (914) 691-3777
Builders of the ELCO replicas

Eliminator
10795 San Sevaine
Mira Loma, CA 91752
Tel: (714) 681-1222
Fax: (714) 685-4187
*Eliminator manufactures more
than 30 different models of
sport, ski, and offshore
power-boats*

Ellis Boat Co., Inc.
Box 20
Seawall Rd.
Manset, ME 04656
Tel: (207) 244-9221
Fax: (207) 244-9222
*Builders of lobster-boat-style
cruising yachts*

Envision Boats, Inc.
P.O. Box 706
500 W. Harlem Ave.
Monmouth, IL 61462
Tel: (309) 734-4365
Fax: (309) 734-4159
Builder of sport boats

Excel
1651 Whitfield Ave.
Sarasota, FL 34243
Tel: (813) 751-7896
*Builders of the Excel line of
runabouts and sport boats*

Express Marine Boats
9483 Smith St.
Algonac, MI 48001
Tel: (313) 794-5551
Fax: (313) 794-1054
Offshore catamaran powerboat

Fairbanks Yachts, Inc.
4720 Cowley Crescent
Richmond, B.C. V7B 1C1
CANADA
Tel: (604) 273-3955
Fax: (604) 273-7236
*Sport-fishing and pleasure
boat builder*

Falmouth Yachts, Inc.
510 D 31st St.
Newport Beach, CA 92663
Tel: (714) 723-4225
*Importers of the Fleming line
of motor yachts*

Florida Bay Coaster Co.
957 Bulkhead Rd.
Green Cove Springs, FL 32043
Tel: (904) 284-2230
*Builders of the Florida Bay
coaster trawler yachts*

Flye Point Marine, Inc.
P.O. Box 217
Brooklin, ME 04616
Tel: (207) 359-4641
Fax: (207) 359-2372
Builders of lobster-boat-style
cruising yachts

Foley Boatbuilding, Inc.
Cutts Island
Kittery Point, ME 03905
Tel: (207) 439-3601
Fax: (207) 439-8889
Builders of the Sisu
lobster-boat-style craft

Forester Boat Co., Inc.
124 North Walnut
Mora, MN 55051
Tel: (612) 679-5700
Fax: (612) 679-3820
Builder of pleasure and
sport-fishing boats

Fortier Boats, Inc.
P.O. Box 264
34 Riverside Ave.
Somerset, MA 02726
Tel: (508) 673-5253
Fax: (508) 677-3211
Builders of Bassboats, lobster
boats, and pleasure craft

Fountain Powerboats
P.O. Drawer 457
2200 W. Monroe St.
Washington, NC 27889
Tel: (800) 736-7686
  or (919) 975-2000
Fax: (919) 975-6793
Builders of the Fountain line of
high-speed, deep-V powerboats

Four Winns, Inc.
4 Winn Way
Cadillac, MI 49601
Tel: (616) 775-1351
Fax: (616) 779-2359
Builders of the Four Winns
family sport boats

Game Fisherman, Inc.
4905 S.E. Dixie Hwy.
Stuart, FL 34997
Tel: (407) 220-4850
Fax: (407) 220-4851
Sport-fishing boats

Garwood Boat Co.
329 Broadway
Watervliet, NY 12189
Tel: (518) 273-2654
Fax: (518) 273-2654
Replica wooden runabouts

General Marine, Inc.
Airport Industrial Park
Biddeford, ME 04005
Tel: (207) 284-7517
Lobster-boat-style custom,
pleasure, or tuna boats

H.T. Gozzard & Associates
P.O. Box 373
Goderich, Ontario N7A 4C6
CANADA
Tel: (519) 524-6393
Fax: (519) 524-9180
Builders of the Pilgrim power
cruising yacht line

Godfrey Marine
22787 County Rd. 14
Elkhart, IN 46516
Tel: (219) 522-8381
Fax: (219) 522-5120
Builders of the Hurricane
series of sport boats

Grady-White Boats
P.O. Box 1527
Greenville Blvd.
P.O. Box 1527
Greenville, NC 27835-1527
Tel: (919) 752-2111
Fax: (919) 752-4217
Grady White sport-fishing
boats have an enviable
reputation

Grand Banks Yachts Ltd.
563 Steamboat Rd.
Greenwich, CT 06830
Tel: (203) 869-9274
Importers of the Grand Banks
line of trawler yachts

Hacker Boat Company
Route 9-N
Silver Bay, NY 12874
Tel: (518) 543-6731
Fax: (518) 543-6732
Builder of mahogany
runabouts

Hallett Boats
5820 Martin Rd.
Irwindale, CA 91706
Tel: (818) 969-8844
Builders of a line of
performance ski, racing, and
pleasure boats

Halvorsen Marine, Ltd.
P.O. Box 79259
Mongkok Post Office
Kowloon
HONG KONG
Tel: (+852) 497-6298

Harbors Cove Marina, Inc.
5550 Merrick Rd.
Massapequa, NY 11758
Tel: (516) 797-6700
Fax: (516) 797-6705
*Dealers for the Fastlane 40
deep-V, high-performance boat*

Harley Boat Co.
300 S. First Ave.
Bartow, FL 33830
Tel: (813) 533-2800
Fax: (813) 533-0787
*Production and
semi-production sport and
motor yachts*

Hatteras Yachts
P.O. Box 2690
2100 Kivett Dr.
High Point, NC 27261
Tel: (919) 889-6621
Fax: (919) 889-4257
*Builders of the Hatteras line of
yachts*

Henriques Boat Works
198 Hilton Ave.
Bayville, NJ 08721
Tel: (908) 269-1180
Fax: (908) 269-1606
*Builders of sport-fishing boats
and lobster-style workboats*

**High-Tech Yacht and Ship,
Inc.**
1535 S.E. 17th St.,
Ft. Lauderdale, FL 33316
Tel: (305) 524-6911
Fax: (305) 524-7107

The Hinckley Co.
P.O. Box 699
Shore Rd.
Southwest Harbor, ME 04679
Tel: (207) 244-5531
Fax: (207) 244-9833

Hi-Star Yachts
ZK Marine 801 N.E. 3rd St.
Dania, FL 33004
Tel: (305) 923-7441

Holiday Mansion
Division of Mohawk, Inc.
2328 Hein Ave.
Salina, KS 67401
Tel: (913) 827-4602
Fax: (913) 827-8138
*Holiday mansion manufacture
a line of tour boats, ferry boats,
and patrol boats*

Hoog Boats, Inc.
10481 S.W. 184th Terr.
Miami, FL 33157
Tel: (305) 255-1651
Fax: (305) 252-0289
23, 24 foot bass boats

Huckins Yacht Corp.
3482 Lakeshore Blvd.
Jacksonville, FL 32210
Tel: (904) 389-1125
*Builders of luxurious
performance sport-fishing
boats*

Hustler Industries, Inc.
124 Springville Rd.
Hampton Bays, NY
11946-3028
Tel: (516) 728-8282
Fax: (516) 728-8203
Offshore performance boats

Hydra-Sports
OMC Fishing Boat Group
880 Butler Dr.
Murfreesboro, TN 37130
Tel: (615) 895-5190
Fax: (615) 895-5195
Builders of sport-fishing boats

Infinity Yachts
2698 S.W. 23rd Ave.
Ft. Lauderdale, FL 33312
Tel: (305) 581-3313
Fax: (305) 797-8986

Intrepid Powerboats, Inc.
6101 45th St. N.
St. Petersburg, Fl 33714
Tel: (305) 922-7544
Fax: (305) 922-3858
Builder of Intrepid yachts

Invader Marine
P.O. Box 420
Giddings, TX 78942
Tel: (409) 542-3101
Builder of sport-fishing boats

Island Gypsy/Halvorsen
138 Wharf Rd.
Warwick, RI 02889
Tel: (401) 737-2233
Fax: (401) 737-2207
*Importers of the Island Gypsy
line of cruising power yachts
(see also Halvorsen Marine
under Foreign Boatbuilders)*

Island Hopper Boats, Inc.
P.O. Box 3958
Ft. Pierce, FL 34984
Tel: (800) 827-2480
   or (407) 468-6796
*Builders of commercial and
pleasure fishing boats*

**James Anthony
Powerboats**
222 Read St.
Northville, NY 12134
Tel: (518) 863-2626
*Builders of a gentleman's
runabout replica*

Jarvis Newman Boats
P.O. Box 707
Shore Rd.
Southwest Harbor, ME 04679
Tel: (207) 244-3860
*Builders of lobster-style
workboat hulls*

Javelin Boats
880 Butler Rd.
Murfreesboro, TN 37129
Tel: (615) 895-5190
Fax: (615) 895-5195
Javelin bass boats

Jeantot Marine
1650 SE 17th St.
Suite 204
Ft. Lauderdale, FL 33316
Tel: (305) 462-6506
*Builders of large cruising
catamarans*

Jefferson Yachts, Inc.
P.O. Box 790
700 E. Market St.
Jeffersonville, IN 47130
Tel: (812) 282-8111
Fax: (812) 288-7783
*Builders of a line of
comfortable motor yachts*

Jersey Yachts, Inc.
P.O. Box 588
Lumberton, NJ 08048
Tel: (609) 267-9200
Fax: (609) 261-6588
Sport-fishing boat builder

John M. Williams Co.
Hall Quarry
Mt. Desert, ME 04660
Tel: (207) 244-7854

Kadey-Krogen Yachts, Inc.
1310 N.W. 18th Ave.
Miami, FL 33125
Tel: (305) 326-0266
Fax: (305) 326-1498
*Builders of the Kadey-Krogen
trawler yacht*

Knight & Carver Marine
1500 Quivira Way
San Diego, CA 92109
Tel: (619) 222-6488

Knowles Boat Co.
450 S.W. Salerno Rd.
Stuart, FL 33497
Tel: (407) 286-5663
*Builders of high-quality
sport-fishing boats*

Larson Boats
Paul Larson Memorial Dr.
Little Falls, MN 56345
Tel: (612) 632-5481
Fax: (612) 632-1439
Sport boats

Lazzarra Yacht Corp.
5300 West Tyson Ave.
Tampa, FL 33611-3224
Tel: (813) 839-0090
Fax: (813) 831-5442
*Builders of a new line of
cockpit motor yachts*

Legnos Boats
973 North Rd.
Groton, CT 06340
Tel: (800) 231-6537
  or (203) 446-8058
*Builders of cruiser/trawler
yachts and work boats*

Lightnin' Fiberglass
P.O. Box 268 Kilauea
Kauai, HI 96754
Tel: (808) 828-1583
Builder of the Cougar Cat

Figure 2: The deck plan of
the Little Harbor 36

Little Harbor Yachts, Inc.
One Little Harbor Landing
Portsmouth, RI 02871
Tel: (401) 683-5600
*Builders of large production
and custom cruising sailboats*

Luhrs Corp.
255 Diesel Rd.
St. Augustine, FL 32086
Tel: (800) 829-5847
  or (904) 829-0500
Fax: (904) 829-0683
*Builders of the Luhrs line of
sport-fishing boats*

MDI Boatworks, Inc.
P.O. Box 60
S.W. Harbor, ME 04679
Tel: (207) 244-0000

Mach 1 Boats, Inc.
by Freedom Boats, Inc.
P.O. Box 410
600 W. 10th Ave.
Monmouth, IL 61462
Tel: (309) 734-2175
Fax: (309) 734-7645

Magic Boats, Inc.
2000 Industrial Blvd.
Lake Havasu City, AZ
Tel: (800) 776-7007
Fax: (602) 680-7667
Builders of catamaran
performance deck boats for
waterskiing and family fun

Magnum Boats
18204 Bothell Hwy.
Bothell, WA 98012
Tel: (206) 481-2628
Builders of aluminum work
boats and skiffs

Magnum Marine Corp.
2900 N.E. 188th St.
N. Miami Beach, FL 33180
Tel: (305) 931-4292
Fax: (305) 931-0088
Builders of high-performance
sport yachts

Mainship Motor Yachts
255 Diesel Rd.
St. Augustine, FL 32086
Tel: (800) 829-5847
  or (904) 829-0500
Fax: (904) 829-0683
Builders of the Mainship line
of express yachts between 36
and 47 feet

Mako Marine, Inc.
4355 N.W. 128th St.
Miami, FL 33054
Tel: (305) 685-6591
Fax: (305) 769-0940
Builders of the Mako
sport-fishing boat line

Manta Marine
2405 S.W. 57th Ave.
Hollywood, FL 33023
Tel: (305) 963-5887
Powerboats

Maple Bay Boat Works
1333 N. Northlake Way
Seattle, WA 98103
Tel: (206) 547-4780
Builders of the Maple Bay line
of traditional power cruisers

Mares Inc.
5225 S. Washington Ave.
Titusville, FL 32780
Tel: (407) 264-9929
Builders of the Mares
high-performance catamarans

Mares International
1535 S.E. 17th St.
Ft. Lauderdale, FL 33316
Tel: (305) 523-2287
Fax: (305) 523-2236
Sales office of the Mares
high-performance catamarans

Mariah Boats, Inc.
P.O. Box 1300
Benton, IL 62812
Tel: (618) 435-5300
Fax: (618) 435-3500
Builders of a line of
performance sport boats

Marine Trading
International
P.O. Box 5300
Rt 166
South Toms River, NJ
08754-5300
Tel: (908) 286-4000
Fax: (908) 349-6649
Trawlers and cruising motor
yachts

Marlin Yachts, Inc.
507 N.W. First Ave.
Ft. Lauderdale, FL 33301
Tel: (305) 728-9787
Fax: (305) 728-9783
Builders of sport-fishing boats

Master Craft Boat Co.
869 Binfield Rd.
Maryville, TN 37801
Tel: (615) 983-2178
Fax: (615) 977-9223
Runabouts and ski boat
builders

Maxum Marine
A division of US Marine
P.O. Box 9019
Everett, WA 98206-9029
Tel: (800) 829-9545
Fax: (206) 435-8034
Builders of the Maxum and
Quantum series of sport boats

Maxum Marine
A division of US Marine
P.O. Box 3900
Peoria, IL 61614-0986
Tel: (800) 635-7500
Builders of the Maxum series
of sport boats

Mediterranean Yachts
2500 S. Susan St.
Santa Ana, CA 92660
Tel: (714) 556-8920
Fax: (714) 241-9635
Builders of high-quality sport-fishing and cruising boats

Mediterranean Yachts
10445 49th St., N.
Clearwater, FL 34622
Tel: (813) 573-5413
Fax: (813) 572-4755
Builders of high-quality sport-fishing and cruising boats

Midnight Lace
Rex Mayer Yachts
1470 Dolgner Place
Sanford, FL 32771
Tel: (407) 323-6108

Mikelson Yachts
2330 Shelter Island Dr.
Suite 202
San Diego, CA 92106
Tel: (619) 222-5007
Builders of 48 and 50 foot sedan cruisers

Monterey Boats, Inc.
P.O. Box 70
212 Magnolis Dr.
Archer, FL 32618
Tel: (904) 495-3624
Fax: (904) 495-2044
Builders of the Monterey cruiser line of bowrider, cuddy and sport boats

Montgomery Yacht & Shipbuilding, Inc.
P.O. Box 550
Brick Kiln Rd.
Crisfield, MO 21817
Tel: (410) 968-3889
Builders of the Montgomery coaster trawler yachts

Nauset Marine, Inc.
Rt. 6A, Box 357
Orleans, MA 02653
Tel: (508) 255-0777
Builders of lobster-boat-style work boats

Neptunis Canada, Ltd.
8 Keefer St.
St. Catherine, Ontario L2M 7N9
CANADA
Tel: (416) 937-3737
Fax: (416) 937-2365
Builders of a line of luxurious sedan cruisers

Nordic Sportboats
770 N. Lake Havasu Ave.
Lake Havasu, AZ 86403
Tel: (602) 855-7420
Fax: (602) 855-0332
Builders of the Nordic line of sport boats

Nordic Tugs, Inc.
1197 Westar Lane
Burlington, WA 98233
Tel: (206) 757-8847
Builders of a line of pleasure tugs

North American Fiberglass Corp.
P.O. Drawer C
Greenville, NC 27835
Tel: (919) 758-9901
Fax: (919) 758-4387
Power catamarans

Ocean Designs, Inc.
P.O. Box 981
Biloxi, MS 39533
Tel: (601) 875-3267
Builders of the Manta power catamaran

Ocean Master Marine, Inc.
1142-B 53rd Court North
W. Palm Beach, FL 33407
Tel: (407) 863-7191
Fax: (407) 842-8340
Solidly built sport-fishing boats

Ocean Tech Marine, Inc.
P.O. Box 547
Dowell Rd./Calvert Marina
Solomons, MD 20688
Tel: (410) 326-2886

Ocean Yachts, Inc.
P.O. Box 312
Egg Harbor City, NJ 08215
Tel: (609) 965-4616
Fax: (609) 965-4914
Builders of the Ocean series of motor and sport-fishing yachts

Offshore Marine Performance, Inc.
7811 N.W. 62nd St.
Miami, FL 33166
Tel: (305) 477-7822
Fax: (305) 477-7840
Builders of the Advance line of high-speed powerboats

Offshore Yacht Builders
4501 Ulmerton Rd.
Clearwater, FL 34622
Tel: (813) 572-9921
*Builders of inshore
sport-fishing boats*

Off Soundings Yachts
308 Line Rd.
Manorville, NY 11949
*Builders of 27 and 34 foot
sport-fishing boats*

Olympic Boat Co.
P.O. Box 328
18310 Cascade View Dr.
Monroe, WA 98272
Tel: (206) 794-7541
Fax: (206) 794-3732
*Builder of sport-fishing boats,
18 to 26 feet*

Onset Yachts
P.O. Box 6231
Solomons Island Rd.
Annapolis, MD 21401
Tel: (410) 266-3898
*Importers of sport-fishing
boats*

Orca Yachts, Inc.
515 Seabreeze Blvd.
Ft. Lauderdale, FL 33316
Tel: (305) 522-4535
Fax: (305) 522-4716

**Otis Enterprises Marine
Corp.**
Prospect St.
Searsport, ME 04974
Tel: (207) 548-6362
*Semi-custom lobster and
sport-fishing boat builder*

P.A.E. Yacht Builders
P.O. Box 874
Dana Point, CA 92629
Tel: (714) 496-4848

Pacific Boat Sales, Inc.
P.O. Box 4010
Kailua-Kona, HI 96740
Tel: (808) 325-5000
Fax: (808) 325-7023
*Builders of the Kevlacat
International*

Pantera Boats
3205 N.E. 188th St.
N. Miami Beach, FL 33180
Tel: (305) 933-3278
Fax: (305) 933-3299
High-performance boats

**Penn Yan Manufacturing
Co.**
Waddell Ave.
Penn Yan, NY 14527
Tel: (315) 536-7755
Fax: (315) 536-0107
*Fishing, cruising and sport
boats*

Malcolm L. Pettigrew, Inc.
P.O. Box 1160
Seal Cove Rd.
Southwest Harbor, ME 04679
Tel: (207) 244-5082
Fax: (207) 244-5084
*Lobster-boat-style yachts and
fishing boats*

**Phoenix Marine
Enterprises, Inc.**
1775 W. Okeechobee Rd.
Hialeah, FL 33010
Tel: (305) 887-5625
Fax: (305) 885-0432

**Pilgrim Live-Aboard
Yachts**
850 N.E. 3rd St. #11
Dania, FL 33004
Tel: (305) 920-0974
Fax: (305) 920-0548

Pilot Cove Boat Co.
P.O. Box 452
Somerset, MA 02726
Tel: (508) 679-3353
*Builders of downeast-style
fishing boats*

Post Marine Co., Inc.
100 Post Rd.
Mays Landing, NJ 08330
Tel: (609) 625-2434

Powerquest Boats, Inc.
2385 112th Ave.
Holland, MI 49424
Tel: (616) 772-9474
Fax: (616) 772-7334
Sport boats

President Marine, Ltd.
2901 N.E. 185 St.
North Miami Beach, FL 33180
Tel: (305) 935-7511

Privateer Boats
P.O. Box 57
Belhaven, NC 27810
Tel: (919) 943-3737
*Builders of commercial and
sport-fishing boats*

Priviledge Yachting
1650 S.E. 17th St.
#204
Ft. Lauderdale, FL 33316
Tel: (305) 462-6706
Fax: (305) 462-6104
*Importers of the French
designed and built Euphorie
40 catamaran*

Profile Boats, Inc.
Hwy. 93 West
Sumner, IA 50674
Tel: (319) 578-8556
Builders of Profile performance boats

Pro-Line Boats, Inc.
1520 S. Suncoast Blvd.
Homasassa, FL 32646
Tel: (800) 866-2771
  or (904) 795-4111
Fax: (904) 795-4374
Builders of sport-fishing boats

Provincial Boat & Marine Ltd.
P.O. Box 125
Kensington, Prince Edward Island C0B 1M0
CANADA
Tel: (902) 836-3533
Fax: (902) 836-3937
Lobster boat style work and pleasure boats

Pursuit Fishing Boats
3901 St. Lucie Blvd.
Ft. Pierce, FL 34946
Tel: (407) 465-6006
Builders of sport-fishing boats

Python Marine, Inc.
6067 Holiday Rd.
Buford, GA 30518
Tel: (404) 271-9803
Fax: (404) 271-9804
Builders of performance sport boats

Quantum Marine
A Division of US Marine
P.O. Box 3900
Peoria, IL 61614-0908
Builders of Quantum fishing and water skiing boats

Quest Boats
880 Butler Rd.
Murfreesburo, TN 37130
Tel: (615) 895-5190
Fax: (615) 895-5195
Center-console fishing boats

Rampage Yachts
Division of Cruistar, Inc.
804 Pecor St.
Oconto, WI 54153
Tel: (414) 834-2211
Fax: (414) 834-2797
Builders of sport-fishing boats

Ranger Boat Co.
Wood Mfg. Co., Inc.
P.O. Box 179, Hwy 178
Flippin, AR 72634
Tel: (501) 453-2222
Builders of sport-fishing boats

Regal Marine Industries
2300 Jetport Dr.
Orlando, FL 32809-7895
Tel: (800) US REGAL
  or (407) 851-4360
Fax: (407) 857-1256
Builders of a range of sport boats

Regulator Marine
P.O. Box 49
187 Peanut Dr.
Edenton, NC 27932
Tel: (919) 482-3837
Fax: (919) 482-5577
Builders of the Express series of sport-fishing boats

Renken Boat Mfg. Co.
1750 Signal Point Rd.
Charleston, SC 29412
Tel: (803) 795-1150
Fax: (803) 795-6854
Builders of the Seamaster line of sport-fishing boats

Rinker Boat Co., Inc.
300 W. Chicago St.
Syracuse, IN 46567
Tel: (800) 231-7738
Fax: (717) 524-5704
Builders of the Rinker Fiesta and Captiva sport boats

Rio America Yacht Co.
901 Fairview Ave. N. #A140
Seattle, WA 98109
Tel: (206) 292-6264

Riva Yachts, Inc.
P.O. Box 476
120 Chubb Ave.
Lyndhurst, NJ 07071
Tel: (800) 444-RIVA
  or (210) 460-9600
Fax: (201) 460-9392
Importers of Riva yachts

Riviera Yacht Distributors, Inc.
2002 Eastwood Rd.
Wilmington, NC 28403
Tel: (919) 256-5135
Builders of the Riviera line of convertible cruising yachts

Robalo Marine
P.O. Box 9019
Everett, WA 98206
Tel: (800) 828-2811
  or (206) 435-6534
Builders of the Robalo series of sport-fishing boats

Ronin Yachts
Box 562023
Miami, FL 33156
Tel: (305) 238-8026

Rosborough Boats Ltd.
P.O. Box 188
Armdale, Nova Scotia B3L 4J9
CANADA
Tel: (902) 477-1415
Fax: (902) 479-2980

**Donzi Yachts by Roscioli
International, Inc.**
3201 State Rd. 84
Ft. Lauderdale, FL 33312
Tel: (305) 581-9200
Fax: (305) 791-0958

Rybovich Yachts
4200 N. Dixie Hwy.
W. Palm Beach, FL 33401
Tel: (407) 844-4331
*Builders of high-performance
sport-fishing boats*

Saber Marine
P.O. Box 8426
Grand Rapids, MI 49518
Tel: (616) 949-3779
*Builders of Saber performance
powerboats*

Sabre Corp.
Hawthorne Rd., Box 134
South Casco, ME 04077
Tel: (207) 655-3831
*Builders of the Sabreline
cruising power yachts*

Sea-Pro Boats, Inc.
769 Chapin Rd.
Hwy. 76
Chapin, SC 29036
Tel: (803) 345-1063
Fax: (803) 345-6621
Fishing boat builders

Sea Ray Boats, Inc.
2600 Sea Ray Blvd.
Knoxville, TN 37914
Tel: (800) SRBOATS
 or (615) 522-4181
Fax: (615) 523-2129
*Builders of a wide range of
sport and fishing boats*

SeaSport Boats
4654 Guide Meridian
Bellingham, WA 98226
Tel: (206) 733-3380

Sea Sprite Boat Co.
P.O. Box 80
Hwy. 24 East
Crescent City, IL 60928
Tel: (815) 683-2155
Fax: (815) 683-2389
*Fishing and cuddy cabin boat
builders*

Seaswirl
A division of Outboard Marine
Corp.
P.O. Box 167
7th & C St.
Culver, OR 97734
Tel: (503) 546-5011
 or in Canada: (705)
876-BOAT
Fax: (503) 546-5011
*Builders of a line of runabouts
and fishing boats*

Seebold Powerboats
940 Biltmore Dr.
Fenton, MS 63026
Tel: (314) 349-1404
*Builders of the Seebold
high-performance sport boat*

Shamrock Marine, Inc.
P.O. Box 150189
905 S.E. 9th Terr.
Cape Coral, FL 33915
Tel: (813) 574-2800
Fax: (813) 574-7489
Builders of sport-fishing boats

Shannon Yachts
Box 388
Bristol, RI 02809
Tel: (401) 253-2441
Fax: (401) 254-1202
*Builders of the Shannon line of
offshore cruising yachts*

**Silverton Marine
Corporation**
301 Riverside Dr.
Millville, NJ 08332-6798
Tel: (609) 825-4117
Fax: (609) 825-1824
*Builders of the Silverton line of
cruising yachts*

Skipjack Boats, Inc.
1763 Placentia Ave.
Costa Mesa, CA 92627
Tel: (714) 646-2451

Smoker Craft
68143 Clunette St.
New Paris, IN 46553
Tel: (219) 831-2103

Sonic Power Boats
American-Industries, Inc.
3600 N. 29th Ave.
Hollywood, FL 33020
Tel: (305) 922-5535

Southern Skimmer
P.O. Box 949
Highway 101
Beaufort, NC 28516
Tel: (919) 728-2755
Fax: (919) 728-6109
Builders of commercial and
pleasure sport-fishing boats

South Shore Boat
P.O. Box 332
Belfast, ME 04916
Tel: (207) 338-4004
Lobster-boat-style work and
pleasure craft

Sportcraft, Inc.
500 Houck Rd.
Perry, FL 32347
Tel: (904) 584-5679
Fax: (904) 584-9395

Stamas Yacht, Inc.
300 Pampas Ave.
Tarpon Springs, FL 34689
Tel: (800) 782-6271
Builder of sport-fishing and
cruising boats

Starfire Boats
619 South 600 West
Salt Lake City, UT 84101
Tel: (801) 363-5159

Sterling Yachts
International
3350 S.E. Slater St.
Stuart, FL 34997
Tel: (407) 220-9685
Fax: (407) 220-9632
Builder of the System
high-performance luxury
cruisers

Stingray Boat Co.
P.O. Box 669
Hartsville, SC 29550
Tel: (803) 383-4507
Builder of the Stingray line of
sport boats

Storm Bird Boats
RD #2, Box 277
Delhi, NY 13753
Tel: (607) 746-3604

Stratos Boats
931 Industrial Rd.
Old Hickory, TN 37138
Tel: (615) 847-4034
Fax: (615) 847-4020
Builder of high-performance
deep-V offshore fishing and
cruising boats

Stryker Boat Co.
3090 Jordan Lane
Huntsville, AL 35806
Tel: (205) 859-2883
Fax: (205) 851-6802
Builders of high-performance
Boats

Sunbird Boat Co.
2348 Shop Rd.
Columbia, SC 29201
Tel: (803) 799-1125
Builders of a line of sportboats

Sunsation Boats
5827 Hessen Rd.
Casco, MI 48064
Tel: (313) 725-8020

Sunseeker International
1650 Route de L'Eglise
St. Antoine de Tilly, Quebec
GOS 2CO
CANADA
Tel: (514) 654-6542
British designed
high-performance craft

Superboats
275 Dixon Ave.
Amityville, NY 11701
Tel: (516) 842-1560
Builders of high-performance
catamarans

Super Hawaii
Manufacturing Co.
6101 45th St. N.
St. Petersburg, FL 33714
Tel: (813) 528-1086
Fax: (813) 528-1749
Builders of the Intrepid series
of sport-fishing boats, plus a
line of high-performance boats

Surf Hunter Corp.
50 Fort St., Box D-4
Fairhaven, MA 02719
Tel: (508) 996-6022

S2 Yachts, Inc.
725 E. 40th St.
Holland, MI 49423
Tel: (616) 392-7163
Fax: (616) 394-7466
Builders of Tiara fishing and
sport boats

Talon Marine Co.
2253 Industrial Blvd.
Sarasota, FL 34234
Tel: (813) 355-0710
Fax: (813) 351-8908
Builders of a line of sport boats

Tashmoo Boat Corp.
Box 2027
Edgartown, MA 02539
Tel: (508) 693-8560
Fax: (508) 696-7680
Builders of lobster-boat-style power and workboats

Thompson Boat Co.
7535 Martin Rd.
St. Charles, MI 48655
Tel: (517) 865-8281
Fax: (517) 865-6691
Powerboat builders

Thunderbird Products
P.O. Box 1003
2200 W. Monroe St.
Decatur, IN 46733-5003
Tel: (800) 736-7635
  or (218) 724-9111
Fax: (219) 724-1103
Builders of the Formula deep-V, high-performance boat

Tiara Yachts
725 E. 40th
Holland, MI 49423
Tel: (800) 843-3172
  or (616) 392-7163
Builders of Tiara sport and fishing boats

Tides Boat Work
P.O. Box 480
Irvington, VA 22480
Tel: (804) 435-3028

Tiffany Yachts, Inc.
Rt. 3, Box 133
Burgess, VA 22432
Tel: (804) 453-3464

Tollycraft Yachts
2200 Clinton Ave.
Kelso, WA 98626
Tel: (206) 423-5160
Builders of contemporary motor yachts

Trojan Yachts
P.O. Box 1010
790 Markham Dr.
Pulaski, WI 54162-1010
Tel: (414) 822-3214
Fax: (414) 822-8820
Builders of motor yachts

Ultress Boats
P.O. Box 7115
Hilton Head, SC 29938
Tel: (803) 757-5790
Builders of the Ultress catamaran

Vantare
Rex Meyer Yachts
1470 Dolgner Pl.
Sanford, FL 32771
Tel: (407) 323-6108

Viking Yacht Company
Rt. 9
New Gretna, NJ 08224
Tel: (609) 296-6000
Fax: (609) 296-3956
Builders of luxurious motor yachts from 50 to 80 feet LOA

VIP Marine Industries, Inc.
950 N.W. 72nd St.
Miami, FL 33150
Tel: (305) 696-3232

Vista Yachts Co., Inc.
P.O. Box 2430
Patchogue, NY 11772
Tel: (516) 758-6166

Wahoo! Boats Unlimited
708 Air Park Rd.
Ashland, VA 23005
Tel: (804) 798-2780
Fax: (804) 798-4658
Sport-fishing boats

Webb Boats, Inc.
13614 N. Old Hwy. 169
Collinsville, OK 74021
Tel: (918) 371-2571

Wellcraft Marine
1651 Whitfield Ave.
Sarasota, FL 34243
Tel: (800) 336-3044
  or (813) 753-7811
Fax: (813) 751-7808
Builders of a wide range of sport boats and high-performance craft

West Bay SonShip Ltd.
8295 River Rd.
Delt, British Columbia V4G 1B4
CANADA
Tel: (604) 946-6226
Fax: (604) 946-8722
Motor yachts

Westerly Marine
660 W. 17th St.
Costa Mesa, CA 92627
Tel: (714) 642-0146

Westship, Inc.
1441 S.E. 16th St.
Ft. Lauderdale, FL 33316
Tel: (305) 463-0700

Lee S. Wilbur Yachts
Seawall Rd.
Manset, ME 04656
Tel: (207) 244-5000
*Builders and brokers of
lobster-boat-style yachts and
boats*

Willard Marine, Inc.
1250 N. Grove St.
Anaheim, CA 92806
Tel: (714) 666-2150

Xylem Technologies
1155 Hastings Ave.
Traverse City, MI 49684
Tel: (616) 929-0598

Young Brothers & Co., Inc.
53 Cranberry Pt. Rd.
Corea, ME 04624
Tel: (207) 963-7467
Fax: (207) 963-7224
*Builders of some of the fastest
lobster boats in Maine*

Figure 3: The 3300 Offshore sportfishing boat is built by Tiara Yachts of Holland, MI.

Boat Builders: Production Sail

Over 90% of the boats built today are by production builders, so it is likely that your new boat will be a production one. How do you decide which production boat is best for you? If you are like many people, you may simply decide that they want a boat that is X feet long, with Y number of berths, and costs Z dollars. Unfortunately, this often results in the purchase of a boat unsuited to your particular type of sailing.

After making the decision to buy a new boat, your first step should be to determine what type of sailing you do. Then write to the builders listed in this book and ask for their brochures, with their price list, for the size boat you want. With the brochures in hand, you should make a careful comparison of all the features. This comparison should include numerical data on performance, costs (of both the basic boat and extras), and any information you can glean about the boat's actual performance.

DETERMINE YOUR SAILING HABITS

If we assume that you have a family of four with $65,000 to spend on a boat, your first step is to make a list of your sailing habits. This will help you determine a boat's suitability for your type of sailing. The list might look like this:

- The boat will be on a mooring during the week.

- We sail from Friday evening to Sunday evening almost every summer weekend.
- We race two evenings per week at the local club.
- We take three weeks in the summer to cruise. Usually the cruise is more than 100 miles from home.
- We do not sail more than 20 miles away from land at any time.
- We rarely sail at night, but instead find a marina or mooring.
- We always eat onboard.
- We sail as a family.

Now we'll look at what this list means in terms of purchasing a boat.

- As the boat will often be anchored at night, the anchor handling gear should be substantial with no sharp edges.
- With four people on board over a weekend, the boat should have plenty of stowage space, and sails should preferably be stowed on the spars to keep them out of the main cabin.
- On weekends and the summer cruise, the family eats aboard. This means that the galley should be fairly large. You might also want to include the cook's preferences for the galley.
- As the boat will not be sailing very far from land, it need not be greatly overbuilt. This will save costs on the yacht's structure.

Obviously, the more comprehensive this list is, the better your new boat will be suited to your sailing needs.

ANALYZING BROCHURES

By now you have a list of the ideal features you want in your new boat and a pile of brochures. How do you match one to the other? The first step is to work up the numbers. That is, make a list of the LOA, LWL, beam, draft, displacement, ballast, sail area, fresh water capacity, fuel oil capacity, and cost of each boat. The list should also include the sail area to displacement ratio, displacement-to-length ratio, fuel-to-displacement ratio, freshwater-to-displacement ratio, and (if you can obtain it) each boat's righting moment.

For a typical 35 footer, the list will probably look like this:

Statistics:

- LOA: 34 ft. 3 in.
- LWL: 27 ft. 5 in.
- Beam: 11 ft. 1 in.
- Draft: 5 ft. 0 in.
- Displacement: 10,800 lbs.
- Ballast: 4,600 lbs.
- Sail area: 558 sq. ft.
- Fresh water: 40 gals.
- Fuel oil: 25 gals.

Ratios:

- Displacement/Length ratio: 120
- Sail area/Displacement ratio: 18.28

- Fuel oil/Displacement ratio: 1.74
- Fresh water/Displacement ratio: 2.96
- Righting moment: 760 ft. lbs.

Costs:

- Base Price: $58,990
- Extras: $17,450
- Total cost afloat: $76,440
- Cost per pound displacement with keel: $7.1/lb.
- Cost per pound displacement less keel: $12.33/lb.

WHAT THE RATIOS TELL YOU

By looking at the ratios carefully you can get a very rough feel for a boat. For instance, a displacement/length ratio of 120 tells you that the boat is quite light, making it a good performer in lighter going offwind. Going upwind it will take some careful handling to get the best out of it. A sail area-to-displacement ratio of 18.28 says the boat has a fair amount of sail and will be at its best in moderate going. A fuel oil-to-displacement ratio under 2% is slightly under average for this size of boat, and a freshwater-to-displacement ratio of 2.96% says you will have to watch the water level constantly to avoid running out.

The cost per pound with keel simply gives you a non-dimensional method of comparing how much each pound of weight in the boat costs. A more accurate figure is obtained from the cost per pound less keel. In this case, it is $12.33/lb. which is about average. Cost per pound figures

The Ratios

Displacement/length ratio - This ratio serves as a rough indication of acceleration. A lighter boat will accelerate faster than a heavier boat. A displacement length ratio under 60 generally indicates that the boat will plane, but most sailboats have displacement length ratios over 100

$$\frac{Displacement/2240}{(Waterline\ Length/100)^3}$$

Sail area to displacement ratio - The sail area to displacement ratio is an indicator of light air ability. A boat with a high number will sail better in light winds than a boat with a lower number.

$$\frac{(Sail\ Area)^{2/3}}{(Displacement/64)}$$

Ballast ratio - I am not a great believer in the value of the ballast ratio, but here it is.

$$\frac{Ballast\ x\ 100}{Displacement}$$

Freshwater to displacement ratio - The freshwater to displacement ratio gives you a method of comparing how much water the boat caries. In general, a value of less than 2% is for racing boats or boats with a watermaker. Up to 5% is good for weekend cruisers. Over 5% is best for long distance cruisers without a watermaker.

$$\frac{Fresh\ water\ in\ gallons\ x\ 8\ x\ 100}{Displacement}$$

Fuel oil to displacement ratio - The fuel oil ratio gives you an idea of the range of the boat. A high number means that the boat can travel further on a full tank than a boat with a low number.

$$\frac{Fuel\ oil\ in\ gallons\ x\ 7.5\ x\ 100}{Displacement}$$

Righting moment - Provided by the builder or designer. This number should be in foot-pounds and will be small (about 800 or 900 ft-lbs for a 20 footer to 3,500 ft lbs for a 70 footer.

Cost per pound - This is the best indicator of the value of a boat. A low number tells you that the boat is either stripped out or built inexpensively. If the quality is low and the number is low, you should check with other owners for possible problems. If both the number and the quality are high then the boat is well built. A more accurate number can be obtained by adding all the extras to the cost of the basic boat.

$$\frac{Cost\ of\ basic\ boat}{Displacement}$$

Cost per pound less ballast - On sailboats a more accurate number can be obtained by removing the cost of the lead ballast. (Lead costs only a few pence per pound, but by the time the keel has been molded and poured, its cost can be reckoned around a dollar per pound.)

$$\frac{Cost\ of\ boat\ (either\ basic\ or\ fully\ equipped)}{Displacement\ minus\ ballast}$$

can vary, of course. For instance, a high-tech yacht might be in the region of $25/lb.

SEEING THE BOAT

Having looked over all the brochures and made all the calculations, you have probably narrowed your search down to a half dozen boats. Now it is time to see each of these. This can be done at a boat show or, if the builder is nearby, you may see the boat at the factory.

When going aboard, walk around the deck and look it over carefully. Ask yourself, are the hatches substantial? Am I going to be concerned about taking the family out in this boat? Is the deck gear fitted properly and in the right place? Is the cockpit comfortable for sailing and for sitting in when in a marina? Is the steering system strong enough and is the feel light enough?

Now go below and make the same kind of checks in the interior. Can you sit in the navigation area comfortably? Can the entire family sit around the dining table? Can you use the head underway? Is there enough headroom? Is the icebox large enough? Can an adult reach the bottom of it? Do you need a stove with an oven? Do you need a second icebox for sodas? Check the width of the bunks. They should be comfortable for the entire family. These and many more questions should be answered to your total satisfaction before you commit to buying a boat.

THE SAIL TRIAL

Having narrowed your choices even further, the next step is to get a test sail before making your final decision. After all, buying a boat without sailing it is like buying a car without driving it. When going aboard for a test sail, you will usually find that the builder wants you to sit back and enjoy the sail. But if you are to get the best value out of your trial you should ask if you can do all the things you normally do on your own boat. For instance, you should handle the boat under power, back it down, and see how it steers. Walk up forward to check how the sail is hoisted, and then go to the mast to make sure the halyards can easily be led to their winches and cleats. If you normally sheet in the sails, try doing it. You may find that your hands hit the lifelines and that the winch will need to be moved. Try steering the boat, both upwind and down, to make sure you like the feel of the helm. Remember anything that nags you on a trial sail will doubly nag you when you own the boat.

Next go down below and check how comfortable the chart table is when you are under sail. Check to see if you have to lean against electrical breakers when you sit in the nav area and the boat is heeled. Do all the navigation instruments have a place, or do they crash around in the chart table? Is there adequate lighting in the nav area? Can you talk to the helmsman easily from the nav area?

Try sitting on the head. Check to see if water backs up into the head while the boat is heeled. Check in the galley to see if the lockers stay closed and whether seawater backfills into the sink. If it does, you may have to remember to turn the seacock off every time you go sailing. Check to see if handholds that were comfortable when the boat was upright are still usable. Lean against the table and see if it moves. Will it stay in place if you fall against it? Can you climb the companionway ladder at sea? You might want to check the bunks to see how comfortable they are, especially if you plan to sail at night.

While you are below deck, check to see how loud the engine noise is. If you have to shout, you might want to add more insulation or move on to another boat. You should be able to carry on a normal conversation with the engine running. Check, too, if you can get easy access to the engine to check the oil and fresh water cooling. If access is difficult, these chores may not get done properly, leading to an engine failure

at an inopportune time. Having made all your checks, write down your comments on each boat. By this time, you should have a comprehensive file of information on three or four boats.

Armed with that information, you should next get costs on insurance, commissioning, mooring, and haulout, as well as estimates of the cost of general upkeep before making your final decision. When you've decided, contact the builder or broker and request a contract. Have your lawyer check the contract before signing it. He or she may find clauses that are unacceptable. If the builder is relatively unknown, you might also want to have a surveyor make a check of the boat before you sign. If you are buying a used boat, a surveyor should definitely check it to make sure it is in good shape.

Finally, comes the day that you become the proud owner of a new boat, one that is entirely suited to your sailing needs and hopefully one that you will enjoy for years to come.

Manufacturers of Domestic Production Sailboats over 20 Feet LOA

Abbott Boats Ltd.
1458 London Rd.
Sarnia, Ontario N7S 1P7
CANADA
Tel: (519) 542-2771
Fax: (519) 542-2324
Builders of Solings and boats up to 36 feet

Albin Marine
143 River Rd.
Cos Cob, CT 06807
Tel: (203) 661-4341
Fax: (203) 661-6040

Alden Yachts
1909 Alden Landing
Portsmouth, RI 02871
Tel: (401) 683-4200
Fax: (401) 683-3668
Builders of the Alden 43, 45, 48 and 50

Baltic Yachts Ltd.
68555 Bosund
Pietarsaari
FINLAND
Tel: (358) 67-72-83070
Fax: (358) 67-72-83216

Barnegat Yacht
P.O. Box 1181
Pt. Pleasant, NJ 08742
Tel: (908) 295-8707

B Boats, Inc.
359 Sheridan St.
Corona, CA 91720
Tel: (714) 279-0781
Builders of the B-25

Beneteau (U.S.A.) Ltd.
8720 Red Oak Blvd.
Suite 102
Charlotte, NC 28217
Tel: (704) 527-8244
Fax: (704) 527-0760
The French owned Beneteau company, the largest boat builder in the world, produce a range of boats from the First 235 to the Oceanis 53

Bennett Brothers Yachts, Inc.
808 Market St.
Wilmington, NC 28405
Builders of the Marek 44, a Klegecell-cored racer designed by Bruce Marek, with a cruising version also available

Bridges Point Boatyard
HCR 63
Box 342
Brooklin, ME 04616
Tel: (207) 359-2713
Bridges Point 24 builder

C & C International Yachts
526 Regent St.
Niagara-on-the-lake, Ontario
LO5 1JO
CANADA
Tel: (416) 468-2101
Fax: (416) 468-4743
Builders of the well known C & C racing and cruising yachts

Cabo RicoYachts, Inc.
2258 S.E. 17th St.
Ft. Lauderdale, FL 33316
Tel: (305) 462-6699
Fax: (304) 462-1317
With their solid teak interiors, these comfortable cruising yachts are reknown for the high standard of their joiner work and finish

Caliber Yacht Corp.
4551-107 Circle North
Clearwater, FL 34622
Tel: 813-573-0627
Fax: 813-573-2413
Production cruising yacht builders of the Caliber 33, 38, and 47, comfortable sailing yachts at an affordable price

Cape Dory Yachts
334 S. Bayview Ave.
Amityville, NY 11701
Tel: (516) 264-1313
Fax: (516) 264-1316

Capital Yachts, Inc.
25914 President Ave.
Harbor City, CA 90710
Tel: (310) 530-1311
Builders of the Newport and Gulf line of production cruisers

Capri Sailboats
21200 Victory Blvd.
Woodland Hills, CA 91376
Tel: (818) 884-7700
Fax: (818) 884-3810
Builders of the Capri line of sailboats

Carrera Performance Yachts, Inc.
1855 University Parkway
Sarasota, FL 34243
Tel: (813) 351-0557
Fax: (813) 351-0383
Builders of performance sailboats

Carroll Marine Ltd.
91 Broad Common Rd.
Bristol, RI 02809
Tel: (401) 253-1263
Fax: (401) 253-5860
Race-winning cruising boats aimed primarily at the IMS and PHRF rules; their boats have won almost all the major regattas and numerous lesser races

Catalina Yachts
21200 Victory Blvd.
Woodland Hills, CA 91367
Tel: (818) 884-7700
Fax: (818) 884-3810
Builders of a range of yachts in many different sizes, known for their affordability and solid construction

Catalina Yachts
Morgan Division
7200 Bryan Dairy Rd.
Largo, FL 33543
Tel: (813) 544-6681
Fax: (813) 546-7303
Catalina now builds the entire line of Morgan sailboats

Cherubini Boat Co.
51 Norman Ave.
Delran, NJ 08075
Tel: (609) 764-1112
Fax: (609) 764-8240
Builders of the Cherubini line of sailboats

Classic Sailing Vessels Ltd.
401 Campus Ave.
Chestertown, MD 21020
Tel: (301) 778-2460
Fax: (301) 778-2460
Builders of the Classic 69 and larger vessels

Crosby Yacht Yard, Inc.
72 Crosby Circle
Osterville, MA 02855
Tel: (508) 428-6958
Fax: (508) 428-0323
Builders of the Crosby Club launch

Custom Yacht Builders
1710 Charles St.
Whitby, Ontario L1N 1C 2
CANADA
Tel: (416) 430-8299
Fax: (416) 961-7830
Builders of the Custom 46

Dashew Offshore
428 N.E. 3rd Ave.
Ft. Lauderdale, FL 33301
Tel: (305) 761-1035
Fax: (305) 761-7661
Builders of the Sundeer 64, a long distance offshore cruiser

Edey & Duff
128 Aucoot Rd.
Mattapoisett, MA 02739
Tel: (508) 758-2591
Builders of the Stone Horse and several smaller craft which are reknown for their simplicity and ease of handling

Endeavour International Corp.
6021 142nd Ave.
Clearwater, FL 34622
Tel: (813) 535-1269
Builders fo Endeavour cats

Ericson Yachts
1301 E. Orangethorpe
Fullerton, CA 92631
Tel: 714-879-1601
Fax: 714-879-5454
Most of the Ericson series of comfortable cruiser / racers are designed by Bruce King and built by Pacific Seacraft, giving them an enviable pedigree

Excel Yachts
9045 Shoreham Dr.
Los Angeles, CA 90069
Tel: (213) 271-3218
Fax: (213) 271-3268

Formula Yachts, Inc.
145 Pearl St.
Noawk, CT 06340
Tel: (203) 572-1110
Builders of Evelyn yachts and racing sailboats

Fort Myers Yacht and Shipping
2909 Frierson St.
Fort Myers, FL 33916
Tel: (813) 332-7800
Fax: (813) 332-0940
Fort Myers Yacht and Shipping builds the cruising boat that some owners have called the ideal Yacht, the Brewer 42

Freedom Yachts, Inc.
305 Oliphant Ln.
Middletown, RI 02840
Tel: (401) 848-2900
Fax: (401) 848-2904
The innovative Gary Mull designed Freedom yachts are built to Lloyds 100 +A1; with interiors in teak, ash, or cherry, they are both comfortable and fast.

H. T. Gozzard & Associates
P.O. Box 373
Goderich, Ontario N7A 4C6
CANADA
Tel: (519) 524-6393
Fax: (519) 524-9180
Builders of a line of sailboats

Hans Christian Yachts
7078 Bembe Beach Rd.
Port Annapolis Marina
Annapolis, MD 21403
Tel: (301) 268-4213
Fax: (301) 268-9229
Importers of cruising yachts

The Hinckley Company
P.O. Box 699
Shore Rd.
Southwest Harbor, E 04679
Tel: (207) 244-5531
Fax: (207) 244-9833
The Hinckley Company is a builder of luxurious cruising boats featuring hand-crafted custom-built interiors in production hulls. The line ranges from the Hinckley 38 to the Sou'wester 59

Hinterhoeller Yachts
630 Read Rd.
St. Catherines
Ontario, L2R 7K6
CANADA
Tel: (416) 646-2300
Fax: (416) 646-5420
Builders of the Niagara series of cruising yachts since 1977

Holby Marine
97 Broad Common Rd.
Bristol, RI 02809
Tel: (401) 253-1711
Fax: (401) 253-1712
Builders of the Clearwater 35

Hunter Marine Corp.
P.O. Box 1030
Rt. 441
Alachua, FL 32615 Customer Hotline (800) 771-5556 or in Florida (800) 940-5556
Tel: (904) 462-3077
Fax: (904) 462-4077
Hunter Marine are known for their large number of affordable and comfortable cruising yacht

Hutchins Company, Inc.
1195 Knapp Drive
Clearwater, FL 34625
Tel: (813) 443-4408
Fax: (813) 443-1088
Builders of a line of comfortable cruising yachts known as the Com-Pac series

Impulse Marine, Inc.
10610 Metric Dr.
Suite 145
Dallas, TX 75243
Tel: (800) 526-7245
  or (214) 340-3111
Fax: (214) 340-3112
Builders of the Impulse 21 and 26

Island Packet Yachts
1979 Wild Acres Rd.
Largo, Fl 34641
Tel: (800) 828-5678
  or (813) 535-6431
Fax: (813) 530-5806
With their long traditional keel shape, Island Packet yachts offer comfortable cruising in a boat capable of sailing to Bermuda right out of the box

J Boats, Inc.
Box 90
Newport, RI 02840
Tel: (401) 846-8410
Fax: (401) 846-4723
Known worldwide as builders of one-design cruiser/racers from the J22 to the J44

Jeanneau North America
128 Howard St.
New London, CT 06320
Tel: (203) 444-2072
Fax: (203) 442-8789
Jeanneau of France build a number of catamarans and fast cruising monhulls

Kadey-Krogen Yachts, Inc.
1310 N.W. 18th Ave.
Miami, FL 33125
Tel: (305) 326-0266

Kanter Yachts
9 Barrie Blvd.
St. Thomas, Ontario N5P 4B9
CANADA
Tel: (519) 633-1058

Kirie Amerique
1204 Chemin Industriel
Bernieres
Quebec G7A 1A9
CANADA
Tel: (418) 831-2522
Fax: (418) 831-3406
Builders of the Elite sailboat line

Bill Lee Yachts
3700B Hilltop Rd.
Soquel, CA 95073
Tel: (408) 475-9627
Fax: (408) 475-0867
The Santa Cruz line of ULDBs need little explanation, having won the Transpac so many times that Bill Lee's name has become synonymous with the event

Figure 1: The Little Harbor 54 is a fine yacht for cruising the world's oceans.

Little Harbor Yachts, Inc.
One Little Harbor Landing
Portsmouth, RI 02871
Tel: (401) 683-5600
Fax: (401) 683-3009
*The Little Harbor line of
imported yachts are known for
their excellent quality and
cruising amentities
incorporated in a fast,
shallow-draft hull form*

**Lyman-Morse Boatbuilding
Co.**
49 Knox Street
Thomaston, ME 04861
Tel: (207) 354-6904
*The builder of the Seguin line
of offshore cruising yachts*

MacGregor Yacht Corp.
1631 Placentia Ave.
Costa Mesa, CA 92627
Tel: (714) 642-6830
Fax: (714) 642-5379
*The long, lean MacGregor 65 is
intended to be an ultra
high-performance,
long-distance cruising yacht*

Mariah Yachts, Inc.
119 W. Riverglen
Worthington, OH 43085
Tel: (614) 431-8831

Marine Concepts
159 Oakwood St. E.
Tarpon Springs, FL 34689
Tel: (813) 937-0166

Marshall Marine
P.O. Box P-266
S. Dartmouth, MA 02748
Tel: (508) 994-0414
*Probably the premier catboat
builders in New England*

Melges Boat Works
P.O. Box 1
Zenda Rd.
Zenda, WI 53195
Tel: (414) 248-6621
Fax: (414) 275-8012
Builders of the Melges 24

Moore Sailboats
1650 Commercial Way
Santa Cruz, CA 95065
Tel: (408) 476-3831
Builder of the Moore 24

Morris Yachts
Clark Point Road
P.O. Box 58
Southwest Harbor, ME 04679
Tel: (207) 244-5509
Fax: (207) 244-5866
*Morris Yachts have a
reputation for building a
comfortable attractive sailing
yacht*

Morgan Marine
7200 Bryan Dairy Rd.
Largo, FL 34647
Tel: (813) 544-6681
Fax: (813) 546-7303
Builders of Morgan sailboats

Figure 2: A Nautor built Swan
47 under full sail.

Oy Nautor Ab.
P.O. Box 10 68601
Pietarsaari
FINLAND
Sales Offices:
USA East Coast
55 America's Cup Ave.
Newport, RI 02840
Tel: (401) 846-8404
300 Alton Rd.
Miami Beach, FL 33139
Tel: (305) 673-4600
Fax: (305) 673-2560
USA West Coast
Swan Pacific, Inc.
2505 West Coast Hwy.
Suite 202
Newport Beach, CA 92663
Tel: (714) 645-4600
USA Northwest
McKee And Mooney, Inc.
1530 Westlake Ave. N.
Suite 300
Seattle, WA 98109
Tel: (206) 284-0144
USA Gulf Coast
P.O. Box 891386
Houston, TX 77289-1386
Tel: (713) 334-7926
*Nautor's line of Swans have an
international reputation for
high-quality and speed*

Nimble Boats, Inc.
6135 142 Ave.
North Clearwater, FL 34620
Tel: (813) 539-6444
Fax: (813) 539-6933

Nordic Sailing Yachts, Inc.
P.O. Box 5908
Bellingham, WA 98227
Tel: (206) 380-2101
Fax: (206) 380-2110
*Nordic sailing yachts are
solidly built world-class
cruising yachts*

Nor'Sea Marine
P.O. Box 14
Dana Point, CA 92629
Tel: (714) 489-8227
Builders of the Nor'Sea 27, a round-sterned, comfortable cruising yachts

Offshore Yachts
145 Water St.
S. Norwalk, CT 06854
Tel: (203) 853-0753
Fax: (203) 855-9862

Pacific Asian Enterprises
P.O. Box 874
Dana Point, CA 92629-0937
Tel: (714) 496-4848
Importers of a Mason designed line of sailboats

Pacific Seacraft Corporation
1301 E. Orangethorpe
Fullerton, CA 92631
Tel: (714) 879-1610
Fax: (714) 879-5454
Selected by Fortune magazine as the manufacturer of one of America's 100 best products, this company produces attractive, well-built cruising yachts designed by W.B. Crealock

Passport Yachts East, Inc.
326 First St.
Suite 14
Annapolis, MD 21403
Tel: (301) 263-0008
Fax: (301) 263-5705
Builders of large cruising yachts, Passport offers a 49 and 50 footer

Passport Yachts International, Inc
2330 Shelter Island Dr. # 20
San Diego, CA 92106
Tel: (619) 222-0446

P.D.Q. Yachts, Inc.
1710 Charles St.
Whitby, Ontario L1N 1C2
CANADA
Tel: (416) 430-2582
Fax: (416) 430-8306
PDQ Yachts

Precision Boat Works
1511 18th Ave. Dr. E.
Palmetto, FL 34221
Tel: (813) 722-6601
Builders of the Precision line of small sailboats

Quickstep Sailboats
17 Broad Common Rd.
Bristol, RI 02809
Tel: (401) 254-0400
Builders of Quickstep sailboats

Randle Yacht Corp
1210 Pipeline Rd.
Port Coquitlam, British Columbia V3B 4S1
CANADA
Tel: (604) 941-1688
Fax: (604) 941-3693
Builders of the Wylie Super 39, Coast 34, Bristol Channel Cutter, and others

Reliance Sailing Craft Co.
P.O. Box 8
Beaconsfield Montreal, Quebec
H9W 5T6
CANADA
Tel: (514) 695-2271

Robinhood Marine Center, Inc.
Robin Hood, ME 04530
Tel: (800) 255-5206
Fax: (207) 371-2899
Builders of the Robinhood 40

Royal Yachts International
326 1st St., Suite 14
Ross Marine, Inc.
P.O. Box 776
Oak Bluffs, MA 02557
Tel: (508) 693-5383
The 23 foot LOA open cockpit Sonar and her sister ship the pocket racer, Blazer, are the only two boats produced by this company

Royal Yachts International
326 1st St., Suite 14
Annapolis, MD 21403
Tel: (410) 263-0008

Sabre Corp.
P.O. Box 134
Hawthorne Rd.
S. Casco, ME 04077
Tel: (207) 655-3831
Fax: (207) 655-5050
The fleet ranges from the Sabre 28 to the 442, all of which are well built comfortable cruising yachts

W.D. Schock Corp.
23125 Temescal Canyon
Corona, CA 91719
Tel: (714) 277-3377
Fax: (714) 277-4104
Builders of the Santana line of sailing cruisers

Shannon Boat Co.
Box 388
19 Broad Common Rd.
Bristol, RI 02809
Tel: (401) 253-2441
Fax: (401) 253-1202

Siltala Yacht/Nauticat
P.O. Box 4325
Annapolis, MD 21403
Tel: (301) 261-9005
*Importers of the Nauticat
motor sailers*

Smart Boats
233 Needham St.
Newton, MA 02614
Tel: (617) 964-0900
Fax: (617) 965-3006
Builders of the Tripp 26

SR> Sailboats
1150 19th St. N.
St. Petersburg, FL 33713
Tel: (813) 822-7663

Sonar International
100 Pattonwood Dr.
Rochester, NY 14617
Tel: (716)342-1040
Fax: (716) 266-4722
*Builders of the Kirby designed
Sonar*

Tartan Yachts
A Navstar Marine Company
P.O. Box 308
320 River St.
Grand River, OH 44055-0308
Tel: (216) 354-3111
Fax: (216) 354-6162
*Tartan Marine built its
reputation with an S & S
designed line of fast cruising
sailboats*

Thomas Marine, Inc.
2300 Oakton
Arlington Height, IL 60005
Tel: (800) 833-4141
  or in Illinois (708) 640-8373
Builders of the T35 and T35C

Tillotson Pearson, Inc.
P.O. Box 328
Rte 136, Market St.
Warren, RI 02885
Tel: (401) 245-1200
Fax: (401) 245-2669
*Builders of J boats, Freedom
Yachts*

Westwind Yachts, Inc.
1610 Placentia Ave.
Costa Mesa, CA 92627
Tel: (714) 650-9083

Figure 3: The Valiant 42 is
suitable for world cruising.
It is based on the Valiant
40 hull and incorporates all
the changes that Rich
Worstall and his team
have made to the 40 over
the years .

Valiant Yachts
Rt. 1, Box 37
Gordonville, TX 76245
Tel: (903) 523-4899
Fax: (903) 523-4077
*The Valiant rounded-stern
cruisers are well known*

Wylie Yachts
86 Ridgecrest Canyon, CA
94516
Tel: (415) 376-7338
Fax: (415) 376-7982

X-Yachts
P.O. Box 908
Englewood Cliffs, NJ 07632
Tel: (201) 567-8952
Fax: (201) 567-8953

**Xiamen Celestial Yacht,
Ltd.**
158 University Rd.
Xiamen, Fujian Province
P. R. C.
U. S. Dealer:
United Shores Corporation
6501 Americas Parkway, Suite
695
Albuquerque, NM 87110
Tel: (800) 688-7433
  or (505) 880-0138
Fax: (505) 880-0630

Yachting USA, Inc.
1650 S.E. 17th St. Ste 204
Ft. Lauderdale, Fl 33316
Tel: (305) 467-6600
*Importers of the Centurion line
of yachts built by Waquiez in
France*

Boat Builders: Under 20 Feet LOA

SAILBOATS

In Europe, most people learn to sail on a boat under 20 feet overall. Yacht clubs on lakes, reservoirs, and ponds enable huge numbers of people to get out on the water. Interestingly, the state with the largest number of boat owners in America is Michigan, which has a large number of lakes. However, most of these owners are fishermen. In America, most small boat sailing is frostbiting, even though you might think that frostbiters might want bigger boats to safely hold their hot drinks on.

Why own a small boat? The most obvious answer is that it is less expensive to buy, maintain, and operate. With a smaller boat, you can also learn all about boat-handling without having a large crew to manage. And a small boat can be launched in a few minutes, sailed all day, and then hauled ashore very quickly.

There is a vast armada of small boats available. I learned to sail on a Wayfarer dinghy and have always had a soft spot for them. It was a Wayfarer I sailed on Nairobi dam when the skipper casually mentioned that we didn't want to capsize here because of the crocs, and then pointed to a basking croc about fifty yards away. If you want something smaller, a Laser might be more to your style. For something larger, you might try a Sonar or Ideal 18. These are forgiving boats aimed at the beginning sailor.

When selecting a dinghy, first decide what you want to do with it. Will it be left at the yacht club, or will it be trailed and brought home after each sail? Will it be launched by one person or two? Will it be sailed in sheltered costal waters, on a lake, on a small pond, or out in the open sea? A boat that is to be brought home after every sail will need a road-worthy trailer. A dinghy that will be launched and retrieved by one person should be as light a possible. If the job becomes a chore, the dinghy will not get used much. A dinghy that is to be sailed in open waters will need more protection than a dinghy that is to be sailed in a sheltered pond. All these questions should be anwered long before you go to a boat show or dealer to look for a dinghy.

Once you have selected a dinghy, make sure that you and your crew always wear a lifejacket or PFD, as the Coast Guard calls them. Also make sure you have a bailer and sponge, or a pump handy. In addition, you should carry a paddle or oars in case you are becalmed, a flashlight in case you stay out after dark, and a whistle in case of capsize.

POWERBOATS

Small power boats under 20 feet overall are mainly used for fishing. With modern materials and construction they can go a fair distance offshore, but should head for the beach at the first sign of bad weather. Boats of this size can have a cuddy cabin or a center console. Both have advantages in certain situations. The cuddy cabin allows you to stay at your favorite fishing hole longer or even overnight, while the center console gives you a 360 degree walk-around capability when the fish are hitting. Both have disadvantages, too, such as the openness of the center console in a driving rain, and its lack of a head, and the fact that you will have to stand on the cuddy top to cast at fish in front of the boat.

When looking for your ideal boat, first decide what you want to do with it and the price you can afford, then check out what is being offered. At the smallest end of the scale, sport fishing boats are often little more than a flat bottomed skiff that can run in waters less than eight inches deep. These little skiffs give a hard, washboard like ride, but are ideal for working mud flats and other shallow areas. As hull size increases so does the deadrise angle of the hull, the power of the engine, the range, and the freeboard, making them more like their off-shore cousins.

Manufacturers of Boats under 20 Feet LOA

Sailboats

Abbott Boats Ltd.
1458 London Rd.
Sarnia, Ontario N7S 1P7
CANADA
Tel: (519) 542-2771
Fax: (519) 542-2324
Builder of Wayfarer dinghies

Tom Allen Boat Co.
655 Fuhrman Blvd.
Buffalo, NY 14203
Tel: (716) 842-0800
Fax: (716) 842-0113
Builder of the Lightning and Highlander class boats.

Alvis Marine
104-80 Orwell St.
N. Vancouver, British
Columbia
CANADA
Tel: (604) 985-3905
Fax: (604) 985-4552
Builders of Optimist, Pirate, Tasar, and B-14s

American Sail, Inc.
7350 Pepperdam Ave.
Charleston, SC 29418
Tel: (803) 552-8548
Fax: (803) 552-7770
Maker of the car-topped 14 foot Aquafinn and Aquacat

Ampro Recreational Products, Inc.
231 Delot Diniere
P.O. Box 67
Dorion-Vaudreuill, Quebec
J7V 8P2
CANADA
Tel: (514) 455-6183
Fax: (514) 455-9004
Builder of 12, 14, and 16 foot day sailers.

The Anchorage, Inc.
57 Miller St.
Warren, RI 02885
Tel: (401) 245-3300
Fax: (401) 245-3302
Builder of Dyer dhows

Barnett Boat Company
534 Commercial Ave.
Green Lake, WI 54941
Tel: (414) 294-6351
Builders of the Barnett 1400

Bauteck Marine Corp., Inc.
2060 Dobbs Rd.
St. Augustine, FL 32086
Tel: (904) 824-8826
Builder of the Baur 10

Booth Enterprises
114 Wildwood Ave.
Victoria, British Columbia
V8S 3V9
CANADA
Tel: (604) 386-9622
Builder of the Thunderbird and other dinghies

Burtis Boat Works
3 Maple Pl.
Glen Head, NY 11545
Tel: (516) 676-4201
Builder of the Penguin class dingy

Byte Boats, Inc.
1400 Pomba St.
St. Laurent, Quebec H4R 2A1
CANADA
Tel: (514) 337-3041
Fax: (514) 336-2763
Builder of one-design sailboats

Figure 1: The Herreshoff designed H-12 1/2 is built by Cape Cop Ship Building.

Cape Cod Shipbuilding Co.
Wareham, MA 02571
Tel: (508) 295-3550
Builder of the Herreshoff H-12 1/2 and Cape Cod Knockabout

Cardinal Yachts
Rt. 3, Box 1080
Gloucester, VA 23061
Tel: (804) 693-5928
Builder of the Buccaneer class dinghy

Catalina Yachts
21200 Victory Blvd.
Woodland Hills, CA 91367
Tel: (818) 884-7700
Fax: (818) 884-3840
Makers of the Capri line of small sailboats

Crosby Yacht Yard, Inc.
72 Crosby Circle
Osterville, MA 02655
Tel: (508) 428-6958
Fax: (508) 428-0323
Builder of the Wyanno

Custom Fiberglass Products of Florida, Inc.
8136 Leo Kidd Ave.
Port Richey, FL 34668
Tel: (800) 554-0640
 or (813) 847-5798
Maker of the Sovereign, Custom Hen, and Island Express sailboats

Defender Industries, Inc.
255 Main St.
P.O. Box 820
New Rochelle, NY 10801
Tel: (914) 632-3001
Fax: (914) 632-6544
Dinghies and inflatables

Doughdish, Inc.
Marion, MA 02738
Tel: (508) 748-0334
Builder of the Doughdish 15 footer

Edey & Duff
128 Aucoot Rd.
Mattapoisett, MA 02739
Tel: (508) 758-2591

Flying Scot, Inc.
Rt. 3, Box 1525
Cemetary St.
Deer Park, MD 21550
Tel: (301) 334-4848
Fax: (301) 334-8324
Over 100 active fleets and 5,000 boats sailing

Gavia Yachts International
4629 Cedar Lake Rd.
St. Louis Park, MN 55416
Tel: (612) 377-5484
Builder of one-design and racing sailboats

General Boats
Rt. 4, Box 369F
Edenton, NC 27932
Tel: (919) 482-4372
Builder of trailerable cabin sailboats

Gilmer Mfg.
13030 S. Colman Rd.
Empire, MI 49630
Tel: (616) 228-6575
Canoes and rowboats

Howmar Boats
Box 783
Moosup, CT 06354
Tel: (800) 428-7305
Fax: (203) 564-1592
Builder of Designers Choice dinghies

Hobie Cat Co.
4925 E. Oceanside Blvd.
Oceanside, CA 92056
Tel: (619) 759-9100
Fax: (619) 758-1841
Maker of Hobie cats

HMS Marine, Inc.
904 West Hyde Park Blvd.
Inglewood, CA 90302
Tel: (213) 674-4540
Importers of the West Wight Potter, a 15 footer built in England

Ideal 18 Sailboats
100 Pattonwood Dr.
Rochester, NY 14617
Tel: (716)342-1040
Fax: (716) 266-4722
*Builder of the Kirby-designed
Ideal 18 footer*

Johannsen Boat Works
2900 S.W. 28th Ln.
Miami, FL 33133
Tel: (305) 445-7534
Fax: (305) 445-8445
Builder of Trinka dinghies

Johnson Boat Works
4495 Lake Ave.
White Bear Lake, MN 55110
Tel: (612) 429-7221
Fax: (612) 429-3248
*Builder of the Johnson
Optimist dinghy*

Jolly Boat, Inc.
1100-43 Metro Pkwy.
Ft. Myers, FL 33912
Tel: (813) 275-2040
*Builder of a range of sailing
and rowing dinghies*

JY Sailboats, Inc.
38 Bayside Ave.
Noank, CT 06340
Tel: (800) 333-5 915
Fax: (203) 536-9848
Builder of the JY 15

Larson Boats
Paul Larson Memorial Dr.
Little Falls, MN 56345
Tel: (612) 632-5481
Fax: (612) 632-1439
Sport boats

Mariah Yachts, Inc.
119 W. Riverglen
Worthington, OH 43085
Tel: (614) 431-8831
Builder of the Mariah 27

Figure 2: Marshall Marine's
18 ft. catboat.

Marshall Marine
P.O. Box P-266
S. Dartmouth, MA 02748
Tel: (508) 994-0414
*Marshall Marine is probably
the premier catboat builder in
New England*

Matrix Marine, Inc.
49 Fir St.
Mahtomedi, MN 55115
Tel: (612) 426-3922
Fax: (612) 426-7935
*Builder of the Supercat 20 and
22*

Maverick Boat Co.
3054 Industrial 31st St.
Ft. Pierce, FL 34946
Tel: (407) 465-0631
Fax: (407) 489-2168
Master Angler boats

Menger Boatworks, Inc.
121 Maple Ave.
Bay Shore, NY 11706
Tel: (516) 968-0300
Builder of the Menger cats

Merryman Boats
4915 Delta River Dr.
Lansing, MI 48906
Tel: (517) 482-9333
Fax: (517) 323-0132
*Builder of the Tadpole and
Frog sailing dinghies*

**New England Skiff
Builders, Inc.**
P.O. Box 267
Wakefield, RI 02879
Tel: (401) 789-4609
*Builder of the Puddleduck
dinghy*

Old Town Canoes
58 Middle St.
Old Town, ME 04468
Tel: (800) 848-3673
Canoes

Porta-Bote International
1074 Independence Dr.
Mountain View, CA 94043
Tel: (800) 227-8882
Fax: (415) 961-3800
Maker of the Porta-Bote

Precision Boat Works
1511 18th Ave. Dr. E.
Palmetto, FL 34221
Tel: (813) 722-6601
Maker of the Precision 18

Raudaschl Sails Canada
3140 Lakeshore Blvd. W.
Toronto, Ontario M8V 1L4
CANADA
Tel: (416) 255-3431
Fax: (416) 259-9136
*One to three person
Electra-Sail day sailer*

SR> Sailboats
1150 19th St. North
St. Petersburg, FL 33713
Tel: (813) 822-7663
Builder of the SR Max>

Figure 3: The Laser can provide hours of fun for young sailors.

Sunfish Laser
200 Highpoint Ave.
Portsmouth, RI 02871
Tel: (800) 966-SAIL
  or (401) 683-5900
Fax: (401) 683-9640
Builder of Sunfish and Lasers

U.S. One Design, Inc.
P.O. Box 176
Armonk, NY 10504
Tel: (914) 273-5240
Fax: (914) 273-5243
Builders of an International 14

Figure 4: Vanguard Racing Sailboats build the 420 dinghy.

Vanguard Racing Sailboats
16 Peckham Dr.
Bristol, RI 02809
Tel: (401) 254-0960
Fax: (401) 253-2950
Maker of the International 420 and the Club/Collegiate 420

XS International, Inc.
156 84th St., S.W.
Grand Rapids, MI 49315
Tel: (616) 281-4740
Fax: (616) 281-3120
Maker of the XS Surfcat

Yankee Boatworks
P.O. Box 422
Westport, CT 06881
Tel: (203) 221-0900
Builder of the Yankee Classic daysailer

Windsurfers

Bic Sport
565 Bic Dr.
Milford, CT 06460
Tel: (203) 783-2500
Fax: (203) 783-2510

More Sports, Inc.
601 Oak St.
Hood River, OR 97031
Tel: (800) 424-4359
Fax: (503) 386-6373

Mistral Windsurfing
7222 Parkway Dr.
Dorsey, MD 21076
Tel: (410) 712-4755
Fax: (410) 712-0960

Powerboats

Answer Marine
9500 N.W. 128th St.
Miami, FL 33054
Tel: (305) 836-1033
Builder of sport-fishing boats

Aquasport
A Genmar Industries Company
1651 Whitfield Ave.
Sarasota, FL 34243-3948
Tel: (813) 755-5800
Fax: (813) 751-7808
Builder of sport-fishing boats

Boston Whaler, Inc.
1149 Hingham St.
Rockland, MA 02370
Tel: (800) WHALERS
  or (617) 871-1400
Fax: (617) 871-6462
Builder of the unsinkable Boston Whalers

Cajun Boats
Rt. 3, Box 333
Winnsboro, LA 71295
Tel: (318) 435-9431
Fax: (318) 435-6918
Builder of bass boats

Cape Craft
5567 Doug Taylor
St. James City, FL 33956
Tel: (813) 283-1626
Fax: (813) 283-4676
Builder of Cape Craft sport-fishing boats

Celebrity Boats, Inc.
P.O. Box 394
451 E. Illinois Ave.
Benton, IL 62812
Tel: (800) 328-1422
  or (618) 439-9444
Fax: (618) 435-4063
Builder of the Celebrity line of sport cruisers and fishing boats

Champion Boats, Inc.
Hwy. 201 Spur S.
Mountain Home, AR 72653
Tel: (501) 425-9850
Builder of Champion bass fishing boats

Crownline Boats, Inc.
Rt. 4, Box 339A
W. Frankfort, IL 62896
Tel: (618) 937-6426
Fax: (618) 937-2277
Builders of bow rider, cuddy cabin, and cruising boats

Dusky Marine
110 N. Bryan Rd.
Dania, Fl 33004
Tel: (305) 922-8890
Builder of sport-fishing boats.

Henry O Boats
Rt. 1, Box 65
Bolivia, NC 28422
Tel: (919) 457-9080
Builder of sport-fishing boats.

Hewes Mfg.
3054 Industrial 31st. St.
Ft. Pierce, FL 34946
Tel: (407) 461-0885
Fax: (407) 489-2168
Fishing boats

Hoog Boats, Inc.
10481 S.W. 184th Terr.
Miami, FL 33157
Tel: (305) 255-1651
Fax: (305) 252-0289
Builder of bass boats

Hydra-Sports
OMC Fishing Boat Group
880 Butler Dr.
Murfreesboro, TN 37130
Tel: (615) 895-5190
Fax: (615) 895-5195
Builder of sport-fishing boats

Invader Marine
P.O. Box 420
Giddings, TX 78942
Tel: (409) 542-3101
Builder of sport-fishing boats

Key West Boats
Rt. 1, Hwy. 27, Box 399
Ridgeville, SC 29472
Tel: (803) 871-2670
Builder of sport-fishing boats

Mako Marine, Inc.
4355 N.W. 128th St.
Miami, FL 33054
Tel: (305) 685-6591
Fax: (305) 769-0940
Builder of the Mako sport-fishing boat line

Nissan Marine & Power Products, Inc.
1420 Valwood Pkwy.,
Bldg 2, Suite 200
Carrilton, TX 75006
Tel: (214) 243-7981
Fax: (214) 243-6806
Builder of bass boats and ski boats

Privateer Boats
P.O. Box 57
Belhaven, NC 27810
Tel: (919) 943-3737
Builder of commercial and sport-fishing boats

Figure 5: The Pro-Line 170 Sportsman is built by Pro-Line Boats, Inc.

Pro-Line Boats, Inc.
1520 S. Suncoast Blvd.
Homasassa, FL 32646
Tel: (800) 866-2771
  or (904) 795-4111
Fax: (904) 795-4374
Builder of sport-fishing boats

Pursuit Fishing Boats
3901 St. Lucie Blvd.
Ft. Pierce, FL 34946
Tel: (407) 465-6006
Builder of sport-fishing boats

Quest
880 Butler Rd.
Murfreesburo, TN 37130
Tel: (615) 895-5190
Fax: (615) 895-5195
Center-console fishing boats

Renken Boat Mfg. Co.
1750 Signal Point Rd.
Charleston, SC 29412
Tel: (803) 795-1150
Fax: (803) 795-6854
*Builder of the Seamaster line
of sport-fishing boats*

Robalo Marine
P.O. Box 9019
Everett, WA 98206
Tel: (800) 828-2811
  or (206) 435-6534
*Builder of the Robalo series of
sport-fishing boats*

Sea Ray Boats, Inc.
2600 Sea Ray Blvd.
Knoxville, TN 37914
Tel: (800) SRBOATS
  or (615) 522-4181
Fax: (615) 523-2129
*Builder of a wide range of
sport and fishing boats*

Shamrock Marine, Inc.
P.O. Box 150189
905 S.E. 9th Terr.
Cape Coral, FL 33915
Tel: (813) 574-2800
Fax: (813) 574-7489
Builder of sport-fishing boats

Sportcraft, Inc.
500 Houck Rd.
Perry, FL 32347
Tel: (904) 584-5679
Fax: (904) 584-9395
Builder of sport-fishing boats

Stamas Yacht, Inc.
300 Pampas Ave.
Tarpon Springs, FL 34689
Tel: (800) 782-6271
*Builder of sport-fishing and
cruising boats*

Stratos Boats
931 Industrial Rd.
Old Hickory, TN 37138
Tel: (615) 847-4034
Fax: (615) 847-4020
*Builder of high-performance,
deep-V offshore fishing and
cruising boats*

Sunbird Boat Co.
2348 Shop Rd.
Columbia, SC 29201
Tel: (803) 799-1125
Builders of a line of sport boats

Wahoo! Boats Unlimited
708 Air Park Rd.
Ashland, VA 23005
Tel: (804) 798-2780
Builder of sport-fishing boats

Wellcraft Marine
1651 Whitfield Ave.
Sarasota, FL 34243
Tel: (800) 336-3044
  or (813) 753-7811
Fax: (813) 751-7808
*Builders of a wide range of
sport boats and
high-performance craft*

Figure 6: The Pro-Line 190 Sportsman.

Boat-Building Supplies

Builders and do-it-yourselfers are constantly faced with finding a particular boat-building item or material. Professionals generally network among themselves, but a D-I-Y builder has to painstakingly search stores and catalogs. Often the D-I-Yer has a job just to find the catalogs. The following adddresses will help you locate most boat building equipment.

Many companies do not supply directly to individuals. For instance, you would probably not have much luck going into Amoco headquarters to buy a quart of resin, even though they make huge amounts of resin. When trying to get supplies or information from large corporations, sometimes even from smaller ones, your best approach is to ask for the names of dealers in your area. Dealers usually have retail outlets as well as delivery trucks. If they do not have the material in stock, they can often get it within a few days.

Manufacturers of Boat-Building Supplies

Composite Supplies

Advanced Composites Ltd.
Yacht Haven West
Box 450
Stamford, CT 06904-0450
Tel: (203) 359-2767
Agents for Monitor Marine Products

Advanced Textiles
1580 Mclaughlin Run Rd.
Suite 203
Pittsburgh, PA 15241
Tel: (800) 338-2839

Airtech International, Inc.
2542 East Del Amo Bvd.
P.O. Box 6207
Carson, CA 90749-6207
Tel: (312) 603-9683
Fax: (312) 603-9040

Airtech Europe S. A.
Zone Industrielle
L-4562 Differdange
LUXEMBOURG
Tel: (+352) 584934
Fax: (+352) 584935

Bean Fiber Glass Inc.
Jaffrey, NH 03452
Tel: (603) 532-7765
Fiberglass materials and resins

Boatex Fiberglass Co.
11 Tech Circle
Natick, MA 01760
Tel: (508) 655-2000
Fax: (508) 655-5045

The Brandau Co.
1737 Anderson Hwy.
Powhaton, VA 23139
Tel: (804) 794-1357
Fax: (804) 794-3052

Erskine-Johns Co.
4677 Wirth St.
Los Angeles, CA 90063
Tel: (213) 269-0131
Fax: (213) 669-3882

Erskine-Johns Co.
3621 Seaport Blvd.
W. Scaramento, CA 95691
Tel: (916) 371-2000

Erskine-Johns Co.
2330 N.W. 31st. St.
Portland, OR 97210
Tel: (503) 223-0935

Fiber Glass Industries
Edson St.
Amsterdam, NY 12010
Tel: (518) 842-4000
Fax: (518) 842-4408
E glass manufacturers

Fibre Glass Developments Corp.
1944 Neva Dr.
Dayton, OH 45414
Tel: (800) 821-3283

Fibre Glass Evercoat
6600 Cornell Rd.
Cincinnati, OH 45242
Tel: (513) 489-7600
Fax: (513) 489-9229
Resins, fiberglass, putties

Film Technology, Inc.
P.O. Box 230228
Houston, TX 77223
Tel: (713) 921-3456
Fax: (713) 928-2324
Vacuum bag films

FRP Supply
55 Scotland Blvd.
P.O. Box 608
Bridgewater, MA 02324
Tel: (508) 697-1600
Fax: (508) 697-7808
Suppliers of resins, coatings, fabrics, and chemicals

FRP Supply
P.O. Box 2219
Columbus, OH 43216
Tel: (614) 889-4272
Fax: (614) 889-4012
Suppliers of resins, coatings, fabrics, and chemicals

Harris Marine Supply
511 Riverside Industrial Pkwy.
Portland, ME 04103
Tel: (800) 286-2811 in ME

Hexcel Corp.
Trevarno Division
11555 Dublin Blvd.
Dublin, CA 94568
Tel: (510) 828-4200
Fax: (510) 829-1698
Advanced fibers and materials

Glas-Craft
5845 W. 82nd St.
Suite 102
Indianapolis, IN 46278
Tel: (317) 875-5592
Fax: (317) 875-5456

High Modulus NZ Ltd.
P.O. Box 150
Warkworth
NEW ZEALAND
Tel: (+64) 9 770-327
  or (+64) 846 8023
Fax: (+64) 846 7286
Advanced fibers, prepregs, analysis and design of composite systems

Hoechst Celanese Corp.
P.O. Box 5887
Spartanburg, SC 29304
Tel: (800) 845-7597
  or (803)-579-5914
Fax: (803) 579-5930

Laminex
Dynatron/Bondo Corporation
3700 Atlanta Industrial Pkwy. N.W.
Atlanta, GA 30331-1098
Tel: (800) 241-3386
  or (404) 696-1098
Fax: (404) 699-0073

Oceana Limited
P.O. Box 6691
Annapolis, MD 21401
Tel: (800) 523-8890
  or (410) 269 6022
Fax: (410) 268-6528
Resins, epoxies, adhesives

Orcon Corp.
1570 Atlantic St.
Union City, CA 94587-3299
Tel: (415) 489-8100
Fax: (415) 471-3410
Makers of uni-directional carbon, Kevlar, and glass materials

Polyfoam Products, Inc.
P.O. Box 11323
Spring, TX 77383-1132
Tel: (713) 350-8888
Fax: (713) 288-6450

RP Associates, Inc.
P.O. Box 568
Minturn Farm Rd.
Bristol, RI 02809
Tel: (800) 343-3030
  or (401) 253-4800
Fax: (401) 253-4720
Suppliers of resins, epoxies, and fiberglass

Seemann Fiberglass
6117 River Rd.
Harahan, LA 70123
Tel: (800) 358-1666
Fax: (504) 738-6014
Distributors of C-Flex & FRP supplies

**Structural Polymer
Systems Ltd.**
Cowes
Isle of Wight PO31 7BS
ENGLAND
Tel: (+44) 983 298451
*Makers of resins and
structural fabrics*

Core Materials

Boatex Fiberglass Co.
11 Tech Circle
Natick, MA 01760
Tel: (508) 655-2000
Fax: (508) 655-5045
Airex

Diversified Materials Co.
8250 Commercial St.
La Mesa, CA 91942
Tel: (619) 464-4111
Fax: (619) 464-4186

Baltek Corp.
P.O. Box 195
Northvale, NJ 07467
Tel: (201) 767-1400
Fax: (201) 387-6631
Balsa core and Duravcore

Baltek S. A.
61, Rue la Fontaine 75016
Paris FRANCE
Tel: (+33) 1 46 47 58 50
Fax: (+33) 1 46 47 66 58
Balsa core and Duracore

**Barracuda Technologies,
Inc.**
315 Seahawk Dr.
DeSoto, TX 75115
Tel: (214) 224-844
Fax: (214) 228-2667
*Manufacturers of Divinycell
foam cores for boat
construction*

Hexcell
11711 Dublin Blvd.
Dublin, CA 94568
Tel: (415) 828-4200
Fax: (415) 828-7101
*Manufacturers of Nomex
honeycomb core*

Klegecell Polimex
204 North Dooley
Grapevine, TX 76051
Tel: (817) 481-3547
Fax: (817 488-4816
*Manufacturers of Ductile,
Klegecell, and other marine
cores*

ProBalsa
204 North Dooley
Grapevine, TX 7651
Tel: (817) 481-3337
Fax: (817 488-4816

Tricel Corp.
3841 Swanson Court
Gurnee, IL 60031
Tel: (708) 336-1321
Fax: (708) 336-1311

Decking Materials

Dri-Dek Corp.
2706 S. Horseshoe Dr.
Naples, FL 33942
Tel: (800) 348-2398
Fax: (813) 643-2376
PVC deck covering material

Hecht Rubber
6161 Phillips Hwy.
Jacksonville, FL 32216
Tel: (800) USA-3401
Fax: (904) 730-0066
*Rubberized and Safetywalk
decking*

Mateflex-Mele
1712 Erie St.
Utica, NY 13402-3337
Tel: (800) 635-6353
*Fax: 315 733-3183 Mateflex
interlocking tiles*

Shipyard Supply Co.
85 Water St.
So. Norwalk, CT 06426
Tel: (800) 442-2111
  or (800) BOAT-WIRE
*Full stock of teak and other
exotic woods*

Teak Connection
2391 S.E. Dixie Hwy.
Stuart, FL 34996
Tel: (800) 274-TEAK
Fax: (407) 287-5031
*Suppliers of teak and
accessories*

Teak Decking Systems
6050 Palmer Blvd.
Sarasota, FL 34232
Tel: (813) 377-4100
Fax: (813) 377-5727
Pre-made teak deck system

Tra-Con
55 North St.
Medford, MA 02155
Tel: (617) 391-5550
Fax: (617) 391-7380

W. H. Salisbury & Co.
7520 N. Lona Ave.
Skokie, IL 60077
Tel: (708) 679-6700
Fax: (708) 679-2401

Viscom International, Inc.
507 Hopmeadow St.
Simsbury, CT 06070
Tel: (203) 658-2201
Fax: (203) 651-8406
TBS non-skid deck coverings

Epoxies

Chem Tech
4669 Lander Rd.
Chagrin Falls, OH 44022
Tel: (216) 248-0770

Fiberglass Coatings Inc.
P.O. Box 60457
St. Petersburg, FL 33784
Tel: (800) 272-7890
  or   (813) 822-3689

Fibre Glass Evercoat
6600 Cornell Rd.
Cincinnati, OH 45242
Tel: (513) 489-7600
Fax: (513) 489-9229
*Resins, epoxies, and paint
sundries*

Gougeon Brothers, Inc.
P.O. Box 908
Bay City, MI 48707
Tel: (517) 684-7286
Fax: (517) 684-1374
*Suppliers of the well-known
WEST system epoxies*

ITW Devcon Corp.
30 Endicott St.
Danvers, MA 01923
Tel: (800) 933-8266
Fax: (800) 765-4329
Epoxies

Fasteners

Attwood Corp.
1016 N. Monroe St.
Lowell, MI 49331
Tel: (616) 897-9241
Fax: (616) 897-8358
*Marine fasteners, hinges, and
other fittings*

Eastern Fastener Co.
P.O. Box 8128
Berlin, CT 06037
Tel: (203) 829-0556
Fax: (203) 829-0552

**Chesapeake Marine
Fasteners**
P.O. Box 6521
Annapolis, MD 21401
Tel: (800) 526-0658
  or   (410) 266-9336
Fax: (410) 266-0709

Jamestown Distributors
28 Narragansett Ave. P.O.
Box 348
Jamestown, RI 02835
Tel: (800) 423-0030
  or   (401) 423-2520
Fax: (401) 423-0542

Jamestown Distributors
Hwy. 17 & 21
Gardens Corner
Rt. 1, Box 375
Seabrook, SC 29940
Tel: (803) 846-9500
Fax: (803) 846-9005

Merit Metal Products Corp.
242 Valley Rd.
Warrington, PA 18796
Tel: (215) 343-2500
*Clasps, hasps, hinges, and
other fittings*

S & J Products
P.O. Box 2099
Chicago, IL 60690
Tel: (312) 549-7983
Fax: (312) 871-4070

Standard Fastenings
P.O. Box 51208
800 Mt. Pleasant St.
New Bedford, MA 02745
Tel: (800) 678-8811
Fax: (508) 995-3886

Impregnators

Binks Manufacturing Co.
9201 Belmot Ave.
Franklin Park, IL 60131

Fabric Impregnator
RR 3, Box 419-C Shore Rd.
#7 Windover Turn
Westerly, RI 02981
Tel: (401) 322-7474
Fax: (401) 322-7474

Venus-Gusmer
1862 Ives Ave.
Kent, WA 98032
Tel: (206) 854-2660
Fax: (206) 854-1666

Panels

Atlantic Plywood
8 Roessler Rd.
Woburn, MA 01801
Tel: (617) 933-7700

Aristech Acrylic Sheet
Aristech Chemical Corp.
7350 Empire Dr.
Florence, KY 41042
Tel: (800) 354-9858

Baltek Corp.
P.O. Box 195
Northvale, NJ 07467
Tel: (201) 767-1400
Fax: (201) 387-6631
Decolite panels

Baltek S. A.
61, Rue la Fontaine 75016
Paris FRANCE
Tel: (+33) 1 46 47 58 50
Fax: (+33) 1 46 47 66 58

Bruynzeel North America
JMB & Assoc
19942 Doyle Pl. W.
Grosse Pointe, MI 48236
Tel: (313) 884-7880
Fax: (313) 884-7912
Bruynzeel marine plywood

Harbor
1401 Russel St.
Baltimore, MD 21230-2089
Tel: (800) 345-1712
  or (410) 727-0106
Fax: (410) 752-0739

King Starboard
King Plastic Corp.
P.O. Box 1475
Venice, FL 34284-1475
Tel: (813) 493-5502
Fax: (813) 497-3274

Daytona Plastix, Inc.
P.O. Box 9425
Daytona Beach, FL 32120
Tel: (800) 874-7512
Fax: (904) 274-4241
*Marine-Tuff Polymer, and
Propanel, Proboard PVC sheets*

Daytona Plastix, Inc.
3141 N. 35th Ave.
Pheonix, AZ 85017
Tel: (800) 227-7963
Fax: (602) 278-8031
*Marine-Tuff Polymer and
Propanel, Proboard PVC sheets*

Nida-Core
P.O. Box 1571
New York, NY 10013-1571
Tel: (212) 529-NIDA
Fax: (212) 529-7030

Quality Woods
P.O. Box 205
Lake Hiawatha, NJ 07034
Tel: (201) 584-7554
Fax: (201) 584-3875

Simpson Panel Products
Third & Franklin
Shelton, WA 98548
Tel: (800) 445-2442

Teak Connection
2391 S.E. Dixie Hwy.
Stuart, FL 34996
Tel: (800) 274-TEAK
Fax: (407) 287 5031

Resins and Resin Cleaners

Ad-Tech Plastic Systems
P.O. Box 437
Charlotte, MI 48813
Tel: (517) 543-7510

Alpha Resins Corp.
P.O. Box 370
Collierville, TN 38027

Aquachelle International Corp.
20 Greenvale Ct.
Ruther Glen, VA 22546
Tel: (804) 448-1633

Amoco Chemical
MC 4106
200 East Randolph Dr.
Chicago, IL 60601
Tel: (800) 621-0626 ext. 20

Ashland Chemical Co.
P.O. Box 2219
Columbus, OH 43216
Tel: (614) 889-3767

Eastman Chemical Co.
P.O. Box 431
Kingsport, TN 37662
Tel: (800) EASTMAN

Ferro Corp.
4150 E. 56th St.
Cleveland, OH 44105
Tel: (216) 641-3752

Hybri-Chem
Polymer Development
Laboratories, Inc.
212 W. Taft Ave.
Orange, CA 92665
Tel: (800) 235- 4201
Fax: (714) 921-2300

International Speciality Products
1361 Alps Rd.
Wayne, NJ 07470
Tel: (201) 623 3110
Resin cleaner

CoRezyn
Interplastic Corp.
Commercial Resins Division
1225 Wolters Blvd.
Vadnais Heights, MN
55110-5145
Tel: (612) 481-6860
Fax: (612) 481-9836

Max-Pro-Coat
Pier Pressure Marine Systems
800 Fifth Ave.
Suite 198
Seattle, WA 98104-3191
Tel: (800) 621-3833
Fax: (206) 545-3556

Oceana Ltd.
P.O. Box 6691
Annapolis, MD 21401
Tel: (800) 523-8890
  or (410) 269-6022
Fax: (410) 268-6528

System Three Resins, Inc.
P.O. Box 70436
Seattle, WA 98107
Tel: (206) 782-7976

Sunrez Corp.
1374 Merrit Dr.
El Cajon, CA 92020
Tel: (619) 442-3353

Sealants and Adhesives

Amoco Chemicals
P.O. Box 87759
Chicago, IL 60680
Tel: (312) 861-5115

Adhesive Engineering and Supply
Unit 36
Lafayette Commercial Park
Seabrook, NH 03874
Tel: (800) 888 GLUE

Alpha Systems, Inc.
21680 Protecta Dr.
Elkhart, IN 46516
Tel: (800) 462-4698
  or (219) 295-5206

Bostik
Boston St.
Middleton, MA 01949
Tel: (508) 777-0100
Fax: (508) 774-7376

Darworth Co.
50 Tower Ln.
Avon, CT 06001
Tel: (203) 843-1200
Fax: (203) 674-8659
Polyseamseal, seamseal

Polybond/Corebond
ATC Chemical Corp.
1051 Clinton St.
Buffalo, NY 14206
Tel: (716) 836-1943
Fax: (716) 836-2362

Boatlife Calk
205 Sweethollow Rd.
Old Bethpage, NY 11804
Tel: (516) 454-0055
Fax: (516) 454-0452

Bondo Marine Products
Dynatron/Bondo Corp.
3700 Atlanta Industrial Pkwy.
Atlanta, GA 30331
Tel: (800) 241-3386
  or (404) 696-2730
Fax: (404) 699-0073

Chem Tech
4669 Lander Rd.
Chagrin Falls, OH 44022
Tel: (216) 248-0770

Fibre Glass Evercoat
6600 Cornell Rd.
Cincinnati, OH 45242
Tel: (513) 489-7600
Fax: (513) 489-9229
Resins, fiberglass, putties

Gougeon Brothers, Inc.
P.O. Box X-908
Bay City, Ml 48707
Tel: (517) 684-7286
Fax: (517) 684-1374
WEST system resin

Industrial Formulators of Canada
3824 William St. Burnaby,
British Columbia V5C 3H9
CANADA
Tel: (604) 294-6315
Fax: (604) 294-8052

ITW Adhesive Systems
37722 Enterprise Ct.
Farmington Hills, MI 48331
Tel: (313) 489-9344
Fax: (313) 489-1545

Owens-Corning Fiberglass Corp.
Resins and Coatings Division
Fiberglass Tower
Toledo, OH 43659
Tel: (419) 248-8657

Pemco
1108 Auburn Dr.
Auburn, IL 46706
Tel: (219) 925-3368

Shipyard Supply Co.
85 Water St.
So. Norwalk, CT 06426
Tel: (800) 442-2111
  or (800) BOAT-WIRE
Suppliers of sealants and adhesives

Sika Corp.
Chemseco Division
4800 Blue Pkwy.
Kansas City, MO 64130
Tel: (800) 323-5926
Fax: (816) 923-8200
Sikaflex

Sta-Put
C. J.'s Inc.
120 Wansly Dr.
Cartersville, GA 30120
Tel: (800) 346-2803
Fax: (404) 386-8676
Spray adhesive systems

Permalite Plastics
1537 Monrovla Ave.
Orange, CA 92663
Tel: (714) 548-1137

Cutraouds Aerospace
5430 San Fernando Rd.
Glendale, CA 91203
Tel: (818) 702-8900
Fax: (818) 247-2710

Surebond, Inc.
500 E. Remmington Rd.
Schaumburg, IL 60173-4540
Tel: (708) 843-1818
Fax: (708) 843-0765

3M Corporation
Marine Trades Building
223-6N-01
St. Paul, MN 55144
Tel: (612) 733-5273

Tra-Con
55 North St.
Medford, MA 02155
Tel: (617) 391-5550
Fax: (617) 391-7380
Adhesives

System Three Resins
P.O. Box 70436
Seattle, WA 98107
Tel: (206) 782-7976
System Three Resins and Chem Tech resins

Trim and Moldings

American Foreign Industries
2210 Gladstone Dr.
Pittsburg, CA 94565
Tel: (510) 427-2341
Fax: (510) 427-2342
Teak trim and moldings

Barbour Plastics, Inc.
932 North Montello St.
P.O. Box 2158
Brockton, MA 02405
Tel: (508) 583-8200
Fax: (508) 583-4113
Plastic rub rails and extrusions

Standard Products Co.
2401 South Gulley Rd.
Dearborn, MI 48124-2486
Tel: (800) 333-3265

Taco Metals, Inc.
50 N.E. 179th St.
Miami, FL 33162
Tel: (800) 226-8201
  or (305) 652-8566
Fax: (305) 653-1174
Metal trim and moldings, toerails and extrusions

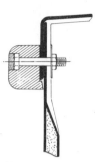

Figure 1: Trim pieces are used to cover hull/deck joints .

Trim-Lok, Inc.
6855 Hermosa Circle
Buena Park, CA 90622-6180
Tel: (714) 562-0500
Fax: (714) 562-0600

Ultra Poly, Inc.
2926 South Steele
Tacoma, WA 98409
Tel: (800) USA-UHMW
  or (206) 272-1217
Fax: (206) 272-1457

Wood

Boatply
Cascade Pacific Industries
P.O. Box 1351
Eugene, OR 97440
Tel: (503) 726-5686

Boulter Plywood Corp.
24 Broadway
Somerville, MA 02145
Tel: (617) 666-1340
Fax: (617)628-3531

M.L. Condon Co.
258 Ferris Ave.
White Plains, NY 10603
Tel: (914) 946-4111
Fax: (914) 946-3779

Dean Hardwoods, Inc.
1 Cowan St.
P.O. Box 1595
Wilmington, NC 28402
Tel: (919) 763-5409
Fax: (919) 763-3748

The Dean Co.
Olympic Manufacturing
Division
P.O. Box 426
Gresham, OR 97030
Tel: (503) 665-2161
Fax: (503) 665-6336

**East Teak Trading Group,
Inc.**
Drake Rd.
Donalds, SC 29639
Tel: (800) 338-5636
Fax: (803) 379-2116

East Teak of Saltan
33521-SR2
Saltan, WA 98294
Tel: (800) 537-3369
Fax: (206) 793-7835

Harbor
1400 Russel St.
Baltimore, MD 21230-2089
Tel: (800) 345-1712
   or   (410) 727-0106
Fax: (410) 752-0739

Shipyard Supply Co.
85 Water St.
So. Norwalk, CT 06426
Tel: (800) 442-2111
   or   (800) BOAT-WIRE
*Full stock of teak and other
exotic woods*

Teak Decking Systems
6050 Palmer Blvd.
Sarasota, FL 34232
Tel: (813) 377-4100
Fax: (813) 377-5727
Teak suppliers, teak decks

Teak Connection
2391 S.E. Dixie Hwy.
Stuart, FL 34996
Tel: (800) 274-TEAK
Fax: (407) 287-5031
*Suppliers of teak and
accessories*

Figure 2: Teak Decking
Systems provide a high quality
pre-fabricated deck for sail and
powerboats.

Boat Cushions and Fabrics

What do you look for when you have to buy new bunk or cockpit cushions? First is the cushion thickness. In general, bunk cushions are three inches thick, but four inches gives a more restful sleep if the bunk flat is made of plywood. If the bottom of the bunk is webbing or canvas, a two-inch cushion will suffice. Note also the type of foam rubber used to make the cushion. It should be a closed cell foam to limit water penetration. Denser foams give a harder cushion, while less dense foam make the cushion very soft.

The material that covers the cushion should be mildew-resistant, water-resistant, and something other than plastic. Plastic cushion covers make a sleeper sweat heavily, and they stick to the skin in warm weather. Unfortunately, many waterproof fabrics have a plastic backing or liner, and a buyer has to be extremely cautious about specifying them.

When getting fabrics for settee berths, make sure the material is not knobby. A knobby material can be uncomfortable when it is covered with a thin sheet on a hot summer night. You should also avoid positioning sofa buttons and other trim features in the middle of the cushion. They, too, are uncomfortable to sleep on.

Ideally, cockpit cushions should also be non-plastic. In hot weather, crews often wear shorts or a swim suit, and sitting on a hot plastic seat can sometimes cause quite a painful burn. Ideally, cushion fabrics should be fairly light in color for tropical areas. Dark colored fabrics tend to absorb heat.

Manufacturers and Installers of Bedding and Cushions

Almo Products
210 Maryland Rte. 3 S.
Millersville, MD 21108
Tel: (410) 987-2121

Bed Mates
P.O. Box 134
Poquonock, CT 06064
Tel: (203) 688-0468
Tailor-made sheets, blankets, and shams

Bottom Siders
4403 Russell Rd.
2A-7
Lynnwood, WA 98037
Tel: (800) 666-3626
Cockpit cushions

C. Cushions
206 Hwy. 35 So.
Rockport, TX 78382
Tel: (800) 531-1014
Fax: (512) 729-1260
Custom cockpit cushions

Handcraft Mattress Co.
605 E. Alton #E
Santa Ana, CA 92705
Tel: (714) 241-7751
Fax: (714) 241-8316
Tailored inner springs, and specially shaped mattresses

Kent Sporting Goods
433 Park Ave.
New London, OH 44851
Tel: (800) 537-2970
Fax: (419) 929-1769
Cushions

Nautical Image Ltd.
2530 Spring Grove Ave.
Cincinnati, OH 45214
Tel: (800) 989-4433
 or (513) 421-6951
Fax: (513) 421-6982
*Fitted bedding and bath
specialists*

Oakum Bay
9 State St.
Marblehead, MA 01945
Tel: (617) 631-8983

RV N' Sea Superbag
26516 Lope De Vega
Mission Viejo, CA 92691
Tel: (714) 830-1292
Custom sleeping bags

Safegard
P.O. Box 2044
Covington, KY 41012
Tel: (606) 431-7650
Fax: (606) 431-1355

Shoreline Design
1090-C Court Dr.
Duluth, GA 30136
Tel: (404) 945-8314
Cockpit cushions

So-Pac
4918 Leary Ave. N.W.
Seattle, WA 98107
Tel: (206) 782-7700
Fax: (206) 782-4531
*Foam fenders and cockpit
cushions*

Todd Enterprises
530 Wellington Ave.
Cranston, RI 02910
Tel: (401) 467-2750
Fax: (401) 467-2650

**Weatherworthy by VME,
Inc.**
P.O. Box 748
Floyd, VA 24091
Tel: (703) 745-2680
Fax: (703) 745-2901
*Fully upholstered cushions
and matresses capable of
withstanding rain and sun*

Boat Design Software

By Stephen M. Hollister

Stephen M. Hollister is the president of New Wave Systems, designers of the Nautilus software. He is a graduate of the naval architecture program of Michigan University and now lectures in computer science and mathematics at Salve Regina University in Newport, RI.

Although there is nothing more flexible and powerful than the human mind, computers have become an inseparable part of the design and construction of boats. The two biggest advantages of using computers are speed of calculation and ease of hull shape definition and fairing. With a computer, a designer can calculate any volumetric, stability, or performance prediction in seconds and can define and fair a hull shape without drawing grids and without matching the shape in all three views. The computer program can then automatically plot the lines drawings, print a table of offsets, or plot full-size construction templates. Computer software thus eliminates the drudgery of calculations and the tedious hand-fairing of lines. The designer can focus on the creative aspects of yacht design.

Some of the computer programs that yacht designers and builders use are created specially for them, while others are more general-purpose. The following sections list various types of programs and how they can be applied to yacht design and construction.

WORD PROCESSING / DESK-TOP PUBLISHING

These programs allow you to combine text and pictures together into one printable document, with no need to cut and paste. They are best used for correspondence, newsletters, and advertising brochures. Since they have little or no ability to create pictures, you need to have a separate drawing or computer-aided design (CAD) program. Drawing programs (sometimes called "paint" programs) are aimed at creating artistic and colorful drawings using computer versions of paint brushes, spray cans, and pencils. CAD programs, in contrast, are aimed at designers and architects who need to create accurate line drawings for design and construction purposes. Most word processors and desk-top publishing programs use the graphics output from either of these sources.

SPREADSHEET PROGRAMS

These programs allow you to organize text and numbers into tables with automatic calculation of numerical results. For example, you could set up a spreadsheet to create a bill of materials report for a vessel and to calculate its total weight and center of gravity. The columns might consist of "Part Description," "Part Number," "Supplier," "Cost," "Weight," "Longitudinal Weight

Location," "Vertical Weight Location," "Longitudinal Weight Moment," and "Vertical Weight Moment." The rows of the table would then be filled with each part or item that appears on the boat. You can also tell the spreadsheet program to sum the "Cost," "Weight," "Longitudinal Weight Moment," and "Vertical Weight Moment" columns to give you a total for each, and you can have the spreadsheet divide the sum of the "Longitudinal Weight Moment" and the sum of the "Vertical Weight Moment" columns by the total of the "Weight" column to find the center of gravity for the vessel. Anything that can be reduced to a tabular row and column format can be implemented on a spreadsheet.

GENERAL CALCULATION PROGRAMS

These programs, such as TK! Solver and MathCAD, allow you to perform calculations too tedious for calculators. Many come with pre-defined sets of calculations covering electrical, structural, and mechanical design problems. You can also create your own boat design calculations just by typing in the equations using names for all variables. Then all you have to do is fill in all but one value and the program will calculate the value of the unknown. These programs will also plot relationships between any two variables.

COMPUTER-AIDED DESIGN (CAD) PROGRAMS

These programs allow designers to produce many of the required structural, arrange-

ment, and detail drawings. The programs fall into two categories: low cost (under $500), mostly 2-dimensional (2D) programs, such as Generic CAD and FastCAD, and high cost (above $2500), 2-dimensional and 3-dimensional (3D) programs, such as AutoCAD and CADKey. Although some designers are using the 3D capabilities, the best use of a CAD is in producing the required 2D drawings. CAD programs really begin to pay off when you start building extensive libraries of standard parts (like deck hardware, lockers, berths, etc.) which can be quickly scaled and inserted into any drawing. Studies have shown that drafting with a CAD program is not much faster than drafting by hand, except when you use standard parts libraries or when a drawing needs to be revised or edited.

If you are thinking about purchasing a CAD system, most programmers recommend the following hardware: IBM PC, AT, or compatible computer. Machines using an 80486 and an 80487 math co-processor or 80386 CPUs are fastest, but the older 80286 and 8088 based machines are acceptable. You'll need at least one disc drive and a minimum 20 meg hard drive. You also need a color graphic adapter or enhanced graphics adapter and screen. While most programs allow input via the keyboard, a mouse or digitizer is best. The Summagraphics MM1201 digitizer is one of the most well known.

HULL SHAPE DESIGN AND FAIRING PROGRAMS

Although CAD programs are good at producing many 2D and 3D drawings, they often have no ability to define and fair 3-dimensional curved hull shapes. Therefore, most designers use a special-purpose 3D hull definition and fairing program. These programs, which are written specifically for boat design, allow you to define and fair hull shapes on the computer screen. In addition, they can calculate all shape-based values such as volume, center of buoyancy, and righting moment, and they can plot either full-size or scaled lines drawings. The programs eliminate drawing lines by hand and eliminate the need to match up the three views of the boat. When you change the shape of the hull in the section view, the other views are automatically and accurately updated. These programs change a highly skilled process that takes days to perform to one that can be performed by anyone in a couple of hours. Remember that these programs do not guarantee a "good" design. They merely simplify the lines drawing process.

Some of these programs also allow you to match up existing designs by typing in a table of offsets and performing the lofting process on screen. The process is much faster than lofting by hand, and any frame, waterline, buttock, or derived hull shape can be plotted very accurately at full size to be used as a template. Some designers are even creating frame and plate shapes to be cut automatically by numerically-controlled (NC) cutting machines.

HULL VOLUMETRIC CALCULATIONS

These programs perform more detailed volumetric and stability calculations than

those performed by the hull design and fairing programs. These calculations include those required by the Coast Guard for boats such as passenger and fishing vessels. The designer includes many of these calculations in a "Stability Booklet," which specifies the safe operating conditions for tankage, cargo, and passengers. Imagine a passenger vessel out to watch the America's Cup races with all of its passengers leaning over the starboard rail with their binoculars. The designer needs to know that, for reasonable wind and wave conditions, the boat will be stable. These hydrostatic and stability programs are created specifically for such calculations.

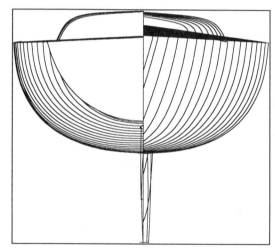

Figure 1: Sectional views of a 35 ft. LOA sailboat developed and faired using the Nautilus System.

DESIGN ANALYSIS PROGRAMS

This category refers to a broad collection of programs created especially for yacht designers. For example, there are programs that allow designers to determine the horsepower required to push a planing hull at any given speed and its trim or angle of attack. This information can then be used as input for another program that selects the most efficient propeller. For sailboats, there are "Velocity Prediction Programs" (VPPs) that predict boat speed for any combination of wind speed and angle. Still other programs help select the size of various structural components.

Suppliers of Boat Design Software

**Programs for IBM
Compatible
Microcomputers**

Aerohydro, Inc.
P.O. Box 684
Main St.
Southwest Harbor, ME 04679
Tel: (207) 244-7347
*Leading-edge software
developed from Dr. John
Letcher's association with the
America's Cup*

Albacore Research Inc.
3080 Uplands Rd.
Victoria, British Columbia
V8R 6B4
CANADA
Tel: (604) 595-0576
*ShipCAM is capable of lofting,
fairing, and generating
numerically controlled
computer codes for ship
builders*

AutoSHIP
Coastdesign, Inc.
#201-12837-76th Ave.
Surrey, British Columbia
V3W 2V3
CANADA

Tel: (604) 599-1278
Fax: (604) 599-1287
*AutoSHIP has 3D graphics,
hydrostatics, stability, weight
editor, offset editor, and section
editor modules.*

British Marine Technology
Feltham, Middlesex
TW14 0LQ
ENGLAND
Tel: 01-890-8989
Fax: 01-890 3992
*Ship design and analysis
software. Extensive CAD
software, including ship
structural design and
performance predictions*

Fast Yacht
Design Systems & Services,
Inc.
105 Eastern Ave.
Suite 102
Annapolis, MD 21403
Tel: (301) 268-5551
Fax: (301) 268-6150
*Fast Yacht software ranges
from keel design to
performance review and
analysis programs.*

General Hydrostatics
Creative Systems, Inc.
P.O. Box 1910
Port Townsend, WA 98368
Tel: (206) 385-6212
Fax: (206) 385-6213
*Several programs of
hydrostatics, yacht design,
trim and stability, and salvage*

**International Marine
Software Associates**
45 James Farm-Lee
P.O. Box 865
Durham, NH 03284
Tel: (603) 659-2660
Fax: (603) 659-6667
*A cooperative of software
developers with complementary
design products including Fast
Ship, General Hydrostatics,
NavCad, and ShipCAM*

The Nautilus System
New Wave Systems, Inc.
79 Narragansett Ave.
Jamestown, RI 02835
Tel: (401) 423-1852
*A complete naval architecture
design package comprised of a
free executive package and
eight modules, each of which
can be purchased separately*

PC-SHCP 4
C. Tremblay & Associes, Inc.
Consulting Naval Architects
3157 Douai St.
Ste-Foy, Quebec
CANADA
PC-SHCP 4 ship hull
characteristics program
supports the latest IMO
regulations concerning damage
stability and subdivision

SHIPFLOW
FLOWTECH International AB
P.O. Box 24 001
S-400 22 Gothenburg
SWEDEN
Tel: (+46) 31 41 50 60
  or (+46) 31 41 05 06
Fax: (+46) 31 41 50 60
A computer code developed as
a complement to towing tank
testing, based on
computational fluid dynamics

Vacanti Yacht Design
17226 163 Pl. S.E.
Renton, WA 98058
Tel: (206) 277-0288
Fax: (206) 277 0288
Keel and winged keel lift/drag
and lofting programs, hull
design and resistance
programs, American Bureau of
Shipping scantling design
programs

Wolfson Unit for Marine
Technology
University of Southampton
Highfield, Southampton
SO9 5NH
ENGLAND
Tel: (+44) 703-585044
Extensive range of programs
available from one of
England's most respected
universities: propeller design,
nozzle data, propulsive
coefficients, and power
prediction for fast craft

Programs for Apple Macintosh Computers

Macsurf
Chance and Co., Inc.
Pratt St.
Essex, CT 06426
Tel: (203) 767-2161
Fax: (203) 767-2162
Surface fairing and design
program for hull and sail
design

Macsurf
Island Computer Systems
41 Horsebridge Hill
Newport, Isle of Wight
PO30 5TJ
ENGLAND
Tel: (+44) 983 821717
Fax: (+44) 983 521608
Surface fairing and design
program for hull and sail
design

Stand-Alone Software for Structural Design

Ambush
Tanton, Inc.
P.O. Box 270
Newport, RI 02840
Tel: (401) 847-4112
Program to "Ambush" the
American Bureau of Shipping
scantling rules

Copan/II
Parados Technical Services
2165 W. Stadium Blvd.
Ann Arbor, MI 48103
A composite material database
and calculation system

Hullforms, Inc.
3667 Woodland Dr. RD3
Baldwinsville, NY 13027
Tel: (315) 622-3933

Structure-Pak 1
C. Tremblay & Associes, Inc.
Consulting Naval Architects
3157 Douai St.
Ste-Foy, Quebec
CANADA
Programs for hull fairing only

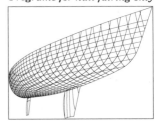

Figure 2:   A   three
dimensional view of a 35 ft.
LOA sailboat designed using
the Nautilus System

Boatshows

Going to a boat show? If so, here are some suggestions on visiting a show and purchasing a new boat. First, wear the right shoes. Leather-soled shoes and boats do not mix. Also, if you want to board a boat, your rubber-soled shoes should not have the remains of last week's gardening chores still stuck to them. After all, you wouldn't board your own boat with muddy shoes.

Second, finish your drinks or ice cream before climbing aboard a boat. Boat salespeople tend to get a little upset when the carefully installed carpet is stained on the first day of the show.

Third, ask questions, by all means, but remember, many answers can easily be found by reading the brochure or looking the boat over for two minutes. When you stop to look at a boat, stand to one side of the dock. There is a flow of traffic along the dock and a sudden stop can result in deadlock. Ask permission to come aboard if you want to look around. From a salesperson's point of view, there is nothing worse than being in the middle of a sales pitch and having a family climb aboard and wander all around the boat.

Once you are aboard, look over the boat, but be considerate. Try not to bounce on cushions or hog the navigator's seat while you explain the working of the loran set to your buddy. The boat is there for everyone to look at, and the salesperson is trying to sell it (or others like it). He wants to have as many people as possible look over his product, and your explaining the loran isn't going to help him. By the same token, after you have finished looking over the craft, don't sit in the cockpit and discuss the six other boats you have seen that morning, unless you have been invited to do so by the salesman. If you feel that you have missed something on your tour, you can always go back aboard again later.

If you are a serious customer, ready to make a purchase, be sure to do your homework. First, look over the various brochures. Make a list of the features you want and check the brochures to see which of these are included in the base price and which are extra. For some boats, such as the Hunter and Luhrs line, about all you have to purchase is the diesel fuel and you are on your way. Others require options that can double the price of the boat.

Having made out your list of features, look over the different boats carefully. Ask opinions of experts on the boat of your choice, especially people who have taken a trip aboard it. Quite often, if you ask, the salesman can give you a list of owners who would be willing to talk about their boat. From them, you can probably find out about any problems the boat might have.

Having narrowed your list down to two or three, ask if you can trial sail the boat. Usually manufacturers have demo boats available to take prospective customers out after the show. When you are aboard, make sure the boat does all the things you intend to do with it. For instance, if your wife normally helms while you sleep in the cockpit, have her drive while you try to stretch out and get comfortable.

When you have decided upon a vessel, hire a surveyor to look it over. It might cost you a few hundred dollars, but unnoticed problems can cost you thousands of dollars more. If you are buying a used boat, it should definitely be surveyed before purchase no matter what the owner says.

Figure 1: An aerial view of the Newport International Sailboatshow held in Newport, RI.

Major Boatshows

Note: In the northern Hemisphere the boat show season is assumed to begin during late summer and early fall. The dates of the major boat shows vary from year to year. In this listing only the approximate dates are given. Check with the show organizers for specific dates.

August

Auckland International Boat Show
Tel: (+64) 9 444 6376
Fax: (+64) 9 444 3798
Held around the second week of August on the Auckland Waterfront, Auckland, New Zealand.

Boston In-Water Boat Show
Tel: (301) 268-8828
Held during the third week of August at the World Trade Center in Boston, MA.

Dallas Marine Trade Show
Tel: (800) 999-0292
  or (214) 760-6080
Fax: (214) 760-6967
Held in the Dallas Market Hall around the middle of August. The Dallas Marine Trade Show, 3811 Turtle Creek Blvd., Suite 950, Dallas, TX 75219

Amsterdam Boat Show
Tel: (+31) 20 549 1212
Fax: (+31) 20 646 4469
Held at the Amsterdam Maritime Museum around the end of August.

Racine In-Water Boat Show (an NMMA boat show)
Tel: (312) 836-4740
Fax: (312) 329-9815
Held at Reef Point Marina, Racine, WI, during the second or third week of August.

Michigan City In-Water Boatshow
Tel: (216) 621-3618
Held at Washington Park, Michigan City, MI, during the third week of August.

September

Newport International Boat Show
Tel: (401) 846-1600
Usually held during September at the Newport Yachting Center. Commercial Wharf, America's Cup Ave., Newport RI 02840

Stockholm Boat Show
Tel: (+46) 8 744 02 20
Fax: (+46) 8 744 18 29
Held at Wasahammen, Djurgaarden, Stockholm during the early part of September.

Dockside Toronto Show
Tel: (416) 695-0311
Fax: (416) 695-0381
Held during early September at the North Marina. Ontario Place, Toronto, Ontario, Canada

Penn's Landing In-Water Boat Show (an NMMA boat show)
Tel: (215) 449-9910
Fax: (215 449-1143
Held at Penn's Landing, Philadelphia, PA, during the middle of September.

Atlantic City In-Water Powerboat Show
Tel: (609) 767-0800
Usually held around the second week of September at Sen. Frank S. Farley State Marina, Atlantic City NJ.

La Rochelle Boat Show
Tel: (+33) 46 44 46 39
Fax: (+33) 46 45 32 24
Held at Port des Minimes, La Rochelle, France, during the middle of September.

IMTEC - International Marine Trades Exhibit & Convention (an NMMA Boat Show)
Tel: (212) 922-1212
Held at McCormick Place, Chicago, IL, during the second or third week of September.

Cannes Boat Show
Tel: (+33) 1 42 89 41 04
Fax: (+33) 1 45 61 12 00
Held at the Old Harbour, Cannes, France, during the middle of September.

Dockside Toronto Show
Tel: (416) 695-0311
Held at North Marina, Ontario Place, Toronto, Canada, during the middle of September.

Southampton International Boat Show
Tel: (+44) 703 737311
Fax: (+44) 703 736840
Held during the middle of September on the Western Esplanade, Southampton, England.

North American Sail & Power Show
Tel: (216) 621-3618
Held at Cedar Point, Sandusky, Ohio, during the second or third week of September.

International In-Water Boat Show

Tel: (713) 526-6361
Fax: (713) 526-6454
Usually held around the third week of September at the Watergate Yachting Center, Clear Lake Shores, TX.

Boat Show USA

Tel: (313) 886-7887
Held at Metro Beach, Metro Park, Mt. Clemens, MI, around the third week of September.

Palma De Mallorca Boat Show

Tel: (+34) 71 455500
Fax: (+34) 71 451221
Held at the West Pier, Palma Harbor, during the middle of September.

Miami's Boat Show in the Grove

Tel: (305) 764-7642
Held at the the Coconut Grove Exhibition Center, Miami, FL, around the third week of September.

Norwalk International In-Water Show (an NMMA boat show)

Tel: (212) 922-1212
Fax: (212) 922-9607
Held around the third week of September in Norwalk, CT.

Norfolk In-Water Boat Show (an NMMA boat show)

Tel: (215) 449-9910
Fax: (215) 449-1143
Held at the Waterside Marina Norfolk, VA, toward the end of September.

North Atlantic Sailboat Show

Tel: (301) 268-8828
Usually held the week following the Norwalk show at Yacht Haven Marine Center, Stamford, CT.

Friedrichshafen Boat Show

Tel: (+49) 75 41 7080
Fax: (+49) 75 70810
Held at the Friedrichshafen Trade Fair Center, Friedrichshafen, Germany, around the end of September.

October

Houston International In-Water Boat Show

Tel: (713) 526-6361
Usually held the first week of October at the Watergate Yachting Center Kemah, TX. Houston International Boat, Sport & Travel, 26000 Southwest Freeway, Suite 305, Houston, TX 77098

Fish Expo

Tel: (207) 594-6222
Held at the Boston Exposition Center Boston, MA, during the early part of September. Sponsored by National Fisherman.

United States Sailboat Show

Tel: (301) 268-8828
Usually held either the second or third week of October (alternates with powerboat show) at the Annapolis City Dock and Harbor, Annapolis, MD. Annapolis Boat Shows, Inc., P.O. Box 4997, Annapolis, MD 21403

Genoa Boat Show

Tel: (+39) 10 589371
Fax: (+39) 10 553104
Held around the third week of October at the Genoa Exhibition Center, Genoa, Italy.

United States Powerboat Show

Tel: (301) 268-8828
Usually held either the second or third week of October (alternates with the sailboat show) at the Annapolis City Dock and Harbor, Annapolis, MD. Annapolis Boat Shows, Inc, P.O. Box 4997, Annapolis, MD 21403

Hamburg International Boat Show

Tel: (+49) 40 35692140
Fax: (+49) 40 35692149
Held around the end of October at the Hamburg Fairgrounds and City Marina, Hamburg, Germany.

November

Ft. Lauderdale International Boat Show
Tel: (305) 764-7642
Fax: (305) 764-4140
Held during the last week of October/first week of November at the Broward County Convention Center, Ft. Lauderdale, FL.

Kobe International Boat Show
Tel: (+81) 680 7525
Fax: (+81) 680 0587
Held at the Kobe Exhibition Center and Marina at the beginning of November.

Pacific Marine Expo
Tel: (207) 594-6222
Held at the Washington Trade & Convention Center during the middle of November. Sponsored by National Fisherman.

Ft. Myers Boat Show
Tel: (305) 570-7785
Held at the Ft. Myers Exhibition Hall and Yacht Basin, Ft. Myers, FL, during the third week of November.

Marine Equipment Trade Show (METS)
Tel: (+31) 20 549 1212
Fax: (+31) 20 646 4469
Held during the second or third week of November at the RAI Exhibition Center, Amsterdam, Holland.

San Diego International Boat Show (an NMMA boat show)
Tel: (619) 274-9924
Fax: (619) 274-6760
Held in San Diego, CA, in late November.

Barcelona Boat Show
Tel: (+34) 3 423 31 01
Fax: (+34) 3 426 33 73
Held at the Barcelona Fair Precincts, Barcelona, Spain.

December

International Work Boat Show
Tel: (207) 772-3005
Fax: (207) 772-5059
Held in the New Orleans Convention Center, New Orleans, LA, during the early part of December. Sponsored by WorkBoat and National Fisherman.

Antigua Charter Boat Show
Tel: (809)
Fax: (809)
Usually held during the first week of December in Antigua, West Indies.

Paris International Boat Show
Tel: (+33) 1 45 55 10 49
Fax: (+33) 1 47 53 94 75
Held during the second week of December at the Parc des Expositions, Porte de Versailles, Paris, France.

January

London International Boat Show
Tel: (+44) 784 473377
Fax: (+44) 784 439678
Held during the first two weeks of January at Earl's Court, London, England.

Portland Boat Show
Tel: (503) 246-8291
Held at the Exposition Center, Portland, OR, during the early part of January.

Chicago Boat, Sports, and RV Show
Tel: (312) 836-4740
Fax: (312) 329-9815
An NMMA show Held at McCormick Place, Chicago, IL, during early January.

Houston International Boat, Sport, and Travel Show
Tel: (713) 526-6361
Held at the Houston Astrohall, Houston, TX, during the second week of January.

Nashville Boat and Sports Show (an NMMA show)
Tel: (314) 567-0020
Fax: (314) 567-1810
Held during the middle of January in Nashville, TN.

San Francisco Sports and Boat Show
Tel: (415) 931-2500
Fax: (415) 931-2385
Held at the Cow Palace, San Francisco, CA, during the middle of January.

Toronto International Boat Show (an NMMA boat show)
Tel: (416) 591-6772
Fax: (416) 591-3582
Held during the second week of January at the Coliseum Building, Exhibition Place, Toronto, Canada.

New York National Boat Show
Tel: (212) 922-1212
Fax: (212) 922-9607
Held during the first and second week of January at the Jacob K. Javits Center in Manhattan, New York.

Rhode Island Boat Show
Tel: (401) 885-5044
Held at the Providence Civic Center, Providence, RI, around the end of January.

The Boat Show
Tel: (612) 827-5833
Held at the Minneapolis Convention Center, Minneapolis, MN during the third week of January.

Mid-America Boat Show
Tel: (216) 621-3618
Held at the International Exposition Center, Cleveland, OH, during the middle of January.

Seattle International Boat Show
Tel: (206) 634-0911
Held at the Kingdome, Seattle, WA, during the last part of January.

Dusseldorf Show
Tel: (+49) 211 4560 01
Fax: (+49) 211 4560 668
Held around the third week of January at the Fairgrounds, Dusseldorf, Germany.

Iowa's January Boat Show
Tel: (616) 530-1919
Held in the Unidome at Cedar Falls, IA, during the middle of January.

Tampa International Boat Show (an NMMA boat show)
Tel: (813) 264-0490
Fax: (813) 264-3639
Held around the third week of January at the Tampa Convention Center, Tampa, FL.

Philadelphia Boat Show (an NMMA boat show)
Tel: (215) 449-9910
Fax: (215) 449-1143
Held around the fourth week of January at the Philadelphia Civic Center, Philadelphia, PA.

Boston Boat Show
Tel: (617) 536-8152
Held at the World Trade Exhibition Center, Boston, MA, near the end of January.

Los Angeles Boat Show
Tel: (714) 633-7581
Fax: (714) 633-9498
Held around the end of January at the Los Angeles Convention Center, Los Angeles, CA.

February

Chesapeake Bay Boat Show (an NMMA boat show)
Tel: (215) 449-9910
Fax: (215) 449-1143
Held at the Baltimore Convention Center in Baltimore, MD, during the early part of January.

Southern California Boat Show
Tel: (714) 633-7581
Held at the Los Angeles Convention Center, Los Angeles, CA, around the end of January or early February.

St. Louis Boat and Sports Show (an NMMA show)
Tel: (314) 567-0020
Fax: (314) 567-1810
Held in St. Louis, MO, during the middle of February.

Dallas Boat Show
Tel: (713) 439-5890
Held at Market Hall, Dallas, TX, during the first week of February.

International Boatbuilders Exhibition and Conference (IBEX)
Tel: (203) 852-0500
Fax: (203) 838-3710
A show for marine industry professionals held around the beginning of February at the Radisson Center, Miami, FL. c/o CMC, 200 Connecticut Ave. Norwalk, CT 06856-4990

Sail Expo
Tel: (401) 841-0900
Fax: (401) 847-2044
A show held for the first time in 1993 during the first week of February at Atlantic City, NJ.

Spokane Boat Show
Tel: (509) 747-1868
Held at the Interstate Fairgrounds, Spokane, WA, during the middle of February.

Gothenburg Boat Show
Tel: (+46) 31 109100
Fax: (+46) 31 160330
Held at the Swedish Exhibition Center Gothenburg, Sweden, around the middle of February.

Chesapeake Bay Boat Show
Tel: (215) 449-9910
Fax: (215) 449-1143
Held during February at the Baltimore Convention Center, Baltimore, MD.

Geneva International Boat Show
Tel: (+41) 1 318 7111
Fax: (+41) 1 318 7101
Held during the second or third week of February at Palexpo, Geneva, Italy.

The Brokerage Yacht Show
Tel: (305) 764-7642
Fax: (305) 462-4140
Held around the middle of February at 47th St. & Collins Ave., Miami Beach, FL.

New Orleans Boat Show (an NMMA boat show)
Tel: (504) 885-9709
Fax: (504) 455-4966
Held at the Lousiana Superdome, New Orleans, LA, around the end of February.

Exponautique Internationale de Montreal
Tel: (514) 257-7600
Fax: (514) 257-7362
Held during the second or third week of February in Montreal, Canada.

Helsinki International Boat Show
Tel: (+358) 0 15091
Fax: (+358) 0 142358
Held during the second week of February in Helsinki, Finland.

Vancouver Boat Show
Tel: (604) 291-6651
Fax: (604) 291-0412
Held at the B.C. Place Stadium, Vancouver, during the middle of February.

Halifax International Boat Show
Tel: (416) 695-0311
Held in the Atlantic Winter Fair Building, Halifax, Nova Scotia, during the middle of February.

Tokyo International Boat Show
Tel: (+81) 33 567 6707
Fax: (+81) 33 567 0635
Held during the second or third week of February at the Tokyo Fair ground, Tokyo, Japan.

Boat-A-Rama
Tel: (904) 724-3003
Fax: (904) 725-9993
Held during the middle of February at the Prime Osborne Convention Center in Jacksonville, FL.

Miami International Boat Show & Sailboat Show (an NMMA Boat Show)
Tel: (305) 531-8410
Fax: (305) 534-3139
Held the second or third week of February at the Miami Beach Convention Center, Biscayne Bay Marriot Marina, and the Miami Beach Marina, Miami, FL.

Long Island Boat Show
Tel: (516) 737-4422
Held at the Nassau Veterans Memorial Coliseum in Uniondale, Long Island, NY, during the third week of February.

Danish International Boat Show
Tel: (+45) 75 92 25 66
Fax: (+45) 93 21 49
Held around the end of February in Frederica, Denmark.

New England Boat Show
Tel: (617) 242-6092
Held at the Bayside Exhibition Center, Boston, MA, during the last week of February.

Grand Center Boat Show
Tel: (616) 530-1919
Held at Grand Center, Grand Rapids, MI, during the last week of February or early March.

March

Central Florida Boat Show
Tel: (407) 298-1167
Held at the Orange County Convention Center, Orlando, FL, during the last week of February/first week of March.

HISWA Amsterdam Boat Show
Tel: (+31) 20 549 1212
Fax: (+31) 20 646 469
Held at the end of February/first week of March in Amsterdam, Holland.

Genoa Trade Show
Tel: (+39) 10 589371
Fax: (+39) 10 5531104
Held at the Genoa Exhibition Center, Genoa, Italy, during the first week of March.

Suncoast Boat Show
Tel: (305) 764-7642
Held at City Island, Sarasota, FL, during the second week of March.

Copenhagen International Boat Show
Tel: (+45) 32 52 88 11
Fax: (+45) 31 51 96 36
Held during the second week of March in Copenhagen, Denmark.

Danish International Boat Show
Tel: (+45) 75 92 25 66
Fax: (+45) 93 21 49
Held during the second week of March.

Norwegian International Boat Show
Tel: (+47) 2 430 420
Fax: (+47) 2 551 560
Held during the second week of March at Sjosenteret Herben Marina, Oslo, Norway.

Maine Boat Show
Tel: (207) 865-1196
Held at the Cumberland County Civic Center, Portland, ME, during the third week of March.

Stockholm International Boat Show
Tel: (+46) 8 749 4100
Fax: (+46) 8 99 2044
Held during the second or third week of March in Stockholm, Sweden.

Canadian Spring Boat & Cottage Show
Tel: (416) 695-0311
Held at the International Center, Toronto, Canada, around the end of March.

Istanbul International Boat Show
Tel: (+90) 1225 0290
Fax: (+90) 1225 0933
Held during the last week of March at the Istanbul Hilton Convention & Exhibition Center, Istanbul, Turkey.

April

Tacoma Dome Boat Show
Tel: (206) 756-2121
Held at the Tacoma Dome in Tacoma, WA, around the beginning of April.

Newport Spring Power & Sailboat Show
Tel: (714) 757-5959
At the Lido Marina Village, Newport Beach, CA, during the first week of April.

St. Petersburg Spring Boat Show
Tel: (305) 764-7642
Held at the Bay Front Center Yacht Basin, St. Petersburg, FL, during the middle of April. Yachting Promotions, 1115 N.E. 9th Ave., Ft. Lauderdale, FL 33304

Annapolis Spring Boat Show
Tel: (410) 268-8828
Fax: (410) 280-3903
Held at the Annapolis Yacht Basin, Annapolis, MD, during the middle of April. International Boat Shows Inc., Box 4997 Annapolis, MD 21403

May

Newport Used Boat Show
Tel: (401) 849-3033
Held at the Newport Yachting Center, Newport, RI, during the last week of May or first week of June.

San Remo Charter Boat Show

Held in San Remo, France, during the first week of May.

Boat Show USA

Tel: (313) 886-7887

Fax: (313) 886-1347

Held at the Metropolitan Beach Metro Pk., Mt. Clemens, MI during the middle of May. Recreational Promotions, Inc., 1177 Cadieux Rd., Grosse Point Pk., MI 48230

Super Yacht Show

Tel: (+44) 814 238666

Fax: (+44) 814 238686

In 1993 this show is to be held at the Acropolis, Nice, France, but time and location may vary. Gillan Beach Ltd., Bydell House, Sudbury Hill, Harrow, Middlesex, England

The Middle East International Boat Show

Held at the Dubai World Trade Center, Dubai, during the latter part of May.

June

Marina Del Rey Boat Show

Tel: (714) 757-5959

Held at Burton Chace Park, Marina Del Ray, CA, during the early part of June.

July

Melbourne Boat Show

Tel: (+61) 3 853 3633

Fax: (+61) 3 853 2659

Held during the early part of July at the Royal Exhibition Building, Melbourne, Australia.

Dallas Summer Boat Show

Tel: (713) 439-5890

Held at Market Hall in Dallas, TX, during the third week of July.

Sydney International Boat Show

Tel: (+61) 2 438 2077

Fax: (+61) 2 439 3983

Held during the last week of July at the Exhibition Center at Darling Harbor, Sydney, Australia.

Boots and Shoes

I wear sailing shoes most of the year and have tried out many, many different kinds, both on boats and on shore. My wife tells me that I am hard on shoes and clothes. I usually wear my boat shoes down to virtually nothing and then wrap them in duct tape and use them for gardening. So I get the maximum amount of wear from them. Even so, I go through two pairs a year.

After trying almost every manufacturer's shoes, I have definite opinions. The sailing shoes with thin (about 1/4 inch thick) rubber soles, I don't like much. They have no give when they are worn and you can feel almost every bump or dip in the deck or street. I also think this type of sole is poor on slippery surfaces.

Another type of boat shoe I have tried has a thick (about 1/2 to 3/4 inch) rubber sole. The ones with the soft rubber wear down so quickly that these shoes need resoling within four months if used for street wear. They do, however, have good non-slip capability. The thick-soled shoes with Vibram soles last a long time and are great for street wear, but they do not have much non-slipability. The solution may be to have two pairs: one with Vibram soles for street wear and another with soft rubber soles for the boat.

As for the uppers of a boat shoe, I prefer leather rather than canvas or plastic. Canvas uppers tend to wear out long before the sole goes. Plus repairing cloth shoes can be almost impossible. As I write this, I am wearing a pair of leather Rockports which have been resoled twice, but still have good uppers.

While I prefer not to purchase shoes with oiled leather uppers (I find they make my feet sweat), I have found that oiling sailing shoes on a regular basis prolongs their life and keeps them supple. Although salt deposits seem to form more easily on well-oiled shoes that get soaked on a regular basis, as mine do, the white film doesn't seem to harm the shoe in any way, except for aesthetics.

As for boots, I prefer the good, solid, old-fashioned sailing boots that come almost up to my knees. That's the only real way to keep your feet dry. The types with holes around the top and drawstrings I found let more water in than out, and the short calf-high boots could only have been designed by a person who'd never been to sea. In fact, I prefer not to wear boots in really inclement conditions, because they hold more water than shoes and keep your feet bathed in seawater. In my opinion, sailing boots are best when it is raining steadily and you want to keep your feet dry. If you are in heavy seas and gale force winds, your boots will soon fill, and you'll spend the rest of your watch sloshing around in your own private wading pools.

Suppliers of Boots and Shoes

Euro Marine Trading
64 Halsey St. #Z7
Newport, Rl 02840
Tel: (800) 222-7712
Fax: (401) 849-3230
Vredestein boots

Gilmer Mfg.
13030 S. Colman Rd.
Empire, MI 49630
Tel: (616) 228-6575
Scupper boat shoes

Harken Yacht Equipment
1251 E. Wisconsin Ave.
Pewaukee, Wl 53072
Tel: (414) 691-3320
Fax: (414) 691-3008
Harken boat shoes

Hecht Rubber
6161 Phillips Hwy.
Jacksonville, FL 32216
Tel: (800) USA-3401
Fax: (904) 730-0066

International Sailing Products
319 Main St.
P.O. Box 389
New Rochelle, NY 10802
Tel: (800) 645-7676
 or (914) 576-4050
Fax: (914) 632-2732

K-Swiss
12300 Montague St.
Pacoima, CA 91331
Tel: (818) 897-3433

Musto, Inc.
333 West 76th St.
New York, NY 10023
Tel: (800) 553-0497
 or (212) 580-3653
Fax: (212) 799-3395
M1 yacht boots

Nike
9000 S.W. Murray Blvd.
Beaverton, OR 97005
Tel: (503) 626-6453
Fax: (503) 626-6494

Watersport Footwear, Inc.
100 Main Street, #16
Somersworth, NH 03878
Tel: (603) 692-6509
Fax: (603) 692-2957
Importer and distributor of Okespor boots and shoes

Omega
130 Condor St.
E. Boston, MA 02128
Tel: (617) 569-3400
Fax: (617) 569-3617

The Rockport Company, Inc.
220 Donald Lynch Blvd.
Marlboro, MA 01752
Tel: (800) 343-WALK
Fax: (508) 624-4299
Rockports

W C. Russell Moccasin
285 S. W. Franklin St.
Berlin, Wl 54923
Tel: (414) 361-2252
Fax: (414) 361-3274
Moccasins and shoes

Sebago, Inc.
P.O. Box 3000
72 Bridge St.
Westbrook, ME 04098
Tel: (207) 854-8474
Fax: (207) 856-7114

Stride-Rite Corp.
5 Cambridge Center
Cambridge, MA 02142
Tel: (617) 491-8800
Fax: (617) 491-8298
Sperry Top-Siders

Timberland
11 Merrill Industrial Dr.
Hampton, NH 03842-5050
Tel: (603) 926-1600
Fax: (603) 926-9239

Wavelengths
6111 Birkdale St.
Long Beach, CA 90815
Tel: (310) 429-4062
Women's boots and clothes

Figure 1: The M5150 boatshoe is available from The Rockport Company.

Canvaswork

Since man learned to sail, boats have needed canvaswork. Canvaswork is used to shelter gear and equipment from the elements, to protect crew from the sun, wind, or waves, and to cover gear that might snag a sail or a person. Good canvaswork should have certain features. It should have reinforced grommets, so that ropes used to tie the awning or bimini down will not pull out of the material. It should have extra patches, usually leather ones, at corners that are likely to be chaffed or abraded as the canvas flaps or works. Good canvaswork should also have a snug fit. It should not blow off as soon as the wind gets up.

There are other features to look for in particular kinds of canvaswork. Dodgers should not only fit snugly, they should also have windows in them to enable the crew to spot oncoming vessels. The windows should be made of a UV-resistant plastic that will remain flexible over its lifetime. Try to avoid clear plastics that gradually harden and eventually crack, neccessitating repairs.

Bimini tops should have reinforced grommets at the corners and middle, plus anti-chafe patches where the canvaswork bears on its supports. Biminis should also be made of a UV- and water-reisitant material for long wear.

Compass, winch, and equipment covers should also be UV- and water-resistant.

They should have a drawstring to secure them in a strong breeze, or, alternatively, a separate length of line to secure them to a nearby cleat or padeye. If the equipment being protected is likely to corrode, the cover should be made of a fabric that will keep moisture out but allow air to circulate under the cover.

Leecloths on lifelines generally have the yacht's name or number on them. They should have reinforced corners, plus patches where stanchions or winches are likely to abrade them. Leecloths on bunks need to be strongly secured so that a person falling against them will not rip the grommets out of the cloth or the securing screws out of the bunk flat.

Sail covers should be made of UV-resistant and waterproof material. They should have a string tie at the mast and at the outboard end of the boom, and, ideally, be open at the bottom. This will allow any water that gets in to run out, rather than remaining in the sail folds and possibly leaving stains.

Covers for lifeline turnbuckles, steering wheels, chainplates, and tangs are usually made of leather. They help to prevent snags and improve the look of the deck. Occasionally they should be removed to check for corrosion. *Note:* Many sailmakers also make sail covers, biminis, dodgers, and cushion covers.

Manufacturers of Canvaswork

American Marine Covering
3975 N.W. 25th St.
Miami, FL 33142
Tel: (305) 871-6116
Fax: (305) 871-2916
Marine canvas manufacturers

Canvas Products Co.
10411 Capital Ave.
Oak Park, MI 48237
Tel: (313) 398-3500
Fax: (313) 398-0680
Boat Covers and Bimini tops

The Canvas Store
265 Broadway
Huntington Station, NY 11746
Tel: (516) 549-0970
Dodgers and awnings

Classic Canvas
(Div. Cameron Sails)
3222 Nasa Rd. 1
Seabrook, TX 77586
Tel: (713) 326-5566
Fax: (713) 326-5567

**Comfy Companionway
Covers**
433 North Harvey
Oklahoma City, OK 73102
Tel: (405) 235-0311
Companionway covers

Dow Canvas Products
4230 Clipper Dr.
Manitowoc, WI 54220
Tel: (800) 558-7755
Fax: (414) 682-5891

Fairclough Sailmakers
108 W. Main St.
Milford, CT 06460
Tel: (203) 882-8433

Genco Marine Ltd.
544 King St. W.
Toronto, Ontario M5V 1M3
CANADA
Tel: (416) 364-2891
Fax: (416) 364-6635

Gordon Marine Accessories
1209 S.E. 10th St.
Cape Coral, FL 33990
Tel: (813) 574-5232

Griffolyn Reef Industries
P.O. Box 750250
Houston, TX 77275-0250
Tel: (800) 231-6074
 or (713) 943-0070
Fax: (713) 947-2053

Harbor Custom Canvas
1609 W. Anaheim
Long Beach, CA 90813
Tel: (310) 436-7708
Fax: (310) 495-3504

Island Nautical, Inc.
Box 207
225 Fordham St.
City Island, NY 10464
Tel: (212) 885-2295
Fax: (718) 885-0813
Dodgers

Oakum Bay
9 State St.
Marblehead, MA 01945
Tel: (617) 631-8983

Protect-A-Boat
1260 E. Woodland Ave.
Springfield, PA 19064
Tel: (215) 328-3031
Fax: (215) 328-5907
Shrinkwrap for boats

Raudaschl Sails Canada
3140 Lakeshore Blvd. W.
Toronto, Ontario M8V lL4
CANADA
Tel: (416) 255-3431
Fax: (416) 259-9136
*Awnings, canvaswork,
harnesses and bosun's chairs*

S&S Fabric Products
1 Maritime Dr.
Portsmouth, RI 02871
Tel: (401) 683-5858
Fax: (800) 441-2252
*Dodgers, cushion covers, and
awnings*

The Sailors' Tailor
1480 W. Spring Valley
Paintersville Rd.
Spring Valley, OH 45370
Tel: (513) 862-7781
Fax: (513) 862-7701

Thomas Clark Sailmakers
37 Pratt St.
Essex, CT 06426
Tel: (203) 767-8278
Dodgers and sails

**Santa Barbara Sailmakers
& Canvas Co.**
208 Gray Ave.
Santa Barbara, CA 93101
Tel: (805) 962-2835
Fax: (805) 962-2835

Shoreline Design
1090-C Court Dr.
Duluth, GA 30136
Tel: (404) 945-8314
*Sail covers, cockpit cushions,
and wheel covers*

Nelson A. Taylor
10 W. 9th Ave.
Gloversville, NY 12078
Tel: (518) 725-0681
Fax: (518) 725-4335
Canvas covers and other gear

Tumacs Covers
50 Terence Dr.
Pittsburgh, PA 15236
Tel: (800) 24-TUMAC
Fax: (412) 653-4670
Boat covers

Time Saver Tool Corp.
6806 Indianapolis Blvd.
Hammond, IN 46324
Tel: (219) 845-2500
Fax: (219) 845-2058
Vice Grip attachments to install snaps, etc.

Weblon
Fox Island Rd.
P.O. Box 190
Port Chester, NY 10573
Tel: (914) 937-3900
Fax: (914) 937-0232
Awnings, dodgers, convertible tops

William J. Mills & Co.
P.O. Box 2126
Front St.
Greenport, NY 11944
Tel: (516) 477-1500
Fax: (516) 477-1504
Awnings, dodgers, and convertible tops

ZUSE Unlimited
800 Village Walk
Guilford, CT 06437
Tel: (203) 458-3295
Fax: (203) 458-8902
Custom personalized kevlar duffles, seabags, seats / backs, and totes

Figure 1: This view of the Newport International Boatshow illustrates how many awnings, dodgers, sailcovers, tents, and banners are needed for just one show.

Charts and Books

CHARTS

When you go on a trip by car, you use a road map to tell you how to find your destination. At sea, sailors use charts. Charts show many things: the depth of water, the type of bottom, where the rocks are, the buoys and lighthouses along the way, and identifiable features on land, such as water towers, high bridges, and power-station chimneys. Charts also show the direction of true and magnetic north, precautionary areas such as traffic lanes and anchorages, and dredged channels. Charts, then, are essential to getting around on the ocean.

A number of different agencies and organizations produce charts. The most commonly used charts worldwide are British Admiralty charts, followed by the U.S. National Oceanic and Atmospheric Administration (NOAA) charts, and then the charts printed by other countries. Some charts are overprinted with loran, omni, or decca lines to make plotting easier. Other charts are overprinted with features such as power or telephone lines that cross a harbor or estuary. These charts are usually available from the local utility company.

When purchasing a chart, look first to see that it is the latest version. On NOAA charts, the latest revision date is printed in the bottom left-hand corner. Next check the scale. If you are looking for a chart showing Narragansett Bay in Rhode Island, or Mis-sion Bay in California, get the one with the largest scale showing that particular area. Don't buy a chart that shows the entire Atlantic coast, from Cape Sable to Cape Hatteras, or a chart of the entire Pacific coast, because the area of interest will be too small on them. If you are buying charts for a long trip, buy small-scale ones for the route, and larger-scale ones for the harbors at each end of the route. You might also want to get one or two charts for harbors along the route, in case rough weather forces you to seek refuge.

If possible, stow your charts flat. They will be easier to use. If you cannot stow them completely flat, then fold them, but only make them small enough to fit into the chart table. I do not like to store charts rolled. They stay curled and need weights on each corner to use them. Weights often slide off the chart table, causing damage along the way.

BOOKS

Books can be a useful source of information on almost any topic. Many of the bookstores listed in the sourcelist have mail-order catalogs, which make them especially useful to sailors who do not live nearby. Quite often, nautical bookstores also have a selection of charts. For instance, the Armchair Sailor in Newport, Rhode Island, carries charts from many foreign countries.

There are a few books that every person who goes to sea should have onboard. This list represents the books I would recommend. They contain a lot of basic information, as well as more advanced topics.

Useful Books

- *Annapolis Book of Seamanship* by John Rousmaniere. Published by Simon & Schuster.
- *Boatowner's Mechanical and Electrical Manual* by Nigel Calder. Published by International Marine Publishing.

- *International Code of Signals* (Pub. # 102). Defense Mapping Agency DMAHTC, Superintendent of Documents, U.S. Government Printing Office, Washington, DC 20402.
- *Offshore Racing Council's Special Regulations*. US Sailing, P.O. Box 208, Newport, RI 02840. For sailboaters only.
- *Reeds Nautical Almanac*. Thomas Reed Publications, Inc., 122 Lewis Wharf, Boston, MA 02110.
- *Waterway Guide*. 6151 Powers Ferry Rd., N.W., Atlanta, GA 30339. Tel: (404) 618-0313, Fax: (404) 618-0348.

Book and Chart Source List

Retail Sellers of Books and Charts

Note: A selection of nautical bookshops with the widest range of books. (My thanks to Oscar at Robert Hale & Co. for help compiling this list.)

Ala Wai Marine, Ltd.
1651 Ala Moana
Honolulu, HI 96815
Tel: (808) 946-4213
Fax: (808) 943-1495

American Boat & Chart
P.O. Box 9711
Arnold, MD 21012
Tel: (800) 933-9463

Armchair Sailor Bookstore
543 Thames St.
Newport, RI 02840
Tel: Orders (800) 292-4278
  or (401) 847-4252
Fax: (401) 847-1219

Armchair Sailor
3 Lockwood Dr. #202
Charleston, SC 29401
Tel: (803) 577-0254

Armchair Sailor
546 Highway 98 East
P.O. Box 698
Destin, FL 32541
Tel: (904) 837-1577

Armchair Sailor
2110 Westlake Ave.
Seattle, WA 98108
Tel: (206) 283-0858
Fax: (206) 285-1935

Armchair Sailor Book & Navigation Center
42 Caledonia St.
Sausalito, CA 94965
Tel: (415) 332-7505

Alexander Marine Ltd.
570 Davis St.
Vancouver, British Columbia
V6B 2G4
CANADA
Tel: (604) 689-5972

Bahia Mar Marine Store
801 Seabreeze Blvd.
Ft. Lauderdale, FL 33316
Tel: (305) 764-8831
Fax: (305) 764-8919

Baker Lyman & Co., Inc.
8876 Gulf Freeway
Suite 110
Houston, TX 77017
Tel: (717) 943-7032

Beckson Marine, Inc.
165 Holland Ave.
Bridgeport, CT 06605
Tel: (203) 333-1412
Publishers of chart books

Bennet Marine Book & Video
730 Washington St.
Marina del Rey, CA 90292
Tel: (800) 262-8862
Fax: (310) 306-3162

B. H. Blackwell Ltd.
Hythe Bridge St.
Oxford OX1 2ET
ENGLAND
Tel: (+44) 865 244944

Better Boating Association
P.O. Box 407
Needham, MA 02192
Tel: (800) 242-7854
Fax: (617) 449-0514

Bluewater Books & Charts
1481 S.E. 17th St. Causeway
Ft. Lauderdale, FL 33316
Tel: To order: (800) 942-2583
 or (305) 763-6533
Fax: (305) 522-2278

Boating Almanac
203 McKinsey Rd.
Severna Park, MD 21146
Tel: (301) 647-0084

Boating Books & Charts, Australia Pty. Ltd.
214 St. Kilda Rd.
St. Kilda
Melbourne, Victoria 3182
AUSTRALIA
Tel: (+61) 3 537 2511
Fax: (+61) 3 534 4203

Captain's Nautical Supplies
1723 West Nickerson St.
Seattle, WA 98119
Tel: (206) 283-7242
Fax: (206) 281-4921

Captain's Nautical Supplies
138 N.W. 10th
Portland, OR 97209
Tel: (503) 227-1648
Fax: (503) 227-0168

Captain's Nautical Supplies
1914 4th Ave.
Seattle, WA 98101
Tel: (206) 448-2278
Fax: (206) 448-2235

Clipper Ship Book Shop
12 N. Main St.
P.O. Box 323
Essex, CT 06426
Tel: (203) 767-1666

Fawcett's Boat Supply, Inc.
110 Compromise
P.O. Box 4817
Annapolis, MD 21403
Tel: (410) 267-8681
Fax: (410) 224-0979

L.J. Harri
120 Lewis Wharf
Boston, MA 02112
Tel: (617) 248-0996

Intl. Specialized Book Services
5602 N.E. Hassalo St.
Suite 54
Portland, OR 97213-3640
Tel: (800) 547-7734
Fax: (503) 284-8859

Kelvin Huges
145 Minories
London EC3H 1NH
ENGLAND
Tel: (+44) 71 709-9706
Fax: (+44) 71 481-1298

Motion Smith
78 Shenton Way 01-03
SINGAPORE 0207
Tel: (+65) 220 5098
Fax: (+65) 225 4902

Mystic Seaport Museum Stores
39 Greenville Ave.
Mystic, CT 06355
Tel: (203) 331-2664
Fax: (203) 572-8260

Munro's Bookstore
1108 Government St.
Victoria, British Columbia
V8W 1Y2
CANADA
Tel: (604) 382-2464

Nanaimo Maps & Charts
8 Church St. Nanaimo,
British Columbia V9R 5H4
CANADA
Tel: (604) 754-2513

Nautical Mind Bookstore
Hotel Admiral
249 Queen's Quay West
Unit 108
Toronto, Ontario M5J 2N5
CANADA
Tel: (416) 869-3431

New York Nautical
140 West Broadway
New York, NY 10013
Tel: (212) 962-4522
Fax: (212) 406-8420

The Owl & the Turtle
8 Bayview St.
Camden, ME 04843
Tel: (207) 236-4769

**Pilothouse Nautical Books
& Charts**
1100 S. Delaware Ave.
Philadelphia, PA 19147
Tel: (215) 336-6414
Fax: (215) 336-6415

Powell's Books
7th N.W. Ninth
Portland, OR 97209
Tel: (503) 228-4651

Seabreeze Ltd.
1256 Scott St.
San Diego, CA 92106
Tel: (619) 223-8989

Ship's Store
14025 Panay Way
Marina Del Ray, CA 90292
Tel: (213) 823-5574
Fax: (213) 823-5514

**Warsash Nautical
Bookshop**
31 Newtown Rd.
Warsash, Southampton
Hampshire SO3 6FY
ENGLAND
Tel: (+44) 489 572384
Fax: (+44) 489 885756

**West Marine (Corporate
Headquarters)**
500 Westridge Dr.
Watsonville, CA 90576

Witherby & Co., Ltd.
32-36 Aylesbury St.
London EC1 OET
ENGLAND
Tel: (+44) 71 251-5341
Fax: (+44) 71 251-1296

Book Publishers

Adlard Coles Nautical
35 Bedford Row
London WC1R 4JH
ENGLAND
Tel: (+44) 071-242 0946

Cornell Maritime Press
P.O. Box 456
Centreville, MD 21617
Tel: (800) 638-7641

Hearst Marine Books
105 Madison Ave.
New York, NY 10016
Tel: (212) 889-3050
Fax: (212) 689-9139

**International Marine
Publishing**
Division of Tab Books
P.O. Box 220
Camden, ME 04843

Naval Institute Press
2062 Generals Hwy.
Annapolis, MD 21401
Tel: (301) 224-3378
Fax: (301) 224-2406

W. W. Norton & Co.
500 Fifth Ave.
New York, NY 10110
Tel: (212) 354-5500
Fax: (212) 869-0856

Oxford University Press
200 Madison Ave.
New York, NY 10016
Tel: (212) 679-7300

Sheridan House
145 Palisades St.
Dobbs Ferry, NY 10522
Tel: (914) 693-2410
Fax: (914) 693-0776

St. Martin's Press
175 Fifth Ave.
New York, NY 10010-7848
Tel: (212) 674-5151
Fax: (212) 420-9314

Chart Producers (US)

Gulf Stream Charts
Oceanographic monthly survey
Tel: (301) 763-8133

National Weather Service
8060 13th St.
Silver Spring, MD 20910
Tel: (301) 427-7278

NOAA Charts
NOAA-National Oceanic &
Atmospheric Agency
Distribution Branch N/CG33
Chartering & Geodetic Service
Riverdale, MD 20737-1199
Tel: (301) 436-6990

Hydrographic Offices in
Other Countries

**Service Hydrographique
des Forces Navales**
Boite postale 78
35320 Bordj El Bahri
Boumerdes
ALGERIA

**Servicio de Hidrografia
Naval**
Avenida Montes de Oca 2124
1271 Buenos Aires
ARGENTINA

Royal Australian Navy
Hydrographic Service
161 Walker St.
North Sydney, NSW 2060
AUSTRALIA

Department of
Hydrography
Biwta Bhaban
Bangladesh Inland Water
Transport Authority
141-143 Motijheel Commercial
Area
Dacca 2
BANGLADESH

Dienst der Kust
Hydrografie
Administratief Centrum
Vrijhavenstraat 3
B-8400 Oostende
BELGIUM

Directoria de Hidrografia e
Navigacao
Rua Barao de Jaceguay S/No
Ponta da Armacao
24040 Niteroi-RJ
BRAZIL

Canadian Hydrographic
Service
615 Booth St.
Ottawa, Ontario K1A OE6
CANADA

Servicio Hidrograficio y
Oceanograficio de la
Armada
Casilla 324
Valparaiso
CHILE

Maritime Safety
Administration
Ministry of Communications
10 Avenue de Fuxing Beijiing
PEOPLE'S REPUBLIC OF
CHINA

Institutio Cubano de
Hidrgrafia
Aparto 606
Marianao 13
Cuidad de la Havana
CUBA

Farvandsveesenet
Overgaden oven Vaudet 628
P.O. Box 1919
DK-1023 Copenhagen K
DENMARK

Departamento
Hidrografico
Marina de Guerra
Sans-Souci
Santo-Domingo
DOMINICAN REPUBLIC

Instituto Oceanografico de
la Armada
Casilla de Correos 5940
Guayquil
ECUADOR

Shobat Al Misala Al
Baharia
Ras el Tin
Alexandria
EGYPT

Merenkulkuhallitus
Merikarttaosasto
Vourimiehenkatu 1
Helsinki
FINLAND

Establissement Principal
de Service Hydrographique
et Oceanographique de la
Marine
13 rue du Chatellier BP426
29275 Brest Cedex
FRANCE

Bundesamt Fur
Seeschiffarht Und
Hydrographie
Bernhard-Nocht-Strasse 78
Postfach 30 12 80
D-2000 Hamburg 36
GERMANY

Bundesant Fur
Seeschiffarht Und
Hydrographie Austenstelle
Rostock
Dierkower Damm 45
02540 Rostock 40
GERMANY

Hellenic Navy
Hydrographic Service
TGN 1040
Athens
GREECE

Sjomaelingar Islands
Seljavegur
Reykjavik
ICELAND

Naval Hydrographic Office
Post Box No 75 Dehra
Dun-248 001 (UP) INDIA

Dinas Hidro-Oseanografi
Jalan Pantai Kuta V No 1
Ancol Timur
Jakarta
INDONESIA

Istituto Idrografico della Marina
Passo Osservatorio 4
16134-Genova
ITALY

Kaijohoan-Cho Suiro-Bu
3-1 Tsukiji
5-chome Chuo-Ku
Tokyo 104
JAPAN

Taehanmin-Guk
Suroguk
1-17, 7-ga
Hang-dong
Chung-gu
P.O. Box No. 56
Inchon 400-600
KOREA

Hydrographic Department
Royal Malaysian Navy
Ministry of Defence
Jalan Padang Tembal
50634 Kuala Lumpur
MALAYSIA

Direccion General de Oceanografia Naval
Calle Pedro Sainz de Baranda
S/N
Edifico B
1 er Nivel
Col. Los Cipreses
Delegacion Coyoacan
C.P. 04830
MEXICO DF

Naval Hydrographic Service
Myanmar Navy
55-61 Strand Rd.
Vangon
MYANMAR

Dienst der Hydrografie
Koninklijke Marine
171, Badhuisweg
P.O. Box 90704
2597 LS-'s-Gravenhage
NETHERLANDS

Hydrographic Office
Royal New Zealand Navy
P.O. Box 33341
Takapuna, Auckland 9
NEW ZEALAND

Norges Sjokartverk
Lervgsveien 36
Boks 60
4001 Stvanger
NORWAY

Hydrographic Department
Naval Headquarters
Islamabad
PAKISTAN

Direccion de Hidrografia y Navegacion de la Marina
Avda
Gamarra No 500
Chucuito
Callao 1
PERU

Coast and Geodetic Survey Department
National Mapping and
Resource Information
Authority
421 Barraca St.
Binondo Branch
P.O. Box 1620
Manila
PHILIPPINES

Biuro Hydrograficzne Marynarki Wojennej
81-912 Gdynia 12
POLAND

Instituto Hidrografico
Rua das Trinas-49
1296 Lisbon
PORTUGAL

Hydrographic Department
Port of Singapore Authority
7 Keppel Rd.
No 02-28 Tanjong Pagar
Complex
Singapore 0208
SINGAPORE

Solomon Islands Hydrographic Unit
Survey and Cartographic
Division
P.O. Box G13
Honiara
SOLOMON ISLANDS

Hydrographic Office
Private Bag XI
Tokai 7966
Cape Town
SOUTH AFRICA

Instituto Hidrografico de la Marina
Tolosa Latour No 1
1107 Cadiz
SPAIN

Sjokarteavdelningen
S-601 78
Norrkoping
SWEDEN

Chinese Naval Hydrographic and Oceanographic Office
P.O. Box No 8505
Tso-Ying
Kao-Hsiung
TAIWAN, ROC

Krom Utoksastr
Royal Thai Navy
Aroon-Ameriu Rd.
Bangkok 10600
THAILAND

Hydrographic Unit
P.O. Box 1104
Port of Spain
TRINIDAD AND TOBAGO

**Seyir Hidrografi ve
Osinografi Dairesi
Baskanligi**
Cubuklu 81647
Istanbul
TURKEY

**Servicio de Oceanografia
Hidrografia y Meteorologia
de la Armada**
Capurro 980
Casilla de Correo 1381
Montevideo
URUGUAY

**Glavnoe Oupravlenie
Navigatsii I Okeanografii**
Ministerstvo Oborony
8, 11 Iiniya B-34
St. Petersburg
RUSSIA

**Comandancia General de la
Armada**
Direccion de Hidrografia y
Navegacion
Apartado Postal No.
6745-Carmelitas
Caracas
VENEZUELA

Chart Kit/BBA
P.O. Box 404
Rockland, MA 02370
Tel: (617) 982-4060
Fax: (617) 878-7334

Figure 1: The Armchair Sailor Bookstore in Newport, R.I., has a large inventory of books and charts for all parts of the world.

Coatings, Paints, Varnishes, and Sealers

The hull and deck of most production boats is protected from ultra violet radiation, degradation, and abrasion by the gelcoat that is laid in the mold before the fiberglass laminates are wetted out and laid up. But without proper protection, it will only protect the boat for about ten or twelve years before it deteriorates. Custom boats, boats that have just been retrofitted, and boats where the gelcoat has already deteriorated need to be repainted.

PAINTING

The repainting job should be done by an expert. It is not generally known, but the sanding job should not be too smooth. In other words, there is no need to sand the hull using 400 grit paper. Eighty or 100 grit is fine. Sanding to this smoothness will look good when painted and will give the paint a rough enough surface to adhere to. The painter may have to undercoat the job before applying the topcoat and should use an undercoat that is compatible with the topcoat.

Amateurs should not attempt to spray paints such as Awlgrip or Imron. Professionals know the best methods of spraying them and how to get the best results. They also have the respirators and other protective clothing needed when spraying polyester-based paints, which these are. When looking at the paint finish, check for runs, areas of "orange peel," and other defects. A good paint job will not show any of these.

Which paint should you use? The most well known hull finish is Awlgrip from U.S. Paint Corp. It was originally developed for aircraft about thirty years ago and has become the leading paint of the industry. Not so well known are Imron, Sterling, and Interspray. Imron is made by DuPont, Sterling by Sterling Laquer Company, and Interspray by Courtalds Coatings. Awlgrip and Sterling have the hardest finishes, Imron the softest. Hardness is a relative term, in that any of the hull paints listed will be damaged if the impact is heavy enough. Unfortunately, the hardness affects the sprayability of the paint, making Awlgrip and Sterling hardest to spray. All paints should be applied in a humidity- and temperature-controlled and well ventillated shop. That is why you see more and more yards building dedicated spray shops with heat lamps, heavy-duty exhaust fans, temperature and humidity controls, and special drain systems.

VARNISHING

A carefully varnished piece of wood looks and feels like it is much more expensive that its unvarnished counterpart. But how do you get that perfect sheen? The first step is to get the wood surface as smooth as possible. This means that you may have to use 400 grit sandpaper. Once the wood is smooth, use a dry tack rag to wipe off the dust, then apply a coat of varnish that has been cut with mineral spirits or the appropriate thinner. The first coat should be 30% varnish and 70% thinner, the second coat 50-50, and the third coat 70% varnish and 30% thinner. After that, you can use undiluted varnish. You should apply the varnish on days when the humidity is low. If moisture gets into your work, it can cloud the varnish. Try to work in the middle of the day and finish the job before any dew is likely to fall. If you need to build up protection quickly, you can apply a second coat as soon as the first coat is tacky, but don't apply more than three coats without letting the varnish dry completely. For a really glistening finish, you should try to get eight or ten coats on the job.

Manufacturers of Coatings, Paints, Varnishes, and Sealers

Coatings

Armorcote IMC
Cook Composites and Polymers
P.O. Box 419389
Kansas City, MO 64141-6389
Tel: (800) 436-2628
 or (816) 391-6000
Fax: (816) 391-6216

Duratec Polyester Primers & Coatings
Hawkeye Industries, Inc.
3050 Brookview Dr.
Marietta, GA 30068
Tel: (404) 977-3336
Fax: (404) 565-5084

Ferro Corp.
1301 N. Flora St.
Plymouth, IN 46563
Tel: (219) 935-5131

Fax: (219) 935-5278
Gelcoats, colorants and dispersions

Futura Coatings
9200 Latty Ave.
Hazelwood
St. Louis, MO 63042
Tel: (314) 521-4100
Fax: (314) 521-7255

International
Courtaulds Coatings
P.O. Box 4806
Houston, TX 77210-4806
Tel: (800) 654-7692
International BlueLine marine coatings

Interplastic Corp.
1225 Wolters Blvd.
Vadnais Heights, MN 55110
Tel: (612) 331-6850

Max Pro-Coat
Pier Pressure Marine Systems, Inc.
5400-28th Ave. N.W.
Seattle, WA 98107
Tel: (206) 782-8711
Fax: (206) 782-8717

The Mearl Corp.
41 East 42nd St.
New York, NY 10017
Tel: (212) 573-8500
Fax: (212) 557-0945

Oceana Ltd.
P.O. Box 6691
Annapolis, MD 21401
Tel: (800) 523-8890
 or (410) 269-6022
Fax: (410) 268-6528
Paints and resins

Classic Yacht
P.O. Box 309
Montgomeryville, PA 18936
Tel: (215) 855-8450
Antifoulant

VC Systems (Courtauld Coatings)
2270 Morris Ave.
Union, NJ 07083
Tel: (908) 686-1300
Fax: (201) 467-4481

Paints

American Colors, Inc.
P.O. Box 397
Sandusky, OH 44871-0397
Tel: (419) 625-2173
Fax: (419) 625-3979

Awlgrip N.V.
Bouleven 1
Industriezone Klein Gent
B-2280 Grobbendonk
BELGIUM
Tel: (+32) 14 23 00 01
Fax: (+32) 14 23 08 80
Hull paints

Bayshore Manufacturing, Inc.
6312 Fairfield Dr.
Flourtown, PA 19031
Tel: (215) 836-7559
Fax: (215) 836-0165
Bottom paints

Fibre Glass Evercoat
6600 Cornell Rd.
Cincinnati, OH 45242
Tel: (513) 489-7600
Fax: (513) 489-9229
Resins, epoxies, and paint sundries

Interlux Paints
2270 Morris Ave
Union, NJ 07083
Tel: (800) INTRLUX
  or (800) 468-7589
  or (908) 686-1300
Fax: (908) 467-4481
Paints, resins, and bottom paints

Oceana Limited
P.O. Box 6691
Annapolis, MD 21401
Tel: (800) 523-8890
  or (410) 269 6022
Fax: (410) 268-6528
Resins, epoxies, and adhesives paints

Pettit Paint Co.
36 Pine St.
Rockaway, NJ 07866
Tel: (201) 625-3100
Fax: (201) 625-8303
Paints, resins, and bottom paints

POR 15
P.O. Box 1235
Morristown, NJ 07962-1235
Tel: (800) 526-0796
  or (201) 887-1999

Rule Industries
70 Blanchard Rd.
Burlington, MA 01803
Tel: (617) 272-7400,
Fax: (617) 272-0920

Sterling Laquer Mfg. Co.
3150 Brannon Ave.
St Louis, MO 63139
Tel: (314) 776-4450
Fax: (314) 771-18548

US Paint
831 So. 21st St.
St. Louis, MO 63103-3092
Tel: (314) 621-0525
Fax: (314) 621- 0722

Woolsey/Z Spar Marine Paint
36 Pine St.
Rockaway, NJ 07866
Tel: (800) 221-4466
Fax: (201) 625-8303

Varnishes and Sealers

Epiphanes USA
1218 S.W. First Ave.
Ft. Lauderdale, FL 3315
Tel: (305) 467-8325

Epiphanes Canada
R.R. #3
Hastings, Ontario KOL 1YO
CANADA
Tel: (705) 696-2554

Detco
P.O. Box 1246
Newport Beach, CA 92663
Tel: (800) 845-0023
  or (714) 631-8480

Target Enterprises
P.O. Box 1582
Rutherford, NJ 07070
Tel: (800) 752-9922
Fax: (201) 939-0518

Woolsey/Z Spar Marine Paint
36 Pine St.
Rockaway, NJ 07866
Tel: (800) 221-4466
Fax: (201) 625-8303

Davits and Boat Lifts

Taking your boat to sea is the fun part of ownership, but when you boat is not in use it must be kept somewhere. Many owners who live close to the shore or on a seawall opt to moor the boat at their own dock, either on davits or on a boat lift.

DAVITS

Davits have a miriad of uses. While most of us think of davits as something to lift the anchor or raise the dinghy inboard, they can be used to hold the boarding ladder, lift sacks of coal or food inboard, hold the fuel line clear of the deck, or even lift people onboard.

On large vessels, davits are specially designed to hold liftboats inside the hull and to project that same lifeboat out over the side when it needs to be lowered. On smaller craft, davits may be located on the transom or along the beam. Most sailboats have davits at the transom for the dinghy, while power yachts have cranes to lift the dinghy up onto the main deck over the heads of people.

When selecting a davit, make sure it is either aluminum or stainless steel, and that it is large enough for the combined weight of the dinghy and its motor. You also might want to add in the fuel tank and any other stores that might be lifted onboard with the dinghy. If the davit is to be used for the anchor, make sure it is large enough to hold not only the anchor, but also its chain and several feet of wet anchor rode.

If you decide upon a collapsible davit, be sure it has a positive locking mechanism and will only collapse when you want it to. There have been cases of collapsible davits folding up as soon as the dinghy load is put on them. Ideally, two lines or falls from the davit to the dinghy are best. They enable the person lifting the dink to control it as it is being lifted. If one line must be used, have an additional person hold the dinghy painter to ensure that the dinghy doesn't bang on the hull as it is being lifted.

BOATLIFTS

In contrast to davits, boat lifts or elevators raise a boat by sinking into the water far enough to allow the boat to float over the lift. Then the lift is raised and the boat comes out of the water. This type of lift is seen only on very large yachts or on shore, either in a boat yard or on a waterfront owner's property. For boats with a submerged prop, a boat lift requires a special cradle for the vessel's hull. If the lift is dedicated to one boat, you can have a cradle built especially for that boat, rather than using chocks which can become displaced.

Manufacturers of Davits and Boat Lifts

Ace Boat Hoist
2211 S. Tamiami Trail
Venice, FL 33595
Tel: (800) 826-3573
  or (813) 493-8100
*America's oldest manufacturer
of boat lifts*

Acme Hoist, Inc.
690 Montauk Hwy. Bayport,
NY 11705
Tel: (516) 472-3030
Fax: (516) 472-3103
Boat hoists

Akerboom
P.O. Box 260
Leiden
HOLLAND
Tel: (+31) 071-761 600
Fax: (+31) 071-312 904
Yacht davits and cranes

Atkins & Hoyle
71 Portland St.
Toronto, Ontario M5V 2MB
CANADA
Tel: (416) 596-1818
Alloy davits

Atlantic Boat Lifts, Inc.
1111 Old Griffin Rd.
P.O. Box 126
Dania, FL 33004
Tel: (305) 524-2000
Fax: (305) 923-9271
*Cradle lifts, davits, and boat
elevators*

Avon Seagull Marine
1851 McGaw Ave.
Irvine, CA 92714
Tel: (714) 250-0880
*Roskelley/Olsson stern-tilt
davits and Simpson-Lawrence
davits*

Davit Master Corp.
5560 Ulmerton Rd.
Clearwater, FL 34620
Tel: (800) 878-5560
  or (813) 573-4414
Fax: (813) 572-0590
Epoch davits and boat lifts

Edson International
10-G Industrial Park Rd.
New Bedford, MA 02745
Tel: (508) 995-9711
Fax: (508) 995-5021
*Davits, steering gear, and deck
gear*

Erie Industries, Inc.
400 N. Buckeye St.
Bellevue, OH 44811-0270
Tel: (419) 483-3840
Kleeco boat hoists

Forespar
22322 Gilberto, Rd.
Santa Margarita, CA 92688
Tel: (714) 858-8820
Fax: (714) 858-0505
Folding Cargo Mate davits

Ft. Lauderdale Boat Lifts
500 S.W. 21st Terrace A103
Ft. Lauderdale, FL 33312
Tel: (305) 581-8587
Fax: (305) 792-1666
Davits and boat lifts

**Galva-Foam Marine
Industries**
Rt. 67, Box 19
Camdentown, MO 65020
Tel: (314) 346-3323
Fax: (314) 346-4025
Boat lifts and docks

GMP Corp.
3771 North Dunlop
Arden Hills, MN 55112
Tel: (612) 490-1899
Fax: (612) 490-1071
St. Croix removable davits

Hi-Tide Sales, Inc.
3181 S.E. Waaler St.
Stuart, FL 34997
Tel: (800) 544-0735
  or (407) 220-3778
*Hi-Tide aluminum and
stainless steel boat lifts*

Hoist-A-Weigh
P.O. Box 148
Marysville, MI 48040
Tel: (313) 364-7150
Fax: (313) 364-7925
*Lifting aid for anchors,
outboards, or dinghies*

Hydrohoist Boat Lifts
P.O. Box 1286
Claremore, OK 74018
Tel: (918) 341-6811
Fax: (918) 341-1178
Boat lifts

Inflex Corp.
1543 Warwick Ave.
Warwick, RI 02886
Tel: (401) 738-2552
Fax: (401) 732-5231
Outboard davit

Little Lift
604 Washington St.
Woodstock, IL 60098
Tel: (800) 942-LIFT
  or (815) 338-3553
Hi- Lift manufacturers

Mar-Quipt
231 S.W. 5th St.
Pompano Beach, FL 33060
Tel: (305) 942-0440
Fax: (305) 942-0447
Tenderlift boat cranes

Nautical Structures
10351 72nd St. N.
Largo, FL 34647
Tel: (800) 832-5438
  or (813) 541-6664
Fax: (813) 541-6353
Yacht cranes and boat lifts

Nautical Structures
Belship
Merwedeweg 3c
3621 LP Breukelen
HOLLAND
Tel: (+31) 3462 65544
Fax: (+31) 3462 65475
Yacht cranes and boat lifts

Nick Jackson Co.
17725 N.E. 65th
Suite A-175
P.O. Box 3398
Redmond, WA 98052
Tel: (206) 481-1381
Fax: (206) 882-2054
The west coast's most popular davit

Offshore Marine Products
P.O. Box 36025
Greensboro, NC 27406
Tel: (704) 636-6458
Fax: (704) 636-6609
Stainless steel davits

Pipe Welders
701 Old Avalon Blvd.
Avalon, NJ 08202
Tel: (609) 368-8228
Fax: (609) 368-8778
Lo-Pro davits

Pipewelders Marine
2965 W. State Rd. 84
Ft. Lauderdale, FL
33312-4867
Tel: (305) 587-8400
Fax: (305) 587-3007
Davits

Quality Boat Lifts, Inc.
1946 Dana Dr.
Ft. Myers, FL 33907
Tel: (800) 545-5603
Alum-A-Vator boat lifts

R & G Marine Products
83 Anderson Rd.
Buffalo, NY 14225
Tel: (716) 892-0224
Fax: (716) 892-0218
Aluminum platform lifts, beacher railway, and boathouse lifts

R. C. Plath
5300 S.E. Johnson Creek Blvd.
Portland, OR 97222
Tel: (503) 777-2441
Fax: (503) 777-2450
Alloy davits

Simpson-Lawrence
P.O. Box 11210
Bradenton, FL 34282-1210
Tel: (813) 746-7161
Fax: (813) 746-7166
Simpson-Lawrence davits

Tops-In-Quality
P.O. Box 148
Marysville, MI 48040
Tel: (313) 364-7150
Fax: (313) 364-7925
Davits

Vetus - Den Ouden, Inc.
P.O. Box 8712
Baltimore, MD 21240-0712
Tel: Orders (800) GO-VETUS
  or (410) 712-0740
Fax: (410) 712-0985
Goliath davits

Williamson Boat Lift
P.O. Box 93
Tahoe City, CA 9645
Tel: (916) 583-2998
Boat lifts

World Wide Marine, Inc.
1100 Lee Wagner Blvd.
Suite 202
Ft. Lauderdale, FL 33315
Tel: (305) 359-9870
Fax: (305) 359-5438
Davits and dinghy lifting systems

Deck Gear

There is a very wide range of marine deck hardware, all of it designed for specific tasks. When buying new hardware there are several points to be kept in mind:

- The hardware should be either stainless steel, aluminum, or brass. Most other metals will corrode.
- If you have a surface that will be bearing a load, such as the faces of a jamb cleat, do not get plastic fittings. The plastic can be burned away by a highly loaded rope pulling through them.
- Eliminate sharp corners. For instance, I prefer cleats with smoothly rounded corners rather than angular corners, which can cause the rope to chafe under load. On a stemhead fitting, check to see if it has sharp corners. Many do. Should a line cross it, the line can chafe, leading to loss of the boat.
- Make sure the gear is large enough. Usually a manufacturer sizes gear to suit a certain sail area or boat displacement. Be sure you know your boat's statistics when you purchase deck gear.
- If you are going to buy anchor-handling gear, the size of the gear is related to the boat's displacement or the size of the anchor. Be sure you know both.
- Bow cleats should be at least one size larger than stern cleats, because bow cleats may be used to tow the boat.

- Make sure stanchions are tall enough. Twenty four inches is the norm, but 27 inch ones are often used on larger cruising boats. Stanchions should be lightweight as well as strong.
- Pushpits and pulpits should be made of at least 1-inch diameter, thick-walled tubing. Make sure the bow pulpit is supplied with wiring and foundations for the bow lights, with line and halyard attachment points, and with strongly welded feet. Pulpits and stanchions should all be through-bolted.
- When purchasing blocks and sheaves, buy the best you can afford. They will last longer and do the job more efficiently than less expensive ones.
- When mounting deck gear, always be sure to install a backing plate or some other form of reinforcement behind the piece of gear. Also, be sure a cored deck is properly filled.
- Check to see if gear can do more than one job. For instance, a pushpit might have the stern light, the flagpole socket, the horseshoe lifering holder, the transom ladder, the barbeque holder, and the outboard bracket all mounted on it.
- Always align gear before bolting it down. For instance, if you are installing a cleat or a fairlead, make sure the line leads properly before bolting down the hardware.

Manufacturers of Deck Gear

A & B Industries
1261 Andersen Dr.
Suite C
San Rafael, CA 94901
Tel: (415) 258-9300
Fax: (415) 258-9461
Wide range of marine deck hardware

Accon, Inc.
14350 60th St. N.
Clearwater, FL 34620
Tel: (813) 536-0411
Fax: (813) 535-9053
Pop-up cleats

Atlantic Main Corp.
319 Main St.
P.O. Box 389
New Rochelle, NY 10802
Holt-Allen dinghy gear

Attwood Corp.
1016 N. Monroe St.
Lowell, MI 49331
Tel: (616) 897-9241
Fax: (616) 897-8358
Lifeline fittings

Avon Seagull Marine
1851 McGaw Ave.
Irvine, CA 92714
Tel: (714) 250-0880
Fax: (714) 250-0740

Bay Sailing and Equipment
986 Cherry St.
Fall River, MA 02720
Tel: (508) 678-4419
Lifelines

Beckson Marine, Inc.
165 Holland Ave.
Bridgeport, CT 06605
Tel: (203) 333-1412
Fax: (203) 384-6954
Opening ports, deck plates, ventilators, and pumps

Buck Algonquin Marine Hardware
370 N. Main St.
Smyrna, DE 19977-1011
Tel: (302) 659-6990
Fax: (302) 659-6909
Bitts, chocks, hinges, hawser pipes, and deckplates

C. Sherman Johnson
East Haddam Industrial Park
East Haddam, CT 06423
Tel: (203) 873-8697
Lifeline fittings

Deep 7 Co.
14260 Innerarity Point Rd.
Pensacola, FL 32507
Tel: (904) 492-0250
Fax: (904) 492-4484
Anchor stowage accessories

The Edson Corp.
476 Industrial Park Rd.
New Bedford, MA 02745
Tel: (508) 995-9711
Fax: (508) 995-5021

Euro Marine Trading, Inc.
64 Halsey St.
Newport, RI 02840
Tel: (800) 222-7712
  or (401) 849-0060
Fax: (401) 849-3230
Suppliers of Antal blocks and tracks

Figure 1: Euro Marine Trading, Inc. can supply this Antal lockoff.

Figure 2: An Antal sheet lead from Euro Marine Trading.

D. B. Follansbee, Inc.
12 Alice Ct.
Pawcatuck, CT 06379
Tel: (203) 599-1849
Fax: (203) 599-2316
Various deck gear items

Fentress Marine
P.O. Box 6102
Clearwater, FL 34618
Tel: (813) 581-9991
Fax: (813) 584-4215
Bow and stern pulpits, dive platforms

Forespar
22322 Gilberto Rd.
Santa Margartia, CA 92688
Tel: (714) 858-8820
Fax: (714) 858-0505

Garhauer Marine Corp.
1082 W. Ninth St.
Upland, CA 91786
Tel: (714) 985-9993
Fax: (714) 946-3913
Blocks

Goiot S.A.
28 rue du Frere-Loius
44062 Nantes Cedex 02
FRANCE
Tel: (+33) 40 75 68 39
Fax: (+33) 40 75 43 56
*Winches, hatches, blocks,
toerails, cleats*

GEM Products, Inc.
140 Industrial Loop
Orange Park, FL 32073
Tel: (800) 874-4506
  or (904) 264-5905
Fax: (904) 264-0173
*Lights, clasps, hatch pulls,
cleats, fishing pole holders*

Hayn Yacht Hardware
498 E. Main St.
Middletown, CT 06457
Tel: (203) 346-4784
Fax: (203) 346-7787
*Lifeline fittings and other deck
gear*

Harken
1251 E. Wisconsin Ave.
Pewaukee, WI 53072
Tel: (414) 691-3320
Fax: (414) 691-3008
*Winches, hatches, blocks,
bearings, and travellers*

Figure 3: A Harken stanchion lead block for roller furling.

Figure 4: Harken line organisers.

Hollaender Mfg.
10285 Wayne Ave.
P.O. Box 156399
Cincinnati, OH 45215-6399
Tel: (513) 772-8800
Fax: (513) 772-8806
*T and component fittings for
handrails and pulpits*

Holt-Allen
The Embankment
Putney, London SW15 1LG
ENGLAND
Tel: (+44) 1 870 9044

Homer Mfg & Co., Ltd.
Sales Office
P.O. Box 22-23 Taichung
TAIWAN, R.O.C.
*Shackles, Lifeline
fittings,cleats, clasps, hatch
pulls, and rowlocks*

Homer Mfg. & Co. Ltd.
Manufacturing Plant
360, Sec. 1
Shin Rd.
Ty Ya Hsiang
Taichung Hsein
TAIWAN, R.O.C.
Tel: (+886) 4- 5661433
Fax: (+886) 4-5672783

Figure 5: IM/Lewmar lock-off with a clean European design look.

IM/Lewmar Inc.
New Whitfield St.
Guilford, CT 06437
Tel: (203) 458-6200
*Winches, hatches, cleats,
tracks, and blocks*

Imtra Corp.
30 Barnet Blvd.
New Bedford, MA 02745
Tel: (508) 990-7000
Fax: (508) 998-5359
Barton hardware

Figure 6: This IM/Lewmar sheet lead makes changing lines easy.

International Sailing Products
319 Main St.
P.O. Box 389
New Rochelle, NY 10802
Tel: (800) 645-7676
 or (914) 576-4050
Fax: (914) 632-2732
Holt-Allen distributor in the USA

ITC, Inc.
401 W. Washington St.
P.O. Box 166
Zeeland, MI 49464
Tel: (616) 772-9411
Fax: (616) 772-9470
Rod holders, grab handles, Surfit leg and table base systems

Johnson Marine
Industrial Park
East Haddam, CT 06423
Tel: (203) 873-8697
Turnbuckles, padeyes, and tangs

Jukova
Oy Colt Ab
PB 115, Bulevardi 42
SF-00121 Helsinki
FINLAND
Tel: (+358) 0-618831
Fax: (+358) 0-61883397
Aluminum Cleats, hatches, ladders, grilles, and stanchion bases

Jukova, Ltd.
7 Hyde St.
P.O. Box 4180
Stamford, CT 06907-0180
Aluminum cleats, hatches, ladders, grilles and stnchion bases

Kaydot Enterprises
86 Allen Blvd.
Farmingdale, NY 11735
Tel: (516) 694-7422
Fax: (516) 249-5139
Manufacturers of stainless steel marine hardware

Loos & Co., Inc.
One Cable Rd.
Pomfret, CT 06258
Tel: (203) 928-7981
Fax: (203) 928-6167
Lifeline and rigging fittings

Lunenburg Foundry & Engineering
P.O. Box 1240
Lunenburg, Nova Scotia
B0J 2C0
CANADA
Tel: (902) 634-8827
Fax: (902) 634-8886
Bronze and brass hardware

M & G Industries
300 Wampanog Trail
E. Providence, RI 02915
Tel: (401) 438-9853
Lifeline fittings and wire

Merit Metal Products Corp.
242 Valley Rd.
P.O. Box 130
Warrington, PA 18976
Tel: (215) 343-2500
Cleats, hasps, lock sets and hardware for tops

Nautalloy Products
140 Olive St.
Elmyria, OH 44035
Tel: (216) 323-3285
Fax: (216) 322-6388
Cleats, bilge pumps, tracks, and other fittings

New Found Metals
240 Airport Rd.
Pt. Townsend, WA 98368
Tel: (206) 385-3315
Fax: (206) 385-6097
Bronze hardware

Nicro Marine
2065 West Ave. 140th
San Leandro, CA 94577
Tel: (510) 357-8332
Fax: (510) 351-5465
Shackles, blocks, ventilators, and solar vents

Norseman Marine, Inc.
516 West Olas Blvd.
Ft. Lauderdale, FL 33312
Tel: (305) 467-1407
Fax: (305) 462-3470
Blocks, tracks, shackles,vangs, and rigging

Orbex
620 S. 8th St.
Minneapolis, MN 55404
Tel: (612) 333-1208
Fax: (612) 333-9043
Drinkholders

**R.C. Marine Products Co.
Ltd.**
6-10 Parkway Dr.
Mairangi Bay
Auckland
NEW ZEALAND
Tel: (+64) 478-9185
Large selection of deck gear

Rieker Instrument Co.
P.O. Box 150
Clifton Hts., PA 19018
Tel: (215) 622-4545
Fax: (215) 622-7367
Clinometers

Rondal bv
P.O. Box 52
8325 ZH
Vollenhove
NETHERLANDS
Tel: (+31) 0 5274 3500
Fax: (+31) 0 5274 3900
*Tracks, blocks, hatches, and
vents for larger craft*

Ronstan Marine, Inc.
805 Court St.
Clearwater, FL 34616
Tel: (813) 443-7661
Fax: (813) 447 0867
  or (604) 325-0326
  or (416) 291-3446
Cleats and blocks

Scanvik, Inc.
980 36th Court S.W.
Vero Beach, FL 32968
Tel: (407) 567-2877
Fax: (407) 567-9113
Hardware

Schaefer Marine, Inc.
Industrial Park
New Bedford, MA 02745
Tel: (508) 995-9511
Fax: (508) 995-4882
*Blocks, shackles, track,
travellers, tangs, and
stanchions*

G. G. Schmitt and Sons
2821 Old Tree Dr.
Lancaster, PA 17603
Tel: (717) 394-3701
Fax: (717) 291-9739
*Manufacturers of stainless
steel hardware*

Sea-Dog Line
P.O. Box 479
Everett, WA 98201
Tel: (206) 259-0194
Fax: (206) 339-1345
*Marine hardware
manufacturers*

**Seabrite Stainless Steel of
Florida**
424 DeLeon Ave.
Titusville, FL 32796
Tel: (508) 823-6779

Shelby Industries, Inc.
P.O. Box 308
Shelbyville, KY 40066
Tel: (502) 633-2040

S & I Products
P.O. Box 2099
Chicago, IL 60690
Tel: (312) 549-7983
Fax: (312) 871-4070
Very large selection of items

Spinlock USA,
20 Barnett Blvd.
New Bedford, MA 02745
Tel: (508) 995-7000
Fax: (508) 994-4919
*Blocks, rope clutches, and
boom vangs*

SSI (Sailing Specialties)
P.O. Box Box 99
Commerce Ave.
St. Mary's Industrial Pk.
Hollywood, MD 20636
Tel: (301) 373-2372
Fax: (301) 373-2734
*Winch handle holders and
mast boots*

Sun Co.
14025 W. 66th Ave.
Arvada, CO 80004
Tel: (303) 424-4651
Fax: (303) 467-1104

Taco Metals, Inc.
50 N.E. 179th St.
N. Miami Beach, FL 33162
Tel: (305) 652-8566
Fax: (305) 653-1174
*Extrusions, trim, and
moldings for rubrails and
towers*

Watrous
P.O. Box 996
Cutchogue, NY 11935
Tel: (516) 734-5504
Fax: (516) 734-7931
Clinometers

**Wellborn Marine &
Industrial Products**
805 Court St.
Clearwater, FL 34616
Tel: (813) 443-7661
Fax: (813) 447-0867

Vetus - Den Ouden, Inc.
P.O. Box 8712
Baltimore, MD 21240-0712
Tel: Orders (800) GO-VETUS
 or (410) 712-0740
Fax: (410) 712-0985
*Fenders and holders, rod
holders, bollards, stanchions,
and ports*

Whitewater Marine
P.O. Box 610-595
Port Huron, MI 48060
Tel: (313) 987-4837

Wilcox-Crittenden Division
A Gulf & Western
Manufacturing Co.
Middletown, CT 06457
Tel: (203) 632-2600
*Steering wheels, oarlocks,
cleats, and horns*

Viking Marine
1630 W. Cowles
Long Beach, CA 90813
Tel: (213) 432-2259
*Deck plates, fat bags, and cat
bags*

Figure 7: A Wichard padeye
from Viscom International,
Inc.

Viscom International, Inc.
507 Hopmeadow St.
Simsbury, CT 06070
Tel: (203) 658-2201
Fax: (203) 651-8406
*Shackles, backstay adjusters,
and carbine hooks*

United Yachting
2190 South Hill Rd.
Milford, MI 48381
Tel: (313) 423-5879
Fax: (313) 685-2093
*Line stoppers, power storage
reels, and line/pole holders*

YS Fittings Ltd.
The Embankment
Putney, London SW15 1LG
ENGLAND
Tel: (+44) 1 870 9044

Diving Equipment

By David Sipperly

David Sipperly is a graduate in Marine Fisheries and Aquaculture from the University of Rhode Island where he is currently the chief SCUBA instructor. A NAUI instructor and instructor trainer, he has received the NAUI Outstanding Service Award. With fourteen years of diving experience, he has taught all levels, from openwater one to instructor. He has also traveled and lectured extensively. Sipperly is an accomplished underwater photographer, a nationally-ranked free-diving/spearfishing competitor, and a member of the MARE's advisory team.

MASKS

Facemasks provide a layer of air between the water and the diver's eyes to restore the diver's vision. A mask should cover the eyes and nose and permit pressure equalization through the nose into the mask to prevent mask squeeze. Remember that the combination of water, glass, and air that light rays must travel through to reach the diver's eyes results in the refraction (bending) of light, thus making objects appear 25% larger and closer. Always select a mask with safety or tempered glass which will not shatter if broken. Avoid plastic instead of glass because it scratches easily, restricting your view.

Low-volume masks are preferred over high-volume masks because they are easily cleared should the mask become flooded. Low-volume masks are ideal for snorkeling and free diving because smaller volume changes occur, reducing the severity of mask squeeze.

Older style, neoprene rubber masks (generally black) are not preferred today. In the late seventies, silicone masks appeared and today account for 90% of all sales. Silicone is more expensive than black rubber, but it offers many advantages. Silicone is more durable and impervious to ultraviolet radiation. It is also hypoallergenic should the diver have sensitive skin. Silicone is usually clear or translucent, allowing light to pass through so the diver doesn't feel claustrophobic as some people do with black rubber masks.

It is possible to purchase prescription masks to correct for common vision defects. You can either have your prescribed corrective lenses bonded to the glass of your existing facemask, or you can buy a mask with removable lenses and replace the standard ones with diopter lenses. This second method works well for most people, but the prescription is not exact, nor will it work for people with astigmatism.

If you wear soft contact lenses, you are permitted to dive with them. But be aware that they can become easily lost should the mask become flooded. Is is not recommended that people dive with hard contact lenses.

Fit is the most important criteria when selecting a mask. To test for proper fit, simply place the mask on your face (it is not necessary to place the strap over your head) and inhale gently through your nose. The mask should stay on your face without the use of hands or strap. If a suction does not occur, the mask does not fit and you should choose a different one. A mask that doesn't fit right will simply leak and be a distraction while you are diving.

When you have purchased a new mask, wash it inside and out with toothpaste or a very mild detergent to remove any protective or manufacturing residues that would cause the mask to fog. Rinse it in freshwater after every use and avoid prolonged exposure to direct sunlight. A mask should be stored in its box to prevent distortion of the mask skirt once it has dried.

SNORKELS

Many types of snorkels are available today. With a basic, non-purge snorkel, there is no purge valve to fail or break, but purge snorkels are easier to clear than non-purge snorkels. The most important consideration when selecting a snorkel is the mouthpiece. It should fit comfortably in the mouth without any irritation. Smaller bore snorkels are generally suited for smaller individuals. For larger individuals, a large bore snorkel is recommended. Remember, the larger the bore, the more water that needs to be cleared upon surfacing. Simply rinse a snorkel with fresh water after every use.

FINS

Fins are used to increase the mobility and efficiency of the diver. There are basically two types of fins: the open-heel fin and the full-foot fin. The open-heel fin is generally used for SCUBA. It has a broad blade and adjustable heel strap. It was designed to be worn with booties for protection and warmth, so you should wear booties when trying them on. The full-foot fin is generally smaller and more flexible than the open-heel fin, and it provides less thrust. It is usually used in pools and warm water. Booties are not necessary with these fins, although many people wear a neoprene sock to prevent chafing. It is important that divers choose a fin that best matches their leg strength. Smaller, more flexible fins are best suited for smaller people. It is important to pick a fin that is neither too soft and flexible, nor too stiff. Fins should fit snugly and feel like a natural extension of the leg. Remember to rinse the fins with freshwater after each use.

WETSUITS

A wetsuit provides thermal protection by insulating a diver from the water. A thin layer of water is often trapped between the suit and the diver's skin. The body warms this water, and the neoprene rubber provides the insulation to keep the water warm.

The two main factors that determine warmth are thickness and fit. Thicknesses can range from 1/8 to 3/8 of an inch. Common thicknesses are 1/8, 3/16, and 1/4 of an inch in the English system, and 2, 3, 5, 6, and 6.5 mm in the metric system. The 1/4 (6.5mm) suit is considered standard for diving in cold waters such as those in New England. The thicker the material, the more insulation. Yet as thickness increases, mobility decreases and the amount of lead to compensate for buoyancy increases. Thinner neoprene suits and lightweight suits such as shorties are preferred for warm water diving where temperatures are 75 degrees F or greater.

A suit should fit as snugly as possible without interfering with circulation. The snugger the suit, the less water can enter and the warmer you will be. Critical areas include the arm pits, the small of the back, and the groin. These areas tend to trap and accumulate cold water. People who are planning to dive in cold water should consider a spine pad. A spine pad is a strip of neoprene that fills the void of the spinal curve. Knee pads are also recommended to prolong the life of any suit.

Custom wetsuits can be manufactured for people who cannot find a suit that fits them properly. Custom suits are not much more expensive than a standard "off the rack" suit. For many people, the comfort and warmth outweighs the extra cost. Being measured for a custom suit requires a visit to a local dive shop for about 30 minutes. Turn-around time is usually one to two weeks.

DIVE SKINS

Many warm water suits are available to both the skin diver and SCUBA diver. They are manufactured from lycra or darylex

and are properly referred to as dive skins. The purpose of the dive skin is to provide thermal protection, protection from the sun, and protection from biotic factors, such as jellyfish stings and coral abrasions. The advantage of a dive skin over a similar neoprene suit is that the dive skin is neutrally buoyant and does not require the use of lead. It also takes minimal space when packing for a warm-water vacation.

DRYSUITS

People who dive on a regular basis in waters colder than 55 degrees F should consider a drysuit. A drysuit is a thick, insulated under-garment. Drysuits come in a variety of styles. You should receive special instruction from one of the certifying dive agencies before attempting to dive in a drysuit.

TANKS

Tanks are cylinders that hold compressed air and form the backbone of the self-contained underwater breathing apparatus. Tanks sizes in North America are expressed in cubic feet (cft), while in Europe sizes are expressed in liters (L). Sizes range from 15 cft (2 L) to 160 cft (24 L). The most popular sizes are 80 cft (12 L) and 50 cft (8 L).

SCUBA tanks are manufactured from two types of metal: steel and aluminum. Steel tanks are more wear-resistant than aluminum ones because steel is a harder material. Steel tanks are used by many seasoned divers because these tanks do not create any buoyancy changes. Aluminum tanks become positively buoyant as the air inside them is depleted. This buoyancy change is about five pounds. Remember that divers should be neutrally buoyant and able to hover at a depth of 10 to 15 feet for a precautionary stop at the end of a dive. The major disadvantage of steel is that it rusts and must be serviced regularly to prolong its life. Aluminum doesn't rust, but it corrodes. When aluminum corrodes, it produces a compound called aluminum oxide which inhibits any further corrosion. The longevity of an aluminum tank is much greater than a steel one. However, with the proper care and maintenance, most tanks should last a long time.

Tanks should be kept secured in an upright position so that if moisture is inside them, the corrosion will occur at the bottom where the tank is the thickest. If a tank cannot be secured upright, it is best to lie it down. A tank should never be depleted of its contents; a minimum of 300 to 500 psi should be kept in at all times. This is to prevent any moisture or particles from entering the tank.

Tanks should be visually inspected once a year and hydrostatically tested every five years. A professional dive shop can take care of this for you. Tanks should be stored in a cool dry place. They should never be put in areas with extreme temperatures and should be condemned if they are in an areas that exceeds 200 degrees F. Every time you use a tank, rinse it in freshwater before storage.

TANK VALVES

Valves transmit air from the SCUBA tank to the regulator. There are three types of valves: the K, J, and DIN. The K valve is a simple on/off valve with rated operating pressures of 3000 psi. The J valve is the same as the K valve, but it has a built-in reserve of 300 to 500 psi. If a diver is using a J valve, and at the end of the dive finds it difficult to breathe, he or she can reach back and manually activate the reserve to permit the remaining 300 to 500 psi of air to flow. The DIN valve is the newest valve on the market and is used when the working pressures of the SCUBA equipment exceed 3000 psi. Like the K valve, it is a simple on/off valve.

REGULATORS

Regulators are devices engineered to decrease the high pressure of a SCUBA tank to ambient pressure and to provide air to the diver on a demand basis. Ambient pressure refers to the pressure surrounding the diver. At sea level, the ambient pressure is one atmosphere or 14.7 psi. The type of regulators used today are demand, single-hosed, and open-circuit. This simply means that air is inhaled from the tank and then exhaled into the water column where it bubbles away. Sport divers do not use closed-circuit systems, such as the military uses, where the gases are recycled and rebreathed, or systems that provide free-flowing air.

The volume of regulators vary. High-volume regulators are for people involved in advanced activities such as deep-diving, wreck-diving, or cave-diving. They ensure an adequate volume of air regardless of the demand. Lower-volume regulators are for people who plan on doing occasional dives to moderate depths well within the recreational guidelines.

Regulators consist of two stages. The first stage attaches to the tank valve and reduces the high tank pressure to an intermediate pressure of about 130-165 psi above ambient pressure. First stages can either be balanced or unbalanced. Divers should purchase a balanced regulator, which means that the ease of breathing is the same regardless of tank pressure. With an unbalanced regulator, breathing becomes more difficult as the tank pressure drops.

The second stage of a regulator, which includes the mouthpiece, reduces the intermediate pressure to ambient pressure and provides air on a demand basis. Most second stages today incorporate a downstream valve. In case of a malfunction, the regulator will not stop the air flow but instead causes a free flow of air. An octopus is an additional second stage that can be attached to your first stage. It is an alternate air source that allows air to be shared safely with an out-of-air buddy. It should be fastened to the front of your buoyancy compensator (BC) with a quick release mechanism. It should never be allowed to drag across the bottom or be put into an inaccessible BC pocket.

In order for your regulator to be complete, you must have a submersible pressure gauge to read the amount of air inside your tank. The gauge should be easy to read, luminous, and connected to the high-pressure port of the first stage of your regulator. Remember that a pressure gauge is a delicate instrument and avoid knocking it around.

Always rinse your pressure gauge and regulator in fresh water after every use. Never depress the purge button on the regulator when rinsing unless it is attached to the tank and the air is on. Avoid prolonged exposure to direct sunlight. Store the regulator by hanging it or coiling it loosely. Avoid any sharp bends and creases. Hose protectors are valuable in extending the life of your hoses. Once a year have your regulator serviced by a professional. Also be cautious about buying an old used regulator. Consult your local dive shop about the proper regulator for you.

DEPTH GAUGES

There are primarily two types of depth gauges for sport diving: the capillary and the bourdon tube. The capillary depth gauge is inexpensive and only good for shallow depths of 0 to 50 feet. It allows a clear tube to fill up with water and you read the water/air interface to find your depth. It works on the Boyle's Law principle. The disadvantages of capillary depth gauges are that some people find them difficult to read and they can become easily clogged. They also require dedicated rinsing and cleaning.

The bourdon tube depth gauge is the most common gauge on the market today.

It is oil filled and sealed. Pressure is transmitted through a rubber membrane to a curved metal tube. As the pressure increases with depth, the tube tries to straighten out. The tube is connected to gears and linkage that control a needle which reads the depth. Bourdon tube depth gauges are easy to read and operate from 0 to 165 feet. They are most accurate in the 50 to 100 foot range. All depth gauges should be luminous and rinsed after each use.

BUOYANCY COMPENSATORS

A buoyancy compensator is a device used to maintain neutral buoyancy during a dive. At the surface, it acts as a support vest. A diver usually wears a neoprene wetsuit which increases buoyancy. A weightbelt offsets the buoyant force of the wetsuit, but as depth increases, the volume of the wet suit compresses and loses its buoyant force, making the diver negatively buoyant. By putting air into the BC, the diver compensates for this loss of buoyancy. However, as the diver ascends, the wetsuit expands back to its normal size, and the air in the BC also expands, causing greater lift. The diver must remember to dump the air out of the BC to achieve neutral buoyancy.

The most common type of BC is the vest or stability jacket, which may have a soft or hard backpack for the tank. This type of BC should fit comfortably when fully inflated, without restricting the diver's breathing or mobility. It should also have the following: a power inflator, an oral inflator, an over-pressure relief valve, a quick dump valve, and a whistle.

The recent trend in BC's is toward low-volume types. It is not necessary for divers to have large volume BC's if they are properly weighted. This low volume is achieved by having a bladderless BC. It is made of a waterproof cordura or nylon that is tear- and puncture-resistant. This kind of BC can be easily repaired with Aquaseal should it become torn.

To properly maintain your BC, rinse it inside and outside with fresh water. Avoid prolonged exposure to direct sunlight. Store the BC with some air in it to retain its shape. Do not crush it.

Suppliers of Diving Equipment

Air Supplies

Atlantic Engineering Co. Ltd.
495 W.Windsor Rd.
North Vancouver, British Columbia V7N 2N5
CANADA
Tel: (604) 980-2936
Fax: (604) 983-3051

Brownies Third Lung
940 N.W. 1st St.
Ft. Lauderdale, FL 33311
Tel: (305) 462-5570
Fax: (305) 462-6115
Third Lung surface breathing gear

Innovative Designs, Inc.
3785 Alt. 19 N.
Suite C
Palm Harbor, FL 34683
Tel: (813) 934-4619
Suppliers of the Super Snorkel unlimited air supply

Cameras and Housings

A B Sea Photo
9136 Sepulveda Blvd.
Los Angeles, CA 90045
Tel: (310) 645-8992
Fax: (310) 645-3645

Accu Gear
724 7th Ave.
New York, NY 10019
Tel: (212) 247-7605
Fax: (212) 307-1858

Amphibico, Inc.
9563 Cote de Liesse
Dorval, Quebec H9P 1A3
CANADA
Tel: (514) 636-9910
Fax: (514) 636-8704

Aqua Vision Systems
7730 Trans Canada Hwy.
Montreal, Quebec H4T 1A5
CANADA
Tel: (514) 737-9841
Fax: (514) 737-7685
Aquatica housings

Gates Underwater Products
5111 Santa Fe St.
Suite H
San Diego, CA 92109
Tel: (619) 272-2501
Fax: (619) 272-1208

Hypertech USA
3675 N.W. 124 Ave.
Coral Springs, FL 33065
Tel: (305) 344-1884
Fax: (305) 344-1887

Ikelite Underwater Systems
50 W 33rd St.
Indianapolis, IN 46208
Tel: (317) 923-4523

GMI Photographic, Inc.
125 Schmitt Blvd.
P.O. Drawer U
Farmingdale, NY 11735
Tel: (516) 752-0066
Fax: (516) 752-0053
Sea & Sea cameras

Leisure Components, Inc.
P.O. Box 13144
Sarasota, FL 34278
Tel: (800) 753-6296
Nautiview underwater housings

Nikon Inc.
19601 Hamilton Ave.
Torrance, CA 90502-1309

Pioneer Marketing and Research, Inc.
216 Haddon Ave.
Westmont, NJ 08108
Tel: (800) 257-7724
  or (609) 854-2424
Ewa housings

Quest Marine Video
1005 Muirlands
Suite M
Irvine, CA 92718
Tel: (714) 855-6376
Fax: (714) 855-4609

Tussey Underwater Systems
5724 Dolphin Pl.
La Jolla, CA 92037
Tel: (619) 551-2600
Fax: (619) 551-8778

Cylinders and Valves

Cylinders International, Inc.
12720 Dupont Circle
Tampa, FL 33626
Tel: (813) 855-1199
Fax: (813) 855-9707

U.S. Divers, Inc.
3323 W. Warner Ave.
Santa Ana, CA 92704
Tel: (714) 540-8010

Dive Computers

Apollo Sports USA
620 Price Ave.
Redwood City, CA 94063
Tel: (415) 306-0909
Fax: (415) 306-0923

Beuchat USA, Inc.
1321 N.W. 65th Pl.
Ft. Lauderdale, FL 33309
Tel: (305) 978-1204
Fax: (305) 978-1207

Cressi-Sub USA
10 Reuten Dr.
Closter, NJ 07624
Tel: (201) 784-1005
Fax: (201) 784-1142

Dacor Corp.
161 Northfield Rd.
Northfield, IL 60093
Tel: (708) 446-9555
Omni dive computer

Digital Dive Research Corp.
P.O. Box 30070
Santa Barbara, CA 93130
Tel: (805) 568-3647
Fax: (805) 962-6033

Dive Rite Mfg., Inc.
Rt. 14, Box 136
Lake City, FL 32055
Tel: (904) 752-1087
Fax: (904) 755-0613

Global Mfg. Corp.
1829 S. 68th St.
West Allis, WI 53214
Tel: (414) 774-1616
Fax: (414) 774-9568

International Divers, Inc.
14747 Artesia Blvd. #5-A
La Mirada, CA 90638
Tel: (714) 994-3900
Fax: (714) 994-5342

Mares
4801 N. 63rd St.
Boulder, CO 80301
Tel: (800) 257-5100
 or (303) 530-2000
Fax: (303) 530-1418

Ocean Edge
7992 Miramar Rd.
San Diego, CA 92126
Tel: (619) 695-9130
Fax: (619) 695-9402

Oceanic
14275 Catalina St.
San Leandro, CA 94577
Tel: (510) 352-5001
Fax: (510) 352-4803

ORCA
Division of EIT, Inc.
45625 Willow Pond Plaza
Sterling, VA 20164
Tel: (703) 478-0333
Fax: (703) 478-0815
Service Center:
644 Cypress St.
Kennet Sq., PA 19348
Tel: (215) 444-9080
Fax: (215) 444-9106

Parkway Imperial
241 Raritan St.
South Amboy, NJ 08879
Tel: (908) 721-5300
Fax: (908) 721-4016

Princeton Techtronics
261 Rt. 130
Bordentown, NJ 08505
Tel: (609) 298-9331
Fax: (609) 298-9601

Prosub-Professional Sports
341 E. Alondra Blvd.
Gardena, CA 90248
Tel: (310) 538-2955
Fax: (310) 538-5143

Salvas USA
1732 N.W. 82 Ave.
Miami, FL 33126
Tel: (305) 477-0001
Fax: (305) 477-0005

Scubapro
3105 E. Harcourt St.
Rancho Dominguez, CA 90221
Tel: (310) 639-7850
Fax: (310) 605-0293

Seaquest
2151 Las Palmas Dr.
Carlsbad, CA 92009
Tel: (619) 438-1101
Suunto diving instruments

Sherwood Scuba
P.O. Box 399
Lockport, NY 14094
Tel: (716) 433-3891
Fax: (716) 433-1275

Sport Divers Mfg.
1923 N.E. 150th St.
Miami, FL 33181
Tel: (305) 947-5692
Fax: (305) 947-9261

**Sunshine Diving
Equipment**
443 Foxbridge Blvd.
Zephyrills, FL 33545
Tel: (813) 788-5207
Fax: (813) 788-3012

Technisub S.P.A.
Piazzale Kennedy 1/D Genoa
ITALY
Tel: (+39) 1 053 0051
Fax: (+39) 1 054 1483

Trident Diving Equipment
20841 Prairie St.
Chatsworth, CA 91311
Tel: (818) 998-7518
Fax: (818) 998 2423

TUSA
2380 Mira Mar Ave.
Long Beach, CA 90815
Tel: (310) 498-3708
Fax: (310) 498-1390

U.S. Divers Co., Inc.
P.O. Box 25018
Santa Ana, CA 92799
Tel: (714) 540-8010
Fax: (714) 432-9340

Dive Suits

Action Plus
17531 Railroad St. # C
City of Industry, CA 91748
Tel: (818) 965-7326

Adrad
5431 Via Aquario
San Diego, CA 92111
Tel: (619) 292-5511
Fax: (619) 275-3703

Bare Sportswear Corp.
P.O. Box 8110-577
Blaine, WA 98230
Tel: (604) 533-7848
Fax: (604) 530-8812

Beuchat USA, Inc.
1321 N.W. 65th Pl.
Ft. Lauderdale, FL 33309
Tel: (305) 978-1204
Fax: (305) 978-1207

Body Glove International
530 6th St.
Hermosa Beach, CA 90254
Tel: (310) 374-4074
Fax: (310) 372-9804

Caribbean Sports
712 N.W. 57th St.
Ft. Lauderdale, FL 33309
Tel: (305) 772-3784
Fax: (305) 772-0782

Cressi-Sub USA, Inc.
10 Reuten Dr.
Closter, NJ 07624
Tel: (201) 784-1005
Fax: (201) 784-1142

Cylinders International, Inc.
12720 Dupont Circle
Tampa, FL 33626
Tel: (813) 855-1199
Fax: (813) 855-9707

Dacor Corp.
161 Northfield Rd.
Northfield, IL 60093
Tel: (708) 446-9555
Fax: (708) 446-7545

Deep Heet Wetsuits
2951 W. Gallaher Ferry Rd.
Knoxville, TN 37932
Tel: (615) 690-1814
Fax: (615) 690-5605

Deep See
18935 59th Ave. N.E.
Arlington, WA 98223
Tel: (206) 435-6696
Fax: (206) 435-4314

Diamond Wetsuits
Northolt Dr.
Bolton
ENGLAND
Tel: (+44) 204 28225
Fax: (+44) 204 31549

Dive Rite Mfg., Inc.
Rt. 14, Box 136
Lake City, FL 32055
Tel: (904) 752-1087
Fax: (904) 755-0613

Diving Unlimited International
1148 Delevan Dr.
San Diego, CA 92102
Tel: (619) 236-1203
Fax: (619) 237-0378

Fathom Dive Equipment Co.
6450 S. Orange Ave.
Orlando, FL 32809
Tel: (407) 851-2202
Fax: (407) 857-2474

Harvey's Skin Diving Supplies, Inc.
2505 252nd St.
Kent, WA 98032
Tel: (206) 824-1114
Fax: (206) 824-3323

Henderson Aquatics
1 Whitall Ave.
Millville, NJ 08332
Tel: (609) 825-4771
Fax: (609) 825-6378

Keene Engineering
9330 Corbin Ave.
Northridge, CA 91324
Tel: (818) 993-0411
Fax: (818) 993-0447

Kokatat
5350 Ericson Way
Arcata, CA 95521
Tel: (707) 822-7621
Fax: (707) 822-8481

Mares
4801 N. 63rd St.
Boulder, CO 80301
Tel: (303) 530-2000
Fax: (303) 530-1418

Nokia
759 W. Fourth Ave.
Escondido, CA 92025
Tel: (619) 746-3834
Fax: (619) 746-1508

O'Brien International
14615 N.E. 91st St.
Redmond, WA 98052
Tel: (206) 881-5900

Ocean Diving/Denizen Wetsuits
750 E. Sample Rd.
Pompano Beach, FL 33064
Tel: (800) 874-6888
  or (305) 943-3337
Fax: (305) 785-3483

Ocean Master
2930 Blandford Dr.
Rowland Heights, CA 91748
Tel: (819) 965-9533
Fax: (819) 965-4375

Oceanic
14275 Catalina St.
San Leandro, CA 94577
Tel: (510) 352-5001
Fax: (510) 352-4803

O'Neill
1071 41st Ave.
Santa Cruz, CA 95062
Tel: (408) 475-7500

O S Systems
P.O. Box 864
Scappoose, OR 97056
Tel: (503) 543-3126
Fax: (503) 543-3129

Oztex, Inc.
15455 New Greenbriar Pkwy.
Suite 210
Beaverton, OR 97006
Tel: (503) 645-5146
Fax: (503) 645-5276
Diveskins

Parkway Imperial
241 Raritan St.
South Amboy, NJ 08879
Tel: (908) 721-5300
Fax: (908) 721-4016

Pic International, Inc.
2611-C Temple Heights Dr.
Oceanside, CA 92056
Tel: (619) 631-0277
Fax: (619) 631-0278

Polar Bears Diving Equipment Ltd.
Units B1/B2
Pennygillam Industrial Pk.
Cornwall PL1 57ED
ENGLAND

Rip Curl
3801 S. El Camino Real
San Clemente, CA 92672
Tel: (714) 498-4920
Fax: (714) 492-3742

S.A.S. Wetsuits
530 6th St.
Hermosa Beach, CA 90254
Tel: (310) 374-4074
Fax: (310) 374-9804

Santiva Ocean Sports
3313 Park Lake
Ft. Worth, TX 76133
Tel: (817) 346-8887
Fax: (817) 346-1030

Scubapro
3105 E. Harcourt St.
Rancho Dominguez, CA 90221
Tel: (310) 639-7850
Fax: (310) 605-0293

Seaquest
2151 Las Palmas Dr.
Carlsbad, CA 92009
Tel: (619) 438-1101
Fax: (619) 438-3142

Sherwood Scuba
P.O. Box 399
Lockport, NY 14094
Tel: (716) 433-3891
Fax: (716) 433-1275
Destiny wetsuits

Sport Products of Tampa, Inc.
2801 Nebraska Ave.
Tampa, FL 33602
Tel: (813) 227-9533
Fax: (813) 221-0555

Sport Suits of Australia
7625 Hayvenhurst #35
Van Nuys, CA 91406
Tel: (818) 376-0402
Fax: (818) 373-7721
Vega wetsuits

Surfer House
4173 Wheaton Way
Bremerton, WA 98310
Tel: (206) 373-9080

Sunshine Diving Equipment
443 Foxbridge Blvd.
Zephyrills, FL 33545
Tel: (813) 788-5207
Fax: (813) 788-3012

Technisub S.P.A.
Piazzale Kennedy 1/D
Genoa
ITALY
Tel: (+39) 1 053 0051
Fax: (+39) 1 054 1483

Typhoon Water Wares Ltd.
1106 Market St.
Pocomoke City, MD 21851
Tel: (410) 957-4417
Fax: (410) 957-4415

U.S. Divers Co., Inc.
P.O. Box 25018
Santa Ana, CA 92799
Tel: (714) 540-8010
Fax: (714) 432-9340

Viking Diving, Inc.
9043 Dutton Dr.
Twinsburg, OH 44087
Tel: (216) 963-0310
Fax: (216) 963-0316

Wetwear USA
P.O. Box 4734
Ft. Walton Beach, FL 32549
Tel: (800) 676-8815
  or (904) 581-5580

Fins

Action Plus
17531 Railroad St. #C
City of Industry, CA 91748
Tel: (818) 965-2667
Fax: (818) 965-7326

Amico
1859 S.W. 31st. Ave.
Hallandale, FL 33009
Tel: (305) 983-7556
Fax: (305) 985-8581

Apollo Sports USA
620 Price Ave.
Redwood City, CA 94063
Tel: (415) 306-0909
Fax: (415) 306-0923

Barracuda Sports
20224 S.W. Hamilton
Portland, OR 97201
Tel: (503) 241-0528
Fax: (503) 227-7814

Beuchat USA, Inc.
1321 N.W. 65th Pl.
Ft. Lauderdale, FL 33309
Tel: (305) 978-1204
Fax: (305) 978-1207

Bob Evans Designs, Inc.
28 Anacapa St.
Santa Barbara, CA 93101
Tel: (805) 966-9628
Fax: (805) 564-8240
Force Fin

Cressi-Sub USA
10 Reuten Dr.
Closter, NJ 07624
Tel: (201) 784-1005
Fax: (201) 784-1142

Dacor Corp.
161 Northfield Rd.
Northfield, IL 60093
Tel: (708) 446-9555

Deep See
18935 59th Ave, N.E.
Arlington, WA 98223
Tel: (206) 435-6696
Fax: (206) 435-4314

Diving Star, Inc.
4065 E. La Palma Ave. #A
Anaheim, CA 92807
Tel: (714) 666-2237
Fax: (714) 666-8072

Dolphin Products
500 Bay Drive S.
Bradenton Beach, FL 34217
Tel: (813) 778-0300
Fax: (813) 778-9303

Go Dive Products
164 N. Bascom Ave.
San Jose, CA 95128
Tel: (408) 294-3483
Fax: (408) 294-3496

International Divers, Inc.
14747 Artesia Blvd. #5-A
La Mirada, CA 90638
Tel: (714) 994-3900
Fax: (714) 994-5342

IST Sports
858 Golden Grove Way
Covina, CA 91722
Tel: (818) 859-7578
Fax: (818) 960-5211

Mares
4801 N. 63rd St.
Boulder, CO 80301
Tel: (800) 257-5100
  or (303) 530-2000
Fax: (303) 530-1418

Netex Products
1420 Claremont Blvd.
Suite 200B
Claremont, CA 91711
Tel: (714) 621-3330
Fax: (714) 621-3361

Ocean Edge
7992 Miramar Rd.
San Diego, CA 92126
Tel: (619) 695-9130
Fax: (619) 695-9402

Oceanic
14275 Catalina St.
San Leandro, CA 94577
Tel: (510) 352-5001
Fax: (510) 352-4803

Parkway Imperial
241 Raritan St.
South Amboy, NJ 08879
Tel: (908) 721-5300
Fax: (908) 721-4016

Salvas USA
1732 N.W. 82 Ave.
Miami, FL 33126
Tel: (305) 477-0001
Fax: (305) 477-0005

Scubapro
3105 E. Harcourt St.
Rancho Dominguez, CA 90221
Tel: (310) 639-7850
Fax: (310) 605-0293

Seaquest
2151 Las Palmas Dr.
Carlsbad, CA 92009
Tel: (619) 438-1101
Fax: (619) 438-3142

Sherwood Scuba
P.O. Box 399
Lockport, NY 14094
Tel: (716) 433-3891
Fax: (716) 433-1275

**Sunshine Diving
Equipment**
443 Foxbridge Blvd.
Zephyrills, FL 33545
Tel: (813) 788-5207
Fax: (813) 788-3012

Technisub S.P.A.
Piazzale Kennedy 1/D
Genoa
ITALY
Tel: (+39) 1 053 0051
Fax: (+39) 1 054 1483

Trident Diving Equipment
20841 Prairie St.
Chatsworth, CA 91311
Tel: (818) 998-7518
Fax: (818) 998 2423

TUSA
2380 Mira Mar Ave.
Long Beach, CA 90815
Tel: (310) 498-3708
Fax: (310) 498-1390

U.S. Divers Co., Inc.
P.O. Box 25018
Santa Ana, CA 92799
Tel: (714) 540-8010
Fax: (714) 432-9340

Knives

Apollo Sports USA
620 Price Ave.
Redwood City, CA 94063
Tel: (415) 306-0909
Fax: (415) 306-0923

Beuchat USA, Inc.
1321 N.W. 65th Pl.
Ft. Lauderdale, FL 33309
Tel: (305) 978-1204
Fax: (305) 978-1207

Bonica Marketing, Inc.
#201-281 H St.
Blaine, WA 98230
Tel: (604) 270-0812
Fax: (604) 270-7278

Cetacea Corp.
1191 Chess Dr.
Suite A
Foster City, CA 94404
Tel: (415) 571-9411
Fax: (415) 571-9412

Clifford & Associates
6610 Snider Plaza
Dallas, TX 75205
Tel: (800) 752-3046
*Blackie Collins Buddie System
knife*

Cressi-Sub USA
10 Reuten Dr.
Closter, NJ 07624
Tel: (201) 784-1005
Fax: (201) 784-1142

Dacor Corp.
161 Northfield Rd.
Northfield, IL 60093
Tel: (708) 446-9555
Fax: (708) 446-7545

Deep See
18935 59th Ave. N.E.
Arlington, WA 98223
Tel: (206) 435-6696
Fax: (206) 435-4314

Dive Rite Mfg., Inc.
Rt. 14, Box 136
Lake City, FL 32055
Tel: (904) 752-1087
Fax: (904) 755-0613

Diving Star, Inc.
4065 E. La Palma Ave. # A
Anaheim, CA 92807
Tel: (714) 666-2237
Fax: (714) 666-8072

Go Dive Products
164 N. Bascom Ave.
San Jose, CA 95218
Tel: (408) 294-3483
Fax: (408) 294-3496

International Divers, Inc.
14747 Artesia Blvd. #5-A
La Mirada, CA 90638
Tel: (714) 994-3900
Fax: (714) 994-5342

IST Sports
858 Golden Grove Way
Covina, CA 91722
Tel: (818) 859-7578
Fax: (818) 960-5211

Mares
4801 N. 63rd St.
Boulder, CO 80301
Tel: (800) 257-5100
  or (303) 530-2000
Fax: (303) 530-1418

Netex Products
1420 Claremont Blvd.
Suite 200B
Claremont, CA 91711
Tel: (714) 621-3330
Fax: (714) 621-3361

Ocean Edge
7992 Miramar Rd.
San Diego, CA 92126
Tel: (619) 695-9130
Fax: (619) 695-9402

Ocean Master
2930 Blandford Dr.
Rowland Heights, CA 91748
Tel: (819) 965-9533
Fax: (819) 965-4375

Oceanic
14275 Catalina St.
San Leandro, CA 94577
Tel: (510) 352-5001
Fax: (510) 352-4803

Parkway Imperial
241 Raritan St.
South Amboy, NJ 08879
Tel: (908) 721-5300
Fax: (908) 721-4016

PIC International, Inc.
2611-C Temple Heights Dr.
Oceanside, CA 92056
Tel: (619) 631-0277
Fax: (619) 631-0278

Scubapro
3105 E. Harcourt St.
Rancho Dominguez, CA 90221
Tel: (310) 639-7850
Fax: (310) 605-0293

Scuda Mfg.
19150 W. Dixie Hwy.
Miami, FL 33180
Tel: (305) 931-5349
Fax: (305) 933-9028

Seaquest
2151 Las Palmas Dr.
Carlsbad, CA 92009
Tel: (619) 438-1101
Fax: (619) 438-3142

Sherwood Scuba
P.O. Box 399
Lockport, NY 14094
Tel: (716) 433-3891
Fax: (716) 433-1275

Sport Divers Mfg.
1923 N.E. 150th St.
Miami, FL 33181
Tel: (305) 947-5692
Fax: (305) 947-9621

Spyderco, Inc.
16399 S. Golden Rd.
Golden, CA 80401
Tel: (303) 279-8383
Fax: (303) 278-2229

Sunshine Diving Equipment
443 Foxbridge Blvd.
Zephyrills, FL 33545
Tel: (813) 788-5207
Fax: (813) 788-3012

Technisub S.P.A.
Piazzale Kennedy 1/D
Genoa
ITALY
Tel: (+39) 1 053 0051
Fax: (+39) 1 054 1483

Trident Diving Equipment
20841 Prairie St.
Chatsworth, CA 91311
Tel: (818) 998-7518
Fax: (818) 998 2423

TUSA
2380 Mira Mar Ave.
Long Beach, CA 90815
Tel: (310) 498-3708
Fax: (310) 498-1390

U.S. Divers Co., Inc.
P.O. Box 25018
Santa Ana, CA 92799
Tel: (714) 540-8010
Fax: (714) 432-9340

Zest International
1500 N. E. Jackson St.
Minneapolis, MN 55413
Tel: (800) 453-8937
Fax: (612) 781-1452

Masks and Goggles

A Plus Marine Supply, Inc.
145 San Remo Dr.
Islamorada, FL 33036
Tel: (305) 664-5194
Fax: (305) 664-5194

Action Plus
17531 Railroad St. #C
City of Industry, CA 91748
Tel: (818) 965-2667
Fax: (818) 965-7326

Adrad
5431 Via Aquario
San Diego, CA 92111
Tel: (619) 292-5511
Fax: (619) 275-3703

Amico
1859 S.W. 31st. Ave.
Hallandale, FL 33009
Tel: (305) 983-7556
Fax: (305) 985-8581

Apollo Sports USA
620 Price Ave.
Redwood City, CA 94063
Tel: (415) 306-0909
Fax: (415) 306-0923

Beuchat USA, Inc.
1321 N.W. 65th Pl.
Ft. Lauderdale, FL 33309
Tel: (305) 978-1204
Fax: (305) 978-1207

Cressi-Sub USA
10 Reuten Dr.
Closter, NJ 07624
Tel: (201) 784-1005
Fax: (201) 784-1142

Curt Walker Optician
3434 Fourth Ave.
Suite 120
San Diego, CA 92103
Tel: (800) 538-2878
Prescription masks

Dacor Corp.
161 Northfield Rd.
Northfield, IL 60093
Tel: (708) 446-9555
Fax: (708) 446-7545

Deep See
18935 59th Ave. N.E.
Arlington, WA 98223
Tel: (206) 435-6696
Fax: (206) 435-4314

Divematics USA, Inc.
145 West Whiting Ave.
Fullerton, CA 92632
Tel: (714) 773-5909
Fax: (714) 773-0471

Diving Star, Inc.
4065 E. La Palma Ave. # A
Anaheim, CA 92807
Tel: (714) 666-2237
Fax: (714) 666-8072

Dolphin Products
500 Bay Drive S.
Bradenton Beach, FL 34217
Tel: (813) 778-0300
Fax: (813) 778-9303

Go Dive Products
164 N. Bascom Ave.
San Jose, CA 95218
Tel: (408) 294-3483
Fax: (408) 294-3496

International Divers, Inc.
14747 Artesia Blvd. #5-A
La Mirada, CA 90638
Tel: (714) 994-3900
Fax: (714) 994-5342

IST Sports
858 Golden Grove Way
Covina, CA 91722
Tel: (818) 859-7578
Fax: (818) 960-5211

Keene Engineering
9330 Corbin Ave.
Northridge, CA 91324
Tel: (818) 993-0411
Fax: (818) 993-0447

Mares
4801 N. 63rd St.
Boulder, CO 80301
Tel: (800) 257-5100
or (303) 530-2000
Fax: (303) 530-1418

Netex Products
1420 Claremont Blvd.
Suite 200B
Claremont, CA 91711
Tel: (714) 621-3330
Fax: (714) 621-3361

Ocean Edge
7992 Miramar Rd.
San Diego, CA 92126
Tel: (619) 695-9130
Fax: (619) 695-9402

Ocean Master
2930 Blandford Dr.
Rowland Heights, CA 91748
Tel: (819) 965-9533
Fax: (819) 965-4375

Oceanic
14275 Catalina St.
San Leandro, CA 94577
Tel: (510) 352-5001
Fax: (510) 352-4803

Parkway Imperial
241 Raritan St.
South Amboy, NJ 08879
Tel: (908) 721-5300
Fax: (908) 721-4016

PIC International, Inc.
2611-C Temple Heights Dr.
Oceanside, CA 92056
Tel: (619) 631-0277
Fax: (619) 631-0278

Salvas USA
1732 N.W. 82 Ave.
Miami, FL 33126
Tel: (305) 477-0001
Fax: (305) 477-0005

Scubapro
3105 E. Harcourt St.
Rancho Dominguez, CA 90221
Tel: (310) 639-7850
Fax: (310) 605-0293

Scuda Mfg.
19150 W. Dixie Hwy.
Miami, FL 33180
Tel: (305) 931-5349
Fax: (305) 933-9028

Sea Vision
P.O. Box 84000
St. Petersburg, FL 33784
Tel: (800) 732-6275
 or (813) 526-0501
Fax: (800) 659- 0284
 or (813) 527-7652

Seaquest
2151 Las Palmas Dr.
Carlsbad, CA 92009
Tel: (619) 438-1101
Fax: (619) 438-3142

Sherwood Scuba
P.O. Box 399
Lockport, NY 14094
Tel: (716) 433-3891
Fax: (716) 433-1275

Sport Divers Mfg.
1923 N.E. 150th St.
Miami, FL 33181
Tel: (305) 947-5692
Fax: (305) 947-9621

Sunshine Diving Equipment
443 Foxbridge Blvd.
Zephyrills, FL 33545
Tel: (813) 788-5207
Fax: (813) 788-3012

Technisub S.P.A.
Piazzale Kennedy 1/D
Genoa
ITALY
Tel: (+39) 1 053 0051
Fax: (+39) 1 054 1483

Trident Diving Equipment
20841 Prairie St.
Chatsworth, CA 91311
Tel: (818) 998-7518
Fax: (818) 998 2423

TUSA
2380 Mira Mar Ave.
Long Beach, CA 90815
Tel: (310) 498-3708
Fax: (310) 498-1390

U.S. Divers Co., Inc.
P.O. Box 25018
Santa Ana, CA 92799
Tel: (714) 540-8010
Fax: (714) 432-9340

Regulators

Apollo Sports USA
620 Price Ave.
Redwood City, CA 94063
Tel: (415) 306-0909
Fax: (415) 306-0923

Beuchat USA, Inc.
1321 N.W. 65th Pl.
Ft. Lauderdale, FL 33309
Tel: (305) 978-1204
Fax: (305) 978-1207

Brownies Third Lung
940 N.W. 1st St.
Ft. Lauderdale, FL 33311
Tel: (305) 462-5570
Fax: (305) 462-6115

Cressi-Sub USA
10 Reuten Dr.
Closter, NJ 07624
Tel: (201) 784-1005
Fax: (201) 784-1142

Dacor Corp.
161 Northfield Rd.
Northfield, IL 60093
Tel: (708) 446-9555
Fax: (708) 446-7545

Divematics USA, Inc.
145 West Whiting Ave.
Fullerton, CA 92632
Tel: (714) 773-5909
Fax: (714) 773-0471

Dolphin Products
500 Bay Drive S.
Bradenton Beach, FL 34217
Tel: (813) 778-0300
Fax: (813) 778-9303

International Divers, Inc.
14747 Artesia Blvd. #5-A
La Mirada, CA 90638
Tel: (714) 994-3900
Fax: (714) 994-5342

IST Sports
858 Golden Grove Way
Covina, CA 91722
Tel: (818) 859-7578
Fax: (818) 960-5211

Mares
4801 N. 63rd St.
Boulder, CO 80301
Tel: (800) 257-5100
  or (303) 530-2000
Fax: (303) 530-1418

Netex Products
1420 Claremont Blvd.
Suite 200B
Claremont, CA 91711
Tel: (714) 621-3330
Fax: (714) 621-3361

Ocean Edge
7992 Miramar Rd.
San Diego, CA 92126
Tel: (619) 695-9130
Fax: (619) 695-9402

Ocean Master
2930 Blandford Dr.
Rowland Heights, CA 91748
Tel: (819) 965-9533
Fax: (819) 965-4375

Oceanic
14275 Catalina St.
San Leandro, CA 94577
Tel: (510) 352-5001
Fax: (510) 352-4803

Parkway Imperial
241 Raritan St.
South Amboy, NJ 08879
Tel: (908) 721-5300
Fax: (908) 721-4016

Salvas USA
1732 N.W. 82 Ave.
Miami, FL 33126
Tel: (305) 477-0001
Fax: (305) 477-0005

Scubapro
3105 E. Harcourt St.
Rancho Dominguez, CA 90221
Tel: (310) 639-7850
Fax: (310) 605-0293

Scuda Mfg.
19150 W. Dixie Hwy.
Miami, FL 33180
Tel: (305) 931-5349
Fax: (305) 933-9028

Seaquest
2151 Las Palmas Dr.
Carlsbad, CA 92009
Tel: (619) 438-1101
Fax: (619) 438-3142

Sherwood Scuba
P.O. Box 399
Lockport, NY 14094
Tel: (716) 433-3891
Fax: (716) 433-1275

Submersible Systems, Inc.
18112 Gothard St.
Huntington Beach, CA 92648
Tel: (714) 842-6566
Fax: (714) 842-4626

**Sunshine Diving
Equipment**
443 Foxbridge Blvd.
Zephyrills, FL 33545
Tel: (813) 788-5207
Fax: (813) 788-3012

Technisub S.P.A.
Piazzale Kennedy 1/D
Genoa
ITALY
Tel: (+39) 1 053 0051
Fax: (+39) 1 054 1483

Trident Diving Equipment
20841 Prairie St.
Chatsworth, CA 91311
Tel: (818) 998-7518
Fax: (818) 998 2423

TUSA
2380 Mira Mar Ave.
Long Beach, CA 90815
Tel: (310) 498-3708
Fax: (310) 498-1390

U.S. Divers Co., Inc.
P.O. Box 25018
Santa Ana, CA 92799
Tel: (714) 540-8010
Fax: (714) 432-9340

Viking Diving, Inc.
9043 Dutton Dr.
Twinsburg, OH 44087
Tel: (216) 963-0310
Fax: (216) 963-0316

Zeagle Systems
37150 Chancery Rd.
Zephyrhills, FL 33541
Tel: (813) 782-5568
Fax: (813) 782-5569

Spearguns

A Plus Marine Supply, Inc.
145 San Remo Dr.
Islamorada, FL 33036
Tel: (305) 664-5194
Fax: (305) 664-5194

A.B. Biller Co.
P.O. Box 316
Bloomingdale, IL 60108
Tel: (708) 529-2776
Fax: (708) 529-4473

Beuchat USA, Inc.
1321 N.W. 65th Pl.
Ft. Lauderdale, FL 33309
Tel: (305) 978-1204
Fax: (305) 978-1207

Cressi-Sub USA
10 Reuten Dr.
Closter, NJ 07624
Tel: (201) 784-1005
Fax: (201) 784-1142

Global Mfg. Corp.
1829 S. 68th St.
West Allis, WI 53214
Tel: (414) 774-1616
Fax: (414) 774-9568

Go Dive Products
164 N. Bascom Ave.
San Jose, CA 95218
Tel: (408) 294-3483
Fax: (408) 294-3496

IST Sports
858 Golden Grove Way
Covina, CA 91722
Tel: (818) 859-7578
Fax: (818) 960-5211

JBL Enterprises, Inc.
426 W. Almond Ave.
Orange, CA 92666
Tel: (714) 633-0860
Fax: (714) 633-1613

Mares
4801 N. 63rd St.
Boulder, CO 80301
Tel: (800) 257-5100
  or (303) 530-2000
Fax: (303) 530-1418

Riffe International
114-B Los Molinos
San Clemente, CA 92672
Tel: (714) 361-2818
Fax: (714) 493-1373

Salvas USA
1732 N.W. 82 Ave.
Miami, FL 33126
Tel: (305) 477-0001
Fax: (305) 477-0005

Scubapro
3105 E. Harcourt St.
Rancho Dominguez, CA 90221
Tel: (310) 639-7850
Fax: (310) 605-0293

Seaquest
2151 Las Palmas Dr.
Carlsbad, CA 92009
Tel: (619) 438-1101
Fax: (619) 438-3142

Technisub S.P.A.
Piazzale Kennedy 1/D
Genoa
ITALY
Tel: (+39) 1 053 0051
Fax: (+39) 1 054 1483

Trident Diving Equipment
20841 Prairie St.
Chatsworth, CA 91311
Tel: (818) 998-7518
Fax: (818) 998 2423

Undersee
5580 Chisolm Rd.
Johns Island, SC 29455
Tel: (800) SUBGUNS
Fax: (803) 559-3780

Training and Certification

American Nitrox Divers, Inc.
74 Woodcleft Ave.
Freeport, NY 11520
Tel: (800) 229-ANDI
  or. (516) 546-2026
Fax: (516) 546-6010

American Watersports Association
2313 Shady Willow Ct.
Bedford, TX 76021
Tel: (817) 354-8996
Fax: (817) 540-5577

Buoyancy Training Systems, Inc.
236 S.W. 171st St.
Seattle, WA 98166
Tel: (206) 241-2634
Fax: (206) 448-5859

International Diving Educators Association (IDEA)
P.O. Box 8427
Jacksonville, FL 32239-8427
Tel: (904) 744-5554

International Association of Nitrox (& Technical) Divers
1545 N.E. 104th St.
Miami Shores, FL 33138
Tel: (305) 751-4873

International Scuba Educators, Inc.
P.O. Box 17388
Clearwater, FL 34622
Tel: (813) 539-6491

**National Academy of Scuba
Educators (NASE)**
1728 Kingsley Ave.
Suite 4
Orange Park, FL 32073-1728
Tel: (904) 264-4104

**National Association of
Scuba Diving Schools
(NASDS)**
8099 Indiana Ave.
Riverside, CA 92504
Tel: (909) 687-8792

**National Association of
Underwater Instructors
(NAUI)**
P.O. Box 14650
Montclair, CA 91763
Tel: (909) 621-5801

**Professional Association of
Diving Instructors (PADI)**
1015 River St.
Scranton, PA 18505
Tel: (717) 342-9434

**Professional Diving
Instructors Corp. (PDIC)**
P.O. Box 3633
Scranton, PA 18505
Tel: (717) 342-9434
Fax: (717) 342-1480

**Professional Scuba
Inspectors, Inc.**
6531 N.E. 198th St.
Seattle, WA 98155
Tel: (206) 486-2252

**Scuba Schools
International (SSI)**
2619 Canton Ct.
Fort Collins, CO 80525
Tel: (303) 482-0883
Fax: (303) 482-6157

**YMCA National Scuba
Program**
Oakbrook Square
6083-A Oakbrook Pkwy.
Norcross
Atlanta, GA 30093
Tel: (404) 662-5172

Ocean Tech
HC 33
#7 Stone Tree Rd.
Arrowsic Island
Bath, ME 04530
Tel: (207) 442-0998
Fax: (207) 442-9042
Advanced diver training

Weights and Belts

A Plus Marine Supply, Inc.
145 San Remo Dr.
Islamorada, FL 33036
Tel: (305) 664-5194
Fax: (305) 664-5194

Action Plus
17531 Railroad St. #C
City of Industry, CA 91748
Tel: (818) 965-2667
Fax: (818) 965-7326

Adrad
5431 Via Aquario
San Diego, CA 92111
Tel: (619) 292-5511
Fax: (619) 275-3703

Cressi-Sub USA
10 Reuten Dr.
Closter, NJ 07624
Tel: (201) 784-1005
Fax: (201) 784-1142

Dacor Corp.
161 Northfield Rd.
Northfield, IL 60093
Tel: (708) 446-9555
Fax: (708) 446-7545

Global Mfg. Corp.
1829 S. 68th St.
West Allis, WI 53214
Tel: (414) 774-1616
Fax: (414) 774-9568

Go Dive Products
164 N. Bascom Ave.
San Jose, CA 95218
Tel: (408) 294-3483
Fax: (408) 294-3496

Mares
4801 N. 63rd St.
Boulder, CO 80301
Tel: (800) 257-5100
  or (303) 530-2000
Fax: (303) 530-1418

Ocean Edge
7992 Miramar Rd.
San Diego, CA 92126
Tel: (619) 695-9130
Fax: (619) 695-9402

Oceanic
14275 Catalina St.
San Leandro, CA 94577
Tel: (510) 352-5001
Fax: (510) 352-4803

Parkway Imperial
241 Raritan St.
South Amboy, NJ 08879
Tel: (908) 721-5300
Fax: (908) 721-4016

Salvas USA
1732 N.W. 82 Ave.
Miami, FL 33126
Tel: (305) 477-0001
Fax: (305) 477-0005

Scubapro
3105 E. Harcourt St.
Rancho Dominguez, CA 90221
Tel: (310) 639-7850
Fax: (310) 605-0293

Seaquest
2151 Las Palmas Dr.
Carlsbad, CA 92009
Tel: (619) 438-1101
Fax: (619) 438-3142

Sherwood Scuba
P.O. Box 399
Lockport, NY 14094
Tel: (716) 433-3891
Fax: (716) 433-1275

Technisub S.P.A.
Piazzale Kennedy 1/D
Genoa
ITALY
Tel: (+39) 1 053 0051
Fax: (+39) 1 054 1483

Trident Diving Equipment
20841 Prairie St.
Chatsworth, CA 91311
Tel: (818) 998-7518
Fax: (818) 998 2423

Watermark Scuba, Inc.
808 Peace Portal Dr.
Suite 21
Blaine, WA 98230
Tel: (604) 530-5615
Seasoft weight belts

Docks and Dock Components

You've just bought waterfront property and have decided to put a dock in. First you'll need to get the necessary permits. These vary in each state, and may affect the materials you can use. Most docks are made out of wooden pilings with some type of decking. The decking can be wood, metal, or some form of synthetic material. But certain features should be included:

- The deck material should have non-skid properties. You don't want the liability of somebody sliding off into the water.
- The materials should be structurally strong enough to withstand the weight of people.
- In bad weather, the sea may be washing up from under the deck, so the deck material should be strongly bolted down.
- The deck should have a strong rail. In some states, this is required by code.

- A floating dock should have enough buoyancy to support the maximum number of people on it.
- Make sure the buoyancy of a floating dock in near the edges and corners. If it is concentrated near the center of the float, the float will be unstable.
- If cleats or rings are to be fitted to the dock, make sure they are strongly through-bolted and have backing plates.
- In bad weather it is often good practice to moor a floating dock away from pilings to prevent damage caused by the dock pounding on the pilings. This means you will need strong cleats or rings on the dock and a heavy line or chain and an anchor.
- If boats are to be moored alongside the dock, you should consider non-abrasive rubrail or fendering around it. This can prevent damage to the dock and the boats.

Manufacturers of Docks, Dock Components, and Racks

Docks

Americon
P.O. Box 1005
Auburn, ME 04211
Tel: (800) 736-3625
Fax: (207) 786-4114
Docks and dock boxes

Carolina Waterworks, Inc.
463 Long Point Rd.
Mt. Pleasant, SC 29464
Tel: (800) 8-FLOATS
  or (803) 884-4832
Fax: (803) 884-1359
Floats, hardware, ramps, and buoys

Custom Marine Systems, Inc.
28 Oxford Rd.
East Rockaway, NY 11518
Tel: (516) 887-9868
Floating docks

Fiberglass Products, Inc.
P.O. Box 1005
Auburn, ME 04211
Tel: (207) 786-4436
Fax: (207) 786-4114
Docks and dock boxes

Figure 1: These covered dock bays, shown shortly after completion, were manufactured by Floating Docks Mfg. Co.

Floating Docks Mfg. Co.
Indianapolis, IN 46254
Tel: (800) 969-DOCK
  or (317) 298-9125
Fax: (317) 291-9287
Breakwaters and docks

Follansbee Dock Systems, Inc.
P.O. Box 610
State St.
Follansbee, WV 26037
Tel: (800) 223-3444
  or (304) 527-4500
Fax: (304) 527-4507
Floating docks and hardware

Galva-Foam Marine Industries
Rt. 67, Box 19
Camdentown, MO 65020
Tel: (314) 346-3323
Fax: (314) 346-4025
Docks and boat lifts

Kracor, Inc.
5625 W. Clinton Ave.
P O. Box 23667
Milwaukee, Wl 53223
Tel: (414) 355-6335
Fax: (414) 355-8782
Dock floats and dock boxes

Shoremaster, Inc.
1 Shoremaster Dr.
Box 358
Fergus Falls, MN 56538-0358
Tel: (218) 739-4641
Fax: (218) 739-4008
Floating docks

Spin-Cast Plastics, Inc.
3300 N. Kenmore St.
South Bend, IN 46628
Tel: (800) 228-DOCK
Fax: (219) 232-6036
Poly Dock deck systems

Sullivan Flotation Systems
P.O. Box 639
Kings Hwy.
Warwick, NY 10990
Tel: (914) 986-7377
Fax: (914) 986-8531
Docks and marina systems

Superdeck Marketing
7753 Beach St. N.E.
Minneapolis, MN 55432
Tel: (612) 571-2247
Fax: (612) 571-3287
Floating docks

Dock Components

Americon
P.O. Box 1005
Auburn, ME 04211
Tel: (800) 736-3625
Fax: (207) 786-4114
Docks and dock boxes

Amerope/Flat Top Cleats
P.O. Box 144141
Coral Gables, FL 33114
Tel: (305) 446-1716
Fax: (305) 442-0687
Flush mounted dock cleats

Beachcomber Fiberglass Technology
2850 S.E. Market Pl.
Stuart, FL 34997
Tel: (407) 283-0200
Fax: (407) 286-0049
Dock components and boxes

Better Way Products
71913 C.R. 23
New Paris, IN 46553
Tel: (219) 831-3340
Fax: (219) 831-3611
Storage, dock boxes, and steps

Brock Mfg.
P.O. Box 2000
St. Rd. 15
Milford, IN 46542-2000
Tel: (219) 658-4191
Fax: (219) 658-4133
Docks and accessories

C & C Fiberglass
3022 Peachtree Industrial Blvd.
Buford, GA 30518
Tel: (800)-DOCKBOX
  or (404) 945-3646
Fax: (404) 945-0766
Dock boxes and lockers

Cal-June, Inc.
P.O. Box 9551
North Hollywood, CA 91609-1551
Tel: (818) 761-3516
Fax: (818) 761-3165
Dock bumpers

C-Loc Retention Systems
P.O. Box 283
Utica, MI 48087-0283
Tel: (313) 731-9511
Fax: (313) 731-9516
Bulkheading material

The Dock Doctors
Rt. 7, Box 1335
Ferrisburgh, VT 05456
Tel: (802) 877-6756
Fax: (802) 877-3147
Components

Dock Hardware & Float Dist.
P.O. Box 686
Geneva, NY 14456
Tel: (800) 826-3433
Fax: (315) 789-4475
Dock hardware

Electronic Production Concepts, Inc.
138 S. Abbe Rd.
Elyria, OH 44035
Tel: (800) 334-5904
Fax: (216) 336-9506
Dockside utility center

Goodhue Marine, Inc.
190 Central St.
Leominster, MA 01453
Tel: (508) 537-0058
Fax: (508) 537-9253
Docks and hardware

Fend Offs, Inc.
750 N.E. 7th Ave.
Dania, FL 33004
Tel: (305) 923-7048
Fax: (305) 922-0698
Dock equipment

Fiberglass Products, Inc.
P.O. Box 1005
Auburn, ME 04211
Tel: (207) 786-4436
Fax: (207) 786-4114
Docks and dock boxes

Flexmaster, Inc.
3995 Pembroke Rd.
Hollywood, FL 33021
Tel: (305) 964-5315
Fax: (305) 964-2715
Dock fenders

Heritage Marine
E. Illinois St.
Assumption, IL 62510
Tel: (217) 226-4409
Fax: (217) 226-4499
Vinyl decking for docks

Materials International
P.O. Box 1484
Lake Charles, LA 70602
Tel: (800) 256-8857
  or (313) 439-8042
Fax: (313) 439-8043
ShoreGuard rigid vinyl sheet piling

Monarch Moor Whips
P.O. Box 6
Normandy Beach, NJ 08739
Tel: (908) 244-4584
Fax: (908) 341-0282
Mooring gear and whips

Mercer Products
37235 St. Rd. 19
Unatilla, FL 32784
Tel: (800) 447-8442
Fax: (904) 357-9660
Bumper guards

Mooring Products International
1189 N. U.S. Hwy. #1
Ormond Beach, FL 32074
Tel: (800) 277-WHIP
Fax: (904) 676-COMM
Dock Ladders, 8 inch and 15 inch cleats, mooring whips

Perimeter Industries
1524 W. 132nd St.
Gardena, CA 90249
Tel: (310) 323-6636
Fax: (310) 323-6637
Dock and pier bumpers, fenders

Rotocast Flotation Products
P.O. Box 1059
Brownwood, TX 76804
Tel: (800) 351-1363
Durafloat pontoons, buoys, and float balls

W. H. Salisbury & Co.
7520 N. Long Ave.
Skokie, IL 60077
Tel: (708) 679-6700
Fax: (708) 679-2401
Bumper and chafe guards.

Sea Technology Ltd.
P.O. Box 489
Gloucester, VA 23061
Tel: (800) 341-8324
  or (804) 642-3568
Fax: (804) 642-3569
Dockside power pedestals

Sentinel Quality
70 Airport Rd.
Hyannis, MA 02601
Tel: (508) 775-5220
Fax: (508) 771-1554
Canoe carriers, bumpers, and towable tubes

Standard Products
Specialtiy Products Division
2401 S. Gulley
Dearborn, MI 48124
Tel: (800) 333-3265
Fax: (313) 562-3305
Dock bumpers

Sternmoor
P.O. Box 150
Spring St.
South Salem, NY 10590
Tel: (914) 763-5917
Fax: (914) 763-9668
Boarding and docking systems

Tara Marine
500 Victory Rd.
North Quincy, MA 02171
Tel: (617) 328-7741
Fax: (617) 328-7570
Snaggletooth dockcleats

World Sport Mfg.
21 Production Pl. #9
Gilford, NH 03246
Tel: (603) 293-1177
Fax: (603) 293-2300
Deckmate floor tiles and dock bumpers

Racks

Coastal Marine Storage, Inc.
P.O. Box 220
High Bridge, NJ 08829
Tel: (908) 725-5553
Fax: (908) 725-5183

Goodhue Marine, Inc.
190 Central St.
Leominster, MA 01453
Tel: (508) 537-0058
Fax: (508) 537-9253
Boat racks

Figure 2: Note the clean styling of a marina pier from Floating Docks Mfg. Co.

Electrical Equipment

Boats, whether they are sail or power, are becoming increasingly dependent upon their electrical and electronic equipment, and the electrical distribution system is essential to these. The electrical distribution system needs to be watertight, fully grounded, and must operate efficiently in an environment that is notoriously inhospitable to electrical gear.

Most small boat electrical systems operate at 12 or 24 volts, while systems on larger vessels run at 110 or 220 volts. With 12 or 24 volt systems, power is supplied by batteries which need periodic recharging, while 110 or 220 volt systems have power supplied by generators or a shore supply system. No matter what voltage is used, both systems have common features. The power is routed to an electrical panel containing circuit breakers. From there, it is distributed to individual circuits by wiring. Each circuit is usually wired to have lights, sockets, motors, or electronics on it, and to minimize interruptions or static between circuits.

PANELS

Electrical panels should be large enough to include the required number of breakers. They should also have indicator lights to show whether there is a short or ground in any circuit. Ideally, the panel should show the battery charging rate, the voltage, the amperage being consumed, and the rate of discharge of the battery. The latest panels have battery and circuit monitors that show the owner the state of the system at any time.

BREAKERS

Ideally, a 12 volt sytem on yachts should have double-pole breakers so that every circuit is completely isolated when the breaker is turned off. That way, there is no possiblity of stray currents causing corrosion. But the ideal world doesn't co-exist very well with economic reality. Most electrical circuits on boats use a single-pole breaker on the positive side and a separate insulated return line on the negative side. This means that should the return wire become damaged, a stray current path could be set up, leading to corrosion.

A 110 or 220 volt circuit should definitely have double-pole breakers throughout the system. In the American wiring system, 220 volts has two live wires (red and black) and a single neutral wire (white), as well as a ground line (green). In Britain, 240 volt circuitry uses three wires: a hot line (black), a neutral (white), and an earth or ground line (green).

The AC system on any boat should be fully floating — that is, totally ungrounded unless a fault develops, at which time the green wire should conduct any stray current to ground. With this system, the breakers should be double-pole rather than single pole. This eliminates the possibility that return currents can exist in a circuit. Because of cost, the usual procedure is to install a double-pole breaker at the main (incoming) breaker panel and single-pole breakers on branch lines.

A breaker that will tell you instantly if the circuit has developed a ground is the ground fault interupter breaker. This type of breaker will flip off if a fault develops in the circuit and stray current passes to ground. However, humidity and dampness can cause these breakers to kick off when no short is present. Consequently, their use is restricted.

WIRING

The most important requirement for electrical wiring is that the wiring be of adequate diameter. Too small a diameter wire creates a high resistance, which leads to high voltage drop along the length of the wire. With wiring that is too small, at the end of a long run (for example up the mast of a sailboat), the voltage could be several volts lower than it is at the battery. This will make lights dimmer and motors run more slowly or not at all.

Electrical wiring should be color-coded as recommended by the American Boat and Yacht Council. This makes it easy for another electrician to follow the original work. Note also, that there are different color codes for DC and AC wiring. For this reason, the ABYC is about to recommend that AC and DC breaker panels should be separated. The ABYC is also working on standards for the amount of moisture in wiring. The dryer the wiring is, the better its insulation qualities are.

TERMINALS

All marine wiring should end in terminals, rather than a soldered or bent connection. The reason for this is that boat vibration can cause soldered wiring to break at the point where the solder ends. Terminals should be crimped onto the wire to ensure a good solid contact. Loose or sloppy contacts can cause a hot spot which, in turn, causes high resistance and a voltage drop in low power systems.

GROUNDING

There should be no breakers in the ground wiring. The idea of ground wiring is to ensure that any faults that develop in the electrical system are conducted safely to ground, rather than passing through a person and then to ground. A boat's main grounding point is usually the engine block. From there, heavy strapping or (usually) 8 gauge wire is run to all other heavy-duty electrical items. All electrical panel cases and cases enclosing any electrical equipment should also be grounded.

CATHODIC PROTECTION

If a bronze propeller and cast iron keel are immersed in seawater, very little corrosion is likely to take place unless they are connected to each other. Suppose we now put

Table 1: The Galvanic Series of Metals in Seawater

Anodic or least noble (most active)

Metal or alloy	Corrosion potential (in Volts)
Zinc	0.9
Alu	0.7
Mild steel	0.6 to 0.75
Cast iron	0.6 to 0.73
Type 316 stainless steel	0.35 to 0.65
Brass	0.3 to 0.4
Tin	0.3 to 0.35
Copper	0.3 to 0.37
Type 410 st. steel (passive)	0.25 to 0.35
Titanium	0.04 to +0.05

Cathodic or most noble (most passive)

a grounding strap between the engine block, which is connected to the prop via the transmission and shaft, and the keel. Because cast iron has a voltage potential of about 0.6 of a volt and bronze has a potential of about 0.24 of a volt, a current is likely to flow. (As long as the voltage potential is over 0.25 of a volt, corrosion is almost certain.) Because the keel has the higher voltage potential, electrons will flow from it to the prop through seawater. Eventually, the keel will corrode. This cannot be stopped as long as both the cast iron keel and the bronze prop are connected and immersed in seawater. It can be controlled, however, by installing a sacrificial block of more corrodable material. On boats, this is usually zinc, which has a voltage potential of almost 1 volt. The flow of electrons from the zinc to the propeller will eventually corrode the zinc. The corrosion rate will depend upon the voltage potential, the rate of flow of water past the hull, and the frequency with which the boat is operated. Faster water flow and greater frequency of use accelerate corrosion.

Zincs usually need to be replaced every year. If you should find that yours is wasting even more quickly, you should check to see if you have an electrical problem. A stray current will corrode the zinc very rapidly since the voltage difference between the stray current and the zinc may be in the 10 or 11 volt range.

Suppliers of Electrical Equipment

Anodes

Electro-Guard
2121 Lincoln Blvd.
Venice, CA 90291
Tel: (310) 821-4158

Essex Machine Works
50 West Ave.
P.O. Box 39
Essex, CT 06426-0039
Tel: (203) 767-8285

Martec Engineering
2257 Gaylord St.
Long Beach, CA 90813
Tel: (310) 435-4494
Fax: (310) 435-7846

Lenco Marine Products
121-26 Dupont St.
Plainview, NY 11803
Tel: (516) 752-3800
Fax: (516) 349-7179

Thermal Reduction Co.
Zincast Products Division
1 Pavilion Ave.
Riverside, NJ 08075
Tel: (609) 461-1400
Fax: (609) 764-8206

Vetus - Den Ouden, Inc.
P.O. Box 8712
Baltimore, MD 21240-0712
Tel: Orders (800) GO-VETUS
  or (410) 712-0740
Fax: (410) 712-0985

Wilcox Crittenden
699 Middle St.
Middletown, CT 06457
Tel: (203) 632-2600

Yacht Corrosion Consultants
2970 Seaborg Ave.
Ventura, CA 93003
Tel: (805) 644-1886
Fax: (805) 644-1895

Z Guard Zinc Anodes
Redlands
Worthing Rd.
Southwater, W. Sussex
RH13 7HE
ENGLAND
Tel: (+44) 403 730032

Electrical Instruments

Charles Industries
5600 Apollo Dr.
Rolling Meadows, IL 60008
Tel: (708) 806-6300
Fax: (708) 806-6231

Faria Corp.
Box 983
Uncasville, CT 06382
Tel: (203) 848-9271
Fax: (203) 848 2704

John Fluke Mfg.
P.O. Box 9090
Everett, WA 98206
Tel: (800) 443-5853

Marine Technologies
1000 Brown St.
Suite 109
Wauconda, IL 60084
Tel: (704) 487-4940
Fax: (704) 487-4952
CO2 detectors

Marinetics
P.O. Box 2676
Newport Beach, CA 92663
Tel: (800) 854-4601
  or (714) 646-8889
Fax: (714) 642-8627
Alarm systems

Solmate Solar Products
11648 Manor Rd.
Glen Arm, MD 21057
Tel: (410) 661-9880

Telcor Instruments
17785 Sky Park Circle
Irvine, CA 92714
Tel: (714) 250-1016
Fax: (714) 250-1014

VDO-Yazaki Instrument Corp.
P.O. Box 2897
980 Brooke Rd.
WincheSuiter, VA 22601
Tel: (703) 665-0100
Fax: (703) 662-2515

Vetus Den Ouden, Inc.
P.O. Box 8712
Baltimore, MD 21240-0712
Tel: (410) 712-0740
Fax: (410) 712-0985
Engine instrument panels, barometers, and weather instruments

Velonex
560 Robert Ave.
Santa Clara, CA 95050
Tel: (408) 727-7370
Fax: (408) 727-0389
Digital panel meters

Ground Fault Interupters and Circuit Breakers

Airpax
807 Woods Rd.
Cambridge, MD 21613
Tel: (410) 228-4600
Fax: (410) 228-8910

Ancor Marine
501 Aaron St.
Cotati, CA 94931
Tel: (707) 792-0312
Fax: (707) 795-7950

Bass Products
50 Grove St.
Salem, MA 01970
Tel: (508) 744-7003
Fax: (508) 744-4844

Carlingswitch
60 Johnson Ave.
Plainville, CT 06062
Tel: (203) 793-9281
Fax: (203) 793-9231

E-T-A Circuit Breakers Group
7400 N. Croname St.
Chicago, IL 60648
Tel: (708) 647-8303
Fax: (708) 647-7494

Eaton Division, Heinemann Products
P.O. Box 6800
Lawrenceville, NJ 08648-0800
Tel: (609) 882-4800
Fax: (609) 896-1631

Professional Mariner
2970 Seaborg
Ventura, CA 93003
Tel: (805) 644-1886
Fax: (805) 644-1895

Sure Power Industries
10189 S.W. Avery
Tualatin, OR 97062
Tel: (503) 692-5360
Fax: (503) 692-9091

Ground Plates and Lightning Protection

Layton Industries
171 Beale St.
Quincy, MA 02170
Tel: (617) 328-9690
Fax: (617) 479-6945

Lightning Electronics
Box 1207
Cabot, AK 72023
Tel: (501) 843-6561
Fax: (501) 843-8996

Panels

ABI Industries, Inc.
1261 Anderson Dr.
Suite C
San Rafael, CA 94901
Tel: (415) 258-9300
Fax: (415) 258-9461

Ample Power Co.
1150 N.W. 52nd St.
Seattle, WA 98107
Tel: (206) 789-5758
Fax: (206) 789-9003

Aqua Signal
1680 E. Fabyan Pkwy.
Batavia, IL 60510
Tel: (312) 232-6425
Fax: (312) 232-9481

Bass Products, Inc.
50 Grove St.
Salem, MA 01970-2245
Tel: (508) 744-7003
Fax: (508) 744-4844

GEM Products, Inc.
140 Industrial Loop
Orange Park, FL 32073
Tel: (800) 874-4506
  or (904) 264-5905
Fax: (904) 264-0173

Hendricks Electric
Fisherman's Terminal C-10
Seattle, WA 98119
Tel: (800) 426-4888
Fax: (206) 285-1736

Marinetics
P.O. Box 2676
Newport Beach, CA 92663
Tel: (800) 854-4601
  or (714) 646-8889
Fax: (714) 642-8627

Michigan Wiring
2638 Bond St.
Rochester Hills, MI 48309
Tel: (800) 624-6300
  or (313) 853-5040
Fax: (313) 853-3189

Newmar
P.O. Box 1306
Newport Beach, CA 92663
Tel: (800) 854-3906
  or (714) 751-0488
Fax: (714) 957-1621

Paneltronics
11960 N.W. 87th Ct.
Hialeah Gardens, FL 33016
Tel: (305) 823-9777
Fax: (800) 833-7802

C. Plath
222 Severn Ave.
Annapolis, MD 21403-2569
Tel: (410) 263-6700
Fax: (410) 268-8713

Shore Power Cabling and Supplies

Bass Products
50 Grove St.
Salem, MA 01970
Tel: (508) 744-7003
Fax: (508) 744-4844

Charles Industries
5600 Apollo Dr.
Rolling Meadows, IL 60008
Tel: (708) 806-6300
Fax: (708) 806-6231
Power cables and adapters

Hubbell
P.O. Box 3999
Bridgeport, CT 06605
Tel: (203) 337-3100
Fax: (203) 579-2892

Kohler
Highland Dr.
Kohler, WI 53044
Tel: (414) 457-4441
Fax: (414) 457-1271

La Marche
106 Bradrock Dr.
Des Plaines, IL 60018
Tel: (708) 299-1188
Fax: (708) 299-3061
Isolation transformers

Marinco
1 Digital Dr.
Novato, CA 94949
Tel: (415) 883-3347

Omnifac
1700 E. Whipp Rd.
Dayton, OH 45440
Tel: (513) 434-8400

Techflex
50 Station Rd.
P.O. Box 119
Sparta, NJ 07871
Tel: (800) 323-5140
Fax: (201) 729-9320
Expandable sleeving for power cords

United Yachting
2190 South Hill Rd.
Milford, MI 48381
Tel: (313) 423-5879
Shore power cable reel

Voltage Regulators

Ample Power Co.
1150 N.W. 52nd St.
Seattle, WA 98107
Tel: (206) 789-5758
Fax: (206) 789-9003

Balmar
1537 N.W. Ballard Way
Seattle, WA 98107
Tel: (206) 789-4970
Fax: (206) 784-0878

CDM Systems
P.O. Box 528
New London, CT 06320
Tel: (203) 447-1024

Cruising Equipment Co.
6315 Seaview Ave. N. W.
Seattle, WA 98107
Tel: (206) 782-8100
Fax: (206) 7823-4336

IM/Vigil
P.O. Box 308
New Whitfield St.
Guilford, CT 06437
Tel: (203) 458-6200
Fax: (203) 453-5669

Wiring and Accessories

Ancor Marine
501 Aaron Dr.
Cotati, CA 94931
Tel: (707) 792-0312
Fax: (707) 795-7950
Wire, terminals, cables, and clamps

Aqua Signal Corp.
1680 East Fabyan Pky.
Batavia, IL 60510
Tel: (708) 232-6425
Fax: (708) 232-9481

Aqua Signal Aktiengesellschatt
P.O. Box 450161
D-2800 Bremen 45
GERMANY
Tel: (+49) 421 4893-0
Fax: (+49) 421 4893210

Baron Wire & Cable
8111 N. St. Louis
Skokie, IL 60076
Tel: (708) 677-5000
Fax: (708) 677-7639

BSP
515 Palmetto Dr.
Simpsonville, SC 29681
Tel: (800) 336-8989
Fax: (803) 963-5352
Wire terminals

Cole Hersee
20 Old Colony Ave.
South Boston, MA 02127
Tel: (617) 268-2100
Fax: (617) 268-9490

Dearborn Wire & Cable L.P.
250 West Carpenter Ave.
Wheeling, IL 60090-6097
Tel: (708) 459-1000
Fax: (708) 459-1008
Marine wire and cable

East Penn Mfg. Co.
Deka Rd.
Lyon Station, PA 19536
Tel: (215) 682-6361
Fax: (215) 682-4781

Electralink Division
National Standard Parts
Associates, Inc.
3825 Navy Blvd.
Pensacola, FL 32507
Tel: (800) 874-6813
  or (904) 456-5771
Fax: (904) 456-5376
Wiring terminals

Hellamarine
Hella, Inc.
201 Kelly Dr.
P.O. Box 2665
Peachtree City, GA 30269
Tel: (404) 631-7500
Fax: (404) 631-7575
Wiring and lighting

Hubbell, Inc.
1613 State St.
Bridgeport, CT 06605
Tel: (203) 579-3100
Fax: (203) 579-2892
Shore supply wiring and terminals

ITT Jabsco
1485 Dale Way
Costa Mesa, CA 92626
Tel: (714) 545-8251
Fax: (714) 957-0609

Klein Tools, Inc.
7200 McCormick Blvd.
P.O. Box 599033
Chicago, IL 60659-9033
Tel: (708) 677-9500
Fax: (708) 677-4476
Wiring tools

Michigan Wiring
2638 Bond St.
Rochester Hills, MI 48309
Tel: (800) 624-6300
Fax: (313) 853-3189

Nartron Corp.
5000 N. U.S. 131
Reed City, MI 49677
Tel: (616) 832-5525

Newmar
P.O. Box 1306
Newport Beach, CA 92663
Tel: (714) 751-0488
Fax: (714) 957-1621

Pass & Seymour
50 Boyd Ave.
Syracuse, NY 13221
Tel: (315) 468-6211
Fax: (315) 468-6296
Wiring terminals, boxes, and other devices

Perko
P.O. Box 64000D
Miami, FL 33164
Tel: (305) 621-7525

S & J Products
1770 W. Berteau Ave.
Chicago, IL 60690
Tel: (800) 255-9837
  or (312) 549-7983
Fax: (312) 871-4070
Terminals, strippers, wire, and cable

Shipyard Supply Co.
85 Water St.
South Norwalk, CT 06426
Tel: (800) 442-2111
  or (800) BOAT-WIRE
Full line of electrical wiring and connectors

Simpson-Lawrence
P.O. Box 11210
Bradenton, FL 34282-1210
Tel: (813) 746-7161
Fax: (813) 746-7166
Waterproof connectors

C. Plath
222 Severn Ave.
Annapolis, MD 21403-2569
Tel: (301) 263-6700
Fax: (410) 268-8713

Wilcox-Crittenden
699 Middle St.
Middletown, CT 06457
Tel: (203) 632-2600
Fax: (203) 632-2636

Emergency Equipment

Coast Guard regulations say that you should have a lifejacket (or Personal Flotation Device in Coast Guardese) for every member of the crew. But that isn't all you should have. Depending on where you intend to sail, you'll also need harnesses, a liferaft, a man-overboard-pole with a dye marker and drogue, flares, a mirror, an EPIRB, and possibly an Argos transmitter. Your boat will need to be fitted with lifelines around the deck, and jacklines for attaching harnesses to. It will also need a place to stow the liferaft that allows the liferaft to be heaved over the side quickly.

LIFEJACKETS

According to the Coast Guard, there has to be a type I, II, III, or IV PFD for everyone on board a recreational boat. If the boat is less than 16 feet overall, that's all you need. If it is over 16 feet, you must have a type I, II, or III for each person and one type IV. A type I PFD is designed to turn an unconcious person face up and must have more than 22 pounds of buoyancy. This type of lifejacket is best for adults in open, rough water. A type II PFD serves the same functions as a type I, but it only has 15.5 pounds of buoyancy. A type II is best for calm inland waters, or where rescue units are nearby. A type III PFD is designed to keep a concious person vertical or slightly backwards in the water. It is best for calm inland waters. A type IV PFD is a ring or cushion that can be thrown to a person in the water to keep that person afloat long enough for the boat to turn around. It must have at least 16.5 pounds of buoyancy. All lifejackets (PFD types I, II, and III) should have a whistle and a small strobe light attached.

LIFERINGS AND HORSESHOES

Coast Guard regulations call for at least one throwable device on every powerboat or sailboat over 16 feet. This may be a lifering, a seat cushion, or a horseshoe. The Offshore Racing Council (ORC), the organization that sets standards for offshore yacht racing, suggests that each boat carry a lifering or horseshoe equipped with a waterproof light and a drogue. When I fell over the side, I found that the wind blew the horseshoe lifering away from me faster than I could swim. Now I would strongly recommend that every boat, whether it is sail or power, have a drogue and a light attached to its lifering. The drogue, or sea anchor, will slow the lifering down enough to enable a person in the water to reach it. For racing yachts that sail offshore, away from sheltered waters, the ORC recommends that a man-overboard-pole is attached to the lifering, together with a dye marker, a drogue, and a self-igniting strobe light.

LIFERAFTS

While the Coast Guard doesn't specifically recommend liferafts, the ORC do. The ORC regulations are based on years of experience setting regulations for sailboat races that vary from an afternoon sail down Long Island Sound to a three week transatlantic race. Given this experience, the ORC recommendations are well worth taking note of. They suggest that any boat which sails out of sight of land carry a liferaft or liferafts capable of carrying the entire crew. The liferaft should be self-inflating, have two buoyancy compartments, a canopy to cover the occupants, a valid annual certificate, and a package of equipment attached to it. This package should contain a sea achor or drogue, a means of inflating the liferaft, a signaling light, three hand flares, a baler, a repair kit, two paddles, and a knife. Usually, this kit is packed in the raft by the manufacturer.

For long distance cruisers, the regulations for the BOC around-the-world race should be taken note of. These regulations recommend keeping a grab bag near the liferaft. This grab bag should contain the following items: clothing for warmth and protection, a waterproof flashlight, two white, two red, and two orange smoke flares, two dye markers, filled unbreakable water bottles, emergency food rations and vitamin tablets, sunscreen lotion, fishing tackle, and a knife. To that, you might want to add a portable still to make water.

HARNESSES

Every offshore sailboat should have a harness or safety belt for every member of the crew. The boat should also have an adequate number of strong points to attach the harnesses to. In the helm station, there should be at least two strong points so that a change of helmsmen can be made without unhooking anyone.

VISUAL DISTRESS GEAR

Aboard each boat there should a bag of flares, a dye marker, and a lamp or flashlight that can be used as a signaling light. Do not use road flares on your boat. They produce hot slag as they burn, which could set the boat on fire. Use special flares that meet the SOLAS (International Convention for the Safety of Life at Sea) specifications, and are designed for use aboard boats. Check the expiration date at the end of every season. Get rid of flares past their expiration date and buy new ones. Your life may depend on it.

According to the Offshore Racing Council, sailboats that stay close to shore (category 4) should carry a minimum of four red hand flares and four white hand flares. If you sail offshore across open oceans (category 1), you should carry twelve white parachute flares, four red hand flares, four white hand flares, and two orange smoke signals. For non-racing sailors, these numbers give you an idea of what to carry. Keep all flares in a watertight container near the companionway.

The dye marker is usually attached by a short length of line to the horseshoe life-ring or man-overboard-pole. When it is immersed in water, a yellow dye will mark an area of about 30 square feet.

FIRE EXTINGUISHERS

Every boat that has an engine should carry at least one fire extinguisher. The Coast Guard says that all open boats under 26 feet must carry one B-I USCG-approved fire extinguisher. Boats from 26 to 65 feet must carry two B-I USCG-approved extinguishers, and boats over 65 feet must meet federal requirements. A B-I extinguisher carries at least 1.25 gallons of foam, 2 pounds of dry chemical, 2.5 pounds of Halon, or 4 pounds of CO_2. Chemical extinguishers are best on fuel or grease fires, while CO_2 extinguishers are best on fires fueled by wood or other solid materials and contained in an enclosed space. Halon extinguishers are best when used in an enclosed space such as the engine compartment. Extinguishers should be checked frequently to ensure they stay fully charged. If yours discharges, get it refilled promptly. You never know when a fire will strike.

Ideally, there should be an extinguisher near (but not actually in) the engine compartment and the galley. If the extinguishers are stored in the engine compartment or the galley, there is a good chance that you may not be able to reach them should fire break out.

THROUGH-HULL FITTINGS

The Offshore Racing Council recommends that wooden bungs of appropriate size be tied to every through-hull fitting. Should the fitting break, the bung can be hammered into the hole to slow the incoming water.

RADAR REFLECTORS

In an ideal world, every boat would have some form of efficient radar reflector secured at least 12 feet above the waterline. Unfortunately, few reflectors are highly efficient, and locating them high up on a powerboat is often difficult. After extensive reading about the value of radar reflectors, I believe that they give the average sailor a false sense of security. Few large ships can easily isolate the return from a single reflector from the background clutter. A radar detector may be a safer bet in that it gives you time to avoid a large ship before that ship has spotted your radar return.

ELECTRONICS

Every boat that goes offshore should carry an EPIRB. This beacon operates on 406 Mhz and the battery expiration date must be valid. Remember, too, that EPIRBs must be registered with NOAA. If you do not sail far offshore, a VHF radio is useful to call for help on channel 16. You can also use other channels to talk to other vessels and to shore. Try not to clutter up channel 16 with your conversation. It is supposed to be an emergency channel only and is listened to by the Coast Guard.

MEDICAL KIT

Most boats should carry a first aid kit and have somebody aboard who knows how to use it. Several companies supply complete kits packed and ready for offshore sailing. At a minimum, the kit should include Bandaids, sunscreen, bandages, cotton or swabs, wound cleaning lotion, rubber gloves, gauze, and antibiotics. You should consult a medical practitioner for information on the type of kit that best suits your application.

TOOLS

Should your engine break down, you should have adequate tools and spare parts aboard to fix the problem. For instance, a kit of spare belts, a spare injector or spark plugs, a spare water pump impeller, and other items as recommended by the manufacturer should always be kept aboard. Many manufacturers give courses in engine maintenance and repair. Which are worth the time and effort for the person who spends a lot of time at sea.

If you are on a sailboat that loses its mast, you should have a pair of bolt cutters, a hacksaw, and several spare hacksaw blades aboard.

ADDITIONAL ITEMS

If your boat has large windows and you expect to stay out at sea for any length of time, you should make storm boards that can cover the largest windows. (Any window over 1 foot square should have a storm board.) A storm board can be made of 1/2 inch (12mm) plywood and should be capable of being screwed over the window in bad weather.

You should carry spare batteries for all flashlights and even a spare flashlight or two. Usually these can be kept in a drawer near the flashlight stowage.

Emergency steering gear is another important item that should be on your emergency list. Ideally, there should be some way that your steering system can be hooked up to get you home should the cables or quadrant break. This might be an emergency tiller that fits on top of the rudder stock or some other device. Make sure that you try it out before you leave the dock and can install it in a seaway.

Sailboats should carry a storm jib and a storm trisail. I no longer believe that on the modern fin and skeg style sailboat you should try to hove-to in a storm. Instead, you should try to sail away from the storm, keeping the wind on the quarter. In this case, you are more likely to use the storm jib and no mainsail or storm trisail. If you are going too fast, stream an anchor rode or docklines to slow the boat down if you do not have a drogue onboard.

A spare set of navigation lights will come in handy if the main lights fail at night. These should be battery-powered and reasonably watertight. You should also have an all-round portable white light to use as an anchor light. If you are caught out in fog, you should have a foghorn and a bell onboard. Coast Guard regulations call for vessels under 26 feet in length to have a portable or mouth-powered horn; boats over that length should have a mechanically-powered horn.

Manufacturers of Emergency Equipment

Distress Signals

American Cyanamid
One Cyanamid Plaza
Wayne, NJ 07470
Tel: (201) 831-2000
Fax: (201) 831-3364
SOS Litesticks

Apache Aerospace
P.O. Box 5763
Bellingham, WA 98227
Tel: (206) 734-8835
Fax: (206) 734-0438
Marine distress signals

Bristol Flare Corp.
P.O. Box 540
Bristol, PA 19007
Tel: (215) 788-3001

Datrex
P.O. Box 1150
Kinder, LA 70648
Tel: (800) 828-1131
Fax: (318) 738-5675
Marine distress signals

Ivec
120A Rose Ct.
York, PA 17402
Tel: (717) 764-3658
Fax: (717) 764-3754

Jim Buoy
A Division of Cal-June, Inc.
P.O. Box 9551
North Hollywood, CA
91609-1551
Tel: (310) 761-3516
Water lights, man-over-board poles

Kilgore Corp.
Rt. 138
Kilgor Drive
Toone, TN 38381
Tel: (901) 658-5231
Fax: (901) 658-4173
  or (901) 658-4533
Marine distress signals

Liferaft & Survival Equipment, Inc.
One Maritime Dr.
Portsmouth, RI 02871
Tel: (401) 683-0307
Fax: (401) 683-2875
Marine signal kits, EPIRBs, and life-rings

Pains-Wessex Ltd.
Marine Dept. High Post
Salisbury, Wiltshire SP4 6AS
ENGLAND
Tel: (+44) 722 411611
Fax: (+44) 722 412121
Pains-Wessex Schermuly flares

Revere Survival Products
603-607 West 29th St.
New York, NY 10001
Tel: (212) 736-5400
Fax: (212) 629-8039
Flare kits

Skyblazer, Inc.
1700 Via Burton
Anaheim, CA 92806
Tel: (714) 956-3881
Fax: (714) 956-4421
Marine distress signals

Standard Fusee/Olin Marine
P.O Box 107
Peru, IN 46970
Tel: (800) 851-5260
Fax: (317) 473-3254
Marine distress signals

Emergency Gear

General Sportcraft
1040 Woodbine St.
Berrgenfield, NJ 07621
Tel: (201) 384-4242
Fax: (201) 387-8128
Man-over-board whistles

**Hathaway, Reiser &
Raymond**
184 Selleck Street
Stamford, CT 06902
Tel: (203) 324-9581
*Storm survival system and
Galerider sea anchor*

Heatpak Industries, Inc.
409 Harding Industrial Dr.
Nashville, TN 37211
Tel: (615) 831-0234
Fax: (615) 831-0218
*Lifepak emergency kit (a first
aid and hypothermia pack)*

**Liferaft & Survival
Equipment, Inc.**
One Maritime Dr.
Portsmouth, RI 02871
Tel: (800) 451-2127
  or (401) 683-0307
Fax: (401) 683-2875
*Marine signal kits, and
liferings*

Neptune Research
2611 Old Okeechobee Rd.
Suite 3
W. Palm Beach, FL 33409
Tel: (407) 683-6992
Fax: (407) 683-8366

Offshore Survival Products
Box 190
Hawthorne, FL 32640
Tel: (800) 707-8823
Offshore survival tube

Port Supply/Lifesling
Port Supply
500 Westridge Dr.
Watsonville, CA 95076
Tel: (408) 761-4270
Fax: (408) 728-3014
*Lifesling and related safety
products*

**PUR, Division of Recovery
Engineering, Inc.**
2229 Edgewood Ave. S.
Minneapolis, MN 55426
Tel: (800) 548-0406
Fax: (612) 541-1313
*PUR Survivor emergency
watermaker for liferafts*

**Quality Marine Products,
Inc.**
4880 Church Ln.
Galesville, MD 20765
Tel: (301) 867-1462
Fax: (301) 867-7139
*Emergency lights and safety
gear*

**School of Survival
Specialities, Inc.**
N. 3808 Sullivan Bldg.
Spokane, WA 99216
Tel: (509) 927-7006
Fax: (509) 928-2832
Signal mirrors

Sporting Lives, Inc.
P.O. Box 518
Meridian, ID 83642
Tel: (208) 888-4184
*Sospenders, harness, and
lifevest*

Survival Cards
P.O. Box 1805
Bloomington, IN 47402
Tel: (812) 336-8206

Survival Products, Inc.
5614 S.W. 25 St.
Hollywood, FL 33023
Tel: (305) 966-7329
Fax: (305) 966-7329

**Survival Technologies
Group**
6418 U.S. Highway 41 N.
Suite 266
Apollo Beach, FL 33572
Tel: (800) 525-2747
Fax: (813) 641-1110
*Makers of MOM8
man-over-board module and
Techvest (an inflatable lifevest)*

Switlik Parachute
P.O. Box 1328
Trenton, NJ 08607
Tel: (609) 587-3300
Fax: (609) 586-6647

EPIRBS (Emergency
Position Indicating Radio
Beacon)

Alden Electronics
40 Washington St.
Westborough, MA 01581-0500
Tel: (508) 366-8851
Fax: (508) 898-2427
Satfind EPIRBs

Cal-June, Inc.
P.O. Box 9551
North Hollywood, CA
91609-1551
Tel: (818) 761-3516
Fax: (818) 761-3165

Emergency Beacon
15 River St.
New Rochelle, NY 10801
Tel: (914) 235-9400
Fax: (914) 576-7075

Dayton-Granger, Inc.
3299 S.W. Ninth Ave.
Ft. Lauderdale, FL 33315
Tel: (305) 463-3451
Fax: (305) 761-3172

Litton Special Devices
750 West Sproul Rd.
Springfield, PA 19064-4084
Tel: (800) 328-0948
  or   (215) 328-4000
Fax: (215) 328-4016

Lokata America
950 Roosevelt Blvd.
Tarpon Springs, FL 34689
Tel: (813) 942-3299

Fire Extinguishers and Extinguishing Systems

American La France
P.O. Box 6159
Charlottesville, VA 22906
Tel: (804) 973-4361
Fax: (804) 973-1589

Ansul Fire Protection
One Stanton St.
Marinette, WI 54143
Tel: (715) 735-7411
Fax: (715) 732-3479,

Fireboy/Xintex
P.O. Box 152
Grand Rapids, MI 49502-0152
Tel: (616) 454-8337
Tlx:(616)4548256

Walter Kidde
1394 S. Third St.
Mebane, NC 27302-9199,
Tel: (919) 563-5911
Fax: (919) 563-3954

Porta-Matic Fire Extinguishing
P.O. Box 353
156 Railroad Ave.
Closter, NJ 07624
Tel: (201) 768-8196

Paul R. Salomon
5000 S. Grand River
Detroit, MI 48208
Tel: (313) 894-2323

Harnesses

Cruising Gear
2751 S.W. 27th Ave.
Miami, FL 33133
Tel: (305) 854-7600
Fax: (305) 854-5984

Genco Sails
544 King St. W.
Toronto, Ontario M5V lM3
CANADA
Tel: (416) 364-2891
Fax: (416) 364-6635

Helly Hansen (US), Inc.
17275 N.E. 67th Ct.
Redmond, WA 98078-9731
Tel: (800) 435-5901
Fax: (206) 885-3882

Holland Yacht Equipment
P.O. Box 452
San Carlos, CA 94070
Tel: (415) 595-2009
Fax: (415) 592-6627

Indiana Mills & Mfg.
18881 US 31 N.
Westfield, IN 46074
Tel: (317) 896-9531
Fax: (317) 896-2142

Lirakis Harness
18 Sheffield Ave.
Newport, RI 02840
Tel: (800) USA-SFTY
Fax: (401) 846-5359

Figure 1: Use a Lirakis harness for offshore safety.

MRC (Mariner Resource)
86 Orchard Beach Blvd.
Port Washington, NY 11050
Tel: (800) 645-6516
Fax: (516) 767-7835

Musto, Inc.
333 West 76th St.
New York, NY 10023
Tel: (212) 580-3653
Fax: (212) 799-3395

Raudaschl Sails Canada
3140 Lakeshore Blvd. W.
Toronto, Ontario M8V lL4
CANADA
Tel: (416) 255-3431
Fax: (416) 259-9136
Harnesses and bosun's chairs

Survival Technologies Group
6418 U.S. Highway 41 N.
Suite 266
Apollo Beach, FL 33572
Tel: (800) 525-2747
Fax: (813) 641-1110

Lifejackets

L. L. Bean
Casco St.
Freeport, ME 04033
Tel: (800) 221-4221

Douglas Gill USA
Div. Weathermark
6087 Holiday Rd.
Buford, GA 30518
Tel: (404) 945-0788

Eastern Aero Marine
3850 N.W. 25th St.
Miami, FL 33142
Tel: (305) 871-4050
Fax: (305) 871-7873

Extrasport
5305 N.W. 35th Ct.
Miami, FL 33142
Tel: (305) 633-2945
Fax: (305) 633-0837
Lifevests

Harishok
R.R. 2, Box 922
Old Grafton Tpk.
Canaan, NH 03741
Tel: (603) 523-7363
Lifejackets

Jim Buoy
A Division of Cal-June, Inc.
P.O. Box 9551
North Hollywood, CA
91609-1551
Tel: (213) 761-3516
*Liferings, PFDs, horseshoes,
floats, and buoys*

Kent Sporting Goods
433 Park Ave.
New London, OH 44851
Tel: (800) 537-2970
Fax: (419) 929-1769
PFDs, lifejackets, and cushions

Mustang META USA Corp.
3870 Mustang Way
Bellingham, WA 98226
Tel: (206) 676-1782
Fax: (206) 676-5014

Northwest River Supplies
P.O. Box 9201
Moscow, ID 83843
Tel: (800) 635-5202
Fax: (208) 883-4787

O'Brien International
14615 N E. 91st St.
Redmond, WA 98052
Tel: (206) 881-5900

Omega Marine Products
1638 Parker Ave.
Fort Lee, NJ 07024
Tel: (800) 966-6342
Fax: (201) 943-9053

Safegard
P.O. Box 2044
Covington, KY 41012
Tel: (606) 431-7650
Fax: (606) 431-1355

Sporting Lives
P.O. Box 518
Meridian, ID 83642
Tel: (208) 888-4184
Fax: (208) 888-4267

Stearns Mfg. Co.
P.O. Box 1498
St. Cloud, MN 56302
Tel: (612) 252-1642
Fax: (612) 252-4425

Stormy Seas, Inc.
P.O. Box 1570
Poulsbo, WA 98370
Tel: (800) 323-7367
  or (206) 779-4439
Fax: (206) 779-8171
*Makers of jackets with
inflatable cells built-in*

**Survival Technologies
Group**
6418 U.S. Highway 41 N.
Suite 266
Apollo Beach, FL 33572
Tel: (800) 525-2747
Fax: (813) 641-1110

Switlik Parachute
P.O. Box 1328
Trenton, NJ 08607
Tel: (609) 587-3300
Fax: (609) 586-6647

**Viking Life-Saving
Equipment (America)**
1625 N. Miami Ave.
Miami, FL 33136
Tel: (305) 374-5115

Wellington Puritan Mills
Monticello Hwy.
Madison, GA 30650
Tel: (800) 221-5054
Fax: (706) 314-0407

West Marine Products
500 West Ridge Dr.
Watsonville, CA 95076-4100
Tel: (408) 728-2700

Liferafts

Autoflug GMBH & Co.
Industriestrasse 10
2084 Rellingen
WEST GERMANY
Tel: 49-4101-300-0
Fax: 49-4101-300-333

SMR Technologies, Inc.
P.O. Box 326
1420 Wolf Creek Trail
Sharon Center, OH 44274
Tel: (216) 239-1000
Fax: (216)239-1352
Crewsaver life rafts

Avon Inflatables/Liferafts
1851 McGaw Ave.
Irvine, CA 92714
Tel: (714) 250-0880
Fax: (714) 250-0740

Cal-June, Inc.
P.O. Box 9551
North Hollywood, CA
91609-1551
Tel: (818) 761-3516
Fax: (818) 761-3165

Chase, Leavitt & Co., Inc.
10 Dana St.
Portland, ME 04112
Tel: (800) 638-8906
  or in ME (800) 244-0675
Viking liferaft sales and service

Datrex, Inc.
P.O. Box 1150
Kinder, LA 70648-1150
Tel: (318) 738-4511
Fax: (318) 738-5675

Dunlop-Beaufort Canada
12351 Bridgeport Rd.
Richmond, British Columbia
V6V 1J4
CANADA
Tel: (604) 278-3221
Fax: (604) 278-7812

Eastern Aero Marine
3850 N.W. 25th St.
Miami, FL 33142
Tel: (305) 871-4050
Fax: (305) 871-7873
Liferafts

Givens Ocean Survival Systems Co., Inc.
1-8 Lagoon Rd.
Tiverton, RI 02871
Tel: (800) 328-8050
  or (401) 683-7400
Water-ballasted liferafts

Imtra
30 Barnet Blvd.
New Bedford, MA 02745
Tel: (508) 990-2700
Fax: (508) 994-4919

Kelvin Hughes
Royal Crescent Rd.
Southampton, Hampshire
SO9 1WB
ENGLAND
Tel: (+44) 703 639411
Fax: (+44) 703 330014

Offshore Repack and Repair
10 Industrial Pk.
P.O. Box 155
Essex, CT 06426
Tel: (800) 243-1176
  or (203) 767-8293

Outfitters USA Services, Inc.
1111 Ingleside Rd.
Norfolk, VA 23502
Tel: (800) 727-BOAT
  or (804) 855-2233
Flares, liferafts, EPIRBs, and PFDs

Pool Inflatables/Marina Safety Equipment Center
Victoria Mill
The Quay
Poole, Dorset BI15 1HA
ENGLAND
Tel: (+44) 202 677777
Fax: (+44) 202 684859

Revere Survival Products
603-607 West 29th St.
New York, NY 10001
Tel: (212) 736-5400
Fax: (212) 629-8039
Liferafts for 2 to 25 persons

Seaco/Elliot
3874 Fiscal Ct.
Rivera Beach, FL 33404
Tel: (407) 842-8900
Fax: (407) 842-0987

SMR Technologies, Inc.
P.O. Box 326
1420 Wolf Creek Trail
Sharon Center, OH
44274-0326
Tel: (216) 239-1000
Fax: (216) 239-1352
Crewsaver liferafts

Switlik Parachute Co., Inc.
P.O. Box 1328
1325 East State St.
Trenton, NJ 08607
Tel: (609) 587-3300
Fax: (609) 586-6647

USA Outfitters Services, Inc.
326 First St.
Annapolis, MD 21403
Tel: (410) 626-1122
Liferaft repacking, sales and service

Viking Life-Saving Equipment (America)
16Z5 N. Miami Ave.
Miami, FL 33136
Tel: (305) 374-5115

Winslow Marine Products
928 S. Tamiani Trail
P.O. Box 888
Osprey, FL 34229
Tel: (813) 966-9791
Fax: (813) 966-6887

Yachting Services
P.O. Box 1045
Pointe Claire, Quebec H9S 4H9
CANADA
Tel: (514) 697-6952
Fax: (514) 695-5912
Liferafts and Tinker inflatables

Zodiac of North America
P.O. Box 400
Thompson Creek Rd.
Stevensville, MD 21666
Tel: (301) 643-4141
Fax: (301) 643-4491

Man-Overboard Alarms

Hewitt Enterprises
510 Ellswarth
Memphis, TN 38111
Tel: (901) 526-4827
Fax: (901) 327-4068

Man-Over-Board Lights

Cal-June, Inc.
P.O. Box 9551
North Hollywood, CA 91609-1551
Tel: (818) 761-3516
Fax: (818) 761-3165

Forespar
22322 Gilberto
R. Santa Margarita, CA 92688
Tel: (714) 858-8820
Fax: (714) 858-0505

Revere Survival Products
603 W. 29th St.
New York, NY 10001
Tel: (212) 736-5400
Fax: (212) 629-8039

Man-Over-Board Poles

Windline Marine
4201 Redwood Ave.
Los Angeles, CA 90066
Tel: (213) 306-8558
Fax: (213) 821-6417

Datrex
P.O. Hox 1150
Kinder, LA 70648
Tel: (800) 828-1131
Fax: (318) 738-5675

Garelick
644 2nd St.
St. Paul, MN 55071
Tel: (612) 459-9795

Genco Sails
544 King St. W.
Toronto, Ontario M5V lM3
CANADA
Tel: (416) 364-2891
Fax: (416) 364-6635

Hinckley Shipstore
Southwest Harbor, ME 04679
Tel: (207) 244-5531

Jamestown Distributors
28 Narragansett Ave.
P.O. Box 348
Jamestown, RI 02835
Tel: (800) 423-0030
or (401) 423-2520
Fax: (401) 423-0542

Jamestown Distributors
Hwy. 17 & 21
Gardens Corner
Rt. 1, Box 375
Seabrook, SC 29940
Tel: (803) 846-9500
Fax: (803) 846-9005

Rotech International Industries, Inc.
115 Saramia Crescent, Unit B
Concord, Ontario L4K 3Z8
CANADA
Tel: (416) 660-9998
Fax: (416) 660-9987

Wellington Puritan Mills
Monticello Hwy.
Madison, GA 30650
Tel: (800) 221-5054

Medical Gear

Essential Emergency Products
5687 Menorca Dr.
San Diego, CA 92124
Tel: (619) 576-8046
First aid kits

Figure 2: Every yacht should carry a first aid kit such as this one from Medical Sea Pak Co.

Survival Foods

Oregon Freeze Dry, Inc.
P.O Box 1048
Albany, OR 97321
Tel: (800) 547-4060
Fax: (503) 967-6527
Freeze-dried foods

Stow-A-Way Industries
P.O. Box 957
E. Greenwich, RI 02818
Tel: (401) 885-6899
Lightweight mail order foods

Survival Suits

Bayley Suit
900 South Fortuna Blvd.
Fortuna, CA 95540
Tel: (707) 725-3391
Fax: (707) 725-6457

Henri-Lloyd
86 Orchard Beach Blvd.
Port Washington, NY 11050
Tel: (800) 645-6516
Fax: (516) 767-7835
SisstemAIR survival suit

Parkway Imperial
241 Raritan St.
South Amboy, NJ 08879
Tel: (908) 721-5300
Fax: (908) 721-4016

Medical Sea Pak Co.
1945 Ridge Rd. E.
Suite 105
Rochester, NY 14622
Tel: (800) 832-6054
  or (716) 266-3136
Fax: (716) 266-3222
First aid kits

Life-Assist, Inc.
11355-B Pyrites Way # 15
Rancho Cordova, CA 95670
Tel: (800) 824-6016
  or (916) 635-3822
Fax: (916) 638-3002
First aid kits and supplies

Coghlan's Ltd.
121 Irene St.
Winnipeg, Manitoba R3T 4C7
CANADA
Tel: (204) 284-9550
Fax: (204) 475-4127
First aid kits

General Scientific Safety Equipment Co.
525 Spring Garden St.
Philadelphia, PA 19123-2899
Tel: (800) 523-0166
Fax: (215) 922-5740

Healer Products
3 Rusciano Blvd.
Pelham Manor, NY 10803
Tel: (914) 738-9300
Fax: (914) 738-9540

Mada Medical
60 Commerce Rd.
Carlstadt, NJ 07072
Tel: (201) 460-0454
Fax: (201) 460-3509
Respiratory products

W. H. Salisbury & Co.
7520 N. Long Ave.
Skokie, IL 60077
Tel: (708) 679-6700
Fax: (708) 679-2401

Survival Technologies Group
6418 U.S. Highway 41 N.
Suite 266
Apollo Beach, FL 33572
Tel: (800) 525-2747
Fax: (813) 641-1110

Engines and Engine Parts

The first decision to be made when choosing an engine is diesel or gasoline. Gasoline engines are lighter, but the fuel can be explosive under the right conditions. Diesel engines are heavier, although some of the latest marine diesels are relatively light. While diesel fuel smells terrible, it is not explosive.

After making a decision on the type of fuel, the next step is to determine engine size. This is a function of the shape of the boat's hull, its displacement, its propulsion system, and the desired speed. The speed at which a displacement craft can travel is directly related to its waterline length and wave-making drag. It is a function of a physical law that cannot be changed. Overpowering such a craft will only result in the stern squatting as the boat tries to climb the bow wave without an increase in speed. It will also burn much more fuel than is necessary. A planing boat, on the other hand, is intended to go fast and can have a larger engine. As the speed increases, the boat rises up onto its bow wave and continues to accelerate until the power available is balanced by the total resistance of the vessel.

Displacement is also important when determining engine size. A lightweight boat planes more readily than a heavy displacement vessel. To some extent, the distribution of this weight is important. Weight high up on the boat makes it less stable, while weight in the bilges tends to increase stability. Weight in the bow may prevent the forward part of the boat from rising up as the craft starts its transition from displacement mode to planing. Weight aft will also make it harder to get up on a plane.

A third factor that plays a part in determining engine size is the boat's wetted surface. A boat with high wetted surface will need a larger engine to overcome the additional low-speed resistance. The curve of the hull's performance is best determined by towing tank testing or by computer simulation. This curve of speed against the hull's resistance can then be matched against the engine's performance curve. For instance, an engine running at 1800 rpm may drive a sport fishing boat at 27 knots, but throttle the engine back to 1400 rpm and speed might drop off dramatically to 15 knots as the power level becomes too low to push the boat onto a plane.

When the hull's performance envelope has been developed, an engine size can be approximated. Then it becomes a matter of checking through manufacturers' catalogs to find an engine of the right size. Remember when looking through engine catalogs, the continuous rating is the number to be concerned with. Maximum rating is only to be used in short-duration emergency situations and may require that the engine be overhauled after it has been used. Some manufacturers divide the continuous rating up even further. For use in a boat making trips of less than an hour, where the engine will be run at high speed over a relatively short period (as on a ferry), the continuous rating is relatively high. In contrast, on a midwater trawler or shallow river barge, where the engine might run for several hours at a relatively high speed and then be throttled back, a medium continuous rating can be used. On offshore tug boats or trawlers, where the engine may run for days at a time without reducing the revs, the rating may be even lower. Most engine manufacturers rate their engines fairly low when the engine is used for a long time at high speed in order to lengthen the time between overhauls.

When selecting an engine, the power-to-weight ratio — that is, the weight of the engine divided by its continuous rated horse power — is one of the simplest and most effective assessment criteria. Suppose you need an engine around 200 hp. The Caterpillar 3208 series is a 210 hp favorite of many builders, but the Cummins 6BT5.9M also rates at 210 hp. The Caterpillar dry weight is 1740 pounds and the

Cummins is 1242 pounds. If we divide 1740 pounds by 210 horsepower, we get 8.296. That is, it weights 8.3 pounds for every 1 horsepower generated. The Cummins wieghs 5.9 pounds for every 1 horsepower generated. Therefore, the Cummins would seem to be a better choice. But you then have to check the power curve of the engine against the resistance curve of your hull to ensure you get the best match.

Note also that the Caterpillar 3208 series can be obtained with various levels of horsepower without a huge increase in weight. For instance, the turbocharged version, which can give up to 290 hp, is only 60 pounds heavier. In this case, the power-to-weight ratio drops to 6.2 lbs/hp, and is much nearer the Cummins.

Of course, other factors, such as ease of maintenance, length of time between overhauls, and reliability may modify your choice of an engine. The size of the engine compartment, the transmission, the prop size and pitch, the familiarity of the operator with a particular engine, and the availability of spare parts can also affect the choice and should be taken into account.

Suppliers of Engines and Engine Parts

Alarms

Altus Technology
11569 Encore Circle
Minnetonka, MN 55343
Tel: (612) 935-6595
Fax: (612) 935-6491
Battery energy gauges

Aqualarm
1151 D Bay Blvd.
Chula Vista, CA 91911
Tel: (619) 575-4011
Fax: (619) 575-4012
Fire, low oil, water cooler, and temperature alarms

Branom Instrument Co.
5500 4th Ave. S.
Seattle, WA 98108
Tel: (206) 762-6050
Fax: (206) 767-5669
Alarms

Floyd Bell, Inc.
897 Higgs Ave.
Columbus, OH 43212
Tel: (614) 294-4000
Fax: (614) 291-0823
Audio alarms

Boat Sentry
271 Rte. 46 W.
Suite A-106
Fairfield, NJ 07006
Tel: (201) 575-5650
Fax: (201) 575-0985
*The Loyal Sentry alarm
control unit*

Brisson Development
13845 Nine Mile Rd.
Warren, MI 48089
Tel: (313) 778-3038
Fax: (313)778-0780
*Boathailers, CO2 and fume
detectors*

Marine Technologies
1000 Brown St.
Suite 109
Wauconda, IL 60084
Tel: (708) 487-4940
Fax: (708) 487-4952
Gas vapor and CO2 detectors

Martrol, Inc.
33 Prince St.
Montreal, Quebec H3C 2M7
CANADA
Tel: (514) 861-6302
Fax: (514) 393-0246
*Water, fuel, oil-level, and
intrusion detectors*

Modern Automation Corp.
1180 Midway Blvd.
Unit 1
Mississauga, Ontario L4Y 3B8
CANADA
Tel: (416) 564-7881
Fax: (416) 564-7891
Fuel and water-level alarms

Nartron Corp.
5000 N. U.S. 131
Reed City, MI 49677
Tel: (616) 832-5525
*Audible alarms, indicator
lights, starter switches, relays,
and blower timer switches*

Sentry Devices
33 Rustic Gate Ln.
Dix Hills, NY 11746
Tel: (516) 491-3191
Fax: (516) 643-5577
Burglar alarms

Controls

IMO Industries, Inc.
Morse Controls Division
21 Clinton St.
Hudson, OH 44236
Tel: (216) 653-7701
Fax: (216) 653-7799
*Engine controls, hydraulic
steering, wheels, and linkages*

Figure 1: Mathers Micro
-Commander controls by
Mathers Controls/MMC

**Mathers Controls/MMC,
Inc.**
675 Pease Rd.
Burlington, WA 98233
Tel: (206) 757-1100
Fax: (206) 757-2500
Mathers MicroCommander

**Rexroth/Pneumatics
Division**
P.O. Box 13597
1953 Mercer Rd.
Lexington, KY 40511
Tel: (606) 254-8031
Fax: (606) 254-4188
*Pneumaticand hydraulic
controls*

Vetus - Den Ouden, Inc.
P.O. Box 8712
Baltimore, MD 21240-0712
Tel: Orders (800) GO-VETUS
   or (410) 712-0740
Fax: (410) 712-0985
*Single and double lever
controls*

Figure 2: A set of controls
from Vetus-Den Ouden, Inc.

Engines

Note: Most engine manufacturers work through a network of dealers. You should inquire about the dealer nearest you.

Alaska Diesel Electric, Inc.
West Coast:
4420 14th Ave. N.W.
Box 70543
Seattle, WA 98107
Tel: (206) 789-3880
Fax: (206) 782-5455
Southeast:
1405 S.W. 6th Ct.
Suite A
Pompano Beach, FL
33069-3505
Tel: (305) 946 7601
Fax: (305) 946 7409
Northeast:
Boston, MA
Tel: (617) 561-2800
Fax: (617) 561-2828
Lugger Northern Light

American Diesel Corp.
Rt. #3 N.
Hillcrest Heights
Kilmamock, VA 22842
Tel: (804) 435-3107
Fax: (804) 435-6420

B.P.M. Motori Marini e Industriali S.R.I.
Via Bosco N. 34
Palazzolo
Verona 37010
ITALY
Tel: (+39) 045 608-0899
Fax: (+39) 045 608-0956
44 to 820 hp marine gas engines

C & G Marine, Inc.
13353 N.E. 17th Ave.
North Miami, FL 33181
Tel: (305) 893-5018
Fax: (305) 891-7218
High-performance engines

Caterpillar, Inc.
Engine Division
P.O. Box 610
Mossville, IL 61552-0610
Tel: (800) 321-7332
Fax: (309) 578-2559

Commander Marine Engines
1125 McCabe Ave.
Elkgrove Village, IL 60007
Tel: (708) 228-9400
Fax: (708) 228-3807

Crusader Engines
7100 E. 15 Mile Rd.
Sterling Heights, MI 48312
Tel: (313) 264-1200
Fax: (313) 264-2344

Cummins Marine
Division of Cummins Engine Co., Inc.
4500 Leeds Ave.
Suite 102
Charleston, SC 29405
Tel: (800) DIESELS
  or (812) 377-5000
Fax: (812) 377-3334

Daytona Marine Engine Corp.
1815 N. US-1
Omond Beach, FL 32174
Tel: (904) 676-1140
Fax: (904) 676-0164

Deere Power Systems
P.O. Box 5100
Waterloo, IA 50704-5100
Tel: (319) 292-6060
Fax: (319) 292-6075

Detroit Diesel Corp.
13400 Outer Dr. W.
Detroit, MI 48239-4001
Tel: (313) 592-5000
Fax: (313) 592-7288

Deutz-MWM
Yacht Engine Division
3131 S.W. 2nd Ave.
Ft. Lauderdale, FL 33315
Tel: (305) 779-7842
Fax: (305) 763-2872

Entec West, Inc.
16710 S.W. 72nd Ave.
Portland, OR 97224
Tel: (800) 458-5069
Fax: (503) 639-2764

Fairbanks-Morse Engine Division
Coltec Industries, Inc.
701 Lawton Ave.
Beloit, WI 53511
Tel: (608) 364-8100

Flagship Marine Engine Co.
200 East Ann St.
Punta Gorda, Fl 33404
Tel: (813) 639-3783
Fax: (813) 575-1285

Ford Motor Co.
19855 West Outer Dr.
Dearborn, MI 48124
Tel: (313) 739-2972
Fax: (313) 730-2905

GE-Alco
2901 E. Lake Rd.
Erie, PA 16531
Tel: (814) 875-5925

Hawker Siddeley/Lister Diesels, Inc.
555 East 56 Hwy.
Olathe, KS 66061
Tel: (913) 764-3512

Hawk Marine Power
3025 N.E. 188th St.
Bldg. B
Aventura, FL 33180
Tel: (305) 932-9230
Fax: (305) 932-9231

Indmar Product Co.
5400 Old Millington Rd.
Millington, TN 38053
Tel: (901) 353-9930
Fax: (901) 358-4292

Isuzu Diesel North America
4039 Robinwood Rd.
York, PA 17402
Tel: (717) 757-6022
Fax: (717) 751-0306

Northeast Isuzu Engines, Inc.
P.O. Box 958
Plattwood Industrial Pk.
Deep River, CT 06417-0958
Tel: (203) 526-5397
Fax: (203) 526-9170

Iveco Aifo S.P.A.
c/o Lister-Petter, Inc.
815 E. 56 Hwy.
Olathe, KS 66061
Tel: (913) 764-3512
Fax: (913)764-5493

KHD Canada/Deutz-MWM
4420 Garand St.
Ville St. Laurent, Quebec
H4R 2A3
CANADA
Tel: (514) 335-3150
Fax: (514) 332-4173

Krupp-Mak Diesel, Inc.
7555 Danbro Cresent
Mississauga, Ontario
L5N 6P9
CANADA
Tel: (416) 542-7810
Fax: (416) 542-7812

Kubota Ltd.
P.O. Box 1124
391 Crossen Ave.
Elk Grove Village, IL 60007
Tel: (312) 437-6675

Lister-Petter, Inc.
815 E. 56 Hwy.
Olathe, KS 66061
Tel: (913) 764-3512
Fax: (913) 764-5493

MAN Marine Engines
6555 N.W. 9th Ave.
Ft. Lauderdale, FL 33309
Tel: (305) 771-9092
Fax: (305) 771-9162

Marine Drive Systems
519 Sunfield Ave.
Raritan Center
Edison, NJ 08837
Tel: (908) 225-3300
Fax: (908) 225-3302

Marine Power, Inc.
1 Marine Power Industrial Pk.
Ponchatoula, LA 70454
Tel: (504) 386-2081
Fax: (504) 386-4010

Mercury Hi-Performance Group
2521 Bowen St.
Oshkosh, WI 54901
Tel: (414) 236-0102
Fax: (414) 236-2535

Mercury Marine
P.O. Box 1939
Fond du Lac, WI 54936-1939
Tel: (414) 929-5410
Fax: (414) 929-5437

Mirrlees-Blackstone (USA), Inc.
2011 Matilda Dr.
Houston, TX 77039
Tel: (713) 449-2253
Fax: (713) 987-1508

Mitsubishi Engine, North America, Inc
610 Supreme Dr.
Bensenville, IL 60106
Tel: (708) 350-9540

Mitsubishi Heavy Industries Ltd.
3000 Tana Sagami Hara-Shi
Kanagana-KEN 229
JAPAN
Tel: (+81) 427 61-1111
Fax: (+81) 427 63-0800

MTU North America
10450 Corporate Dr.
Sugar Land, TX 77478-2825
Tel: (800) 321-2688
  or In Texas: (713) 240-4100

Penninsular Diesel, Inc.
4900 Stecker Ave.
Dearborn, MI 48126
Tel: (313) 584-5800
Fax: (313) 582-3043

Perkins Engines Ltd.
c/o Detroit Diesel Corp.
13400 Outer Dr. W.
Detroit, MI 48239
Tel: (313) 592-5000

**Pleasurecarft Marine
Engine Co.**
Hwy. 76
Little Mountain, SC 29075
Tel: (803) 345-1337
Fax: (803) 345-3309

PRP, Inc.
1017 Spray Ave.
Beachwood, NJ 08722
Tel: (908) 286-6104
Fax: (908) 505-0094

RMP
9040 Burrough Dover Ln.
Pennsauken, NJ 08110
Tel: (609) 662-3811
Fax: (609) 663-1745

Sabre-Lehman Engines
22 Cobman Rd.
Wimborne, Dorset BH21 7AV
ENGLAND
U.S Rep:
Northeast Ford Engines
56 Mitchell Rd.
Ipswich, MA 01938
Tel: (800) 446-1026
   or   (508) 356-2114

Torque Engineering Corp.
52640 Thorne Dr.
Elkhart, IN 46514
Tel: (219) 264-2628
Fax: (219) 264-3600

**Volvo Penta of North
America, Inc.**
1300 Volvo Penta Dr.
Chesapeake, VA 23320
Tel: (804) 436-2800
Fax: (804) 436-5150

Wartsila Diesel
Route 5, Box 116B
709 Morgnec Rd.
Chestertown, MD 21620
Tel: (410) 778-9100
Fax: (410) 778-9107

Wartsila Diesel AB
P.O. Box 920
S-46129, Trollhattan
SWEDEN
Tel: (+46) 520-226 00
Fax: (+46) 520-173 87

Figure 3: The thirty hp 30B
three diesel engine from
Westerbeke.

Westerbeke
Avon Industrial Pk.
Avon, MA 02322
Tel: (508) 588-7700
Fax: (508) 559-9323

Vetus - Den Ouden, Inc.
P.O. Box 8712
Baltimore, MD 21240-0712
Tel: Orders (800) GO-VETUS
   or   (410) 712-0740
Fax: (410) 712-0985

**Yanmar Diesel America
Corp.**
Corporate Grove Dr.
Buffalo Grove, IL 60089
Tel: (708) 541-1900

**Yanmar Diesel Engine Co.
Ltd.**
1-1, 2-chome
Yaesu, Chuo-ku
Tokyo
JAPAN

Exhaust Systems

Apex Equipment, Inc.
4001 21st Ave. W.
Seattle, WA 98199
Tel: (800) 444-3636
   or   (206) 285-3830
Fax: (206) 281-0971
Elastomuffle mufflers

C Breeze Ltd.
P.O. Box 513
Cape May, NJ 08204
Tel: (800) 638-4064
Stainless Steel exhaust flexes

Apex Equipment, Inc.
4001 21st Ave. W.
Seattle, WA 98199
Tel: (206) 283-7380

Barr Marine Products
1505 Ford Rd.
P. O. Box 408
Bensalem, PA 19020
Tel: (215) 639-8941
Fax: (215) 639-9188
System parts

J.A. Chamberlain, Inc.
821 Waterway Pl.
Longwood, FL 32750
Tel: (407) 323-4938
Fax: (407) 323-8926
Exhaust manifolds

De Angelo Marine Exhaust
150 S.W. 33rd St.
Ft. Lauderdale, FL 22215
Tel: (305) 763-3005
Fax: (305) 763-6845
Exhaust systems

Figure 4: High-performance manifolds are available from Gil Marine Corp.

Gil Marine Corp.
97 Corwin Dr.
Box 391
Painesville, OH 44077
Tel: (800) 624-9805
  or (216) 354-6800
Fax: (216) 354-0687
High-performance exhausts

Key Marine, Inc.
4401 E. 11th Ave.
Hialeah, FL 33013
Tel: (305) 688-6546
Fax: (305) 688-6549
Exhaust system parts

Marine Exhaust Systems
3640 D Fiscal Ct.
Riviera Beach, FL 33404
Tel: (407) 848-1238
Fax: (407) 848-1298
Diesel exhaust systems

Marine Exhaust Systems of Alabama
757 Nichols
Fairhope, AL 36532
Tel: (205) 928-1234

Marine Propulsion Equipment Co., Inc.
P.O. Box 1029
Harvey, LA 70059
Tel: (504) 392-6900
Spiral exhaust silencer

Stainless Marine, Inc.
13800 N.W. 19th Ave.
Opa-Locka, FL 33054
Tel: (305) 681-7893
Fax: (305) 685-1457
Exhaust systems

Vetus - Den Ouden, Inc.
P.O. Box 8712
Baltimore, MD 21240-0712
Tel: Orders (800) GO-VETUS
  or (410) 712-0740
Fax: (410) 712-0985
Exhaust systems

Filters

Alfa-Leval Separation
955 Mearns Rd.
Warminster, PA 18974-4895
Tel: (215) 443-4000
Fax: (215) 957-4859
Fuel filters, oil/water separators

Allied Signal
105 Pawtucket Ave.
E. Providence, RI 02916
Tel: (401) 434-7000
Fax: (401) 431-3253
Fuel and air filters

Clark Filter
3649 Hempland Rd.
Lancaster, PA 17601
Tel: (800) 552-5275
Fax: (717) 285-3039
Air, fuel and oil filters

Diesel Research, Inc.
P.O. Box 213
Hampton Bays, NY 11946
Tel: (800) 552-7079
Crank vent, closed-filtered, crankcase ventilation system

Racor Division
P.O. Box 3208
3400 Finch Rd.
Modesto, CA 95353
Tel: (209) 521-7860
Fax: (209) 529-3278
Fuel and oil filters

Stanadyne Automotive Corp.
92 Deerfield Rd.
Windsor, CT 06095
Tel: (203) 525-0821
Modular dry change filter for diesels

Vetus Den Ouden, Inc.
P.O. Box 8712
Baltimore, MD 21240-0712
Tel: (410) 712-0740
Fax: (410) 712-0985

**Walker Engineering
Enterprises**
7405 Hayvenhurst Place
Van Nuys, CA 91406
Tel: (818)782-2154
Fax: (818) 909-7694
AIRSEP filtration device

Inboard/Outboards

Marine Drive Systems
519 Sunfield Ave.
Raritan Center
Edison, NJ 08837
Tel: (908) 225-3300
Fax: (908) 225-3302

Mercruiser
1939 Pioneer Rd.
Fond du Lac, WI 54936
Tel: (414) 929-5000

Outboard Marine Corp.
200 Seahorse Dr.
Waukegan, IL 60085
Tel: (708) 689-6200

**Volvo Penta of North
America, Inc.**
1300 Volvo Penta Dr.
Chesapeake, VA 23320
Tel: (804) 436-2800
Fax: (804) 436-5150

Yamaha Marine Corp.
6555 Katella Ave.
Cypress, CA 90630
Tel: (800) 526-6650

Instruments

Aetna Engineering
Box 7749
Van Nuys, CA 91409-7749
Tel: (800) 776-7962
Fax: (818) 366-7896
Digital tachometer

Astro Electrical Products
13214 4th Avenue W.
Everett, WA 98204
Tel: (206) 742-2000
Fax: (206) 742-9610
Redline gauges

Branom Instrument Co.
5500 4th Ave. S.
Seattle, WA 98108
Tel: (206) 762-6050
Fax: (206) 767-5669
*Alarms and engine monitoring
systems*

IM/Brookes & Gatehouse
7855 126th Avenue N.
Largo, FL 34643
Tel: (813) 536-1400
Fax: (813) 536-1717
Engine sensor displays

Faria Corp.
P.O. Box 983
Uncasville, CT 06382-0983
Tel: (203) 848-9271
Fax: (203) 848-2704
Engine instruments

Floscan Instrument Co.
3016 N.E. Blakely St.
Seattle, WA 98105
Tel: (206) 524-6625
Fax: (206) 523-4961
Fuel monitoring systems

Figure 5: Aqua Meter gauges
are available from Rule
Industries.

Rule Industries
70 Blanchard Rd.
Burlington, MA 01803
Tel: (617) 272-7400
Fax: (617) 272-0920
Aqua Meter tach / sync

Signet Marine
16321 Gothard St.
Unit E
Huntington Beach, CA 92647
Tel: (714) 848-6467
Fax: (714) 848-6009

VDO Yazaki Corp.
P.O. Box 2897
980 Brooke Rd.
Winchester, VA 22601
Tel: (703) 665-0100
Fax: (703) 662-2515
Gauges

Heat Exchangers and Keel Coolers

Champ Products
7615 Matoaka Rd.
Sarasota, FL 34243
Tel: (813) 351-6800
Fax: (813) 351-6590
*Heat exchangers and oil
coolers*

The Walter Machine Co., Inc.
P.O. Box 7700
Jersey City, NJ 07307
Tel: (201) 656-5654
Fax: (201) 656-0318

R.W. Fernstrum & Co.
1716 11th Ave.
P.O. Box 97
Menominee, MI 49858
Tel: (906) 863-5553
Fax: (906) 863-5634

Outboards

American Honda Marine
4475 River Green Pkwy.
Duluth, GA 30136
Tel: (800) 426-7701
or (404) 497-6066
Fax: (404) 497-6008

American Suzuki Motor Corp.
3251 E. Imperial Hwy.
Brea, CA 92621-6722
Tel: (714) 996-7040

Force Outboards
P.O. Box 1939
W6250 W. Pioneer Rd.
Fond du Lac, WI 54936-1939
Tel: (414) 929-5000
Fax: (414) 929-5017

Mariner Outboards
P.O. Box 1939
W6250 W. Pioneer Ave.
Fond du Lac, WI 54936-1939
Tel: (800) 526-6645
or (414) 929-5000
Fax: (414) 929-5017

Mercury Marine
P.O. Box 1939
Fond du Lac, WI 54936
Tel: (800)-MERCURY
or (414) 929-5000
Fax: (414) 929-5017
Mercruiser stern drives and outboards

Nissan Marine & Power Products
1420 Valwood Pkwy.
Bldg. 2, Suite 200
Carrollton, TX 75006
Tel: (214) 243-7981
Fax: (214) 243-6806

Outboard Marine Corp. Drive Systems
200 Seahorse Dr.
Waukegan, IL 60085
Tel: (800) 255-2550
or (708) 689-5701
Fax: (708) 689-5839

Suzuki Motor Corp.-American
3251 E. Imperial Hwy.
Brea, CA 92621
Tel: (714) 996-7040
Fax: (714) 970-6005

Tohatsu Corp.
West Coast:
984 N. Lemon St.
Orange, CA 92667
East Coast:
500 Marathon Pkwy. N.W.
Lawrenceville, GA 30246
Tel: (800) 343-3433
or (404) 339-3510
Fax: (404) 339-3566

Yamaha Motor Co.
6555 Katella Blvd.
P.O. Box 6555
Cypress, CA 90630
Tel: (800) 526-6650
or (714) 761-7300
Fax: (714) 761-7454

Outboard Fins and Parts

Atlantic Watercraft, Inc.
139 East Merrick Rd.
Freeport, NY 11520
Tel: (800) 645-5393
or (516) 378-9800
Fax: (516) 378-9899
Outboard fins

Port Kent Marine
P.O. Box 311
Port Kent, NY 12975-0311
Tel: (514) 637-2566
The Handler, a kort nozzle for outboards

Part Suppliers

A-1 Motors Inc.
740 Deerfield Ave. #3
Deerfield Beach, FL 33441
Tel: (305) 426-6379
Fax: (305) 426-8981
OMC, Indmar, Mercruiser, and Barr marine power parts shipped anywhere

Alexspares
14a High St.
Battle
E. Sussex TN33 0AE
ENGLAND
Tel: (+44) 0424 774888
Fax: (+44) 042 774766
Suppliers of new equipment and spares for yachts

American A & M
105 Hope St.
Longwood, FL 32750
Tel: (407) 767-5280
Engines, stern-drive, and jet boat parts

Aqua Power IMO Industries, Inc.
500-B Edwards Ave.
New Orleans, LA 70123
Tel: (504) 734-5611
Fax: (504) 734-7843
Replacement parts and props

Barr Marine Products
6505 S. Orange Ave.
Orlando, Fl 32809
Tel: (800) 762-5901
  or (407) 851-8641
Largest suppliers of used parts in Florida

Buck Algonquin Marine Hardware
370 N. Main St.
Smyrna, DE 19977-1011
Tel: (302) 659-6900
Fax: (302) 659-6909
Fuel fills, flanges, struts, and brackets

Champ Products
7615 Matoaka Rd.
Sarasota, FL 34243
Tel: (813) 351-6800
Fax: (813) 351-6590
Heat exchangers and oil coolers

The Cincinnati Gear Co.
5657 Wooster Pike
Cincinnati, OH 45227
Tel: (513) 271-7700
Fax: (513) 271-0049
Reduction gears

Flagship Marine Engine Co.
200 East Ann St.
Punta Gorda, Fl 33404
Tel: (813) 639-3783
Fax: (813) 575-1285
Remanufactured OMC and Cobra parts

Giannone Marine
800 S. Federal Hwy.
Pompano Beach, FL 33062
Tel: (800) 950-2628
  or (305) 784-9011
Fax: (305) 942-8511
Mercruiser, Barr and PCM parts shipped anywhere

Gledinning Marine
4753 Hwy. 90
Conway, SC 29526
Tel: (803) 399-6146
Fax: (803) 399-5005
Automatic twin-engine synchronizer

Graymarine
1402 Mt. Vernon St.
Oshkosh, WI 54901
Tel: (414) 231-7909
Engine parts

Kelly Marine & Supply
821 Waterway Pl.
Longwood, FL 32750
Tel: (800) 527-4221
Fax: (407)323-8926
Parts

Lerand Corp.
VA Metal Products Division
4900 N.W. 37th Ave.
Miami, FL 33142
Tel: (305) 633-0018
Fuel line assemblies and manifolds

McDurmon Distibuting, Inc.
G-12238 Fenton Rd.
Fenton, MI 48430
Tel: (800) 621-4130
  or (313) 750-0411
Fax: (313) 750-0188
Sierra parts

Mack Boring & Parts Co.
Engine City
Rt. 22, Box 3116
Union, NJ 07083
Tel: (201) 964-0700

Mack Boring & Parts Co.
587 Granite St.
Braintree, MA 02184
Tel: (617) 848-9300
Fax: (617) 848-0335

Mack Boring & Parts Co.
130 Rt. 110
Farmingdale, NY 11735
Tel: (516) 293-2700

Obt Marine Division of Orbitrade, Inc.
P.O. Box 20069
Jamestown, NC 27282
Tel: (800) 628-3860
Fax: (919) 887-6702
Volvo Penta replacement parts

Osco Motors Corp.
P.O. Box 136
Souderton, PA 18964
Tel: (215) 855-8268
Fax: (215) 855-5976
Manifolds, risers, and elbows

R & D Enterprises
19430 Gerald
P.O. Box 5380
Northville, MI 48167
Tel: (313) 349-7077
Fax: (313) 349-0021
*Oil coolers and heat
exchangers*

Racor/Div. Parker Hannifin
P.O. Box 3208
Modesto, CA 95353
Tel: (800) 344-3268
Fax: (209) 529-3278
*Fuel oil filters for gas and
diesel engines*

Sen-Dure Products
6785 N.W. 17th Ave.
Ft. Lauderdale, FL 33309
Tel: (305) 973-1260
Fax: (305) 968-7213
*Transmission oil, return fuel,
and lube oil cooling systems*

Southwest Marine, Inc.
1118 S.E. 12th Ct.
Cape Coral, FL 33990
Tel: (813) 772-1113
Fax: (813) 772-2677
*OMC and Mercury powerheads
and lower units*

**Stanadyne Automotive
Corp.**
Power Products Division
92 Deerfield Rd.
Windsor, CT 06905
Tel: (203) 525-0821
Fax: (203) 525-7160
Diesel fuel filters

Sturdy Marine
1822 Carolina Beach Rd.
Wilmington, NC 28401
Tel: (919) 763-8261
Fax: (919) 763-2650
*Digital control system and
synchronizers*

Torque Engineering Corp.
52640 Thorne Dr.
Elkhart, IN 46514
Tel: (219) 264-2628
Fax: (219) 264-3600
Headers and parts

United States Marine
at Spinnaker Marina
13301 Biscayne Blvd.
North Miami, FL 33181
Tel: (800) 825-7799
or (305) 940-7576
Fax: (305) 940-0072
*Yamaha, Yanmar, Volvo
Penta, and PCM parts shipped
anywhere*

Vetus - Den Ouden, Inc.
P.O. Box 8712
Baltimore, MD 21240-0712
Tel: Orders (800) GO-VETUS
or (410) 712-0740
Fax: (410) 712-0985
*Flexible couplings and exhaust
systems*

Superchargers and Turbochargers

**American Diesel
Engineering Co., Inc.**
201 Production Dr.
Yorktown, VA 23185
Tel: (804) 596-3100
Fax: (804) 596-9109

B & M Automotive
9152 Independence Ave.
Chatsworth, CA 91311
Tel: (818) 882-6422 ext 249

**Mercury Hi-Performance
Group**
Pioneer Rd.
Fond du Lac, WI 54936-1939
Tel: (414) 929-5000

Turbine Specialities, Inc.
Gulf Coast Division
1900 Industrial Blvd.
Harvey, LA 70058
Tel: (504) 348-4462

Weiand
P.O. Box 65977
Los Angeles, CA 90065
Tel: (213) 225-4138

Transmissions

**Borg-Warner Marine &
Industrial Transmissions**
Theodore Rice Blvd. Industrial
Pk.
New Bedford, MA 02745
Tel: (508) 979-4800

Cincinnati Gear Co.
5657 Wooster Pike
Cincinnati, OH 45227
Tel: (513) 271-7700
Fax: (513) 271-0049

Hurth Marine Gear
Moosacher Strasse 36
8000 Munchen 40
GERMANY
Tel: (+49) 089-3540 1542
Fax: (+49) 089-3540 1516

Tonan America
A Division of Transmission
America
P.O. Box 1764
Lake Charles, LA 70602

Tuit Power
P.O. Box 21368
Ft. Lauderdale, FL
33335-1368
Tel: (800) 462-TUIT ext. 27
 or (305) 467-1508
Fax: (305) 467-1525
Marine transmissions shipped worldwide

Twin Disc
1328 Racine St.
Racine, WI 53403-1758
Tel: (414) 634-1981
Fax: (414) 634-1989

Voith Transmissions, Inc.
25 Winship Rd.
York, PA 17402
Tel: (717) 767-3200
Fax: (717) 767-3210

Volvo Penta North America, Inc.
1300 Volvo Penta Dr.
Chesapeake, VA 23320
Tel: (804) 436-2800
Hydraulic transmissions

Turbines

Allen Industries
309 S. Cloverdale, #D-21
Seattle, WA 98108
Tel: (206) 767-0770
Fax: (206) 764-1220

Codag Marine Turbines, Inc.
8 Fair St.
Newport, RI 02840
Tel: (401) 848-8010
Fax: (401) 846-4289

Pratt & Whitney, Canada, Inc.
Industrial & Marine Division
1000 Marie-Victorin
Longueuil, Quebec J4G 1A1
CANADA
Tel: (514) 677-9411
Fax: (514) 647-3620

Figure 6: This 2,225 shp gas turbine is available from Turbine Power Systems, Inc. 2551 State Rd. 84, F Lauderdale, FL 33312 Tel: (305) 846-9230 Fax: (305) 791-5094.

Fishing Equipment

By Dean Travis Clarke

Dean Travis Clarke, executive editor of both Sport Fishing and Marlin magazines, is a 28 year veteran of the marine industry, a licensed captain, and a relatively adept fisherman since he gets paid to travel all over the world to fish with the great and near great. Unfortunately, he blithely ate his only world record fish without a second thought.

There's an old saying that goes: "God doesn't subtract time spent fishing from your allotted time on earth." If that's true, I guess I've found the closest thing to the fountain of youth there is. I share with you here some very basic information to help you choose fishing gear right for your purposes and budget without boring you to tears.

GETTING STARTED

There are two very basic contradictions you MUST keep in mind when looking for fishing gear:

- Fish don't know and don't care what kind of rod or reel you're using. It could be a $10,000 custom trolling rig or a cane pole with a piece of kite string and a rusty hook. Both can catch fish. But....
- Buy the best gear that you can afford. There's a reason why some tackle is more expensive than others. It will work better and last longer.

Figure 1: You don't need a big boat to fish offshore as long as you keep an eye on the weather. This Grady White 23 caught many large fish 30 miles offshore. (Photo Dean Clarke)

The only real requisite for happier fishing (besides actually catching fish) is to match your tackle. Don't put a 50 pound test line on a 12 pound reel and a 20 pound rod. Make sure all the components match. Figure out what types of fish you are targeting (or likely to catch) and work backwards from there. If you only want to fish so you can have a meal, don't mess around with ultra-light gear. Better to use a little overkill. If you want the sport of fishing to take priority and intend releasing most of your fish, ultra-light tackle fishing is a fantastic pastime. But always match your components.

SELECTING RODS

Once you've decided what type of fishing you are pursuing — trolling, casting, bottom fishing, or flyfishing — you can start looking for a rod to use. One great approach is to fish with friends or professional charters a few times and use their tackle to see what you like. That way, you can usually experience quite a variety of different "actions" and constructions of rods. Action is the pattern of flex the rod exhibits — how the rod feels. A "slow" rod is soft and bends over its entire length above the butt. As the action gets faster, the rod flexes less, and the flexing section moves farther toward the tip. The faster the rod, the stiffer. A slow rod will feel the strike of a fish better, but a fast rod will cast better and have more fighting power.

Graphite is a popular rod material today, but it may not be the answer for all applications. Graphite rods are great for increased casting power and distance because they can handle greater "loading,"

but anglers who are more concerned with fighting fish than casting may want to go with a fiberglass rod. Fiberglass rods are considered by many anglers to be superior to graphite for bottom fishing and big game trolling when you need lots of brute lifting strength and pulling power. If you're fishing from a sailboat, a short fiberglass rod is the wisest choice from the standpoints of trolling. It offers power enough to pull in a fish without luffing, and it allows for easier storage when not in use.

No matter what material rod you choose, they all have one thing in common. The outer wrapping on the core layers has an overlap that creates the "spline." The spline is very much like your backbone. It's critical that your fishing rod have the guides aligned exactly with the spline to avoid twisting and fatigue. And it isn't only the rod that suffers from these conditions. It can damage your reel too. On baitcasters and bottom fishing/trolling rods, the guides go on top of the spline. Spinning and flyrods are just the opposite, with guides along the side away from the spline. When you're in a tackle shop and want to check spline alignment, place the butt end of the rod on the floor against the arch of your foot and, holding the rod midway along its length with one hand (guides up on a conventional rod, guides down on a spinning or fly rod), hold the tip with your other hand and bend the rod down. If the rod isn't wrapped on-spline, it will roll or twist in your fingers in one direction or the other. Be sure to do this several times to make sure. If it doesn't roll over, you have a good one! Remember that spline misalignment has nothing to do with the cost, make, or model of a rod, or its materials. It can show up on rods from even the finest manufacturers. Never buy a rod wrapped off-spline. Check every one.

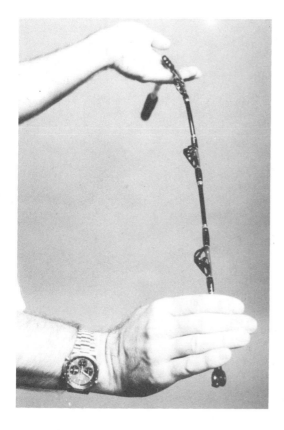

Figure 2: Always check that a rod's spline and guides are matched correctly. A rod wrapped "off spline" should be avoided. (Photo Dean Clarke)

By the way, fiberglass rods have "memory" and can become permanently bent — a condition known as "set." Avoid storing them by leaning them against the wall or supporting them with only a peg on each extremity.

The most common types of guides (those little holes the line runs through) are roller and ceramic. Ball-bearing roller guides are by far the best for trolling and stand-up rods because they cause the least amount of wear. Ceramic guides are another common choice. Although you'll find them offered on all kinds of rods from big-game to ultralight tackle, they're best-suited for baitcasting, fly, and spinning rods where the line needs to "fly" through the guides during casting.

Again, if you plan on standing up and fighting fish with brute strength, choose a stiff, short rod, probably built of fiberglass. Spinning rods can be longer and more flexible. Their "action" is more important. Spinning rods come in sizes from 2-pound up to about 50-pound test and can be used for casting or trolling. They're available in both fiberglass and graphite, as well as several other space-age materials. Experiment with several different actions to determine which is most comfortable for your fishing style. Saltwater flyfishing will usually demand a flyrod anywhere from an 8-weight to 15-weight, depending on the size of fish you're targeting. Most popular saltwater flyrods today are some form of graphite. Again, experiment with many different rods to find which manufacturer and action you prefer.

SELECTING REELS

Several different types of reels have merit for saltwater anglers: trolling reels (which also work for bottom fishing), spinning reels, baitcasting reels, and flyreels. At all costs avoid the spincast reel — the kind with the little button. While these are great for a child's first rig, they aren't worth the aggravation for an adult with any kind of serious fishing aspirations.

A reel is several things. It is a storage and management system for hundreds of yards of thin plastic line that without a reel becomes an incredibly messy and unusable nightmare. It is also a system of gears to give the user a mechanical advantage so that large fish may be brought to the boat.

When considering a reel, the drag system is of prime concern. The drag is basically a brake that applies friction to the spool of the reel so it rotates more slowly. That's how an angler using 10 pound line can catch a one-hundred pound fish. Left just to the line, the feat would be impossible. The drag allows the line to run out smoothly and slowly. Rather than go into the technicalities of different drag materials, let's say they all work pretty well.

Trolling Reels

Trolling reels are what the general public pictures when someone says "fishing reel." They come in all sizes and are good for dragging lures or baits behind your boat or for bottom fishing.

Lever-drag systems are tremendously popular on bluewater trolling reels because the single adjustment point is conveniently located, and is quickly and easily moved from freespool to strike and any setting in between. Star drags remain popular mainly because they are less expensive and work well in applications such as bottom fishing. The adjustments are located around the

Figure 3: Lever drag reels are more expensive than star drags but are easier to use. Drag setting is easily adjusted and can be noted at a glance. (Photo Dean Clarke)

handle of the reel. Unlike the lever drag, you can't tell the drag setting at a glance with a star drag.

Line capacity becomes a more important factor when fast-moving, ocean roaming (pelagic) species are the target. For offshore game, a minimum of 400 yards is recommended. Some trolling reels comes in both standard and wide varieties, the latter accommodating more line.

There are only a few important universal truths to remember about offshore reels. Reel bodies used for medium to big-game species should be aluminum for strength. Spools should also be aluminum for big game, though graphite bodies and spools are acceptable for smaller species. Just remember, there's incredible pressure applied to the center of a spool when a fish runs against the drag. At all costs, avoid plastic reels. They'll blow apart on the first good-size fish you hook up.

Baitcasting Reels

Baitcasting reels have historically been the province of the bass-fishing bubbas. You know, those guys in their metal-flecked boats with matching pickup truck, mega-outboard power pushing them along at 90 mph on a quarter-mile long lake, the ones who wear their Red Man Chewing Tobacco hats backwards so they don't blow off. Well, they're making their way into the saltwater fishing market in ever more advanced forms. The baitcasting reels that is, not the bass fishermen.

Once you get the hang of a baitcaster, you can wing a plug or spoon a country mile with one. However, they're difficult to master. I'm convinced they were never meant for humans to use. But as I said, once you get the educated thumb and hand-switching action indelibly imprinted on your cortex, they are outstanding for casting plugs and spoons to all sorts of small and medium gamefish. They should be matched with a baitcasting rod with either a "pistol" grip or standard casting rod grip. They won't work attached to a spinning or trolling rod.

Spinning Reels

When it comes to casting, most offshore anglers still prefer spinning gear. Spinning reels have the spool on the front of the reel instead of in the center, as with trolling and baitcasting reels, and the drags are located on the front or back rather than the side. Many spinning reels have the ability to be quickly adjusted to suit either left- or right-handed people, whereas most other types of reels are not so accommodating. Whether you are casting or trolling live baits, spoons, or plugs, it is impossible to beat a good spinning rig for all-around utility. In fact, if you can choose only one rod to use for all your fishing applications, logic would dictate that it be a spinning rod. Again, a spinning reel should be matched with the line and rod weight. And, of course, don't mount a spinning reel on anything but a spinning rod.

Flyreels

The fastest growing segment of the offshore fishing market is saltwater flyfishing. Fly-reel ratings translate directly to line weight. A 12- or 13-weight line is what you need for tarpon and most other large offshore gamesters. A 10- to 12-weight reel will handle those two weights of flyline and is also good for smaller species. For greater sport, though, you may wish to use an 8- or 9-weight rig for bluefish, or striped bass, or any of the small tuna family like little tunny or bonito.

Saltwater flyreels should accommodate at least 300 yards of 30-pound dacron backing. This backing then attaches to between 80 and 100 feet (or less) of actual flyline. Another critical feature of a saltwater flyreel is anti-reverse. This means that when a fish is streaking away from you at warp eight and taking line with it, the reel handle isn't spinning like a meat grinder waiting to devour your fingers. Finally, the all important drag system. On those teeny-tiny freshwater flyreels, drag is a virtually non-existent concept. But for saltwater gamefish, without a good drag, don't even

Figure 4: Many former offshore trollers have discovered the comparative peace and solitude of back country saltwater fly fishing. (Photo Dean Clark)

bother trying to catch a fish. Make sure your drag is up to the job you plan to give it. A simple clicker-style won't do.

Electric Reels

I won't go into much detail about electric reels here because they are really for a deepwater fishing specialty that the average recreational angler isn't likely to engage in right off the bat. I mention them, however, because I have several friends who can't use their arms and hands well enough

to fish with standard tackle. Why should they be left out of a sport that can be one of the most soothing and meditative pastimes going? In my friends' cases (and many others), their fishing difficulties have been solved with electric reels. Several manufacturers make self-contained electric reels, and others make simple electric motors that attach to regular reels. Most are lightweight and easily adapted to whatever the immobility challenge of the angler is.

LINES

There are a number of different types of line in use today: stainless steel or monel wire, dacron, and several different kinds of plastic. But the most common is called monofilament. It is amazingly strong stuff for its thickness.

When looking for fishing tackle, the "line class" or "pound test" of the line is probably your first decision. It runs in strengths from 1 pound to over 900 pounds. The most commonly used by recreational anglers is from 2 to 130 pounds.

The pound test of a line is not a terribly exact indicator of its strength. For example, ten pound test, depending upon the brand of line, may mean that the line breaks, when wet, with just 10 pounds of pull, or with as much as 15 pounds. If using a test line that is exactly what is stated on the box is important to you, look for the word "tournament" or "IGFA (International Game Fishing Association) -class" printed on the spool. Otherwise, consider the kilogram rating as a generally more reliable indicator of real line strength.

Table 1: Weights of fishing line and equivalents		
METRIC (KG.)	U.S. (LBS.)	IGFA (LBS.)
1	2	2.20
2	4	4.40
4	8	8.81
6	12	13.22
8	16	17.63
10	20	22.04
15	30	33.06
24	50	52.91
37	80	81.57
60	130	132.27

Figure 5: Offshore trolling lures can easily be rinsed off, stored, and transported in new accessory bags designed for that purpose.

LURES

It used to be that you'd go into your garden and dig up some worms, take them in a can down to your boat, put one on a hook, and go fishing. Not anymore. Like everything else, fishing lures have become far more sophisticated. For those of you still interested in fishing with worms, there's a new electronic device that you stick into the ground, plug into a wall socket, and, like magic, the worms crawl right up to the surface and all but jump into your bait bucket. DON'T USE IT! Four people have been electrocuted already just digging worms.

Today, there are plugs, spoons, spinners, trolling lures, birds, teasers, deadbaits, crankbaits, rattles, tubes, flies, streamers, epoxies, lightsticks, fish scents, artificial softbaits, and the list goes on. All these artificial lures have one thing in common: they are all designed to look and act just like something real that fish already eat.

Most offshore anglers fish artificial lures sometime for the simple reason that they catch fish. There are some circumstances, such as trolling for billfish and tuna, where lures have been known to be more efficient and productive. For trolling purposes, match the lure to both the species of fish you want to catch and the speed of the boat. Different plastic trolling lures work better at different speeds. Some want to be trolled at 4-5 knots, while others are happier in the 12-15 knot range. There are even trolling lures perfectly designed for dragging behind sailboats.

One of the earliest forms, and still the cheapest and simplest trolling lure, is the small plastic squid. It is readily available in every saltwater tackle shop, either rigged or unrigged, and will attract virtually all offshore gamefish, especially tuna.

Many of today's higher speed trolling lures are designed to leave a trail of bubbles much like the vapor trail of a high-altitude jet. This "smoke trail" attracts fish. The concept here is to set the lures out so they rise to the surface and "spray," and then dive below the surface a foot or so and leave the bubble trail. Deadly effective!

The concept of livebait is really the simplest of all. Provide a live specimen of whatever the target fish is already eating. Livebait are usually purchased or caught by throwing a castnet. The baits are then put into a live baitwell until ready to be attached to your hook. As you might expect, there isn't a predatory fish swimming that won't eat a well-presented live bait. For the uninitiated, a live baitwell is much like a running toilet filled with constantly replenished seawater. The water circulates around in the baitwell but always maintains the same level. While many fishing boats (even small ones) now offer live baitwells built-in, there are also a number of portable livewells available. Check this section's list of manufacturers.

If you aren't trolling, then you're probably bottom fishing. Besides livebait, one of the more popular lures for this is called a jig. A jig is a piece of lead weight in the shape of a ball or bullet with a hook sticking out of it. Sometimes there's hair or shiny mylar, and anglers often put a piece of real bait on the hook as well. The idea is to drop the jig to the bottom and then move the rod up and down (jigging). All too often though, when there are fish in the area, the jig never makes it all the way to the bottom before a fish starts tearing line off your reel.

ACCESSORIES

The fishing industry couldn't survive on just rods, reels, line, and lures alone. Neither could the avid fisherman. Unlike fishing in freshwater where the angler can pick his quarry up out of the water by holding the fish by the lips, more often than not, a saltwater denizen would remove your appendages for you if you tried that.

There are accessories galore for handling fish, rigging baits and lures, cutting things, holding things, storing things, carrying things, shipping things, measuring things, releasing fish, tagging fish, and we haven't even scratched the surface. Here are just a few of the really important items you should consider if you plan on catching any fish over 15 pounds.

Gaffs and Fish Tailers

A gaff is a strong sharp hook attached to a long handle used to grab the fish once it's alongside the boat. If you try to simply hoist a heavy fish up by the line alone, you're likely to break it off and lose the fish.

A fish tailer is good for those who would rather not have a super sharp gaff lying about their boat or who are squeamish about "gaffing" a fish. It is a large loop of rope or wire that slips over the fish's tail, then tightens down to hold the tail, which is the main power source on a fish.

Gloves

Every boat used for fishing should have onboard some sort of heavy gloves to wear while bringing a fish aboard, preferably rawhide or welder's gloves.

Tags

In the name of conservation and research, if you plan on releasing your fish, carry a tag stick and tags so the fisheries scientists can make use of information about the fish you caught. If you feel like doing your good deed for the day, you can buy superb tag sticks and the special hydroscopic nylon tags from the non-profit Billfish Foundation in Miami, Florida.

Hand Tools

Small, comprehensive and compact rigging kit carryalls made of nylon mesh and clear plastic with Velcro closure pouches are available from a number of manufacturers. They are a safe, easy, and effective way to carry everything you need for fishing in a neat package. When fully stocked, there are very few rigs that can't be fabricated or repaired with the materials and tools at hand. The typical rigging kit holds a great variety of crimps, beads, thimbles, monofi-

Figure 6: Although you can certainly fish with a rod and reel, adding accessories such as a gimbel belt, stand up harness, or back brace can make the process more comfortable and more fun. (Photo Dean Clark)

lament, wire, and cable leader material. There are also pockets for cutters, pliers, and crimping tools. A file or pocket hook sharpener is critical, since no hook should touch the water without first being touched up, even those directly from the box. Fishing pliers should be carried at all times to remove hooks, cut leaders, bend barbs, tighten knots — the list is endless.

Gimbal Belts and Harnesses

Anyone who has fought a fish of any stature with the butt of the rod pressed into groin or abdomen knows that it doesn't take long for that to become quite painful. The easy and lightweight answer to this is called a gimbal belt. For larger fish, a harness can be worn that distributes the strain of leverage on the fish over the entire back and upper legs rather than just the lower back. It makes all the difference in the world.

Bait Cutting Tables

For people who want to set up chum slicks — long stretches of bait and fish oil laden areas that attract fish — a bait cutting table is a necessity. Ones that mount in ordinary rod holders are available.

Rod Holders

Every boat should have at least three rod holders. Most have two on each side of the cockpit, and holders for rods not in use elsewhere. I've also mounted rod holders on every sailboat I've ever owned or run. Mount them on the stern rail, in the taffrail, or to the backstay. Sailboats make ideal trolling platforms. You'll be amazed at the delicious dinners you can catch with the proper lures, and without even trying.

Knives

A good sharp knife is vitally important for a fisherman. No sailor of any kind should be aboard without a solid, sharp knife with-

in reach at any given moment. It can be used to cut lines, bleed and gut your catch, and for a variety of other tasks.

Figure 7: Offshore fishing demands rock solid equipment that will last. (Photo Dean Clarke)

Ice

Fish can offer up the most debilitating bacteria to poison you if you don't take proper care. Be sure to ice your fish down immediately upon catching it. And it's even better, for warm-blooded fish like tuna, if you bleed and gut it immediately as well. This means that you should have a large icebox on board. Don't use huge chunks of ice, which will need to be broken, but buy the smaller packages.

Manufacturers of Fishing Equipment

Accessories

Accurate Fishing Products
3528 E. 16th St.
Los Angeles, CA 90023
Tel: (213) 269-4985
Gaffs

AFTCO
17351-B Murphy Ave.
Irvine, CA 92714
Tel: (714) 660-8757
Gaffs, rod components, and rigging accessories

American Foreign Industries
2210 Gladstone Dr.
Pittsburg, CA 94565
Tel: (510) 427-2341
Fax: (510) 427-2342
Rod holders

Anglers Image, Inc.
205 Hallene Rd., B-24
Warwick, RI 02886
Tel: (401) 737-0950
Line winder

Birdsall Marine Design
530 Nottingham Blvd.
West Palm Beach, FL 33405
Tel: (407) 832-7879
Bait-cutting tables

Braid Products
616 East Ave. P
Palmdale, CA 93550
Tel: (805) 266-9791
Belts, harnesses, teasers, and offshore lures

Buck Knives
P.O. Box 1267
El Cajon, CA 92022
Tel: (619) 449-1100
Knives

W.R. Case & Sons Cutlery Co.
Owens Way Bradford, PA 16701
Knives

Climax Bluewater Marine
251 NJ Railroad Ave.
Newark, NJ 07105
Tel: (201) 344-3737
Rod holders

Darby Metal Products
208 Saude Ave.
Essington, PA 19029
Tel: (215) 521-9106
Reel-a-rig lure storage system

Dehooker, Inc.
5928 N. Oceanshore Blvd.
Palm Coast, FL 32137
Tel: (800) 772-5804
Hook removers

Donnmar Enterprises
10637 NE Coxley, No. 206
Vancouver, WA 98662
Tel: (206) 892-1006
Hook/knife sharpeners and pliers

Dotline
Mengo Industries, Inc.
4611 Green Bay Rd.
Kenosha, WI 53144
Tel: (414) 652-3070
Fax: (414) 652-9910
Ladders, boathooks, and fishing nets

Gudebrod
P.O. Box 357
Pottstown, PA 19464
Tel: (215) 327-4050
Accessories, Dacron and specialty lines

Fentress Marine
Design Products Division
P.O. Box 6102
Clearwater, FL 34618
Tel: (813) 581-9991
Fax: (813) 584-4215
Rod holders, dive platforms, and cleaning posts

Fishing Friends
P.O. Box 1856
Lodi, CA 95241
Tel: (209) 333-8207
Big fish stringer

Lansky Sharpeners
P.O. Box 800
Buffalo, NY 14221
Tel: (716) 877-7511
Knife and hook sharpeners

Ripoffs
P.O. Box 3270
San Dimas, CA 91773
Tel: (714) 593-5924
Belts, harnesses, and sheaths

Perko
Street address:
16490 Northwest 13th Ave.
Miami, FL 33169-5707
Mailing address:
P.O. Box 64000D
Miami, Fl 33164-0510
Tel: (305) 621-7525
Fax: (305) 620-9978
Outrigger and rod holders

PlayAction Products
P.O. Box 6406
Titusville, FL 32782-6406
Tel: (800) 327-4643
Belts and bait tables

Spirit River, Inc.
2405-68 N.E. Diamond Lake Blvd.
Roseburg, OR 97470
Tel: (800) 444-6916
Fly-tying dispenser

Team Nu Mark
802 E. Pasadena Freeway
Pasadena, TX 77506
Tel: (713) 473-9100
Pliers, harnesses, belts, and accessories

Texas Tackle
P.O. Box 531239
Richardson, TX 75083
Hook sharpeners

Valeo, Inc.
W229 N. 1687 Westwood Dr.
Waukesha, WI 53186
Tel: (414) 547-9474
Stand-up back support belts

Downriggers and Outriggers

Big Jon
14393 Peninsula Dr.
Traverse City, MI 49684
Tel: (800) 637-7590
Downriggers

Bottomline/Cannon
499 E. Corporate Dr.
Meridian, ID 83642
Tel: (800) 456-5432
Fax: (208) 877-2000
Downriggers

Cannon
499 E. Corporate Dr.
Meridian, ID 83642
Tel: (800) 456-5432
Fax: (208) 877-2000
Downriggers

Du-Bro Products
480 Bonner Rd.
Wauconda, IL 60084
Tel: (708) 526-1030
Downriggers, fishing accessories, and tools

Nekton Z-Wing
P.O. Box 460
Danville, NH 03819
Tel: (800) 421-5402
Z-Wing downrigger planes

Proos Mfg. Co.
1037 Michigan St. N.E.
Grand Rapids, MI 49503
Tel: (616) 454-5622
Fax: (616) 454-1424
Downriggers

Rupp Marine, Inc.
4761 Anchor Ave.
Stuart, FL 34997
Tel: (407) 286-5300
Rupp Radial outriggers

Scotty Downriggers
P.O. Box 5788
Concord, CA 94524
Tel: (415) 825-8560

The J.M Roberts Co., Inc.
Box 2383
Alameda, CA 94501
Downriggers and rod holders

Rupp Marine, Inc.
4761 Anchor Ln.
P.O. Drawer F
Port Salerno, FL 34992
Tel: (407) 286-5300
Rupp Sidekick outrigger

Schaefer Marine, Inc.
Industrial Park
New Bedford, MA 02745
Tel: (508) 995-9511
Fax: (508) 995-4882
Outriggers and Redi-Rigger

Walker Downriggers
8100 Neptuna Dr.
Kalamazoo, MI 49009
Tel: (800) 828-4754
  or (616) 385-2727
Fax: (616) 385-1771
Downriggers

Wille Products
P.O. Box 532
Brookfield, WI 53008
Tel: (414) 544-9528
Downriggers, planers, and rod holders

Fighting Chairs

Bluewater Tackle
231 S.W. 28th St.
Ft. Lauderdale, FL 33315
Tel: (305) 522-4238
Fishing chairs

The Marine Concept
A division of Marcon International
41 Commerce St.
Clinton, CT 06413
Tel: (203) 669-5608
Fax: (203) 669-6982

**Murray Brothers
Sportfishing**
1306 53rd St.
West Palm Beach, FL 33407
Tel: (407) 845-1366
Fax: (407) 844-4355

Pompanette
190 Bryan Rd.
Dania, FL 33004
Tel: (305) 925-7304

Release Marine Co.
P.O. Box 1768
27 Magazine Ave.
Savannah, GA 31402
Tel: (912) 236-5717
Fax: (912) 233-1199

Scopinich Fighting Chairs
3716 S.E. Dixie Hwy.
Stuart, FL 34997
Tel: (407) 288-3111
Fax: (407) 288-1893

Fish Boxes and Coolers

Chem-Tainer
361 Neptune Ave.
Babylon, NY 11704
Tel: (516) 661-8300
Portable live-bait tanks

Kracor
5625 W. Clinton Ave.
P.O. Box 23667
Milwaukee, WI 53223
Tel: (800) 255-6335
  or (414) 355-6335
Fax: (414) 355-8782
Marine tanks

**Marine Appliances
International**
2807 Antigua Dr.
Burbank, CA 91505
Tel: (800) 672-8297
  or (818) 842-0226
Fax: (818 953-9847
Ice maker and coolers

Pacific Edge
5044 Edinger
Huntington Beach, CA 92649
Tel: (714) 840-4262
Live-bait tanks

Sailing Specialties, Inc.
P.O. Box 99
Commerce Ave.
Hollywood, MD 20636
Tel: (301) 373-2372
Fax: (301) 373-2734
Coolers

Fishing Tackle Boxes

Flambeau
P.O. Box 97
Middlefield, OH 44062
Tel: (216) 632-1631
Tackle boxes

Plano Moulding Co.
431 E. South St.
Plano, IL 60545
Tel: (708) 552-3111
Fax: (708) 552-8989
Tackle boxes

Trophy Products
9714 Old Katy Rd.
Houston, TX 77055
Tel: (713) 464-8256
Tackle boxes

Rods, Reels, and Lures

Abel Fly Reels
165 Aviador St.
Camarillo, CA 93010
Tel: (805) 484-8789
Fly reels

Abu-Garcia, Inc.
21 Law Dr.
Fairfield, NJ 07004
Tel: (201) 227-7666
*Stock spinning and bait rods,
bait, spinning, and fly reels*

AFTCO
17351-B Murphy Ave.
Irvine, CA 92714
Tel: (714) 660-8757
*Gaffs, rod components, and
rigging accessories*

All Star Rods
9750 Whithorn
Houston, TX 77095
Tel: (713) 855-9603
Spinning, bait, and fly rods

C. Altenkirch & Sons
Box 799
Hampton Bays, NY 11946
Tel: (516) 728-4110
*Custom parts, all types of rods
and reel parts*

American Fishing Wire
205 Carter Dr.
West Chester, PA 19380
Tel: (215) 692-1751
*Leader, rigging wire, custom
parts, all of types reels*

Ande Lines
1310 W. 53rd St.
West Palm Beach, FL 33407
Tel: (407) 842-2474
Monofilament line and leaders

Fred Arbogast
313 W. North St.
Akron, OH 44303
Tel: (216) 253-2177
Plugs and lures for offshore, spoons, jigs, and monofilament line

Area Rule Engineering
32232 Azores Rd.
Laguna Niguel, CA 92677
Tel: (714) 496-7401
Offshore lures, teasers, hooks rigs, T-bar reel handles

Bagley Bait Co.
P.O. Box 810
Winter Haven, FL 33882
Tel: (813) 294-4271
Offshore lures and mono lines

Bally-Hood
700 NW 57th Pl.
Box 11
Ft. Lauderdale, FL 33309
Tel: (305) 351-9246
Ballyhoo bird covers

Bass Pro Shop
1935 S. Campbell
Springfield, MO 65898
Tel: (800) 227-7776
  or (417) 887-1915
Fax: (417) 887-2531
Rods

Bead Tackle Co.
600 Main St.
Monroe, CT 06468
Tel: (203) 459-1213
Offshore lures, spoons, jigs, and rigs

Berkley
One Berkeley Dr.
Spirit Lake, IA 51360
Tel: (712) 336-1520
Monofilament and fly lines, all types of rods

Betts Tackle Ltd.
P.O. Box 57
Fuquay-Varina, NC 27526
Tel: (919) 552-2226
Plugs, spoons, and jigs

Billy Pate Fly Reels
900 NE 40th Ct.
Oakland Park, FL 33334
Tel: (305) 566-0222

Biscayne Rods Mfg., Inc.
425 E. Ninth St.
Hialeah, FL 33010
Tel: (305) 884-0808
All types of stock and custom rods

Blue Fox Tackle Co.
645 N. Emerson
Cambridge, MN 55008
Tel: (612) 689-3402
Plugs, spoons, and artificial lures

Bluewater Lures
P.O. Box 724
Olive Branch, MS 38654-0724
Tel: (601) 895-1117
Offshore lures, and teasers

Boone Bait Co.
440-B Plumosa Ave.
Casselberry, FL 32707
Tel: (407) 830-7474
Offshore lures, plugs, spoons, jigs, and teasers

Braid Products
616 East Ave. P
Palmdale, CA 93550
Tel: (805) 266-9791
Belts, harnesses, teasers, and offshore lures

Burley Custom Rods
1100 NW 53rd St., No. 2
Ft. Lauderdale, FL 33309
Tel: (800) 833-RODS
Custom, trolling, spinning, and bait-casting rods

C&H Lures
142-A Mill Creek Rd.
Jacksonville, FL 32211
Tel: (800) 458-LURE
Offshore/nearshore lures, teasers, rigging accessories

Cabela's
812 13th Ave.
Sidney, NE 69160
Tel: (800) 237-4444
Monofilament and wire; spinning, bait-casting reels; stock spinning, bait-casting, and fly rods

Calcutta Baits
300 Dunbar Ave.
Oldsmar, FL 34677
Tel: (813) 855-7384
Flash-frozen naturals

Castway Graphite Rods
1775 E. Loop 336
Suite 1
Conroe, TX 77301
Tel: (409) 760-3474
Stock, spinning, bait-casting rods

Chatham Squid Co.
P.O. Box 827
Greenville, RI 02828
Tel: (401) 949-4109
Offshore lures, teasers, rigs

Coastal Lures
2175 Kingsley Ave., No. 215
Orange Park, FL 32073
Tel: (904) 272-0562
Plugs

Cortland Line Co.
P.O. Box 5588
Cortland, NY 13045
Tel: (800) 847-6787
Monofilament and fly lines

Culprit Lures
P.O. Box 121249
Clermont, FL 34712
Tel: (407) 656-6133
Offshore lures and plugs

Daiwa Corp.
7421 Chapman Ave.
Garden Grove, CA 92641
Tel: (714) 895-6645
*Spinning, bait-casting, and
trolling reels; all types of rods*

DOA Fishing Lures
3467-B Palm City School Ave.
Palm City, FL 34990
Tel: (407) 287-5001
Artificial lures

Custom Rods by Dru
Andrew Lee International
1911 Juno Rd.
North Palm Beach, FL 33408
Tel: (407) 626-3697
All types of custom rods

Du-Bro Products
480 Bonner Rd.
Wauconda, IL 60084
Tel: (708) 526-1030
*Downriggers, fishing
accessories, and tools*

DuPont Fishing Products
6234 Brandywine Building
Wilmington, DE 19898
Tel: (302) 774-4040
Stren (monofilament line)

Eagle Claw
P.O. Box 16011
Denver, CO 80216
Tel: (303) 321-1481
*Hooks, terminal tackle, fly,
spinning reels; all types of rods*

Elec-tra-mate
Electric Fishing Reel Systems,
Inc.
1700 Sullivan St.
Greensboro, NC 27405
Tel: (919) 273-9101
Electric fishing reels

Falcon Rods
821 W. Elgin
Broken Arrow, OK 74012
Tel: (918) 251-0020
Rods

Fenwick
5242 Argosy Ave.
Huntington Beach, CA 92649
Tel: (714) 897-1066
*Mono, fly lines, all types of
rods*

**FireHawk Fishing Lure
Mfg. Co.**
P.O. Box 6305
Nashua, NH 03063-6305
Tel: (800) 542-2776
Bass lures

Gamefisher Rod Co.
5517 N. Military Tr.
Suite 905
Boca Raton, FL 33496
Tel: (407) 241-6996
All types of custom rods

Grandt Custom Rods
P.O. Box 4373
Arlington Heights, IL
60006-4373
Tel: (708) 577-0848
*Twice national rod building
champion all types, including
split bamboo rods*

Gudebrod
P.O. Box 357
Pottstown, PA 19464
Tel: (215) 327-4050
*Accessories; dacron and
specialty lines*

Hatteras Lures
P.O. Box 1171
Kernersville, NC 27285
Tel: (919) 996-3631
Offshore lures and teasers

Hildebrandt Corp.
P.O. Box 50
Logansport, IN 46947
Tel: (219) 722-4455
Plugs and spoons

Hi-Seas Industries
18-22 Minetta Ln.
New York, NY 10012
Tel: (212) 979-8989
Mono, wire lines, and leaders

Hopkins Lures, Inc.
1130 Boissevain Ave.
Norfolk, VA 23507
Tel: (804) 622-0977
Spoons, jigs, and tubes

Hook Bros.
P.O. Box 17278
Seattle, WA 98107
Tel: (206) 782-4665
Snap baits

Iland Lures
Tournament Tackle
P.O. Box 372820
Satellite Beach, FL 32937
Tel: (407) 259-1903
Offshore lures and teasers

Islander Fly Reels
517 Kelvin Rd.
Victoria, British Columbia
CANADA
Tel: (604) 384-3242

J & B Tackle Co.
41 Commerce St.
Clinton, CT 06413
Custom rods

Johnson Fishing, Inc.
1531 Madison Ave.
Mankato, MN 56001
Tel: (507) 345-4623
Spinning reels

Kennedy Fisher Fly Rods
P.O. Box 3147
Carson City, NV 89702
Tel: (702) 246-5220
Fly rods

Laser Lures
P.O. Box 870076
Mesquite, TX 75150
Tel: (214) 226-0734
Hologram lures

L.L. Bean
Freeport, ME 04033
Tel: (800) 221-4221
Fly reels, rods, and line

LMR Custom Rods
1495 E. Southeast 17th St.
Ft. Lauderdale, FL 33316
Tel: (305) 525-2592
All types of custom rods

Lamiglass, Inc.
P.O. Box U
Woodland, WA 98674
Tel: (206) 225-9436
All types of rods

Lee
8227 NW 54th St.
Miami, FL 33166
Tel: (305) 599-9324
Outriggers, chairs, and accessories

Bill Lewis Lures
P.O. Box 7959
Alexandria, LA 71306
Tel: (318) 487-0352
Plugs

Loki Nets
P.O. Box 5320
Knoxville, TN 37928
Tel: (615) 687-7341
Cast nets

G. Loomis
P.O. Box E
1359 Downriver Dr.
Woodland, WA 98674
Tel: (206) 225-6516
Fly, spinning, and bait-casting rods

Luhr-Jensen
P.O. Box 297
Hood River, OR 97031
Tel: (800) 366-3811
Spoons, plugs, jigs, and rigs

Magnuflex Rods
American Rod Manufacturers
2147 NW 32nd Ave.
Miami, FL 33142
Tel: (305) 633-6360
All types of custom rods

Malin Co.
5400 Smith Rd.
Cleveland, OH 44142
Tel: (216) 642-0090
Wire line and leaders

Manns Bait Co.
604 State Docks Rd.
Eufala, AL 36027
Tel: (205) 687-5716
Plugs, jigs, and artificial lures

Martin Fly Reel Co.
30 E. Main St.
Mohawk, NY 13407
Tel: (315) 866-1690

Mason Tackle Co.
11273 N. State Rd.
Otisville, MI 48463
Tel: (313) 631-4571
Monofilament, wire, specialty lines, hooks, and rigs

Master Fishing Tackle
1009 E. Bedmar St.
Carson, CA 90746
Tel: (213) 631-5188
Spinning and fly reels; all types of rods

Maxima Fishing Lines
Five Chrysler St.
Irvine, CA 92718
Tel: (714) 380-7444
Monofilament

MirrOlure
1415 E. Bay Dr.
Largo, FL 34641
Tel: (813) 584-7691
Plugs and spoons

Miya Epoch of America
P.O. Box 5191
Torrance, CA 90501
Tel: (213) 320-1172
Electric reels

Mold Craft Lures
501 NE 28th St.
Pompano Beach, FL 33064
Tel: (305) 785-4650
Fax: (305) 786-9232
Offshore lures, teasers, and rigs

Momoi Canada, Inc.
165005 Western Ave.
Suite 100
Gardena, CA 90247
Tel: (310) 352-3878
Monofilament

Mud Hole Marine
126 N. Route 9
Forked River, NJ 08731
Tel: (609) 971-1170
Custom tackle

Murray Brothers
207 East Blue Heron Blvd.
Riviera Beach, FL 33404
Tel: (800) 845-3474
Anything you could possibly want

O. Mustad & Son (USA), Inc.
P.O. Box 838
Auburn, NY 13021
Hooks

Carl Newell Mfg.
940 Allen Ave.
Glendale, CA 91203
Tel: (818) 240-9652
Semi-custom offshore bait-casters

Normark
1720 E. 78th St.
Minneapolis, MN 55423
Tel: (612) 869-3291
Tools and Rapala plugs

O. Mustad & Son
P.O. Box 838
Auburn, NY 13021
Tel: (315) 253-2793
Hooks, rigs, and terminal tackle

Offshore Edge Products
P.O. Box 14855
North Palm Beach, FL 33408
Tel: (407) 844-0065
Hook racks

Offshore Outfitters
190 Will St.
East Brunswick, NJ 08816
Tel: (800) 435-6840
Custom, trolling, and spinning rods

Orvis
Historic Route 7A
Manchester, VT 05254-0798
Tel: (800) 548-9548
Fly reels, fly line, fly and spinning rods

Outrageous Rods
12555 Biscayne Blvd.
Suite 756
Miami, FL 33181
Tel: (305) 891-6373
Custom trolling, spinning, and bait-casting rods

Owner American
17165 Von Karman
Suite 111
Irvine, CA 92714
Tel: (714) 261-7922
Hooks and rigs

Pakula Lures
167 Bayview St.
Runaway Bay, Queensland
4216
AUSTRALIA
Tel: (+61) 7 5374-689
Offshore lures and teasers

Peerless Fly Reels
427-3 Amherst St.
Suite 177
Nashua, NH 03063
Tel: (603) 595-2458

Penn Fishing Tackle Mfg. Co.
3028 W. Hunting Park Ave.
Philadelphia, PA 19132
Tel: (215) 229-9415
Fax: (215) 223-3017
Trolling, bait-casting, and spinning reels; all types rods, and downriggers

PFC Wire
4103 Clark Rd.
Sarasota, FL 34233
Tel: (813) 922-5800
Leader and rigging wire

Powell Custom Rods
P.O. Box 4000
Chico, CA 95927-4000
Tel: (800) 228-0615
Custom fly, spinning, and bait-casting rods

Pradco
P.O. Box 1587
Ft. Smith, AR 72902
Tel: (501) 782-8971
*Plugs, spoons, jigs, artificial
lures, Silver Thread
monofilament*

Red Eye Tackle Co.
6619 Oak Orchard Rd.
Elba, NY 14058
Tel: (800) 332-3937
Crankbait lures

Sadu Bluewater Lures
4660 122nd Dr. N.
Royal Palm Beach, FL 33411
Tel: (407) 795-1516
Offshore lures and teasers

Sage
8500 N.E. Day Rd.
Bainbridge Island, WA 98110
Tel: (206) 842-6608
Stock spinning and fly rods

St. Croix
P.O. Box 279
Park Falls, WI 54552
Tel: (715) 762-3226
All types of stock rods

Sampo Tackle
P.O. Box 328
Barneveld, NY 13304
Tel: (315) 896-2606
Terminal tackle and harnesses

Bob Schneider
155 E. Blue Heron Dr.
Riviera Beach, FL 33404
Tel: (407) 845-1994
Offshore lures and teasers

Sea Talons
P.O. Box 2753
Norfolk, VA 23501
Tel: (804) 627-2598
*Offshore and semi-natural
lures*

Seeker
P.O. Box 14744
Long Beach, CA 90805
Tel: (213) 491-0076
*Stock spinning and trolling
rods*

Sevenstrand
899 W. Cowles St.
Long Beach, CA 90813
Tel: (310) 437-1010
Fax: (310) 495-4707
Offshore lures and teasers

Shakespeare
3801 Westmore Dr.
Columbia, SC 29223
Tel: (803) 754-7000
*Monofilament lines; spinning,
fly, trolling, and bait-casting
reels; all types of rods*

Shimano American Corp.
One Shimano Dr.
Irvine, CA 92713-9615
Tel: (714) 951-5003
*Spinning, fly, trolling, and
bait-casting reels; trolling,
spinning, and bait-casting
rods*

Siglon
VIP Distributing
1220 E. 68th, Unit 101
Anchorage, AK 99518
Tel: (907) 349-8924
Monofilament

**Silstar Corp. of America,
Inc.**
P.O. Box 6505
1141 Silstar Rd.
West Columbia, SC 29170
Tel: (803) 794-8521
Fax: (803) 794-8544
*Spinning, fly, trolling, and
bait-casting reels; all types of
rods*

Silver Thread
Pradco Fishing Tackle
P.O. Box 1587
Ft. Smith, AR 72902
Tel: (501) 782-8971
Monofilament

Skipper Lure Co.
128 Oceanside Dr.
Tavernier, FL 33070
Tel: (305) 852-0147
Flying-fish teasers

Smoooooth Drag
5321 Concha Dr.
Mira Loma, CA 91752
Tel: (714) 360-1675
Replacement drag washers

So-Lo Marine
P.O. Box 877
Bridgeport, CT 06601
Tel: (203) 336-2700
Rod holders and accessories

South Bend
1950 Stanley St.
Northbrook, IL 60065
Tel: (708) 564-1900
*Spoons, jigs, rigs, artificial
lures; spinning, fly, and
bait-casting reels; all types of
rods; monofilament and fly
lines*

STH Fly Reels
P.O. Box 816
Marathon, FL 33050
Tel: (800) 232-1359

Storm Lures
P.O. Box 720265
Norman, OK 73070-4199
Tel: (405) 329-5894
Plugs

Star Rods
8538 N.W. 64th St.
Miami, FL 33166
Tel: (305) 592-3134
All types of stock rods

Stuart Industries
526 N.E. 190th St.
North Miami Beach, FL 33179
Tel: (305) 651-3474
Rod components

Talon
736 Davidson Ave.
Woodland, WA 98674
Tel: (206) 225-8247
Stock, fly, bait-casting, and spinning reels

3M/Scientific Anglers
3M Center
Bldg. 225-3N-04
St. Paul, MN 55144-1000
Tel: (612) 733-4751
Fly line; spinning, fly, trolling, and bait-casting reels

Tite-Lok
P.O. Box 219
Topeka, IN 46571
Tel: (800) 848-3565
Rod, net, and gaff holders

Triple Fish
Kenneth Smith & Associates
321 Enterprise Dr.
Ocoee, FL 34761
Tel: (407) 656-7834
Monofilament

Tycoon Fin-Nor
2021 S.W. 31st Ave.
Hallandale, FL 33009
Tel: (305) 966-5509
Trolling and fly reels

Van Staal Engineering
205 Eliot Pl.
Fairfield, CT 06430
Tel: (203) 259-5003
Spinning reels

Versitex Rods
3545 Schuykill Rd.
Spring City, PA 19475
Tel: (215) 948-4442
Spinning, trolling, and bait-casting rods

Viper Lures
P.O. Box 9833
Springfield, MO 65801-9833
Tel: (800) CHEETER
Weedless jigs

Wille Products
P.O. Box 532
Brookfield, WI 53008
Tel: (414) 544-9528
Monofilament and specialty lines; downriggers, planers, and rod holders

Williamson Lures
15495 Eagle Nest Ln.
Suite 100
Miami Lakes, FL 33014
Tel: (305) 362-2727
Offshore lures, teasers, rigs, plugs, spoons, jigs

R.L. Winston Rod Co.
Drawer T
Twin Bridges, MT 59754
Tel: (406) 684-5674
Stock fly rods

Woodstock Line Co.
83 Canal St.
Putnam, CT 06260
Tel: (203) 928-6557
Dacron and specialty lines

Yakima Bait Co.
P.O. Box 310
Granger, WA 98932
Tel: (509) 854-1311
Spoons, plugs, jigs, artificial lures, and rigs

Yo-Zuri Lures
675 N. Eckhoff Suite E
Orange, CA 92668
Tel: (714) 639-9272
Every type of fishing lure

Zebco/Quantum/Motorguide
P.O. Box 270
Tulsa, OK 74101
Tel: (918) 836-5581
Spinning, bait-casting, reels; all types of rods

Figure 8: An Abel fly reel can make your casting easier.

Foul Weather Gear

A not so well-known test was made once. A foul weather gear manufacturer decided to try out its gear by having people wear it in a yacht manufacturer's leak-testing spray booth. The gear maker was absolutely certain that its gear would be better than anything currently on the market. When the soaked crew stepped off the boat, the manufacturer was surprised to find that the foul weather gear leaked like a sieve. At that time, the gear had been on the market for several years with few complaints. Sailors figured that if you got wet at sea, that was just too bad and you changed when you went below. Today, however, with increased recognition of hypothermia and increased time spent on the rail aboard racing boats, foul weather gear has to be very water-resistant. No foul weather clothing, though, will keep you entirely dry.

How do you pick the best gear for your kind of sailing? First, recognize what your needs are. Ask yourself if you want to keep cold out, to cut the power of the wind, or just to keep off salt spray. If you want foul weather gear to keep you warm, you should probably look at a lined jacket and leggings, with mittens and thermal underwear. If you want the gear to keep the wind out, you'll probably need a snug-fitting suit that does not allow wind to blow up inside the jacket or the arms. If you sail in warm waters and just want a light suit that keeps the spray off, your choices will be very different than those designed for warmth or wind protection.

Recognition of your needs basically determines the fabric that your foul weather gear will be made from. Some manufacturers, such as Line 7, use a heavily rubberized fabric with rubberized neck and wrist seals on their foredeck suit. Many other manufacturers use a proprietary waterproof coating over a neoprene fabric. Musto, according to its catalog, makes foul weather gear for specific purposes. For instance, the Musto ocean suit is made of 4 oz neoprene-coated nylon with reinforcing patches on knees and seat. It has neoprene-coated feet that fit inside your boots, a strobe light pocket, and an inflator valve, and it must be worn with this company's combination lifejacket/safety harness. For use in cold latitudes, Musto recommends that its ocean suit is worn with bodywarmer underwear. The company claims that this suit meets or exceeds anything that any other manufacturer produces.

But this type of gear is too hot if you are sailing in warm water. In warm climates, you probably want a lighter suit without all the additional weight. Most lighter suits are made of PVC-coated nylon without extensive linings inside. Under these suits, you might want to wear a light tee shirt to absorb sweat.

If you are a dinghy sailor, you sail close to the water and need a suit with wrist, ankle, and neck seals. These seals may be made of neoprene or latex rubber, and should be a snug fit to keep water out. The suit should not be heavy or confining, because you often have to move very quickly on a small boat.

Safety features are important on any foul weather gear. Some suits come equipped with a safety harness. You should look for this type of suit if you work on deck at night. If the suit you choose does not have a harness built in, look for one with attachement points for a harness. A suit with a built-in harness should have some way of fastening it under the crotch so that, should you fall over the side, the suit will not ride up around your neck as the harness takes the strain. Make sure, too, that there is a place to stow your harness line when not in use. It can be a royal pain to be constantly snagging or tripping over your harness line.

Other suits have a built-in lifejacket, which is great if you plan on falling overboard, but usually foul weather gear with a built-in life jacket is bulky and heavy. All foul weather gear should have orange or yellow reflective strips, so that a person in the water at night can easily be seen. Another good safety feature is a fluorescent yellow hood. This also reflects light at night, which makes it easier to be seen.

Most foul weather gear is designed to be worn over some type of warm clothing. Ideally, thermal underwear or a pile jacket and pants should be worn, but often many light layers of clothing will suffice. When buying foul weather gear, look at that manufacturer's line of warm clothing. Quite often the warm under clothing is designed to compliment the outer garments. Together they will make a complete unit that will function better than clothing from different manufacturers worn together.

Manufacturers and Suppliers of Foul Weather Gear

Atlantis Weathergear
30 Barnett Blvd.
New Bedford, MA 02745
Tel: (508) 995-7000
Fax: (508) 998-5359
Atlantis weathergear

Canterbury Clothing Co. of New Zealand
600 Lincoln Center Dr.
P.O. Box 4699
Foster City, CA 94404
Tel: (415) 349-2990

CB Sports
1 Apollo Dr.
Glens Falls, NY 12801
Tel: (518) 792-2121
Fax: (518) 792-4111

Champion Glove
2200 E. Ovid St.
Des Moines, IA 50313
Tel: (515) 265-2551
Fax: (515) 265-7210
Sailing gloves

Chuck Roast Equipment
29 Odell Hill Rd.
Conway, NH 03818
Tel: (603) 447-5492
Fax: (603) 447-2277

Canyon Gear Sportswear
P.O. Box 4037
Brick, NJ 08723
Tel: (908) 262-0011
Fax: (908) 262-0222
Sport-fishing clothing

Davis Instruments
3465 Diablo Ave.
Hayward, CA 94545-2746
Tel: (415) 732-9229
Fax: (415) 732-9188

Weathermark/Douglas Gill USA
6087 Holiday Rd.
Buford, GA 30518
Tel: (404) 945-0788
Fax: (404) 932-0622

Dritex Rainwear
1725 S. Chesterfield Rd.
Arlington Hts., IL 60005
Tel: (708) 437-2141
Fax: (708) 437-2147

E & B Marine Supply
201 Meadow Rd.
Edison, NJ 08818
Tel: (908) 819-7400

Frostline Kits
2525 River Rd.
Grand Junction, CO 81505
Tel: (800) 548-7872
Kit manufacturers

Harken, Inc.
1251 E. Wisconsin Ave.
Pewaukee, WI 53072
Tel: (414) 691-3320
Fax: (414) 691-3008
Shoes and clothes

Helly Hansen (US), Inc.
17275 N.E. 67th Ct.
Redmond, WA 98078-9731
Tel: (800) 435-5901
Fax: (206) 885-3882

Henry-Lloyd North America
86 Orchard Beach Blvd.
Port Washington, NY 11050
Tel: (800) 645-6516
or (516) 883-8450
Fax: (516) 767-7835

International Sailing Products
319 Main St.
P.O. Box 389
New Rochelle, NY 10802
Tel: (800) 645-7676
or (914) 576-4050
Fax: (914) 632-2732

Kokatat
5350 Ericson Way
Arcata, CA 95521
Tel: (707) 822-7621
Fax: (707) 822-8481

Line Seven
P.O. Box 3114
Annapolis, MD 21403
Tel: (301) 268-8182
Fax: (301) 268-6528

Marathon Rubber Products
510 Sherman St.
Wausau, WI 54401
Tel: (800) 331-4864

Mustang META USA Corp.
3870 Mustang Way
Bellingham, WA 98226
Tel: (206) 676-1782
Fax: (206) 676-5014

Musto
333 W. 76th St.
New York, NY 10023
Tel: (800) 553-0497
Fax: (212) 799-3395

O'Neill
1071 41st Ave.
Santa Cruz, CA 95062
Tel: (408) 475-7500

Patagonia
P.O. Box 150
Ventura, CA 93002
Tel: Advice (800) 523-9597

Patagonia
P.O. Box 8900
Bozeman, MT 59715
Tel: catalog: (800) 336-9090
or order: (800) 638-6464

Peter Storm
6313 Seaview Ave. N.W.
Seattle, WA 98107
Tel: (206) 789-8112
Fax: (206) 789-1137

Peter Storm (Atlantic)
P.O. Box 451
52 Bradford St.
Concord, MA 01742
Tel: (508) 371-0270

Pilgrim Hat Company
Division of Fanning Industries
P.O. Box 451
West Falmouth, MA
02574-0451
Tel: (508) 548-7904
Fax: (508) 540-3390
Long-billed sword-fishing hats

Rainfair
300 S. Memorial Dr.
Box 1647
Racine, WI 53403
Tel: (800) 558-5990
Fax: (414) 554-6655

Sailing Angles
P.O. 331725
Miami, FL 33155
Tel: (800) 666-3616
Fax: (305 661-5551
Protective sailing clothes

W. H. Salisbury & Co.
7520 N. Long Ave.
Skokie, IL 60077
Tel: (708) 679-6700
Fax: (708) 679-2401

Stearns
P.O. Box 1498
St. Cloud, MN 56302
Tel: (800) 328-3208
Fax: (612) 252-4425

Stormy Seas
P.O. Box 1570
Poulsbo, WA 98370
Tel: (800) 323-7327
  or (206) 779-4439
*Foul weather gear with CO2
emergency flotation*

Tom Taylor
425 Alliance Ave.
Toronto, ON M6N 2J1
CANADA
Tel: (416) 769-7288
Fax: (416) 769-0525

Timberland
11 Merrill Industrial Dr.
Hampton, NH 03842-5050
Tel: (603) 926-1600
Fax: (603) 926-9239

Vermont Bird Co.
71 Olive Court
Mountain View, CA 94041
Tel: (415) 967-3123

Walls Industries
P.O. Box 98
Cleburne, TX 76033
Tel: (817) 645-4366
Fax: (817) 645-7946

West Marine Products
500 West Ridge Dr.
Watsonville, CA 95076-4100
Tel: (408) 728-2700

Windsurfing Hawaii
P.O. Box 1746
Goleta, CA 93116
Tel: (805) 683-6333

**Woods Hole Marine
Clothing**
Division of Fanning Industries
P.O. Box 451
West Falmouth, MA
02574-0451
Tel: (508) 548-7904
Fax: (508) 540-3390
Wholesaler of foulweather gear

Figure 1: For a set of top-notch offshore foul weather gear check out this outfit from Musto.

Furling Gear

By Scott Alexander
Scott Alexander is the National Sales Manager of Sailsystems, Inc., Marblehead, Massachusetts. He was previously a sailmaker with Thurston Sails in Bristol, Rhode Island.

When purchasing a roller furling system, the boat owner encounters a myriad of options. The most important thing to remember is that you are buying a piece of equipment that is expected to rotate with little friction under heavy load. The question you should always ask is: "What has the manufacturer done to provide for less friction under sail and rig loads?"

Ease of furling in all headstay systems is a function of the overall number and hardness of the ball bearings, as well as the engineering of the bearings to distribute the load and thereby decrease friction. Since the halyard attaches on the side of the halyard swivel rather than at its center, it exerts an uneven loading. This is referred to as "point loading" and results in increased friction at the point of halyard attachment. Some of the better systems have engineered the bearing races to avoid point loading and to rotate with less friction under heavy rig and sail loads.

The material of the ball bearings also affects the performance of the system. The harder the ball bearings, the longer-lived the system will be and the better at resisting the compression or point loading that

the bearings encounter. The materials most commonly used include: stainless steel, carbon steel, and torlon (plastic). Stainless steel is best for corrosion resistance and hardness. Carbon steel, although hard, must be maintained in a greased condition, usually in a sealed race to avoid rusting. In a harsh marine environment, a race doesn't always maintain its seal. Torlon, a plastic manufactured by Amoco, has the advantage of being a "no maintenance" material, but it suffers from lack of hardness.

Another area to consider is the luff extrusion and its relationship to the headstay. In order to reduce friction, the headstay must be located in the middle of the rotating foil. This is accomplished with a PVC tube or bushing that runs the entire length of the headstay. The bushing centers the stay and protects against chafe and electrolysis between the rotating aluminum extrusion and the stainless steel forestay. Not all manufacturers include this important feature.

The final point to consider is the completeness of the kit. Parts that are needed for a complete installation but are not always included are: stanchion blocks, furling line, halyard fairleads, a sail prefeeder, and often a new headstay.

One of the more common mishaps associated with all furling systems is halyard wrap. This usually occurs because of an insufficient angle between the halyard

and the headstay. The angle of deflection must be between 5 and 10 degrees in order to prevent halyard wrap. The simplest and most effective way of correcting this problem is with a halyard fairlead.

One serious consideration for a blue-water sailor is maintenance. How easily will you be able to service the system? Can you check the wire terminal to insure that everything is in order? If a foil is damaged, can it be easily replaced?

Whether you are a coastal or blue-water cruiser, make sure the system you choose incorporates the correct bearing material and the engineering needed for low friction. This should give you years of carefree sailing.

Figure 1: A Furlex roller furling gear from Sailsystems, Inc.

Manufacturers of Furling Gear

Cruising Design, Inc.
9 Old Sudbury Rd.
Maynard, MA 01754
Tel: (508) 897-5933
Fax: (508) 897-6038
Flexible furler

Figure 2: The Harken roller furling gear stands up to rough weather.

Harken
1251 E. Wisconsin Ave.
Pewaukee, WI 53072
Tel: (414) 691-3320
Fax: (414) 691-3008
Harken furling gear

Hood Ocean Systems
P.O. Box 714
Marblehead, MA 01945
Tel: (617) 631-9549
Hood furling gear

Mariner
2280 Shasta Way # 106
Simi Valley, CA 93065
Tel: (805) 522-9091
Fax: (805) 522-6218
Roller-stay furling gear for sails with hanks

Pacific Marine Rope, Inc.
1879 W. Commonwealth, N.E.
Fullerton, CA 92633
Tel: (714) 879-5161
Superfurl

Proegin, Inc.
401 N.E. 8th St.
Fort Lauderdale, FL 33304
Tel: (800) 272-9511 or (305) 760-9511
Fax: (305) 763-8790
Profurl

Profurl Canada - ACIF Canada
11925 rue Guertin
Montreal, Quebec H4J1V7
CANADA
Tel: (515) 334-4548
Fax: (514) 334-0288
Profurl

Raudaschl Sails Canada
3140 Lakeshore Blvd.
West Toronto, Ontario
M8V 1L4
CANADA
Tel: (416) 255-3431
Fax: (416) 259-9136
Ultrafurl

Riggarna
200 High Point Ave.
Unit B9
Portsmouth, RI 02871
Tel: (401) 683-6727
Fax: (401) 683-6729
*German-made Reckman
furling gear*

Rondal bv
P.O. Box 52 8325 ZH
Vollenhove NETHERLANDS
Tel: (+31) 0 5274 3500
Fax: (+31) 0 5274 3900
*Dutch-built hydraulic furling
gear for larger craft*

Figure 3: The Tuff-Luff
headstay system is available
from ERA Marine Products
Division.

Sailsystems, Inc.
P.O. Box 1218
Marblehead, MA 01945
Tel: (617) 639-0440
Fax: (617) 631-7517
Swedish-built Furlex system

Schaefer Marine, Inc.
Industrial Park
New Bedford, MA 02745
Tel: (508) 995-9511
Fax: (508) 995-4882
Furling gear

Stream-Stay Systems, Inc.
26 Burnside St.
Bristol, RI 02809
Tel: (401) 253-0988
*Stream Stay 1 and 2 furling
gear*

Viscom International, Inc.
507 Hopmeadow St.
Simsbury, CT 06070
Tel: (203) 658-2201
Fax: (203) 651-8406
French-made Facnor system

Luff Groove Systems

ERA Marine Products Div.
2750 Niagara Ln. North
Minneapolis, MN 55447
Tel: (612) 550-1000
Fax: (612) 550-1237
Tuff-Luff headstay system

Figure 4: This cutaway view
shows the range of Furlex
gear available from
Sailsystems.

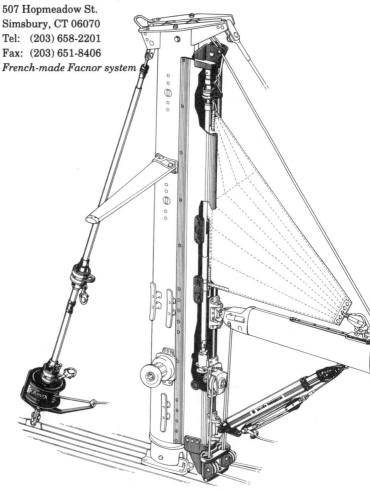

Gelcoat Peeling

Just before the season begins you start to sand the bottom of your boat only to find that strange blisters have appeared. These blisters may be the first sign of a problem with the original resin used to laminate the boat. If the original resin was an ortho-phthalic polyester resin (orthophthalic refers to the acid base used to formulate the resin), it has probably allowed seawater to permeate through the gelcoat and into any tiny voids between the gelcoat and the fiberglass laminate. This seawater mixes with the chemicals in the laminate and expands to produce the charactersitic blisters. Blisters may develop anywhere on a hull and may be severe or very light depending upon the application technique and viscosity of the original gelcoat. Unfortunately, the only solution to eliminating blisters is to remove the faulty gelcoat completely (and often a portion of the laminate behind the gelcoat). Removal of the gelcoat by peeling is considered to give a better,

more even finish than grinding the laminate with a rotary grinder. Once the gelcoat has been removed, a new exterior laminate is applied using isophthalic resin. Isophthalic resins have better resistance to water permeation and generally eliminate blistering problems. Today, almost all yachts are laid up with an isophthalic or vinylester gelcoat in order to prevent blistering.

When looking for a yard to peel a gelcoat, find out how the work will be done. The boat should be undercover so that the peelings can be kept out of the environment and so that heat can be applied to the hull to dry it out before new resin is applied. If the work is done out of doors, rain can wet the hull as soon as it is peeled, making the drying time much longer. Make sure that the new resin is totally compatible with the existing laminate and that it is isophthalic or another specially formulated resin to prevent a recurrence of the problem.

Gelcoat Peeling Source List

Gelcoat Peeling Operators

Hullshield
1 Shipyard Ln.
Cataumet, MA 02534
Tel: (508) 563-7136

Jamestown Boatyard
P.O. 347
Racquet Rd.
Jamestown, RI 02835
Tel: (401) 423-0600
Fax: (401) 423-0060

Oceana Ltd.
1811 Virginia St.
Annapolis, MD 21401
Tel: (800) 523-8890
  or (301) 269-6022
Fax: (301) 268-6528

Manufacturers of Coatings and Resins

Ad-Tech Plastic Systems
P.O. Box 437
Charlotte, MI 48813
Tel: (517) 543-7510

Alpha Resins Corp.
P.O. Box 370
Collierville, TN 38027

Aquachelle International Corp.
20 Greenvale Ct.
Ruther Glen, VA 22546
Tel: (804) 448-1633

Ashland Chemical Co.
P.O. Box 2219
Columbus, OH 43216
Tel: (614) 889-3767

Ferro Corp.
4150 E. 56th St.
Cleveland, OH 44105
Tel: (216) 641-3752

Interlux Paints
2270 Morris Ave.
Union, NJ 07083
Tel: (800) INTRLUX
   or (800) 468-7589

Interplastic Corp.
1225 Wolters Blvd.
Vadnais Heights, MN 55110
Tel: (612)331-6850

Max Pro-Coat
Pier Pressure Marine Systems, Inc.
5400-28th Ave. N.W.
Seattle, WA 98107
Tel: (206) 782-8711
Fax: (206) 782-8717

Pettit Paint Co.
36 Pine St.
Rockaway, NJ 07866
Tel: (201) 625-3100

System Three Resins, Inc.
P.O. Box 70436
Seattle, WA 98107
Tel: (206) 782-7976

US Paint
831 S. 21st St.
St. Louis, MO 63103
Tel: (314) 621-0525

West System/Gougeon Brothers, Inc.
P.O. Box 908
Bay City, MI 48707
Tel: (517) 684-7286
Fax: (517) 684-1374

Figure 1: Jamestown Boatyard's gelcoat peeler in action. Note the smooth, even finish.

Generators

What do you look for when choosing an auxiliary generator? First and foremost is the wattage supplied, followed closely by the weight of the unit and its fuel consumption. Then perhaps you'll look at the noise levels, the air requirements, and the size.

To calculate the capacity of the generator you need, you don't simply add up the power required to run every electrical item onboard. Not every item will be in use all the time, nor will many items be operated at full power. To accurately calculate the power needed, a specialist should figure out the amount of power used over a twenty four hour period. This is done by listing every electrical item onboard and then estimating when and how long that item is used in a typical day. The information can be displayed as a table of watt-hours of consumption over 24 hours. Displayed graphically, it shows the periods of peak power usage. It also gives hints as to how power consumption can be modified to suit a smaller generator. For instance, an electric stove might be used to cook dinner when in harbor, and the clothes dryer might be run at the same time. The stove uses 3 kw and the dryer another 1.5 kw. A generator to cover this peak usage period would have to be at least 6 kw in order to run both the stove and the dryer and a few other incidental pieces of equipment. However, if the dryer is always used at another time, the generator can be smaller.

Remember to make a separate calculation for your boat's air conditioning requirements. These estimates will take into account the size of the boat's windows, the difference in ambient air temperature, the hull material, and the amount of insulation in the hull. (See the section on air conditioning.)

Having made your calculations and found the power required, the next job is to specify fuel. Usually, this would be the same fuel that powers the boat's engines. For example, if the boat's engines are diesel, the the generator should be diesel, too. Although most boat generators are water-cooled, a few are air-cooled. If you want to save weight and use an air-cooled generator, you must locate it where air can circulate around it. Putting an air-cooled generator in a hot engine room is usually asking for trouble. When specifying a water-cooled generator, make sure that the water intakes are easily accessed and are fitted with filters and strainers to prevent sand and seaweed from getting into the engine.

Another requirement is siting the generator in an easily accessible location. This makes the physical size of the generator a factor to consider. Most generators have a sound enclosure which increases the size of the unit, but keeps ambient noise levels down. I would recommend that the sound enclosure be ordered with the generator. You will need to get access to the generator motor to check oil levels and so forth, so the unit cannot just be crammed into a corner.

Having determined the type of generator and where you will put it, you need to supply it with fresh water, air, and fuel, and to lead electrical wires from it. You will also have to find a place to put the starting and running controls, and you will want to make sure the unit runs as quietly as possible. All these tasks make installing a generator difficult, but one that can be handled by a competent mechanic.

Manufacturers and Suppliers of Generators

Alaska Diesel Electric
Box 70543
4420 14th N.W.
Seattle, WA 98107
Tel: (206) 789-3880
Fax: (206) 782-5453
Northern Lights generators

Ample Power Co.
1150 NW 52nd Street
Seattle, WA 98107
Tel: (206) 789-5758
Fax: (206) 789-9003
Battery chargers, and
deep-cycle alternators

Apollo Generators
833 W. 17th St. #3
Costa Mesa, CA 92627
Tel: (714) 650-1240
Custom generators

Auto-Gen Division of
Mercantile Manufacturing.
P.O. Box 895
Minden, LA 71058-0895
Tel: (318) 377-0844

Balmar
1537 N.W. Ballard Way
Seattle, WA 98107
Tel: (206) 789-4970
Fax: (206) 784-0878
Up to 11 kw genset

Clinton Engines
Clark and Maple St.
Maquoketa, IA 52060
Tel: (319) 652-2411
Portable gensets

Cruising Equipment Co.
6315 Seaview Ave. N.W.
Seattle, WA 98107
Tel: (206) 782-8100
Alternators and regulators

Cutter Marine Services
2298 Chapman Way
North Vancouver, British
Columbia V7H 1W1
CANADA
Tel: (604) 929-4444

Entec West
16710 S.W. 72nd St.
Portland, OR 97224
Tel: (503) 639-2764

Generac Corp.-Quicksilver
P.O. Box 8
Waukesha, WI 53187
Tel: (414) 544-4811
8 kw set only

Greenwich
9507 Burwell Rd.
Nokesville, VA 22123
Tel: (703) 439-3277

Hamilton Ferris II Co.
P.O. Box 126
Ashland, MA 01721
Tel: (508) 881-4602
Fax: (508) 881-3846
500 watt to 2 kw gensets

Honda Marine
4475 River Green Pkwy.
Dulutha, GA 30136-9420
Tel: (800) 426-7701
Portable generators

Kawasaki Motors
P.O. Box 25252
Santa Ana, CA 92799-5252
Tel: (714) 770-0400
Portable generators

Kestrel Electronic Designs
(USA)
619 Severn Ave.
Annapolis, MD 21403
Tel: (301) 647-1301

KiloPak
3333 S.W. 13th Ave.
Ft. Lauderdale, Fl 33315
Tel: (305) 763-8216
Fax: (305) 763-1079
6.5 kw to 75 kw gensets

Kohler
Highland Dr.
Kohler, WI 53044
Tel: (414) 457-4441
Fax: (414) 457-1271
4 kw to 32 kw gensets

Marine Development Corp.
P.O. Box 15299
Richmond VA 23227-0699
Tel: (800) 542-7245
  or (804) 746-1313
3 kw AC generator

McDurmon Distibuting, Inc.
G-12238 Fenton Rd.
Fenton, MI 48430
Tel: (800) 621-4130
  or (313) 750-0411
Fax: (313) 750-0188
Alternators

Onan
1400 73rd Ave. N.E.
Minneapolis, MN 85432
Tel: (800) 888-ONAN
4 kw to 95 kw gensets

Power Technology
1200 S. Sherman
Suite 100
Richardson, TX 75081-6500
Tel: (214) 437-0600
Fax: (214) 437-0680
110 volt alternator

PRP
1017 Spray Ave.
Beachwood, NJ 08722
Tel: (908) 505-6839

Ship and Shore Power System
339 Sawmill River Rd.
Yonkers, NY 10701
Tel: (201) 431-1710
Fax: (201) 431-1845

Suzuki Motor
3251 Imperial Hwy.
Brea, CA 92621
Tel: (714) 996-7040

TACK Corp.
4053 Harlan St. #113
Emeryville, CA 94608
Tel: (510) 654-9333
Fax: (510) 658-3996

Viking International
P.O. Box 1004
Eunice, LA 70535
Tel: (318) 546-6035
3 kw to 10 kw gensets

Wagner Products Company, Inc.
P.O. Box 26655
St. Louis, MO 63122
Tel: (314) 966-4444
Replacement alternators

Westerbeke
Avon Industrial Pk.
Box 181
Avon, MA 02322
Tel: (508) 588-7700
Fax: (508) 559-9323
4.4 kw to 32 kw gensets

Yamaha Motor Corp. USA
6555 Katella Ave.
P.O. Box 6555
Cypress, CA 90630
Tel: (714) 761-7612
Fax: (714) 761-7454
Portable generators

Yanmar Diesel Engines USA
1031 Segovia Circle
Placentia, CA 92670
Tel: (714) 630-9415
Fax: (714) 630-1562
Portable generators

Mack Boring & Parts Co.
Engine City
Rt. 22 Box 3116
Union, NJ 07083
Tel: (201) 964-0700
Yanmar marine diesel generators

Mack Boring & Parts Co.
587 Granite St.
Braintree, MA 02184
Tel: (617) 848-9300
Fax: (617) 848-0335
Yanmar Marine diesel generators

Mack Boring & Parts Co.
130 Rt. 110
Farmingdale, NY 11735
Tel: (516) 293-2700
Yanmar marine diesel generators

Vetus Den Ouden, Inc.
P.O. Box 8712
Baltimore, MD 21240
Tel: (301) 796-4740
Fax: (301) 796-1985

Hatches

If your boat lacks adequate ventilation and natural lighting, a new hatch may be the answer. A good hatch has several important features. It should be watertight when closed. (In spite of all the hype to the contrary, very few companionway hatches are truly watertight when shut.) It should have good aesthetics. After all, you wouldn't want to spoil the look of your boat with an ugly hatch or clumsy installation. In my opinion, a good hatch should also be alloy framed with clear openings, a place for a screen, an easy method of propping the hatch open in warm weather, and dogs that move easily without taking the skin off your knuckles. A good hatch should be reasonably lightweight so that the top will not crush people should it fall on them while they are climbing through it, but heavy enough that it will not break when someone is standing on it. The inside faces of a good hatch should be smooth-sided. Nothing is more annoying than falling against or snagging your clothes on a projection for a hatch dog.

A good companionway hatch has some additional features. First, make sure the top and the vertical part of the hatch operate independently of each other. In bad weather, you might want to close the hatchtop and leave the vertical opening ajar. Or in heavy weather, you might need to insert one or two washboards, leaving a small opening for air. Make sure the washboards can be removed. Hinged washboards tend to bang against each other in a seaway. Make sure that both the washboards and the top can be locked securely and that very little water can get into the boat. Ideally there should be a dodger or hatch cover over the companionway to keep rain out. This will also help make the companionway watertight.

If you are buying a deck hatch, look for good construction, ease of use, and watertightness. When installing a deck hatch, always face the opening aft. That way, if a wave comes aboard, it will slam the hatch shut rather than opening it. Also look carefully at the area where you will put the hatch. There should be no deck camber there unless the hatch is specifically made to be cambered. If you bolt a flat hatch on a cambered deck, it will almost certainly leak and probably end up with a severely distorted frame. Water should easily drain away from a properly installed deck hatch. Water that builds up in or around a hatch almost always goes below when the hatch is opened. Make sure that there is adequate reinforcement under the hatch structure. Inserting a hatch in an unreinforced deck can result in distorting the hatch or severely weakening the deck. Finally, make sure the hatch will not trip people walking along the deck. If the hatch is plexiglass, you might also want to put non-skid patches on the top side.

Manufacturers of Hatches and Hatch Hardware

Hatches

Atkins & Hoyle
69-71 Portland St.
Toronto, Ontario M5V 2M9
CANADA
Tel: (416) 596-1818
Aluminum-framed hatches

Beckson Marine, Inc.
165 Holland Ave.
Box 3336
Bridgeport, CT 06605
Tel: (203) 333-1412
Fax: (203) 384-6954
*Newport series of opening ports
and hatches*

The Bomar Co.
Division of Pompanette, Inc.
P.O. Box W
South West St.
Charlestown, NH 03603
Tel: (603) 826-5791
Fax: (603) 826-4125
*Aluminum-framed hatches
and opening ports*

Boomsma
De Steiger 74
1351 AE Almere
NETHERLANDS
Tel: (+31) 365 311524
Fax: (+31) 365 3115190
Gebo hatches and port lights

D. B. Follansbee, Inc.
12 Alice Ct.
Pawcatuck, CT 06379
Tel: (203) 599-1849
Fax: (203) 599-2316

Forespar
22322 Gilberto Rd.
Santa Margarita, CA 92688
Tel: (714) 858-8820
Fax: (714) 858-0505

**Freeman Marine
Equipment, Inc.**
P.O. Box F
28336 Hunters Creek Rd.
Gold Beach, OR 97444
Tel: (503) 247-7078
Fax: (503) 247-2114
*Commercial-duty doors,
hatches, and windows*

Go Industries
20331 Lake Forest Dr., C-1
El Toro, CA 92630
Tel: (714) 837-8241
Fax: (714) 837-9764

Figure 1: The Goiot hatch is available from Goiot in Europe and Viscom International in America (See Deck Gear section for address)

Goiot S.A.
28 rue du Frere-Louis
44062 Nantes Cedex 02
FRANCE
Tel: (+33) 40 75 68 39
Fax: (+33) 40 75 43 56

H & L Marine Woodwork
2965 E. Harcourt
Rancho Dominguez, CA 90221
Tel: (213) 636-1718

Harken, Inc.
1251 E. Wisconsin Ave.
Pewaukee, WI 53072
Tel: (414) 691-3320
Fax: (414) 691-3008

Hood Yacht Systems
Maritime Dr.
Portsmouth, RI 02871
Tel: (401) 683-2900
Fax: (401) 683-2410

**Imperial Marine
Equipment**
8209 N.W. 70th St.
Miami, FL 33166
Tel: (305) 592-0073
Fax: (305) 477-2182
*Custom windshields, windows,
and hatches*

Figure 2: The Lewmar Ocean hatch is available from IM/Lewmar, Inc. in many sizes and shapes.

IM/Lewmar Marine
P.O. Box 308
New Whitfield St.
Guilford, CT 06437
Tel: (203) 458-6200
Fax: (203) 453-5669

Nelson A. Taylor
10 W. 9th Ave.
Gloversville, NY 12078
Tel: (518) 725-0681
Fax: (518) 725-4335

New Found Metals
240 Airport Rd.
Townsend, WA 98368
Tel: (206) 385-3315

Plasticworks Marine Products
Division of ICON, Inc.
8343 N. Clinton
P.O. Box 10240
Fort Wayne, IN 46851-0240
Tel: (800) 426-0208
  or   in Indiana: (800)
942-2398
Fax: (219) 482-4877
Ultrac sliding doors

Rabud
110 N. Bryan Rd.
Dania, FL 33004
Tel: (305) 925-4199

Rondal bv
P.O. Box 52
8325 ZH
Vollenhove
NETHERLANDS
Tel: (+31) 0 5274 3500
Fax: (+31) 0 5274 3900
Tracks, blocks, hatches, and vents for larger craft

Rostand-R.I.
Box 737
Chepachet, RI 02814
Tel: (800) 635-0063

G. G. Schmitt
2821 Old Tree Dr.
Lancaster, PA 17601
Tel: (717) 394-3701

Simpson-Lawrence
P.O. Box 11210
Bradenton, FL 34282-1210
Tel: (813) 746-7161
Fax: (813) 746-7166

Vetus - Den Ouden, Inc.
P.O. Box 8712
Baltimore, MD 21240-0712
Tel: Orders only: (800)
GO-VETUS
  or   (410) 712-0740
Fax: (410) 712-0985
Air vents, sliding hatches, opening hatches, and windshields

Wefco Rubber
1655 Euclid St.
Santa Monica, CA 90404
Tel: (213) 393-0303

Welborn Marine & Industrial Products
805 Court St.
Clearwater, FL 34616
Tel: (813) 443-7661
Fax: (813) 447-0867

Wilcox-Crittenden
699 Middle St.
Middletown, CT 06457
Tel: (203) 632-2600

E. J. Willis
Park Ave.
Middleville, NY 13406
Tel: (315) 891-7602

Young Windows
P.O. Box 387
Conshohocken, PA 19428-0387
Tel: (215) 828-5422
Fax: (215) 828-2144
Windows and window trim

Hatch Hardware

ABI Industries, Inc.
1261 Anderson Dr.
Suite C
San Rafael, CA 94901
Tel: (415) 258-9300
Fax: (415) 258-9461
Hinges, fasteners, hooks, hasps, and latches

American Marine Products
1790 S.W. 13th Ct.
Pompano Beach, FL 33069
Tel: (305) 782-1400
Fax: (305) 782-1404
Windshields, windows, and acrylics

Attwood Corp.
1016 N. Monroe St.
Lowell, MI 49331-0260
Tel: (616) 897-8358
Fax: (616) 897-8358
Hatch hardware

Brassworks Division
Safeguard Lock and Safe
P.O. Box 606
30 N.E. 3rd St.
Ft. Lauderdale, FL 33302
Tel: (305) 467-2515
Hatch hardware, locks, and hinges

Buck Algunquin Marine Hardware
1565 Palmyra Bridge Rd.
Rt. 73
Pennsauken, NJ 08110
Tel: (609) 665-9405

Deep 7 Co.
14260 Innerarity Point Rd.
Pensacola, FL 32507
Tel: (904) 492-0250
Fax: (904) 492-4484

H.S. Getty
Box 169
Allenwood, NJ 08720
Tel: (201) 449-3700
Hook sets, lock sets, hinges,
and hatch handles

Homer Mfg. & Co. Ltd.
Sales Office:
P.O. Box 22-23, Taichung
TAIWAN
Manufacturing plant:
360, Sec. 1
Shin Rd.
Ty Ya Hsiang, Taichung Hsein
TAIWAN
Tel: (+886) 4- 5661433
Fax: (+886) 4-5672783
Clasps, handles, and hinges

Master Tool
6115 N.W. 153rd St.
Miami Lakes, FL 33014
Tel: (305) 557-1020
Fax: (305) 556-0908

Merit Metal Products Corp.
242 Valley Rd.
Warrington, PA 18976
Tel: (215) 343-2500
Brass or bronze clasps, hinges,
cleats, and door trim

Moonlite Marine
776 W. 17th St.
Costa Mesa, CA 92627
Tel: (714) 645-0130

Perko
Street address:
16490 Northwest 13th Ave.
Miami, FL 33169-5707
Mailing address:
P.O. Box 64000D
Miami, Fl 33164-0510
Tel: (305) 621-7525
Fax: (305) 620-9978
Clasps, hinges, and handles

Sea-Dog Line
P.O. Box 479
Everett, WA 98201
Tel: (206) 259-0194
Fax: (206) 339-1345

Spartan International
1845 S. Cedar
Holt, MI 48842
Tel: (517) 694-3911
Fax: (517) 694-7952

Taco Metals, Inc.
Main office:
50 N.E. 179th St.
Miami, FL 33162
Tel: (800) 226-8201
  or (305) 652-8566
Fax: (305) 653-1174
Hinges, clasps, and deck
hardware

Wilcox-Crittenden
699 Middle St.
Middletown, CT 06457
Tel: (203) 632-2600
Hatches and hardware

Vetus Den Ouden, Inc.
P.O. Box 8712
Baltimore, MD 21240-0712
Tel: (410) 712-0740
Fax: (410) 712-0985
Hatch hardware

Heating and Ventilation

If you intend to sail in colder regions or want to extend your sailing season, you might want to consider installing a heating system. There are many types on the market, and you need to determine what is best for you. You'll need to decide upon the size, the fuel, and the location.

SIZING A HEATER

First, you will need to determine how much heat is lost from your boat. If your boat's hull is made of fiberglass, the heat loss will be much greater than if it has a foam-cored hull. The typical foam cores used for boat building have an insulation value of about R5 to 10, depending upon the foam's density. In colder areas, house walls are insulated to R19 or better, which means that even a foam-cored hull has a relatively high rate of heat loss. Heat loss will also be high if the boat has large windows. Typical window glass has an R value of about R2 or R4. Boats, then, are not well insulated.

Another factor that plays a major part in determining the size of the heater needed in a boat is the ambient temperature rise. If it is freezing outside and you want to heat the boat to 70 degrees, the ambient temperature rise is 38 degrees, but if the evening is merely chilly, say 50 degrees, the temperature rise needed is only 20 degrees. The maximum temperature rise required directly affects the size of the heater.

A third factor that affects heater size is the volume of space to be heated. In other words, you need to figure out the interior volume of your boat. Then factor in the degree of heat loss and the ambient temperature rise needed, plus an allowance for heater inefficiency, usually around 10 to 15%. All this information is taken into account in determining the size of the unit you require. With heaters, size is exressed in BTUs (British Thermal Units), a measure of the amount of heat the unit puts out.

FUEL CHOICES

Different fuels have different BTU levels. The options for fuel are propane (LPG), natural gas (CNG), diesel, wood, coal, or electric. (See the section on stoves for comments on fuels). Two factors shouldn't be forgotten in selecting a fuel. The first is carbon monoxide. Because a boat can be sealed up tightly with the occupants inside, the by-products of combustion (such as carbon monoxide) should be vented out of the boat unless the system is specifically designed to be non-vented. Venting usually means that the heater will have a chimney or stack, which, in turn, means that the heating unit cannot be gimballed for sailboat use. Also, with wood, coal, and some types of LPG, oxygen is needed to create combustion, so you should have an external vent to the stove rather than simply letting it use oxygen from the interior. Sailors who don't have an external vent on their boat generally leave a port or hatch open to allow air in.

The second factor not to overlook in selecting a fuel is condensation. Boats are naturally very humid, and some fuels, such as kerosene and diesel can add additional moisture to the air inside the boat. As soon as this moisture hits the cold outer surfaces of the vessel, it will condense. Dry-heating types of heaters alleviate this problem somewhat.

HEATER LOCATION

The location of the heater is another question that should be carefully considered before making a purchase. Usually, wood, coal, and some gas heaters must be located in the main cabin. As these heaters get very hot, abutting surfaces need the proper clearance and must be protected.

Some types of LPG, CNG, diesel, and electric heating systems can be installed in the engine room, and the warm air ducted to the compartment you want to be heated. If your boat has a large engine room this could be a less expensive way to install a heating system, rather than having separate heaters in each compartment.

VENTILATION

It used to be said that you could tell, simply by sniffing, if a boat was well maintained. A well kept boat smelled fresh and sweet. A tightly shut up boat with little ventilation smelled sour, as rot and mildew made their way through the woodwork. These days, few boats are made entirely of wood, but good ventilation is still essential.

The best form of ventilation is an open vent, such as a dorade style, a clamshell vent, or the Nicro solar vent. These vents keep out seawater and allow air to move easily through the boat. Note also that air cannot be pushed through the boat. If you want good airflow, turn the forwardmost vents to face downwind. The venturi effect will draw air out of them and prompt air to be pulled in from the aftermost vents. In fact, the best airflow is usually obtained when all dorade style vents face aft, not forward. Because air is being pulled out of the boat through the vents, fresh air will enter through any other vents, such as openings in the companionway doors.

Inside the boat, try to eliminate restrictions to airflow. Open locker and compartment doors, and the door to the head. Remember, too, to check under the bilges to ensure that air can circulate.

Manufacturers of Heaters and Ventilators

Heaters

Allcraft Corp.
55 Border St.
W. Newton, MA 02165
Tel: (617) 969-7740
Fax: (617) 969-2605
Stainless steel water heaters

Atlantic Marine Stainless Corp.
7176 S.W. 47th St.
Miami, FL 33155
Tel: (305) 665-9900
Fax: (305) 665-9877
Stainless steel water heaters

Figure 1: The Balmar cabin heater from Balmar Products

Balmar Products, Inc.
1537 N.W. Ballard Way
Seattle, WA 98107
Tel: (206) 789-4970
Fax: (206) 784-0878
Stoves and cabin heaters

Ballard Sheet Metal Works, Inc.
4763 Ballard Ave. N.W.
Seattle, WA 98107
Tel: (206) 784-0545
Cole stoves

The Dickinson Mfg. Co. Ltd.
407-204 Caver St.
Coquitlam, British Columbia
V3K 5B1
CANADA
Tel: (604) 525-6444
Fax: (604) 525-6417
Stoves and cabin heaters

Dickinson USA, Inc.
11324 Mukilteo Speedway
Mukilteo, WA 98275
Tel: (206) 347-4028
Fax: (206) 347-8502
Stoves and cabin heaters

Espar Heater Systems
6435 Kestrel Rd.
Missassauga, Ontario L5T 1Z8
CANADA
Tel: (416) 670-0960
Fax: (416) 670-0728
Espar cabin heaters

Fab-All Marine Mfg. Ltd.
#2 3005 Murray St.
Port Moody, British Columbia
V3H 1X3
CANADA
Tel: (604) 461-8522
Fax: (604) 461-2518
Stoves and cabin heaters

Force 10 Marine
23080 Hamilton Rd.
Richmond, British Columbia
V6V 1C9
CANADA
Tel: (604) 522-0233
Fax: (604) 522-9608
Barbeques and stoves

King Marine Air of Florida
8420 Ulmerton Rd.
Largo, FL 34641
Tel: (813) 532-0048
Fax: (813) 531-7130
Manufacturers of King-Air air conditioning and heating systems

Ocean Options, Inc.
50 Fort St.
Favirhaven, MA 02719
Tel: (508) 992-3644
Fax: (508) 999-5338
Espar cabin heaters

Origo
Division of Dometic Corp.
1121 Lewis Ave.
Sarasota, FL 34237
Tel: (813) 365-3660
Fax: (813) 955-2596
Alcohol heaters and stoves

Scan Marine Equipment
2144 Westlake Ave. N.
Suite D
Seattle, WA 98109
Tel: (206) 285-3675
Fax: (206) 285-9532
Ardic hot water heater/furnace and forced-air systems

Shipmate Stove Division
Richmond Ring Co.
Souderton, PA 18964
Tel: (215) 855-2609
Skippy heaters

Simpson Lawrence
P.O. Box 11210
Bradenton, FL 34282-1210
Tel: (813) 746-7161
Fax: (813) 746-7166
Taylor heaters and stoves

South Pacific Associates Ltd.
4918 Leary Ave. N.W.
Seattle, WA 98107
Tel: (206) 782-7700
Fax: (206) 782-4531
So-Pac electric heaters

Thermal Systems
Mottman Industrial Pk.
2757 29th Ave. S.W.
Tumwater, WA 98502
Tel: (206) 352-0539
Fax: (206) 943-6442
CNG and propane heaters

Webasto Heater
1458 E. Lincoln St.
Madison Heights, MI 48071
Tel: (313) 545-8770
Fax: (313) 545-8773
Diesel cabin and water heaters

Vetus - Den Ouden, Inc.
P.O. Box 8712
Baltimore, MD 21240-0712
Tel: Orders only: (800)
GO-VETUS
  or (410) 712-0740
Fax: (410) 712-0985
Calorifiers

Wolter Systems, Inc.
1100 Harrison Ave.
Cincinnati, OH 45214
Tel: (513) 651-2666
Fax: (513) 651-0633
Gas hot-water heaters

Ventilators

A & B Industries
1261 Andersen Dr.
Suite C
San Rafael, CA 94901
Tel: (415) 258-9300
Fax: (415) 258-9461
Wide range of marine deck hardware

Beckson Marine, Inc.
165 Holland Ave.
Bridgeport, CT 06605
Tel: (203) 333-1412
Fax: (203) 384-6954

Buck Algonquin Marine Hardware
370 N. Main St.
Smyrna, DE 19977-1011
Tel: (302) 659-6990
Fax: (302) 659-6909
Transom vent

Goiot S.A.
28 rue du Frere-Loius
44062 Nantes Cedex 02
FRANCE
Tel: (+33) 40 75 68 39
Fax: (+33) 40 75 43 56

GEM Products, Inc.
140 Industrial Loop
Orange Park, FL 32073
Tel: (800) 874-4506
  or (904) 264-5905
Fax: (904) 264-0173

Hood Yacht Systems
1 Maritime Dr.
Portsmouth, RI 02871
Tel: (401) 683-2900
Fax: (401) 683-2410
Dorade vent cowls

Jukova
Oy Colt Ab
PB 115, Bulevardi 42
SF-00121 Helsinki
FINLAND
Tel: (+358) 0-618831
Fax: (+358) 0-61883397
Aluminum cleats, hatches, ladders, grilles, and stanchion bases

Jukova, Ltd.
7 Hyde St.
P.O. Box 4180
Stamford, CT 06907-0180
Aluminum cleats, hatches, ladders, grilles and stanchion bases

Midget Louver
800 Main Ave.
Norwalk, CT 06852
Tel: (203) 866-8266
Fax: (203) 847-7147

Nicro Marine
2065 West Ave. 140th
San Leandro, CA 94577
Tel: (510) 357-8332
Fax: (510) 351-5465
Low-profile solar vents and cowls

Norseman Marine, Inc.
516 West Olas Blvd.
Ft. Lauderdale, FL 33312
Tel: (305) 467-1407
Fax: (305) 462-3470
Aluminum and stainless steel vent cowls

R.C. Marine Products Co. Ltd.
6-10 Parkway Dr.
Mairangi Bay
Auckland
NEW ZEALAND
Tel: (+64) 478-9185

Rondal bv
P.O. Box 52
8325 ZH
Vollenhove
NETHERLANDS
Tel: (+31) 0 5274 3500
Fax: (+31) 0 5274 3900

Sea-Dog Line
P.O. Box 479
Everett, WA 98201
Tel: (206) 259-0194
Fax: (206) 339-1345
Marine hardware manufacturers

Vetus - Den Ouden, Inc.
P.O. Box 8712
Baltimore, MD 21240-0712
Tel: Orders only: (800) GO-VETUS
  or (410) 712-0740
Fax: (410) 712-0985

Viking Marine
1630 W. Cowles
Long Beach, CA 90813
Tel: (213) 432-2259
Deck plates

Wellborn Marine & Industrial Products
805 Court St.
Clearwater, FL 34616
Tel: (813) 443-7661
Fax: (813) 447-0867

Figure 2: A solar powered low-profile vent from Nicro Marine.

Inflatables

If you are, like many sailors, in the market for a new dinghy, you should look at the advantages that an inflatable offers. First, an inflatable large enough to carry your entire crew can be stored deflated in almost any locker. Many sizes of outboards fit an inflatable, plus rowing an inflatable is fairly easy. Some can even be sailed. In a pinch, an inflatable can be used as an emergency liferaft.

Before purchasing an inflatable, there are a number of points that should be carefully checked over:

1. *The number of inflation tubes.* The more tubes an inflatable dinghy has, the less likely it is to dump you in the water if a tube ruptures. Most inflatables have at least two tubes; some have three or five. More than five tubes on a small dinghy means that you will spend more time disconnecting and reconnecting the pump. This can be quite tedious, leading to minimal use of the dinghy.

2. *The construction of the bottom.* Rigid-bottomed inflatables are the best choice for all around use, but they take up more space. The smallest rigid-bottomed craft is in the eight to nine foot range. This means that you will need a deck space of close to that much if you intend to stow the boat on deck. A better compromise might be to purchase a soft-bottomed inflatable that has wooden bottom boards. These dinghies pack away into a valise about the size of a medium liferaft.

3. *The transom.* If you intend to use an outboard motor, make sure the dinghy has a wooden transom. Dinghies without a wooden transom can usually be powered only by a very small outboard. Make sure that the transom has a bung hole to let water out. It makes the boat easier to drain when you scoop water inboard as you launch it.

4. *The towing eyes and securing lines.* Make sure they are strongly attached. If you are going to tow the boat, you will be unhappy if you find yourself towing only a painter with a towing eye attached while somebody else has "rescued" your dinghy.

5. *The size of the packed dinghy.* Be certain that it will fit in the locker you intend to store it in. Remember, too, that you might not be able to pack it as well as the salesman who sold it to you.

6. *The inclusion of a repair kit.* If you inadvertently put a hole in the dinghy at the beginning of a cruise, you want to be able to make temporary repairs.

7. *Secure points to which oars, a bailer, a sponge, and a flashlight can be tied.*

8. *The inclusion of a serviceable pump that will inflate the dinghy quickly and easily. All too often the pump is like a toy*

that falls apart after using it a few times.

9. *Molded-in oarlocks, a lifeline around the boat, and strong lifting handles.* The better inflatables have these features. Molded-in oarlocks make the boat easy to row should the outboard fail. The lifeline helps you get back aboard after going for a swim. The lifting handles will be used every time you bring the dinghy inboard or launch it.

Under use, an inflatable is very forgiving. It is the only dinghy that you can bang against the side of your boat without doing any harm (provided you get the oars inboard). It can be left on the mooring while you take the boat for a sail. (But make sure you have a wire pennant and padlock in areas where it might get stolen.) Rowing an inflatable is just like rowing a regular dinghy, except that an inflatable can be windblown rather easily. This may make your job harder when you are rowing upwind.

Under tow, I have found inflatables to be rather skitterish. The easiest way to tow one is to adjust the length of the towline so that the boat is just in front of the third wave behind the boat. If your dinghy still skitters, a heavy dock line tied to the dinghy's transom and towed behind it will cure the problem. Remember to remove oars and gear which might be lost if the dinghy swamps.

Suppliers of Inflatable Dinghies

AB Inflatables
919 Bay Ridge Rd.
Suite A
Annapolis, MD 21403
Tel: (800) 422-5977
Fax: (410) 267-8020
(Formerly Calypso)

Avon West
1851 McGaw Ave.
Irvine, CA 92714
Tel: (714) 250-0880
Avon inflatables

Achilles West
1407 80th St. S.W.
Everett, WA 98203
Tel: (206) 353-7000
Achilles inflatables

Achilles East
P.O. Box 517
East Rutherford, NJ 07073
Tel: (201) 438-6400
Fax: (201) 438-2618
Achilles inflatables

Bombard USA
P.O. Box 400
Thompson Creek Rd.
Stevensville, MD 21666
Tel: (410) 643-4141
Fax: (410) 643-4143
Bombard inflatables

California Inflatables Co.
2608 Temple Heights Dr.
Oceanside, CA 92056
Tel: (619) 724-8300
Fax: (619) 724-9531
Inflatables and rigid-bottom inflatables

Caribe Inflatables USA
4444 S.W. 71st St.
Miami, FL 33155
Tel: (305) 667-2997
Fax: (305) 667-3813
Caribe inflatables

Caribe Nautica C.A.
1ra. Calle la Industria
Edificio Caribe
Zona Industrial
Palo Verde
Caracas
VENEZUELA
Tel: (+58) 2 21 42 12
Fax: (+58) 2 21 41 22
Caribe inflatables

Defender Industries, Inc.
255 Main St.
P.O. Box 820
New Rochelle, NY 10801
Tel: (914) 632-3001
Fax: (914) 632-6544
Dinghies and inflatables

Dynous by Toyo Tire & Rubber
500 Marathon Pkwy.
Lawrenceville, GA 30245
Tel: (404) 339-3510
Fax: (404) 339-3566
Dynous inflatables

H.B.I
185 South Rd.
Groton, CT 06430
Tel: (203) 445-6390
Fax: (203) 448-1038
Hard-bottomed inflatables

Imtra Corp.
30 Barnet Blvd.
New Bedford, MA 02745
Tel: (508) 990-7000
Fax: (508) 998-5359
Avon inflatables

Intercoastal, Inc.
919A Bay Ridge Rd.
Annapolis, MD 21403
Tel: (410) 267-0850
Fax: (410) 267-8020
Inflatables

International Watercraft
2389 S.E. Dixie Hwy.
Stuart, FL 34996
Tel: (800) 780-RAFT
Fax: (407) 283-0122
Retailer of parts and accessories for inflatables

North Atlantic Rigid Inflatables
31 Lagoon Rd.
Portsmouth, RI 02871
Tel: (401) 683-6588
Fax: (401) 683-6775
Rigid-bottom inflatables

Nautica International
6135 N.W. 159th St., E-17
Miami, Fl 33169
Tel: (305) 556-5554
Fax: (305) 557-0268
Nautica inflatables

Nissan Marine & Power Products
1420 Valwood Pkwy.
Building 2, Suite 200
Carrollton, TX 75006
Tel: (214) 243-7981
Fax: (214) 243-6806
Inflatables

Novamarine America
Division of Leopard Marine Systems
74011 114th Ave.
Suite 503B
Largo, FL 34643
Tel: (813) 545-9997
Fax: (813) 541-4860
Inflatables

Novurania of America, Inc.
8476 N.W. 61st. St.
Miami, FL 33166
Tel: (305) 597-0321
Fax: (305) 471-9614
Novurania inflatables

OMC Express
200 Seahorse Dr.
Waukegan, IL 60085
Tel: (708) 689-5583
Fax: (708) 689-5739
Inflatables

Quicksilver Inflatables
W6250 Pioneer Rd.
P.O. Box 1939
Fond du Lac, WI 54935
Tel: (800) 552-3882
  or (414) 929-5000
Fax: (414) 929-5017
Quicksilver inflatables

Sevylor USA, Inc.
6651 E. 26th St.
Los Angeles, CA 90040-3215
Tel: (213) 727-6013
Fax: (213) 726-0481
Sevylor inflatables

Viking Life-Saving Equipment (America), Inc.
1625 North Miami Ave.
Miami, FL 33136
Tel: (305) 374-5115
Fax: (305) 374-1535

Zeppelin Technologies
2226 S. Federal Hwy.
Ft. Lauderdale, FL 33315
Tel: (305) 764-1161
Fax: (305) 764-2717
Inflatables

Zodiac of North America
Thompson Creek Rd.
Stevensville, MD 21666
Tel: (410) 643-4141
Fax: (410) 643-4491
Zodiac inflatables

Instruments: Electronic

You have just taken delivery of your new boat and have empty spaces in the navigation area waiting for new electronics. What should you buy? In some ways, your choices are dictated by the type of sailing or boating you do. For instance, if you stay within twenty miles of shore, your first item should be a VHF radio, the range of which is essentially line of sight. A VHF radio will enable you to stay in touch with other boaters and with rescue services. After the radio, you should buy a depth sounder to show the bottom contours or depth of water under the boat. If you use your boat for fishing, you might want to buy an instrument that is both a depth sounder and a fish finder. Make sure your depth sounder has shallow water alarms. You may be concentrating on something else and need the alarm to warn you that you are in danger of running aground. With a good VHF radio and a depth sounder, plus a reliable compass, a competent seaman can navigate almost anywhere.

Many inshore sailors, however, would also like a loran. A good loran will enable you to position your boat close by a buoy or get an accurate repeat fix on a favorite fishing ground. But while loran is a good navigation aid, remember that its accuracy is only to within a few hundred feet. And the accuracy can be reduced if the signal passes over land and water, such as the Maine coast, where it crosses islands and

ocean several times. There are also areas where coverage is not available or is very fuzzy — for instance, in parts of the Caribbean. If you sail offshore often, you might want to consider satnav or GPS navigation electronics. The accuracy of these units is considerable. In fact, differential GPS, such as the navy uses, is said to be accurate to within 50 feet. The GPS used by sailors has been downgraded slightly and is said to be accurate to within 500 feet, although this downgrading is now being reviewed, because of the potential for lawsuits.

For sailors, the next most useful piece of electronic equipment to get is a set of wind instruments. A wind instrument package tops the list of electronic gear for racing sailors. Wind instruments should include wind speed, boat speed, wind angle, and wind direction indicators and an electronic compass. These usually come as a complete network. More sophisticated electronic packages enable the navigator to calculate true wind angles and speeds, heel angle, apparent and true wind angles on the next leg of the course, and much more, as well as interfacing with other electronic equipment. Cruising sailors, too, can benefit from wind instruments. Many autopilots interface with wind instruments and loran to keep the boat on track. In fact, a large number of electronic instruments now use the National Marine Electronics Association's (NMEA) interfacing standards to ensure compatibility between equipment from different manufacturers. You should make sure that the instruments you buy use these standards and can interact. For instance, wind instruments, loran, satnav or GPS, and a barometer can all feed information to an electronic chart unit which tells you where the boat is at any time. Plus, it can feed an autopilot steering the boat, make turns at designated waypoints, and even keep you clear of hazards. If you want to get even more sophisticated, all the signals can be fed into a computer and integrated to serve a very large number of functions.

The next piece of equipment to buy is radar. The newer types are smaller, use less power, and have collision-avoidance alerts, as well as a minimum twenty mile range. The radar should be mounted as high as possible on the boat to maximize its range. Radar will also help you get home in fog or periods of low visibility.

If you range further than 20 miles offshore, you should consider a single-sideband radio (SSB) or one of the newer satellite links which will enable you to talk to almost anywhere in the world. These radio and telephone links can be used to keep in touch with friends, family, or business associates. You can even modem or fax documents worldwide. For the offshore sailor, some other pieces of electronic equipment will help make life easier.

First, is an EPIRB or electronic position-indicating radio beacon. Should your boat be damaged or sink, the EPIRB will alert a satellite or aircraft flying overhead and help to direct rescuers to you. Remember that your EPIRB needs to be registered with NOAA or the appropriate authority in order for them to come looking for you. Also, keep in mind that an EPIRB should be left on once it is switched on, so that rescuers can home in on its signal. In addition, a NAVTEX receiver is very useful. This little box is set to pick up notices to mariners and weather forecasts for a particular area. There are about 12 NAVAREAS worldwide, with more expected. Another electronic gizmo for offshore sailors is the Argos satellite tracking system. It is just becoming commercially available, but is already well known because of its involvement with various offshore races. This system operates in a manner similar to an EPIRB and uses the same satellites, but it transmits continuously to ensure your position is known at all times. Argos transmitters can be leased on a long- or short-term basis. You might want to lease one for a single long trip.

Manufacturers of Electronic Instruments

Argos

Service Argos, Inc.
NACLS
9200 Basil Ct.
Suite 306
Landover, MD 20785
Tel: (301) 341-1814
Fax: (301) 341-2130

Depth Sounders and Fishfinders

Apelco
46 River Rd.
Hudson, NH 03051
Tel: (603) 881-9605
Fax: (603) 881-4756

Autohelm
A Raytheon Company
46 River Rd.
Hudson, NH 03051
Tel: (603) 881-9605
Fax: (603) 881-4756

Brookes & Gatehouse
7855 126th Avenue N.
Largo, FL 34643
Tel: (813) 536-1400
Fax: (813) 536-1717

Cetrek, Inc.
254 Church St.
Pembroke, MA 02359
Tel: (617) 826-7497
Fax: (617) 826-2495

Coast Navigation
116 Legion Ave.
Annapolis, MD 21401
Tel: (410) 268-3120
Fax: (410) 268-0389

Datamarine International, Inc.
53 Portside Dr.
Pocasset, MA 02559
Tel: (508) 563-7151
Fax: (508) 564-4707

Eagle Electronics
12000 E. Skelly Dr.
Tulsa, OK 74128
Tel: (918) 437-6881
Fax: (918) 438-3277

Eastern Marine Distibutors
1064 Sun Valley Dr.
Annapolis, MD 21401
Tel: (800) 222-9440
Fax: (301) 757-1048

Furuno U.S.A., Inc.
P.O. Box 2343271
Harbor Way S.
San Francisco, CA 94083
Tel: (415) 873-9393
Fax: (415) 872-3403

Humminbird
One Humminbird Ln.
Eufaula, AL 36027
Tel: (205) 687-6613
Fax: (205) 687-4272

Impulse Technologies
4700 Amon Carter Blvd.
Fort Worth, TX 76155
Tel: (817) 858-3300
Fax: (817) 858-3311

Interphase Technologies, Inc.
1201 Shaffer Rd.
Santa Cruz, CA 95060
Tel: (408) 426-2007
Fax: (408) 426-0965

Lowrance Electronics
12000 E. Skelly Dr.
Tulsa, OK 74128-2486
Tel: (918) 437-6881

Marinetek
2239 Paragon Dr.
San Jose, CA 95131
Tel: (408) 922-0880
Fax: (408) 922-0290

Raytheon Marine
46 River Rd.
Hudson, NH 03051
Tel: (603) 881-5200
Fax: (603) 881-4756

Ross Laboratories
3138 Fairview Ave. E.
Seattle, WA 98102
Tel: (206) 324-3950
Fax: (206) 329-0250

Silva U.S. Marine
4923 Bayshore Blvd.
Tampa, FL 33611
Tel: (813) 839-2266
Fax: (813) 837-2177

Simrad, Inc.
19210 33rd Ave. W.
Lynnwood, WA 98036
Tel: (800) 425-5565
 or (206) 778-8821
Fax: (206) 771-7211

Si-Tex Marine Electronics
P.O. Box 6700
Clearwater, FL 34618
Tel: (813) 535-4681
Fax: (813) 530-7272

S.R. Instruments, Inc.
600 Young St.
Tonawanda, NY 14150
Tel: (800) 654-6360
  or (716) 693-5977
Fax: (716) 693-5854

Standard Communications
P.O. Box 92151
Los Angeles, CA 90009
Tel: (213) 532-5300

Uniden America Corp.
4700 Amon Carter Blvd.
Fort Worth, TX 76155
Tel: (817) 858-3300
Fax: (817) 858-3311

VDO-Yazaki Instruments Corp.
P.O. Box 2897
980 Brooke Rd.
Winchester, VA 22601
Tel: (703) 665-0100
Fax: (703) 662-2515

Vexilar
9252 Grand Ave. S.
Minneapolis, MN 55420
Tel: (612) 884-5291
Fax: (612) 884 5292

Wesmar
18500 68th Ave.
Box 3001
Bothell, WA 98041-3001
Tel: (206) 481-2296
Fax: (206) 486-0909

Electronic Charts

Autohelm
A Raytheon Company
46 River Rd.
Hudson, NH 03051
Tel: (603) 881-9605
Fax: (603) 881-4756

C-Map/USA
P.O. Box 1609
Sandwich, MA 02563
Tel: (800) 424-2627
Makers of chart cartridges

Cetrek, Inc
254 Church St.
Pembroke, MA 02359
Tel: (617) 826-7497
Fax: (617) 826-2495

Datamarine International, Inc.
53 Portside Dr.
Pocasset, MA 02559
Tel: (508) 563-7151
Fax: (508) 564-4707
Chart link systems

Electronic Charts Co. (ECC)
1715 N.W. Market
Seattle, WA 98107
Tel: (206) 782-2535
SeaNav computer-assisted electronic sailing and bathymetric charts

Electronic Marine Systerns
800 Ferndale Pl.
Rahway, NJ 07065
Tel: (908) 382-4344
Fax: (908) 388-5111
Chart viewers

Icom
2380 116th Ave. N. E.
Bellevue, WA 98004
Tel: (206) 454-8155

KVH Industries, Inc.
110 Enterprise Center
Middletown, RI 02840
Tel: (401) 847-3327
Fax: (401) 849-0045
Makers of the Quadro network which uses your existing charts

King Marine Electronics
13830 58th St. N., #47
Clearwater, FL 34620
Tel: (813) 530-3411
Fax: (813) 530-3820

Maptech
2225 Sperry Ave.
Suite 1000
Ventura, CA 93003
Tel: (805) 654-8006
Fax: (805) 654-8147
Uses GPS or loran signal to track course

Micrologic
9610 DeSoto Ave.
Chatsworth, CA 91311
Tel: (818) 998-1216
Fax: (818) 709-3658

Navionics
P.O. Box 722
Woods Hole, MA 02543
Tel: (508) 457-0701
Fax: (508) 548-9030

Raytheon Marine
46 River Rd.
Hudson, NH 03051
Tel: (603) 881-5200
Fax: (603) 881-4756

Si-Tex Marine Electronics
P.O. Box 6700
Clearwater, FL 34618
Tel: (813) 535-4681
Fax: (813) 530-7272

Signet Marine
16321 Gothard St.
Unit E
Huntington Beach, CA 92647
Tel: (714) 848-6467
Fax: (714) 848-6009

Simrad
19210 33rd Ave.
W. Lynnwood, WA 98036
Tel: (206) 778-8821
Fax: (206) 771-7211

Electronic Compasses

Autohelm
A Raytheon Company
46 River Rd.
Hudson, NH 03051
Tel: (603) 881-9605
Fax: (603) 881-4756

Shakespeare Co.
P.O. Box 733
Newberry, SC 29108
Tel: (800) 845-7750
Fax: (803) 276-8940

Electronic Noise Filters

Marine Technology
2667 E. 28th St.
Suite 505
Signal Hill, CA 90806
Tel: (310) 595-6521
Fax: (310) 427-0770

Euro Marine Trading
64 Halsey St. #27
Newport, RI 02840
Tel: (800) 222-7712
Fax: (401) 849-3230
NKE Electronics

Navico
7411 114th Ave. N.
Suite 310
Largo, FL 34643
Tel: (813) 546-4300
Fax: (813) 546-5539

GPS

Apelco
46 River Rd.
Hudson, NH 03051
Tel: (603) 881-9605
Fax: (603) 881-4756

Cetrek, Inc.
254 Church St.
Pembroke, MA 02359
Tel: (617) 826-7497
Fax: (617) 826-2495

Eagle Electronics
12000 E. Skelly Dr.
Tulsa, OK 74128
Tel: (918) 437-6881
Fax: (918) 438-3277

Electronic Marine Systems
800 Ferndale Pl.
Rahway, NJ 07065
Tel: (908) 382-4344
Fax: (908) 388-5111

Euro Marine Trading
64 Halsey St. #27
Newport, RI 02840
Tel: (800) 222-7712
Fax: (401) 849-3230
NKE electronics

Furuno U.S.A., Inc.
P.O. Box 2343271
Harbor Way S.
San Francisco, CA 94083
Tel: (415) 873-9393
Fax: (415) 872-3403

Garmin
9875 Widmer Rd.
Lenexa, KN 66215
Tel: (800) 800-1020
or (913) 599-1515
Fax: (913) 599-2103

Humminbird
One Humminbird Ln.
Eufaula, AL 36027
Tel: (800) 633-1468
or (205) 687-6613
Fax: (205) 687-4272

Impulse Technologies
4700 Amon Carter Blvd.
Fort Worth, TX 76155
Tel: (817) 858-3300
Fax: (817) 858-3311

Koden International, Inc..
14000 Roosevelt Blvd.
Clearwater, FL 34622
Tel: (813) 536-0898
Fax: (813) 530-7272

Magellan Systems Corp.
960 Overland Ct.
San Dimas, CA 91773
Tel: (714) 394-5000
Fax: (714) 394-7050

Micrologic, Inc.
9610 DeSoto Ave.
Chatsworth, CA 91311
Tel: (818) 998-1216
Fax: (818) 709-3658
Admiral GPS

Magnavox
2829 Maricopa St.
Torrance, CA 90503
Tel: (213) 618-1200

Motorola, Inc.
4000 Commercial Ave.
Northbrook, IL 60062
Tel: (800) 421-2477
Traxar GPS

Navstar Electronics
1500 N. Washington Blvd.
Sarasota, FL 34236
Tel: (800) 486-6338
Fax: (813) 366-9335

North Star Technologies, Inc.
30 Sudbury Rd.
Acton, MA 01720
Tel: (508) 897-6600
Fax: (508) 897-7241

Panasonic Co.
Marine Electronics Division
One Panasonic Way
Secaucus, NJ 07094
Tel: (201) 392-6397
Fax: (201) 348-7209

Shakespeare Co.
P.O. Box 733
Newberry, SC 29108
Tel: (800) 845-7750
Fax: (803) 276-8940

Sony Corp. of America
One Sony Dr.
Park Ridge, NJ 07656
Tel: (201) 930-6440
Fax: (201) 930-0491

Trimble Navigation
Marine Division
P.O. Box 3642
Sunnyvale, CA 94088-3642
Tel: (800) TRIMBLE
 or in California (800)
221-3001
Fax: (408) 737-6057
NavTrac GPS

Interfaces

Apelco
46 River Rd.
Hudson, NH 03051
Tel: (603) 881-9605
Fax: (603) 881-4756
GPS to plotter, fish finder, loran, and radar interface

AUSCO
15 Goose Pond Rd.
Tabernacle, NJ 08088
Tel: (609) 268-3081
Hardware link between electronic instruments and computer

Autohelm
A Raytheon Company
46 River Rd.
Hudson, NH 03051
Tel: (603) 881-9605
Fax: (603) 881-4756
Daisy chain for Autohelm instruments

Better Boating Association
P.O. Box 407
Needham, MA 02192
Tel: (800) 242-7854
Fax: (617) 449-0514

Eagle Electronics
12000 E. Skelly Dr.
Tulsa, OK 74128
Tel: (918) 437-6881
Fax: (918) 438-3277

Si-Tex Marine Electronics
P.O. Box 6700
Clearwater, FL 34618
Tel: (813) 535-4681
Fax: (813) 530-7272
Nav-Add system

Loran

Apelco
46 River Rd.
Hudson, NH 03051
Tel: (603) 881-9605
Fax: (603) 881-4756
Loran and loran plotters

Brookes & Gatehouse
7855 126th Avenue N.
Largo, FL 34643
Tel: (813) 536-1400
Fax: (813) 536-1717

Datamarine International, Inc.
53 Portside Dr.
Pocasset, MA 02559
Tel: (508) 563-7151
Fax: (508) 564-4707

Eagle Electronics
12000 E. Skelly Dr.
Tulsa, OK 74128
Tel: (918) 437-6881
Fax: (918) 438-3277

Furuno U.S.A., Inc.
P.O. Box 2343271
Harbor Way S.
San Francisco, CA 94083
Tel: (415) 873-9393
Fax: (415) 872-3403

Heath
Hilltop Rd.
St. Joseph, Ml 49085
Tel: (800) 253-0570
Fax: (616) 983-0699

II Morrow
P.O. Box 13549
2345 Turner Rd. S.E.
Salem, OR 97309
Tel: (503) 581-8101

Interphase Technologies, Inc.
1201 Shaffer Rd.
Santa Cruz, CA 95060
Tel: (408) 426-2007
Fax: (408) 426-0965

Koden International
77 Accord Park Dr.
Norwell, MA O2061
Tel: (617) 871-6223
Fax: (617) 871-6226

KVH Industries
110 Enterprise Center
Middletown, Rl 02840
Tel: (401) 847-3327
Fax: (401) 849-0045

Loran-Card
1173 A 2nd Ave.
Box 150
New York, NY 10021
Tel: (212) 371-9286

Marinetek
2239 Paragon Dr.
San Jose, CA 95131
Tel: (408) 922-0880
Fax: (408) 922-0290

Micrologic
9610 DeSoto Ave.
Chatsworth, CA 91311
Tel: (818) 998-1216
Fax: (818) 709-3658
Mariner and Supersport lorans

Navstar Electronics
1500 N. Washington Blvd.
Sarasota, FL 34236
Tel: (800) 486-6338
Fax: (813) 366-9335

North Star Technologies, Inc.
30 Sudbury Rd.
Acton, MA 01720
Tel: (508) 897-6600
Fax: (508) 897-7241

Ray Jefferson
4200 Mitchell St.
Philadelphia, PA 19128
Tel: (215) 487-2800
Fax: (215) 482-3323

Ross Engineering
12505 Starkey Rd.
Suite E
Largo, FL 34643
Tel: (813) 536-1226
Fax: (813) 535-4248
Navigation and communication equipment

Trimble Navigation
645 N. Mary Ave.
P.O. Box 3642
Sunnyvale, CA 94088-3642
Tel: (800) TRIMBLE
Fax: (408) 730-2997

Uniden
4700 Amon Carter Blvd.
Fort Worth, TX 76155
Tel: (817) 858-3300
Fax: (817) 858-3333

Vigil
7855 126th Ave. N.
Largo, FL 34643
Tel: (813) 536-1400
Fax: (813) 536-1717

Marine Stereo

Automation Design
18 E. Montauk Hwy.
Hampton Bays, NY 11946
Tel: (516) 728-2864
Fax: (516) 728-8124
Audio and video systems

Jensen
25 Tristate
International Office Center
Suite 400
Lincolnshire, IL 60069
Tel: (800) 323- 0707
  or (708) 317-3700
Fax: (708) 317-3826

Maxxima Marine
125 Cabot Ct.
Hauppauge, NY 11788
Tel: (516) 434-1200
Fax: (516) 434-1457

Pioneer Electronics
2265 E. 220th St.
Long Beach, CA 90810
Tel: (213) 835-6177
Fax: (213) 816-0402

Poly-Planar
1800 Mearns Rd.
Unit J
Warminster, PA 18974
Tel: (215) 675-7805
Fax: (215) 675-7920

Radion Sound, Inc.
1031 W. Main St.
Louisville, KY 40202
Tel: (502) 589-9946
Fax: (502) 589-9949

Si-Tex Marine Electronics
P.O. Box 6700
Clearwater, FL 34618
Tel: (813) 535-4681
Fax: (813) 530-7272

SMR Marine Electronics
1401 N.W. 89th Ct.
Miami, FL 33172
Tel: (305) 591-9433
Fax: (305) 593-9693
Marine stereos and speakers

Standard Communications
P.O. Box 92151
Los Angeles, CA 90009
Tel: (213) 532-5300

Navigation Computers

AP Systems
7461 Pollock Dr.
Las Vegas, NV 89123
Tel: (702) 361-7676

Calculated Industries
22720 Savi Ranch Pkwy.
Yorba Linda, CA 92687
Tel: (800) 854-8075
Fax: (714) 921-2799

Celesticomp
8903 S.W. Bayview Dr.
Vashon, WA 98070
Tel: (206) 463-9626
Celesticomp V navigation computer

Conex Electro Systems
P.O. Box 1342
1602 Carolina St.
Bellingham, WA 98227
Tel: (206) 734-4323
Fax: (206) 676-4822

InfoCenter, Inc.
P.O. Box 47175
Forestville, MD 20707
Tel: (800) 526-0649
Sextants and navigation calculators

KVH Industries, Inc.
110 Enterprise Center
Middletown, RI 02840
Tel: (401) 847-3327
Fax: (401) 849-0045
Sailcomp computers and compasses

Litton/C. Plath
North American Division
222 Severn Ave.
Annapolis, MD 21403-2569
Tel: (410) 263-6700
Fax: (410) 268-8713
Weems & Plath Galileo and Tamaya computers

Merlin Navigation
1520 22nd Ave. E.
Suite W
Seattle, WA 98112
Tel: (206) 329-8574
Merlin II sight reduction and navigation computer

NAVTEX

Alden Electronics
40 Washington St.
Westboro, MA 01581
Tel: (508) 366-8851
Faxmate, marine fax, and NAVTEX receivers

Radio Holland U.S.A.
8943 Gulf Freeway
Houston, TX 77017
Tel: (713) 943-3325
Fax: (713) 943-3802

Radar

Furuno U.S.A., Inc.
P.O. Box 2343 271
Harbor Way S.
San Francisco, CA 94083
Tel: (415) 873-9393
Fax: (415) 872-3403

Koden International, Inc.
14000 Roosevelt Blvd.
Clearwater, FL 34622
Tel: (813) 536-0898
Fax: (813) 530-7272

Raytheon
46 River Rd.
Hudson, NH 03051
Tel: (603) 881-9605
Fax: (603) 881-4756

Shakespeare Co.
P.O. Box 733
Newberry, SC 29108
Tel: (800) 845-7750
Fax: (803) 276-8940

Si-Tex Marine Electronics
P.O. Box 6700
Clearwater, FL 34618
Tel: (813) 535-4681
Fax: (813) 530-7272

Koden
P.O. Box 6700
Clearwater, FL 34618
Tel: (813) 535-4681

Panasonic Co.
Marine Electronics Division
One Panasonic Way
Secaucus, NJ 07094
Tel: (201) 392-6397
Fax: (201) 348-7209

Simrad, Inc.
19210 33rd Ave. W.
Lynnwood, WA 98036
Tel: (800) 425-5565
  or (206) 778-8821
Fax: (206) 771-7211

Figure 1: A VHF radio from
Si-Tex Marine Electronics

Vigil
7855 126th Ave. N.
Largo, FL 34643
Tel: (813) 536-1400
Fax: (813) 536-1717

Radio Direction Finders

Apelco
46 River Rd.
Hudson, NH 03051
Tel: (603) 881-9605
Fax: (603) 881-4756

Brookes & Gatehouse
7855 126th Ave. N.
Largo, FL 34643
Tel: (813) 536-1400
Fax: (813) 536-1717

Furuno U.S.A., Inc.
P.O. Box 2343271
Harbor Way S.
San Francisco, CA 94083
Tel: (415) 873-9393
Fax: (415) 872-3403

Icom America, Inc.
2380 116th Ave. N.E.
Bellevue, WA 98004
Tel: (800) 999-9877
  or (206) 454-8155

Kenwood U.S.A.
P.O. Box 22745
2201 E. Dominguez St.
Long Beach, CA 90801-5745
Tel: (213) 639-4200

Koden International, Inc..
14000 Roosevelt Blvd.
Clearwater, FL 34622
Tel: (813) 536-0898
Fax: (813) 530-7272

Ross Engineering
12505 Starkey Rd.
Suite E
Largo, FL 34643
Tel: (813) 536-1226
Fax: (813) 535-4248
*Navigation and
communication equipment*

Sony Corp. of America
One Sony Dr.
Park Ridge, NJ 07656
Tel: (201) 930-6440
Fax: (201) 930-0491

**Tele Comm
Communications**
P.O. Box 3232
Margate, NJ 08402
Tel: (609) 822-8588

Yaesu Communications
17210 Edwards Rd.
Cerritos, CA 90701
Tel: (213) 404-2700
Fax: (213) 404-1210

Radio Telephones

Apelco
46 River Rd.
Hudson, NH 03051
Tel: (603) 881-9605
Fax: (603) 881-4756
*Portable and shelf-mounted
VHF radios*

Furuno U.S.A., Inc.
P.O. Box 2343271
Harbor Way S.
San Francisco, CA 94083
Tel: (415) 873-9393
Fax: (415) 872-3403
VHF and SSB

Humminbird
One Humminbird Ln.
Eufaula, AL 36027
Tel: (800) 633-1468
  or (205) 687-6613
Fax: (205) 687-4272

Hull Electronics
1100-B N. Magnolia Ave.
El Cajon, CA 92020-1919
Tel: (619) 447-0036
Fax: (619) 444-0628

Icom America, Inc.
2380-116th Ave. N.E.
Bellevue, WA 98004
Tel: (800) 999-9877
 or (206) 454-8155
*Portable and shelf-mounted
VHFs*

Impulse Technologies
4700 Amon Carter Blvd.
Fort Worth, TX 76155
Tel: (817) 858-3300
Fax: (817) 858-3311

Intech
2270 Martin Ave.
Santa Clara, CA 95050
Tel: (408) 727-0500
Fax: (408) 748-9489

Kenwood U.S.A. Corp.
Marine Products Division
2201 E. Dominguez St.
Long Beach, CA 90801-5745
Tel: (213) 639-4200
*Shelf-mounted and portable
VHFs*

Maracom Marine, Inc.
7350 N.W. 34th St.
Miami, FL 33122
Tel: (305) 592-3591
Fax: (305) 592-3591
Shelf and portable VHFs

Marinetek
2239 Paragon Dr.
San Jose, CA 95131
Tel: (408) 922-0880
Fax: (408) 922-0290

Maxxima Marine
125 Cabot Ct.
Hauppauge, NY 11788
Tel: (516) 434-1200
Fax: (516) 434-1457

Midland International
1690 N. Topping
Kansas City, MO 64120
Tel: (816) 241-8500
Fax: (816) 245-1144

**Motorola Triton Marine
Communications**
1301 E. Algonquin Rd.
Schaumburg, IL 60196
Tel: (708) 576-6563
Fax: (708) 576-2702

MoTron Electronics
310 Garfield St.
Suite 4
Eugene, OR 97402
Tel: (800) 338-9058
Fax: (503) 687-2492

Navico
7411 114th Ave. N.
Suite 310
Largo, FL 34643
Tel: (813) 546-4300
Fax: (813) 546-5539

Panasonic Co.
Marine Electronics Division
One Panasonic Way
Secaucus, NJ 07094
Tel: (201) 392-6397
Fax: (201) 348-7209

Radio Holland U.S.A.
8943 Gulf Freeway
Houston, TX 77017
Tel: (713) 943-3325
Fax: (713) 943-3802

Ranger Communications
3377 Carmel Mountain Rd.
San Diego, CA 92121
Tel: (619) 259-0287
Fax: (619) 259-0437
*Hand-held and shelf-mounted
VHFs*

Ray Jefferson
4200 Mitchell St.
Philadelphia, PA 19128
Tel: (215) 487-2800
Fax: (215) 482-3323

Ross Engineering
12505 Starkey Rd.
Suite E
Largo, FL 34643
Tel: (813) 536-1226
Fax: (813) 535-4248

SEA, Inc.
7030 220th St. S.W.
Mountlake Terrace, WA 98043
Tel: (206) 771-2182
Fax: (206) 771-2650

**SeaRanger Marine
Electronics**
201 Meadow Rd.
Edison, NJ 08818
Tel: (201) 819-4730
Fax: (201) 819-4794

SGC, Inc.
13737 S.E. 26th St.
Bellevue, WA 98005
Tel: (206) 7466310
Fax: (206) 746-6384
*SG-2000 SSB radios are
American made*

Shakespeare Co.
P.O. Box 733
Newberry, SC 29108
Tel: (800) 845-7750
Fax: (803) 276-8940

Simrad, Inc.
19210 33rd Ave. W.
Lynnwood, WA 98036
Tel: (800) 425-5565
  or (206) 778-8821
Fax: (206) 771-7211

Si-Tex Marine Electronics
P.O. Box 6700
Clearwater, FL 34618
Tel: (813) 535-4681
Fax: (813) 530-7272

SMR Marine Electronics
1401 N.W. 89th Ct.
Miami, FL 33172
Tel: (305) 591-9433
Fax: (305) 593-9693
Portable and shelf-mounted
VHF

Standard Communications
P.O. Box 92151
Los Angeles, CA 90009-2151
Tel: (310) 532-5300
Fax: (310) 515-7197

Tele Comm
Communications
P.O. Box 3232
Margate, NJ 08402
Tel: (609) 822-8588

Uniden Amercia Corp.
4700 Amon Carter Blvd.
Fort Worth, TX 76155
Tel: (817) 858-3300
Fax: (817) 858-3311

Yaesu Communications
17210 Edwards Rd.
Cerritos, CA 90701
Tel: (213) 404-2700
Fax: (213) 404-1210

Satellite Communications
Communications Satellite
Corp.
950 L'Enfant Plaza S.W.
Washington, DC 20024
Tel: (202) 863-6507
Fax: (202) 488-3814/3819

Sonar

American Pioneer
4775 Ballard Ave. N.W.
Seattle, WA 98107
Tel: (800) 927-6627
  or (206) 789-7053

Eagle Electronics
12000 E. Skelly Dr.
Tulsa, OK 74128
Tel: (918) 437-6881
Fax: (918) 438-3277
Accura sonar

Furuno U.S.A., Inc.
P.O. Box 2343271
Harbor Way S.
San Francisco, CA 94083
Tel: (415) 873-9393
Fax: (415) 872-3403

Humminbird
One Humminbird Ln.
Eufaula, AL 36027
Tel: (800) 633-1468
  or (205) 687-6613
Fax: (205) 687-4272

Wesmar
18500 68th Ave.
Box 3001
Bothell, WA 98041-3001
Tel: (206) 481-2296
Fax: (206) 486-0909

Satcom

Magnvox Co.
2829 Maricopa St.
Torrance, CA 90503
Tel: (213) 618-1200

Radar Devices
2955 Merced St.
San Leandro, CA 94577
Tel: (415) 483-1953
Fax: (415) 351-7413

Radio Holland U.S.A.
1509 S.W. 1st Ave.
Ft. Lauderdale, FL 33315
Tel: (305) 764-0130
Fax: (305) 764-0197

SEA
7030 220th St. S.W.
Mountlake Terrace, WA 98043
Tel: (206) 771-2182

Weather Map Receivers

Alden Electronics
40 Washington St.
Westboro, MA 01581
Tel: (508) 366-8851

Phitechnologies
4605 N. Stiles
Oklahoma, OK 73105
Tel: (405) 521-9000
Fax: (405) 524-4254

SEA
7030 220th St. S.W.
Mountlake Terrace, WA 98043
Tel: (206) 771-2182
Fax: (206) 771-2650

Sealutions
9842 Hibert
Suite 145
San Diego, CA 92131
Tel: (619) 429-5850

Sony Corp. of America
One Sony Dr.
Park Ridge, NJ 07656
Tel: (201) 930-6440
Fax: (201) 930-0491

Wind Instruments

Autohelm
A Raytheon Company
46 River Rd.
Hudson, NH 03051
Tel: (603) 881-5838
Fax: (603) 881-4756

Brookes & Gatehouse
7855 126th Ave. N.
Largo, FL 34643
Tel: (813) 536-1400
Fax: (813) 536-1717

Datamarine International, Inc.
53 Portside Dr.
Pocasset, MA 02559
Tel: (508) 564-7151
Fax: (508) 564-4707

Davis Instruments
3465 Diablo Ave.
Harward, CA 94545
Tel: (415) 732-9229
Fax: (415) 732-9188

Moor Electronics
601 Amherst St.
Buffalo, NY 14207
Tel: (716) 876-4970
Fax: (716) 876-0567

Epic
150 Nassau St.
Suite 1430
New York, NY 10038
Tel: (212) 349-2470
Fax: (212) 406-2508

Euro Marine Trading
64 Halsey St. #27
Newport, RI 02840
Tel: (800) 222-7712
Fax: (401) 849-3230
NKE electronics

Navico
7411-114th Ave. N.
Suite 310
Largo, FL 34643
Tel: (813) 546-4300
Fax: (813) 546-5539

Ockam Instruments
26 Higgins Dr.
Milford, CT 06460
Tel: (203) 877-7453
Fax: (203) 878-0572

Robertson-Shipmate
400 Oser Ave.
Hauppauge, NY 11788
Tel: (800) 645-3738
Fax: (516) 273-3270

Rochester Instruments, Inc.
118 Airport Dr.
Suite 205
San Bernardino, CA 92408
Tel: (714) 824-0101
Fax: (714) 983-8359

Signet Marine
16321 Gothard St.
Unit E
Huntington Beach, CA 92647
Tel: (714) 848-6467
Fax: (714) 848-6009

Silva U.S. Marine
4923 Bayshore Blvd.
Tampa, FL 33611
Tel: (813) 839-2266
Fax: (813) 837-2177

R. A. Simerl Instruments
528 Epping Forest Rd.
Annapolis, MD 21401
Tel: (410) 849-8667
Fax: (410) 849-2505

S.R. Instruments, Inc.
600 Young St.
Tonawanda, NY 14150
Tel: (800) 654-6360
 or (716) 693-5977
Fax: (716) 693-5854

Standard Communications
P.O. Box 92151
Los Angeles, CA 90009
Tel: (213) 532-5300

Telcor Instruments
17785 Sky Park Circle
Irvine, CA 92714
Tel: (714) 250-1016
Fax: (714) 250-1014

VDO-Yazaki Instrument Corp.
P.O. Box 2897
980 Brooke Rd.
Winchester, VA 22601
Tel: (703) 665-0100
Fax: (703) 662-2515

Instruments: Non-Electronic

With today's emphasis on electronic navigation, it may seem surprising that a navigator needs non-electronic gear. But a prudent offshore navigator will carry backup charts, and a means of using those charts, plus various other pieces of equipment in case the electrical power fails. The most important piece of gear is the sextant, closely followed by a good stopwatch. You should also have a set of sight-reduction tables and a portable calculator. An inshore navigator will only need a chart, a hand bearing compass, a set of triangles or parallel rules, and a sharp pencil to keep a good track of his position.

A SEXTANT

Knowing how to use a sextant is essential if you plan to spend any length of time offshore. Purchasing a sextant is a major investment, and you can reasonably expect a new sextant to last many years, provided it is properly maintained and cared for.

When buying a sextant keep in mind:

1. If you can afford it, purchase a sextant with a metal frame, not a plastic one. The early plastic types had a tendency for error as the plastic expanded and contracted. Metal-framed sextants have much less of a problem. Brass is the most commonly used metal, with certain lightweight models made from aluminum alloy. A new sextant should have an accuracy within + 15 seconds of arc. Sextants with lower error are more accurate.

2. Both the index mirror and the horizon glass should be silvered on the front to reduce refraction and parallax errors. Less expensive models may be silvered on the back of the glass, which can introduce a slight error. In general, larger mirrors are better, as they allow sights to be taken in marginal conditions.

3. Look for high-quality optics in the telescope. Lower quality optics can make it hard to see in hazy or early evening conditions. In general, a 4 x 40 scope is better for star sights and all-around use, whereas a 6 x 30 lens is better for sun sights as it allows you to more accurately align the sun's lower tangent with the horizon.

4. Check the index arm movement and release lever. It should be smooth and even without any jerkiness. The arm should not move when the release lever is engaged. Check, too, the vernier or micrometer movement. It should also be smooth and even.

5. Look at the shade glasses. They should be optically ground, evenly graded, and of various shades.

6. Look carefully at the curved bottom limb, the arc, and the inscribed index marks. If the index marks are hard to read in the chandlery, imagine how difficult it will be to read them after the sextant has been in use for some time or on a dark hazy evening. Ideally, your sextant should have some form of lighting to illuminate the index marks.

7. If you can afford it, buy a sextant with a prism level so that sextant tilt error is reduced.

8. When trying out a sextant, make sure that it feels comfortable in your hand. The center of gravity should be as near as possible to the handle so that the instrument feels balanced. This also helps to reduce tilt error.

9. Get a flexible eyepiece if you possibly can.

10. More experienced navigators prefer a sextant with some heft to it. Lighter sextants tend to have less stability and wobble more.

11. When buying a sextant, purchase a wooden box and cleaning kit with it. This will reduce the possiblity of incidental damage to your instrument and enable you to keep it clean.

A STOPWATCH

In addition to a sextant, a navigator needs a stop watch. Get one with a large sweep second hand or digital readout that can easily be handled with the sextant. If the stopwatch is battery powered, make sure you carry additional batteries.

A PELORUS

Although they are not often seen on boats today, a good pelorus can be used to take bearings, check compass deviation, and take a three-point fix. In looking for a pelorus, make sure that the instrument is made of a non-corrosive metal. Ideally, the bearing card and sight should be able to be locked down independently of each other, but usually, this feature is found only on the most expensive instruments.

A HAND BEARING COMPASS

A good quality hand bearing compass has largely replaced the pelorus for taking bearings. But few hand bearing compasses are ever aligned with the boat's main compass, which can lead to errors. If you own a hand bearing compass, check the heading obtained from it against the boat's main compass. You'll probably be surprised to find that there may be up to ten degrees difference.

Of all the hand bearing compasses, I prefer the "hockey puck" style, which can hang on a string. Get used to using it and use it often to take quick sights to keep abreast of your position. When buying a hand bearing compass, look for one that feels comfortable in your hand and is easy to use.

A MAIN COMPASS

A yacht's main compass should be chosen with considerable care. After all, this is the instrument by which you will steer the boat whenever it is at sea. A poor compass may put you miles away from you destination. When buying a compass, look for the following features:

1. It should be readable. Most compasses use white letters on a black card, which is easiest to read at night. The divisions on the compass card should not be too close together. Usually, five-degree intervals are easiest to read.

2. Make sure the instrument has an easily seen lubber line. (That is the line at the front of the compass, which indicates the centerline of the yacht.) Many compasses have more than one line, often up to six, at intervals of forty-five degrees. Additional lines make it easier to steer when you are sitting to one side of the compass.

3. Always choose a compass with a metal housing. Metal has a longer life and is usually coated to resist corrosion. If possible, select a compass with a glass dome. Plastic domes sometimes crack or craze, making them hard to read.

4. If you can afford it, always purchase a compass with an expansion diaphragm. This allows the liquid inside the compass to expand when the instrument heats up. Quite often, on compasses without an expansion diaphragm, the liquid will leak out as the compass expands, and a bubble will form, making the compass card hard to read.

5. When trying out a compass in a store, tilt it to see when the card sticks. If your boat heels twenty five degrees and the card sticks at twenty degrees, you'll be without a useful compass for much of your trip.

6. Select the right mounting for your compass. Some compasses are most visible when they are mounted in the bulkhead, others when they are mounted on a bracket on the bulkhead. Most are set on the binnacle, but a few are flush-mounted in the coaming for use when the helmsman is sitting outboard. In general, the binnacle mounting is the safest; bracket-mounted compasses can easily get knocked off the bracket. Also, look for electrical wiring, and metal items stored near the compass. On one boat I sailed on, a number of electrical wires passed directly behind the bulkhead-mounted compass. As soon as the lights were turned on, the compass went haywire.

7. The compass should be swung at least once per season if you are going to sail offshore. Ideally, once or twice a season, you should use your pelorus to check your compass's accuracy. A compass adjuster will give you a table of deviations and put compensating magnets near the compass. Only by having this done regularly are you assured that your compass will remain accurate. On steel boats, it is essential that the compass is compensated properly. If you intend to cruise regulary offshore, you might get the compass checked for deviation when the boat is heeled as well.

SMALLER TOOLS

Under this category comes parallel rules, triangles, pencils, dividers, two- and three arm protractors, a course plotter, and rolling rules. The prudent navigator will keep such items stowed in the chart table. They can either be bought separately or together in a Navpak, such as the one supplied by C. Plath.

A CHRONOMETER

The chronometer features to look for are reliability and accuracy. Make sure the clock keeps accurate time. An error in the time at which sights are taken could put you many miles away from your actual position. If you purchase a battery-powered clock, make sure you carry spare batteries.

BAROMETER OR BAROGRAPH

Weather forecasts can tell you what is coming your way, but quite often the weather forecast is several hours old before you get the information. A more reliable indicator is a barometer or barograph which tells you what the air pressure is around you. For instance, on one offshore trip I took, a tropical storm was forecast for our area with an anticipated arrival time several hours away. We hoped to make port before its arrival, but a plummeting track on the barograph warned us that the storm was nearer than expected and we hove to rather than try to make a tricky entry into port.

A LOG

While not strictly an instrument, the log is a very important part of offshore sailing. If it is kept up-to-date, it provides an accurate track of the boat, and, in the event of the navigator not being able to get a good sight, it can be used for dead reckoning. A good log should have spaces for boat speed and direction, weather comments, course sailed, wind angle, and other items that are of interest to the navigator. For instance, on a track form Newport, Rhode Island, to Bermuda, an additional entry of seawater temperature might be made to tell the navigator when the boat enters the Gulf Stream.

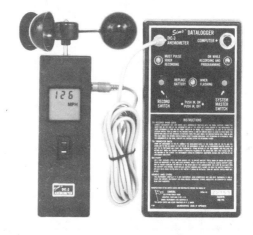

Figure 1: A Sims model DIC-3 anemometer and Data -logger from Simerl Instruments.

Manufacturers and Distributors of Non-Electronic Instruments

(See also the Electronic
Instruments section)
Chronometers, Clocks, and Barometers

A & B Industries
1261 Anderson Dr.
Suite C
San Rafael, CA 94901
Tel: (415) 258-9300
Fax: (415) 258-9461
Clocks

Aldeas
136 Colburn Ave.
Dracut, MA 01826
Tel: (508) 957-0971
*Tide clocks, barometers and
hygrometers*

Armchair Sailor Bookstore
Lee's Wharf
Newport, RI 02840
Tel: (401)8474252
*Clocks, nav gear, chronometers
and much more*

Chelsea Clock
284 Everett Ave.
Chelsea, MA 02150
Tel: (617) 884-0250
Fax: (617) 884-3608
Clocks and barometers

Figure 2: The Russian Made
Poljot chronometer is im-
ported by J.P. Connor & Co.

J.P. Connor & Co.
Box 305
Devon, PA 19333
Tel: (215) 644-1474
Fax: (215) 993-0760
*Marine chronometers and
importer of Poljot
chronometers*

**Feldmar Watch & Clock
Center**
9000 W. Pico Blvd.
Los Angeles, CA 90035
Tel: (213) 272-1196
Fax: (213) 274-2081
  *Retailer of Chelsea clocks,
tide clocks and barometers*

Hollams Yacht Equipment
P.O. Box 452
San Carlos, CA 94070
Tel: (415) 595-2009
Fax: (415) 592-6627
Brass oil lamps

C. Plath, North America
222 Severn Ave.
Annapolis, MD 21403
Tel: (410) 263-6700
Fax: (410) 268-8713
Weems and Plath clocks

Swift Instruments
952 Dorchester Ave.
Boston, MA 02125
Tel: (617) 436-2960
Fax: (617) 4363-232
Clocks and barometers

Seth Thomas
Division of General Time
520 Guthridge Ct.
Norcross, GA 30092
Tel: (404) 447-5300
Clocks and instruments

**Robert E. White
Instruments**
34 Commercial Wharf
Boston, MA 02110
Tel: (800) 992-3045
*Clocks and navigation
instruments*

Compasses and Peloruses

Autohelm
A Raytheon Company
46 River Rd.
Hudson, NH 03051
Tel: (603) 881-5838
Fax: (603) 881-4756
Fluxgate hand-held compass

Airguide Instrument Co.
1110 Lake Cook Rd.
Suite 220
Buffalo Grove, IL 60089
Tel: (708) 215-7888
Fax: (708) 215-7895
*Airguide and Plastimo
compasses*

ARC Industries
P.O. Box 033498
Indialantic, FL 32903
Tel: (407) 254-1917

Cetrek/Wagner, Inc.
300 Oak St.
260 Corporate Park
Pembroke, MA 02359
Tel: (800) 323-8735
  or (617) 826-7497
Fax: (617) 826-2495
Fluxgate compasses

Davis Instruments
3465 Diablo Ave.
Hayward, CA 94545
Tel: (510) 732-9229
Fax: (510) 732-9188
*Hand-held compasses and
peloruses*

H. G. Dietz Products
14-26 28th Ave.
Long Island City, NY
11102-3692
Tel: (718) 726-3347
Fax: (718) 728-3976
*Compasses, peloruses, and
compass-correction kits*

Dirigo Compass
13456 S.E. 27th Pl.
Bellevue, WA 98005
Tel: (206) 746-1786
Dirigo compasses

IMI/Brookes & Gatehouse
7855 126th Ave. N.
Largo, FL 34643
Tel: (813) 536-1400
Fax: (813) 536-1717
Electronic compasses

C. Plath, North America
222 Severn Ave.
Annapolis, MD 21403
Tel: (410) 263-6700
Fax: (410) 268-8713
*Weems and Plath, and
Airguide compasses and
peloruses*

Precise International
15 Corporate Dr.
Orangeburg, NY 10962
Tel: (914) 357-6200
Pathfinder compass

E.S. Ritchie
243 Oak St.
Pembroke, MA 02359
Tel: (617) 826-5131
Fax: (617) 826-7336
*Navigator and Globemaster
compasses*

Rule Industries
70 Blanchard Rd.
Burlington, MA 01803
Tel: (617) 272-7400
Danforth compasses

Henry Browne & Son Ltd.
Sestrel House
Loxford Rd.
Barking, Essex
ENGLAND
Tel: (+44) 1 594-4054
Sestral compasses

Silva US Marine
4923 Bayshore Blvd.
Tampa, FL 33611
Tel: (813) 839-2266
Fax: (813) 837-2177
Silva compasses

Sun Co.
14025 W. 66th Ave.
Arvada, CO 80004
Tel: (303) 424-4651
Fax: (303) 467-1104

Figure 3: A hand held
compass from Suunto USA.

Suunto USA
2151 Las Palmas Dr.
Carlsbad, CA 92009
Tel: (800) 543-9124
Fax: (619) 931-9875
Suunto compasses

Viking Instruments
532 Pond St.
South Weymouth, MA 02190
Tel: (617) 331-3526
Compasses and peloruses

Logs

Knotstick
P.O. Box 6340
Vero Beach, FL 32960
Tel: (407) 567-4445

**Robert E. White
Instruments**
34 Commercial Wharf
Boston, MA 02110
Tel: (800) 992-3045

Navigator's Equipment

Armchair Sailor Bookstore
543 Thames St.
Newport, Rl 02840
Tel: (401) 847-4252
*Sextants, charts, and
navigation gizmos*

Associated Marine
P.O. Box 5421
1650 S. Amphlett Blvd. #118
San Mateo, CA 94402
Tel: (415) 349-1341

Basic Designs
5815 Bennett Valley Rd.
Santa Rosa, CA 95404
Tel: (707) 575-1220
Fax: (707) 578-0378

Better Boating Association
P.O. Box 407
Needham, MA 02192
Tel: (800) 242-7854
Fax: (617) 449-0514

Cassens & Plath
U.S. Baker Lyman & Co.
P.O. Box 838
3220 SI 10 Service Rd.
Metaire, LA 70001
Tel: (504) 831-3685
Sextants

C. Plath
222 Severn Ave.
Annapolis, MD 21403
Tel: (410) 263-6700
Sextants

C-Thru Ruler
6 Britton Dr.
P.O. Box 356
Bloomfield, CT 06002
Tel: (203) 243-0303

Celestaire
416 S. Pershing
Wichita, KS 67218
Tel: (800) 727-9785
   or (316) 686-9785
Fax: (316) 686-8926
*Sextants, instruments, books,
and videos*

Chartmaster
238 Davenport Rd.
Suite 306
Toronto, Ontario M5R 1S6
CANADA
Tel: (416) 536-3997

Davis Instruments
3465 Diablo Ave.
Hayward, CA 94545-2746
Tel: (415) 732-9229
Fax: (415) 732-9188
Sextants and charts

Gurry Enterprises
52 Tropicana Dr.
Punta Gorda, FL 33950
Tel: (813) 637-1998

Holland Yacht Equipment
P.O. Box 452
San Carlos, CA 94070
Tel: (415) 595-2009
Fax: (415) 592-6627
InfoCenter, Inc.
P.O. Box 47175
Forestville, MD 20747
Tel: (301) 420-2468
Navigation instruments

**International Sailing
Supply**
320 Cross St.
Punta Gorda, FL 33950
Tel: (813) 639-7626
Fax: (813) 637-9866

Kleid Technologies
443 Ruane St.
Fairfield, CT 06430
Tel: (203) 259-7161

Landfall Navigation
354 W. Putnam Ave.
Greenwich, CT 06830
Tel: (203) 661-3176
Fax: (203) 661-9613
Sextants and charts

Nautac
607 St. Lucie Crescent
Stuart, FL 34994
Tel: (407) 220-2320
Fax: (407) 288-2111

NET
P.O. Box 187
Acushnet, MA 02743
Tel: (508) 995-4935

Recmar Marine
1937 Blair Ave.
Santa Ana, CA 92705
Tel: (714) 261-8774

E. S. Ritchie & Sons
234 Oak St.
Pembroke, MA 02359
Tel: (617) 826-5131
Fax: (617) 826-7336

Seacraft/Honneus
Box 41
27 Aster Circle
Weymouth Landing, MA
02188
Tel: (617) 337-0520
Fax: (617) 337-0529

Selsi
40 Veterans Blvd.
Carlstadt, NJ 07072
Tel: (201) 935-0388
Fax: (201) 935-5851

Stormproof Martensen
P.O. Box 261
Williamsburg, VA 23187
Tel: (804) 564-8626

**Technical Information
Services**
P.O. Box 24A34
Westwood Station
Los Angeles, CA 90024
Tel: (213) 821-4958

Tidewatch Products, Inc.
P.O. Box 336
Danforth Ln.
Califon, NJ 07830
Tel: (201) 832-9103

Robert E. White Instruments
34 Commercial Wharf
Boston, MA 02110
Tel: (800) 992-3045

Thermometers

Armchair Sailor Bookstore
Lee's Wharf
Newport, RI 02840
Tel: (401) 847-4252

Dytek Laboratories
Division of Charles Marine
Products
5600 Apollo Dr.
Rolling Meadows, IL 60008
Tel: (708) 806-6300
Fax: (708) 806-6231

Lowrance Electronics
12000 E. Skelly Dr.
Tulsa, OK 74128
Tel: (918) 437-6881

Maximum
30 Samuel Barnett Blvd.
New Bedford, MA 02745
Tel: (508) 999-2226
Fax: (508) 994-4919

Wind Instruments

Ahmer Marine
3330 Commercial Ave.
Northbrook, IL 60062
Tel: (800) 728-2441

Airguide Instrument Co.
1110 Lake Cook Rd.
Suite 220
Buffalo Grove, IL 60089
Tel: (708) 215-7888
Fax: (708) 215-7895

Altco Trading International
6 Macaulay St.
E. Hamilton, Ontario
CANADA
Tel: (416) 521-1061
Fax: (416) 521-9721

Davis Instruments
3465 Diablo Ave.
Hayward, CA 94545-2746
Tel: (415) 732-9229
Fax: (415) 732-9188

Dwyer Instruments
P.O. Box 373
Michigan City, IN 46360
Tel: (219) 879-8000

Euro Marine Trading
64 Halsey St. #27
Newport, RI 02840
Tel: (800) 222-7712
Fax: (401) 849-3230
Lago wind direction indicator

Gemini Research
P.O. Box 0
Rochester, NY 14623
Tel: (716) 461-5620

Watrous
P.O. Box 996
Cutchogue, NY 11935
Tel: (516) 734-5504
Fax: (516) 734-7931
Barometers and other weather instruments

Figure 4: Suunto USA imports a number of yacht compasses from Finland.

Insulation

Good insulation is important around the engine, the engine exhaust, and any other noise sources. But noise insulation is only one part of the total insulation picture. It often helps to have insulation in the hull, especially if the boat is painted a dark color. Or if you extend your sailing season and sail when there's frost around, hull insulation will make the interior warmer.

SOUND INSULATION

Sound insulation starts with reducing vibrations. The first step is to make sure that your engine and generator, all the onboard pumps, and any motors are on flexible mountings. This will ensure that the vibrations are not transmitted to the hull where they can cause resonance.

When you have reduced vibrations as far as possible, you should figure out where the major sources of noise are coming from. Ask yourself if a quieter pump or motor can replace a noisy one? If the answer is yes, it should be replaced. If it is impractical to install a quieter unit, then the sound will have to be contained or masked.

To contain sound, you will to build an insulated box around the noisy machinery. If the machinery is an engine, it needs an air intake, so you have to develop a baffled aperture that allows air to enter but muffles noise. Naturally aspirated diesel engines need a certain amount of air for combus-

tion. Turbo-charged engines need much more air, and the larger the engine the larger the air intake needs to be. However, air vents tend to allow noise to escape, so they need expert design. Remember, too, that sound insulation is also a good heat insulator, so you also need a way to let excess heat out in order to prevent fire. Most noise insulation is installed by either gluing it to the inside of the compartment or gluing pins to the compartment face and pushing the insulation over them. A metal or plastic cap secures the insulation on the pin and any excess pin is chopped off.

Sound insulation is usually a layer of about 1 inch fire-retardant plastic foam with a layer of lead (about 1/8 inch) or high-density plastic in the middle. In higher noise areas, the foam may be thicker, sometimes up to 3 inches. The entire lead/foam layer is faced with a coating. This may be perforated plastic, or a perforated reflective metalic coating. There should also be a thin vapor barrier over the inside face to prevent a buildup of oil spray, which could cause an engine room fire.

HEAT INSULATION

Heat insulation is not nearly so demanding to install as sound insulation is, nor are the advantages quiet so noticeable. In fact, many boats may already be fairly well insu-

against heat. These are the boats that have a foam-cored hull. Not only does a foam-core increase structural rigidity, it also increases the insulation value of the hull. For instance, depending upon the thickness and density of the foam, the insulation value of the hull can be up to R 10 per inch of foam core. (By comparison, the R value of house walls in New England are likely to be about R19 with 3 1/2 inches of fiberglass insulation.) In most cases, an increase in the heat insulation value of a hull will not provide high enough returns to make it worthwhile. But if you have an air conditioning system or intend to take a metal boat into very cold climates, you should thoroughly investigate the cost of insulating the hull.

Certain types of insulation are better in a marine environment than others. Foam cores are the best. They are impermeable to water, can be bent to conform to the hull shape, and can be glued in place. Insulations like fiberglass and cellulose tend to mat down when they get wet, are hard to contain unless they are completely sealed, and are hard to install and hold in place.

Manufacturers of Insulation

W. R. Grace & Co.
62 Whittemore Ave.
Cambridge, MA 02140
Tel: (617) 876-1400

Greenwood Forest Products
5895 S.W. Jean Rd.
Lake Oswego, OR 97034
Tel: (503) 635-9271

Hecht Rubber
6161 Phillips Hwy.
Jacksonville, FL 32216
Tel: (800) USA-3401
Fax: (904) 730-0066

Hough Marine & Machine
1111 Northwest Ballard Way
Seattle, WA 98107
Tel: (800) 423-3509
  or   (206) 784-8400
Fax: (206) 783-7323

Noise Reduction Enterprises
6 Dodge St.
P.O. Box 907
Essex, MA 01929
Tel: (508) 768-6487

Soundown Corp.
17 Lime St.
Suite 1
Marblehead, MA 01945
Tel: (800) 359-1036
  or   (617) 631-9611
Fax: (617) 631-9231
Noise and thermal insulation

South Coast Marine
788 W. 16th St.
Costa Mesa, CA 92627
Tel: (714) 646-5445

Wefco Rubber
1655 Euclid St.
Santa Monica, CA 90404
Tel: (213) 393-0303

Noise Control Engineering Companies

J & A Enterprises, Inc.
P.O. Box 853
Marblehead, MA 01945
Tel: (617) 631-9551

W. van Cappellen
Noordhoek 37
3351 LD Papendrecht
HOLLAND
Tel: 31 78 411022
Fax: 31 78 155349
Noise, vibration and thermal insulation consultants

Insurance

By Stephanie Bernardo Johns
Stephanie Bernardo Johns is a contributing edi-
tor to Motor Boating & Sailing magazine. She
lives in Mountain Lakes, New Jersey, and
writes frequently about marine finance and
insurance.

Marine insurance is not mandatory, but if your boat were destroyed by a hurricane, you'd want to replace it. And if you injured another boater in an accident, you'd want to be protected in the event of a lawsuit.

Before you buy separate marine insurance, however, it pays to check your home owner's policy, because you may already have all the coverage you need. Generally, small boats under 16 feet in length, such as canoes, windsurfers, or rowboats, are covered as personal property under many home owners' policies. But be advised that the coverage is limited. Some policies will only cover losses of only $1,500 or less for all watercraft, trailers, furnishings, equipment, and outboard motors. Liability coverage is also provided automatically by some home owner's policies for certain boats: sailboats under 26 feet in length, powerboats with inboard engines of 50 horsepower or less, and boats with outboard motors that do not exceed 25 horsepower.

Even if your boat's size and power fit the limits of your existing home owner's policy, you should still alert your insurer to any boating additions. The added items might not necessarily increase your premiums, but the insurance company still wants to be informed about any increases in potential liabilities.

If your boat is too large or too powerful to be covered under an ordinary home owner's policy, ask your agent how much it would cost to add an endorsement to your policy for the additional coverage. Don't assume that an endorsement will always be cheaper than a separate policy. Do some comparison shopping because sometimes a separate boat owner's policy is the more economical way to go.

WHAT SHOULD YOU LOOK FOR IN A MARINE INSURANCE POLICY?

Most policies provide "all risk, all peril" coverage. That means, that no matter how a boat is damaged — by wind, fire, earthquake, collision, vandalism, or what have you — the boat owner will be compensated. But because there are some states where "hurricane exclusion" policies are still being sold, it is important to read your policy to be sure your vessel is protected from almost every conceivable destructive force.

There are two different types of marine insurance: actual cash value policies and agreed value policies. To ensure that you will be able to replace your 40-foot sportfisherman if it were destroyed in a hurricane, most insurance agents suggest choosing an agreed value or stated value policy. Unlike actual cash value policies (which have lower premiums), claims made under stated value policies are settled without any deductions for depreciation. Under an actual cash value policy, which is written in similar fashion to an automobile insurance policy, the insurer pays claims based on the value of your boat or equipment at the time of loss. This means that the insurer has the option of depreciating the boat. Instead of receiving the full purchase price of, say, $60,000, the owner of a three-year-old boat that had been destroyed or stolen, might receive only $42,000 under an actual cash value policy if the insurance company chose to depreciate the value of the boat by 30 percent.

You must remember to increase the stated value of your boat when you make improvements to it. Keep a file with all receipts and photographs of installed equipment to facilitate making a claim. Proof of loss is required whenever an insurance claim is made. A good documentation system can make the difference between getting paid in a few weeks, or a few months.

As with any insurance, it is important to read the policy carefully to determine exactly what is covered and under what conditions. In most instances, electronic equipment or safety devices that are needed for the safe operation of a boat are covered. Thus, a ship-to-shore radio stolen in June, while a boat is commissioned for the summer season, is typically covered under most insurance policies. But that same radio, stolen in January when the boat is decommissioned for the winter season, might not be covered for theft. Similarly, a television stolen from a built-in entertainment center on a 50-foot yacht might be covered, while a portable TV would have to be claimed on your home owner's insurance policy. While many policies do permit owners to keep a boat in the water year-round, they have special requirements on how the boat should be decommissioned. All electronics have to be removed; fuel and water tanks must be drained; and other security precautions have to be taken to keep the policy in force.

Some policies also state how and where a boat may be used. If your normal cruising waters are New York Harbor and Long Island Sound, you might have to add an endorsement to the policy to take a cruise down the Atlantic coast to Florida. You might also find your boat is not covered during certain times. If, for example, your sailboat is normally raced on the weekends, some policies might exclude the sails from coverage during those times.

HOW MUCH WILL YOU HAVE TO PAY?

How much you pay for insurance will depend upon several factors: the type of boat you own; its size and value; how fast it goes (high speed power boats are the most expensive); how you use it; where you use it; and other variables, such as your boating experience, any safety systems installed on the boat, and the deductible, or the amount you agree to pay per claim. The deductible is often calculated as a percentage of the value of the boat. Typically, deductibles run about $300 for boats costing less than $25,000 and close to one percent of the total value for more expensive boats.

The easiest way to save money on an insurance premium is by raising the deductible from one to two percent. Some insurance companies also offer discounts as high as 20% off current rates for claim-free boaters. And many organizations, such as BOAT/U.S., are able to offer members discounted insurance.

Your amount of liability coverage also enters into how much you pay. In addition to covering physical damage to your vessel, most boat insurance policies also include coverage to pay for damage caused to another person or another person's property. Typically, liability coverage is limited to $300,0000. If you want greater protection for your assets, you need more coverage, say $500,000 or $1 million. It may be cheaper to buy an "umbrella" policy that covers all of your other insurance policies instead of buying increased protection for your boat.

When comparing different policies, there are other factors to consider in addition to price: Is emergency towing covered? Are payments made for damage caused by uninsured boaters? Will any medical bills be covered? All of us love a bargain, but when it comes to insurance it pays to stick with brand names — well-known companies that will be there should you ever have to file a claim. Be on guard if one insurance agent quotes a much lower premium than the other firms you've contacted. Read each contract carefully to determine exactly what coverage will be provided. Because policies vary widely from one company to the next, it is impossible to choose an insurance policy strictly on price. You have to read and reread each policy thoroughly to be certain that you have all the coverage you want and need.

Providers of Marine Insurance and Financial Services

Marine Insurance

John G. Alden Insurance Agency
28 Constitution Rd.
Charlestown, MA 02129
Tel: (800) JG ALDEN
  or   (617) 241-8088

Atlantic Credit Corp.
326 1st St.
Suite 39
Annapolis, MD 21403
Tel: (410) 263-1263
Fax: (410) 263-1463

Berg-Williams Marine Insurance
1535 S.E. 17th St.
Suite 200
Ft. Lauderdale, FL 33316
Tel: (305) 767-9500
Fax: (305) 767-9700

BOAT/USA
880 S. Pickett St.
Alexandria, VA 22304
Tel: (703) 823-9550
Fax: (703) 461-2854

Carle & Carle, Inc.
560 Sylvan Ave.
Englewood Cliffs, NJ 07632
Tel: (201) 568-5010
Fax: (201) 568-3414

Craven Insurance
2317 Northwest Market St.
Seattle, WA 98107
Tel: (800) 826-2344

Essex Insurance Corp.
P.O. Box 364
40 Main St.
Centerbrook, CT 06409
Tel: (203) 767-1424
Fax: (203) 767-8091

**Eugene Horton &
Associates**
600 Stewart St.
Suite 1300
Seattle, WA 98101
Tel: (800) 223-5833
  or   (206) 441-7020
Fax: (206) 441-7025

Gowrie, Barden & Brett
P.O. Box 970
70 Essex Rd.
Westbrook, CT 06498
Tel: (800) 262 8911
  or   (203) 399-5945
Fax: (203) 399-7897
*Insurance and financial
services*

Kelly Agency
447 East Boston Post Rd.
Mamaroneck, NY 10543
Tel: (14) 698-0676
Fax: (914) 381-5060

Kolish Marine Insurance
90 Almeria Ave.
Coral Gables, FL 33134
Tel: (800) 947-0470
  or   (305) 447-8600
Fax: (305) 447-0209

Main Insurance Agency
5525 West Market St.
Greensboro, NC 27419
Tel: (800) 763-0895
  or   (919) 292-8737
Fax: (919) 299-5190

Management Effort, Inc.
325 Lexington Ave.
New York, NY 10016
Tel: (212) 689-4477
Fax: (212) 685-9268
The boat insurance specialists

Marine Agency
191 Maplewood Ave.
Maplewood, NJ 97040
Tel: (201) 763-4711
Fax: (201) 763-1635

**Marine Underwriters
Agency**
8 Drummond Pl.
P.O. Box 8699
Red Bank, NJ 07701
Tel: (800) 631-2147
Fax: (800) 548-0501

Jack Martin & Associates
Rowe Blvd. and Melvin Ave.
Annapolis, MD 21401
Tel: (800) 833-3830
Fax: (301) 268-9764

Alan R. Mott Agency, Inc.
184 E. Main St.
Huntington, NY 11743
28 years of marine insurance

Ocean Underwriters, Inc.
P.O. Box 1968
Cocoa, FL 32923
Tel: (800) 833-0342
  or   (800) 327-0944

Pantaenius (Germany)
Cremon 32
2000 Hamburg 11
GERMANY
Tel: (+49) 040-370 910
Fax: (+49) 040-370 09 11 09

Pantaenius (UK) Ltd.
11 Queen Anne's Battery
Plymouth, Devon
ENGLAND
Tel: (+44)-752-223656
Fax: (+44)-752-223637

Seattle General Agency
1715 West Nickerson
Nordby Bldg.
Fishermen's Terminal
Seattle, WA 98119
Tel: (206) 282-7000
Fax: (206) 283-1419

Ski-Pro
P.O. Box 11128
Montgomery, AL 36111
Tel: (800) 489-0105
Ski-boat insurance

U.S. Power & Sail
625 Spring St.
P.O. Box 6947
Wyomissing, PA 19610
Tel: (215) 374-4040
Fax: (215) 374-2509

Financial Services

Atlantic Credit Corp.
326 1st. St.
Suite 39
Annapolis, MD 21403
Tel: (410) 269-1263
Fax: (410) 269-1463

**CoreStates First
Pennsylvania Bank**
747 Dresher Road
Horsham, PA 19044
Tel: (215) 830-3400
Fax: (800) 362-5234

Essex Credit Corp.
P.O. Box 580
Essex, CT 06426
Tel: (800) 431-5626
  or   (203) 767-2626
Fax: (203) 767-8091

First Commercial Corp.
P.O. Box 439
Allenwood, NJ 08720
Tel: (800) 55-FIRST
  or   (908) 528-3326
Fax: (201) 528-6911

**First New England
Financial**
P.O. Box H
Southport, CT 06490
Tel: (203) 255-5713
Fax: (203) 255-4943

Forward Financial Co.
360 Church St.
Northboro, MA 01532-1240
Tel: (508) 393-5300
Fax: ((508) 393-9571

Ganis Corp.
425 Broad Hollow Rd.
Suite 423
Melville, NY 11747
Tel: (516) 454-9400
Fax: (516) 454-6660

Offshore Financial Corp.
160 Bridge Ave.
Suite 5
Bay Head, NJ 08742
Tel: (908) 899-7733
Fax: (908) 899-8686

Scott Financial Services
914-16 S. Wolfe St.
Baltimore, MD 21231
Tel: (800) 556-0666
Fax: (410) 675-0843
*Marine financing and
documentation*

Security Marine Creditcorp
17 Hanover Rd.
Suite 430
P.O. Box 320
Florham Park, NJ 07932-0320
Tel: (201) 514-1920
Fax: (201) 514-1843

Yegen Marine
Mack Center Dr.
Paramus, NJ 07652
Tel: (800) 523-9419
Fax: (201) 262-7209

Figure 1: You should make sure that your boat is well insured like this Pro-Line 192 Sport TC.

Keels

Suppose you decide that your boat doesn't have enough stability, or that the keel is too deep for the waters you want to sail in. If you think that a new keel will solve the problem, your first step is to ask a boatyard to give you a ball-park price. Add 10 or 15% to their price and you really will be in the ball park. The additional money is to cover getting the keel off the boat. Most keels seem to be magically glued to the hull once they are put in place. Next, you'll need to get a designer to draw up the new keel. If you know the weight of the existing keel and its center of gravity, the new design work should take about a day with the proper computer program. (See the section on boat design software.)

When the design is complete, a patternmaker will have to build a plug. This job is best left to the experts. If the keel is lead, the plug will be slightly larger than the actual keel to allow for lead shrinkage. The plug is then packed in sand or concrete and allowed to set. Next, the keel mold is split apart and the plug removed.

Now you have a female mold of your keel, which is usually filled with hot lead. If the keel is a complex shape, say a keel with wings, the mold may be in three or more parts which can sometimes lead to additional problems. When a new winged keel was poured for a 12 meter with which I was involved, the mold was a four-part unit,

and the top half actually floated on top of the lead (concrete is lighter than lead) and off the mold. As the water main chose that moment to fail, we ended up with several thousand pounds of hot lead on the ground.

If all goes well, the keel is poured and left to cool. Once it has cooled, the mold is removed and the entire keel is sanded to remove mold lines and marks. Now the keel is shipped to the boatyard to be fitted to your boat.

Another method of making a keel is to cast the approximate shape and use a computer aided milling machine to do the final fairing. The resulting keel will be extremely smooth, highly accurate, and an exact fit. The only snag is that the only keelmakers that do milling, to my knowledge, are in Europe — Speedwave in Germany, and Pantotech in Italy — and it can get very expensive shipping a lead keel translantic.

If the keel is cast, either before it is fitted or when it is on the boat, you should make sure that the surface has been carefully smoothed ready for final fairing. If you race your boat, you'll probably want to get templates of the keel sections ready for fairing. Then you should spend time filling hollows and planing off bumps until the surface is perfectly smooth. The last step is to paint the keel with anti-fouling and sand to a smooth finish.

Manufacturers of Keels

I. Broomfield & Son
11 Lehigh St.
Providence, RI 02905
Tel: (401) 941-7361

Canada Metal
721 Eastern Ave.
Toronto, Ontario M4M lE6
CANADA
Tel: (416) 465-4684
Fax: (416) 465-8053

Computer Keels
P.O. Box 39757
Edina, MN 55439
Tel: (612) 829-5670
Templates

Hanover Metal
P.O. Box 27155
Baltimore, MD 21230
Tel: (301) 539-1338
Fax: (301) 539-1341

Keel Makers Division,
Willard Industries
101 New Bern St.
Charlotte, NC 28203
Tel: (704) 523-1230
Fax: (704) 527-8580

Lunar Industries
427 Speers Rd.
Unit 18
Oakville, Ontario L6K 3S8
CANADA

Mars Metal
4130 Morris Dr.
Burlington, Ontario L7L 5L6
CANADA
Tel: (416) 637-3862
Fax: (416) 637-8841

Pantotech Italia SRL
Via Folleraeu, 14
24027 Nembro (Bg)
ITALY
Tel: (+39) 35 520040
Fax: (+39) 35 520772
Milled keels

Speedwave
D-8876 Jettingen
Haupstrasse 112
Stuttgart
GERMANY
Tel: (+49) 0 82 25 821
Fax: (+49) 082 25 887
Milled keels

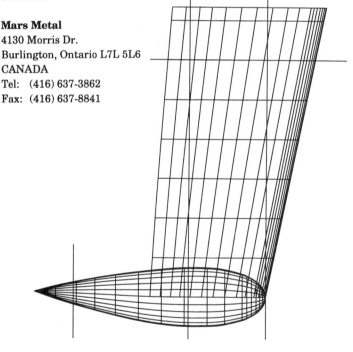

Figure 1: 2 Views of a bulbed keel designed with the Nautilus System for a design of the author's.

Kits and Stock Plans

Suppose you want a custom boat, but cannot afford one. One option is to purchase a set of stock plans or a kit. You can modify the plans to suit your ideas, and either build the boat yourself or get it built. If you are going to build a boat yourself, you should have some experience and know what you are doing.

KITS

Most small boat kits are designed for plywood building and require some woodworking skills, although a few are "stitch and glue." The plywood parts are held together with copper or steel wire, and the seams taped with fiberglass strips. Unless the fiberglass work is done extremely carefully the finished product can look like a real D-I-Y special, and lose all resale value.

A few kits come with a finished fiberglass hull, a deck, a keel, and a rudder, together with the interior parts. All you have to do is finish out the interior, finish the deck, add the keel and rudder stock, and put the hull and deck together. Putting the deck and hull together last can be helpful. If you put the hull and deck together first, you'll have to carry each part of the interior into the boat through the hatches. This can be difficult if you are trying to get a large bulkhead or counter through the companionway.

Another option is to get the boat with the hull, keel, bulkheads, engine, rudder, and deck already in place. All you have to do is fit out the interior and deck. This is, in my opinion, the best way for an amateur to proceed. The number of hours required before you go sailing are fewer, the work is almost all joinerwork, and the major heavy work is already finished.

STOCK PLANS

If you intend to buy stock plans and build a boat from scratch, be prepared to spend a lot of time at it. A typical 48 foot cruiser, professionally built, will take about 8,500 hours; a 30 footer about 4,000 hours. Taking a round figure of 5,000 hours divided into 40 hour work weeks is 125 weeks, or about two-and-half years of full-time labor for one person. An amateur, doing the same work, can add about 10% more to this time.

Only about 28% to 30% of your labor will be spent on building the hull and deck, so don't be deceived into thinking that once you have finished the hull and deck you are almost done. Also don't be fooled into thinking that you can save money by building a boat out of ferro-concrete. A ferro-concrete hull takes up to 50% more time with a material cost only slightly less than a more conventional hull.)

Many designers sell stock plans. Usually stock plans are designs that have already been created for a customer, and are sitting in the designer's file drawer. But a few designers specialize in making up low cost stock plans for mass market sales. The typical cost for stock plans is in the $500 to $2,000 range. If alterations are required, most designers will bill the alteration work at their normal hourly rate.

When you are buying stock plans, make sure you are getting all the drawings needed to build a complete boat. Quite often, detail plans must be added to explain complicated work. (See the section on Naval Architects and Designers.) Ask the designer if any alterations were made to the boat after launching. Sometimes ballast was added to trim the boat out, or a heavy item was moved to make the boat sail better. If you have any doubts whether you have everything you need, take the plans to a qualified builder and ask if the builder can build a boat using those plans. Even if you have to pay for it, ask the builder for an estimate of the hours needed to build the boat. Add 10% to the builder's time estimate to make up for your lack of knowledge in areas where the builder would call in an expert. From this, you'll get an idea of the work in store for you.

You may even find that a good builder can give you a better product for a little more money in less time than you expect. Plus, the professionally-built yacht will have a much greater resale value. Few home-built boats have high resale value, unless the amateur has a very high level of craftsmanship. If your goal is to save money, look at the overall picture and factor in the resale value. Do your homework before purchasing materials.

Suppliers of Stock Plans and Kits

Stock Plans

Atkin & Co.
Box 3005
Noroton, CT 06820

Jay R. Benford
P.O. Box 447-B
605 Talbot St.
St. Michaels, MD 21663
Tel: (301) 745-3235
Fax: (301) 745-9743

Ted Brewer Yacht Designs
117 Harbor Ln.
Anacortes, WA 98221

George Buehler Yacht Design
Box 966
Freeland, WA 98249

George Calkins
Box 222
Nordland, WA 98358-0222

Cape Fear Museum Associates
814 Market St.
Wilmington, NC 28401
Tel: (919) 341-4350

Chesapeake Light Craft
34 S. Pershing Dr.
Arlington, VA 22204
Tel: (703) 271-8787

Classic Boats
P. O. Box 720
Galveston, TX 77553

Clark Craft
16-77 Aqualane
Tonawanda, NY 14150
Tel: (716) 873Z640

Common Sense Designs
11765 S.W. Ebberts Crt.
Beaverton, OR 97005
Tel: (503) 524-8264

Compumarine
P.O. Box 7565-PS
Everett, WA 98201

Cooper Boat Design
P.O. Box 616
Woods Hole, MA 02543
Tel: (508) 548-2297

Norman Cross
4326 Ashton
San Diego, CA 92110
Tel: (619) 276-0910

Arch Davis Design
P.O. Bop 119
Morrill, ME 04952
Tel: (207) 342-4055

Duck Flat Wooden Boats
230 Flinders St.
Adelaide, South Australia
AUSTRALIA
Tel: (+61) 8 232 2344
Fax: (+61) 8 232 2477

Dudley Dix Yacht Design
P.O. Box 26524
Hout Bay, 7872
SOUTH AFRICA
Tel: (+27) 21 790-2838

Arthur Edmonds, Inc.
4310 Windemere Pl.
Sarasota, FL 34231
Tel: (813) 921-1553

Weston Farmer Associates
18971 Azure Rd.
Wayzata, MN 55391

Farr International
613 Third St.
Annapolis, MD 21403
Tel: (301) 263-6600
Fax: (301) 268-1137

Farrier Marine
P.O. Box 1305
Belleview, WA 98009
Tel: (206) 454-4627
Fax: (206) 454-4827

Gerr Marine, Inc.
838 West End Ave.
Suite BB
New York, NY 10025
Tel: (212) 846-7030
Fax: (212) 932-0872

Glen-L Marine Designs
9152 Rosecrans
Box 1804
Bellflower, CA 90706
Tel: (310) 630-6258
Fax: (310) 630-6280

Greene Marine
343 Gilman Rd.
Yarmouth, ME 04096
Tel: (207) 846-3184
Plans for 35 foot multihull

Ken Hankinson Associates
P.O. Box 2551AA
La Habra, CA 90631
Tel: (310) 947-1241

J.P. Hartog, N.A.
750 LaPlaya
Suite 430
San Francisco, CA 94121
Tel: (415) 752-2212
Fishing vessel plans

Headwater Boats
156 Bunker Creek Rd.
Chehalis, WA 98532

Holland Marine, Inc.
P.O. Box 690
Astor, FL 32102
Tel: (904) 759-2121
Fax: (904) 759-3247

Kurt Hughes
612-1/2 W. McGraw
Seattle, WA 98119
Tel: (206) 284-6346
Fax: (206) 283-4106

John R. Marples
4530 Firmont Dr. S.E.
Port Orchard, WA 98366

Roger Marshall, Inc.
44 Fort Wetherill Rd.
Jamestown, RI 02835
Tel: (401) 423-1400
Fax: (401) 423-2322

Richard C. Newick
5 Sheppards Way
Kittery Point, ME 03905
Tel: (207) 439-3768

Charles Neville Associates, Inc.
P.O. Box 4805
2919 Wycombe Way
Palm Harbor, FL 34685
Tel: (813) 789-2689
Fax: (813) 789-5038

Norwalk Islands Sharpie
213 Rowayton Ave.
Rowayton, CT 06853

Parker Marine Enterprises
P.O. Box 3547
Ft. Pierce, FL 34948
Tel: (407) 489-2191

Harold H. Payson & Co.
Beach Rd.
S.Thomaston, ME 04858
Tel: (207) 594-7587

Bruce Roberts International
P.O. Box 1086
Severna Park, MD 21146
Tel: (301) 544-4311

Seven Seas Yachts Ltd.
Box 1073-B
Whistler, British Columbia
VON 1BO
CANADA
Tel: (604) 932-6874
Fax: (604) 938-1186

Ken Swan
P.O. Box 267
Hubbard, OR 97032
Tel: (503) 982-5062

Tanton, Inc.
P.O. Box 270
America's Cup Ave.
Newport, RI 02840
Tel: (401) 847-4112
Fax: (401) 849-8835

Charles W. Wittholz
100 Williamsburg Dr.
Silver Spring, MD 20901
Tel: (301) 593-7711

WoodenBoat Catalog
P.O. Box 78
Brooklin, ME 04616
Tel: (800) 225-5205
Fax: (207) 359-8920

Kits

Booth Enterprises
114 Wildwood Ave.
Victoria, British Columbia
V8S 3V9
CANADA
Tel: (604) 386-9622

Cape Fear Museum Associates
814 Market St.
Wilmington, NC 28401
Tel: (919) 341-4350
Sea skiffs

Clarkcraft
16-77 Aqualane
Tonawanda, NY 14150
Tel: (716) 873-2640
Large selection of kits

Glen-L Marine Designs
9152 Rosecrans
Bellflower, CA 90706
Tel: (213) 630-6258
Large selection of kits

Merryman Boats
4915 Delta River Dr.
Lansing, MI 48906
Tel: (517) 875-3788
Fax: (517) 323-0132

Monfort Associates
Division of Aladdin Products
R.F.D. 2
Wiscasset, ME 04578
Tel: (207) 882-5504

N.L. Silva & Co.
7980 Market St.
Wilmington, NC 28405
Tel: (919) 686-4356
Sea skiffs

Norton Boat Works
535 Commercial Ave.
Green Lake, WI 54941
Tel: (414) 294-6813
Iceboat kits and wooden masts

Southern Lakes Boatbuilding Co.
3436 Sevierville Rd.
Maryville, TN 37804
Wayfarer kits

Tremolino Boat
411 E. 6th St.
Chaska, MN 55318
Tel: (612) 448-6855

Figure 1: Plans for boats such as this dinghy designed by the author are often available inexpensively.

Lighting Equipment

If your boat is reasonably new, the chances are that you have several different types of lights onboard. These lights can be of three different types: incandescent, fluorescent, or halogen. Incandescents are the most common, but they cast a light with a slightly yellow glow and have a relatively high power draw. Fluorescents have the lowest power draw, and cast a white "shadowless" light. They can also cause radio interference. Halogens cast a bright white light and have a medium battery draw. You should be careful when changing a halogen bulb. The oils on your fingers, when transferred to the bulb, can make it heat up and diminish its life.

Increasingly, halogen lights are becoming the light of choice on boats, but each type of light has its place. Incandescent lights are usually used as area or overhead lighting in boat cabins. Quite often, two incandescent lights are fitted in the same fixture, one with a white bulb and the other with a red bulb for night lighting. Flourescent lights are often used in the galley or the head where bright white light is desirable. Often too, they are located over a vanity or under galley lockers as valance lighting. Halogen lights with their strong, concentrated beams, are best used as accent or spot lights. Common positions are over bunks and dining tables, and occasionally in navigation areas.

Other types of below-deck lights are the emergency or night lights. These are usually red incandescent lights that will not hinder night vision. Red lights should be fitted near any ladders, in the galley, in the navigation area, and in other areas where light might be transmittted to the helmsman. Quite often boats have a narrow strip of red lights under bunk and furniture faces, or on step faces to show the way in an emergency situation.

On-deck lights need to be powerful. The most important are the navigation lights. The very minimum you should have are red and green bow lights and a white stern light. Col-Regs (International Regulations for the Prevention of Collisions at Sea) categorize their requirements according to vessel length. Powercraft under 12 meters LOA (39.4 ft.) must have bow lights covering a combined 20 points of arc (225 degrees), a stern light covering 12 points or arc (138 degrees), and a masthead light covering at least 20 points of arc (225 degrees). The masthead light must be at least 1 meter above the bow and stern lights. On powercraft between 12 and 20 meters (39.4 ft. to 65.6 ft.), the masthead light must be carried at least 2.5 meters (8.2 ft.) above the gunwale. For sailboats under 20 meters (65.6 ft.), the requirements for bow and stern lights are similar to those for powercraft, but no masthead light is required. Sailboats, however, can have an optional red-over-green masthead light or a tricolor (red, green, and white) masthead light.

Lights to Col-Regs requirements must be carried on vessels using international waters. But vessels smaller than 65 feet using inland waters have slightly different requirements. Small sailboats and power-boats under 26 feet must have bow lights, but the stern light can be an all-around white light. Boats between 26 and 65 feet should have a white light at the bow, as well as red and green bow lights, plus an all-around white stern light higher than the white bow light. In all cases, the lights should be visible for at least two miles. Dingies and rowing boats should carry a lantern or all-around white light. Other lights used on deck are walkway lights and ladder lights on powercraft, and spreader lights on sailboats. These are usually incandescent or halogen lights and must be watertight.

Manufacturers of Lighting Fixtures

ABI Industries, Inc.
1261 Anderson Dr.
Suite C
San Rafael, CA 94901
Tel: (415) 258-9300
Fax: (415) 258-9461
Overhead and cabin lights

Alpenglow Marine Lights
P.O. Box 415
Eureka, MT 59917
Tel: (406) 8890-3586
Cabin lights

American Foreign Industries
2210 Gladstone Dr.
Pittsburg, CA 94565
Tel: (510) 427-2341
Fax: (510) 427-2342
Interior and spreader lights

Ancor Marine
501 Aaron St.
Cotati, CA 94931
Tel: (707) 792-0312
Fax: (707) 795-7950
Lamps

Aqua Signal Corp.
1680 East Fabyan Pkwy.
Batavia, IL 60510
Tel: (708) 232-6425
Fax: (708) 232-9481
Interior and navigation lighting

Aqua Signal Aktiengesellschatt
P.O. Box 450161
D-2800 Bremen 45
GERMANY
Tel: (+49) 421 4893-0
Fax: (+49) 421 4893210
Interior and navigation lighting

Aqua Signal (Australia) Pty. Ltd.
Unit 1/18 Energy Crescent
Ernest, Old
AUSTRALIA
Tel: (+61) 75 940555
Fax: (+61) 75 940105
Interior and navigation lighting

Asimow Enterprises, Inc.
12941 Killion St.
Van Nuys, CA 91401
Tel: (818) 786-2445
Fax: (818) 786-2446
Masthead lights

Barnegat Light Marine Products
10 W. College Ave.
Yardley, PA 19067
Tel: (215) 493-2777
Fax: (215) 493-1401
Interior and exterior lighting

Bass Electrical Products, Inc.
50 Grove St.
Salem, MA 01970
Tel: (617) 744-7003
Interior lighting and panels

The Guest Corp.
130 Shield St.
West Hartford, CT 06110
Tel: (203) 525-5318
Anchor lights, spotlights, and interior lighting

Hellamarine
201 Kelly Dr.
P.O. Box 2665
Peachtree City, GA 30269
Tel: (404) 631-7500
Fax: (404) 631-7575
Interior and navigation
lighting

Highlights in Lighting, Inc.
1280 S. Powerline Rd., # 184
Pompano Beach, FL 33069
Tel: (305) 739-9049
Spots and strip lights

ITC, Inc.
401 W. Washington St.
P.O. Box 166
Zeeland, MI 49464
Tel: (616) 772-9411
Fax: (616) 772-9470
12 volt lighting

Midland Ross Corp.
Russellstoll Division
530 Mt. Pleasant Ave.
Livingston, NJ 07039
Tel: (201) 992-8400
Watertight lighting for larger
vessels

Figure 1: A flexible wall light
from Modern Boatworks.

Modern Boatworks, Inc.
18 Marshall St.
South Norwalk, CT 06853
Tel: (800) 428-2628
Fax: (203) 838-8351
High quality, architecturally
distinctive interior light
fixtures

Perko
Street address:
16490 Northwest 13th Ave.
Miami, FL 33169-5707
Mailing address:
P.O. Box 64000D
Miami, FL 33164-0510
Tel: (305) 621-7525
Fax: (305) 620-9978
Interior and navigation
lighting

Ramco Industries, Inc.
52896 C.R. 113 N.
Elkhart, IN 46514
Tel: (800) 826-5483
   or (219) 264-2139
Fax: (219) 262-2686
Interior lighting, strip lights,
and switches

RGM Industries, Inc.
3342 Lillian Blvd.
Titusville, FL 32780
Tel: (407) 269-7428
Strip lights

Daniel R. Smith & Assoc.
1338 South Killian Dr., #11
Lake Park, FL 33403
Tel: (407) 842-5704
Fax: (407) 842-5705
Lighting

Supreme Lighting Corp.
Sales Office:
1605 John St.
Ft. Lee, NJ 07024
Tel: (800) 221-1573
   or (201) 947-4111
Fax: (201) 947-9329
Cabin and workshop lights

Supreme Lighting Corp.
122 E. Laurel St.
Mullins, SC 29574
Tel: (800) 922-6693
   or (803) 464-0554
Fax: (803) 464-6135
Cabin and workshop lights

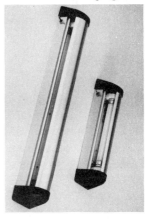

Figure 2: Overhead or wall
lights from Vetus-Den Ouden.

Vetus - Den Ouden, Inc.
P.O. Box 8712
Baltimore, MD 21240-0712
Tel: Orders (800) GO-VETUS
   or (410) 712-0740
Fax: (410) 712-0985
Cabin lights, nav lights, and
spot lights

Low Power Systems

Electrical systems below 56 volts are generally considered low power. With most systems of this voltage the power is supplied by batteries and each battery system must be regulated, charged and switched. If higher power is required, and the boat does not have the capability to generate its own power, an inverter can be used.

BATTERIES

Most boat owners will never have to select their own batteries; their boats come with them. Often, however, an owner increases the amount of electrical equipment onboard and soon the engine has to be run every day to keep the battery fully charged. If you have to run your engine every day to charge the battery, you should think about ways to reduce charging time. For instance, if you currently use a 60AH battery and need to recharge it every 24 hours, a 120AH battery will allow you to go twice as long without recharging. If your battery serves for both engine-starting and house, another alternative is to add a second battery dedicated solely to starting the engine.

If you are starting from scratch in selecting a battery, you will have to calculate how large a battery you will need. You do that by listing the wattage of every piece of electrical and electronic equipment onboard the boat and the amount of time it is used in a day. Multiplying the wattages by the times in use and totaling the results gives you the number of watt-hours of power used aboard the boat daily. Divide this watt-hour total by the voltage to get ampere hours required per day. To be safe, you should probably add about 20% to ensure that the battery is large enough to handle any future purchase of electrical equipment.

For best results, the engine-starting battery should be entirely separate from the house battery. Call your engine maker to find out what size battery is recommended.

The next decision is what type of battery you need: a conventional lead acid type, a deep-cycle battery, or a gel-cell battery. Deep-cycle batteries are better for marine applications because they can be discharged quite deeply before being recharged. Gel-cell batteries can also be deeply discharged, but they are very heavy.

The battery should be installed in its own box, which is securely fastened. If the boat rolls over, you do not want a large heavy battery flying around inside the vessel. Make sure the battery box is located in a spot that will not get too warm and is easily accessible, but not so accessible that it can be kicked or damaged.

Suppliers of Low Power Equipment

Batteries

Ample Power Co.
1150 NW 52nd St.
Seattle, WA 98107
Tel: (206) 789-5758
Fax: (206) 789-9003

Concorde Battery
2009 San Bernardino Rd.
West Covina, CA 91760
Tel: (818) 813-1234
Fax: (800) 237-4209
 or (818) 338-3549
Lifeline batteries

Figure 1: This Amp-Hour indicator is available from Cruising Equipment.

Cruising Equipment
6315 Seaview Ave. N.W.
Seattle, WA 98107
Tel: (206) 782-8100
Fax: (206) 789-1137

Delco Voyager
2401 Columbus Ave. 18-109
Anderson, IN 46018
Tel: (404) 257-3777
Fax: (404) 257-3609

Jack Rabbit Marine, Inc.
425 Fairfield Ave.
Stamford, CT 06902
Tel: (203) 961-8133
Fax: (203) 358-9250
Sealed gel batteries

Johnson Controls, Inc.
Specialty Battery Division
900 East Keefe Ave.
Milwaukee, WI 53212
Tel: (414) 961-6500
Dynasty gel-cell batteries

**Performance Parts
Industries, Inc.**
2480 Dr. Martin Luther King Blvd.
Pompano Beach, FL 33069
Tel: (800) 537-2232
Fax: (305) 970 3322
Lifeline gel-cell batteries

Rolls Battery Engineering
P.O. Box 671
8 Proctor St.
Salem, MA 01970
Tel: (508) 745-3333
Fax: (508) 741-8956
The most complete line of batteries in the industry

Surrette American
Box 249
Tilton, NH 03276
Tel: (603) 286-8974
Fax: (603) 286-7770
Marine battery suppliers

Vetus - Den Ouden, Inc.
P.O. Box 8712
Baltimore, MD 21240-0712
Tel: Orders only: (800) GO-VETUS
 or (410) 712-0740
Fax: (410) 712-0985
Batteries, switches, boxes, and chargers

Battery Chargers

Ample Power Co.
1150 NW 52nd St.
Seattle, WA 98107
Tel: (206) 789-5758
Fax: (206) 789-9003

Balmar Products, Inc.
902 N.W. Ballard Way
Seattle, WA 98107
Tel: (206) 789-4970
Fax: (206) 784-0878

Charles Industries
5600 Apollo Dr.
Rolling Meadows, IL 60008
Tel: (708) 806-6300
Fax: (708) 806-6231

**Cruisair/Marine
Development Corp.**
P.O. Box 15299
Richmond, VA 23227
Tel: (804) 746-1313
Fax: (804) 746-7248

Cruising Equipment
6315 Seaview Ave. N.W.
Seattle, WA 98107
Tel: (206) 782-8100
Fax: (206) 789-1137

Deltona Transformer Corp.
801 U.S. Hwy. 92 E.
Deland, FL 32724
Tel: (800) 456-7901
Fax: (904) 736-0379

Guest
48 Elm St.
Meriden, CT 06450
Tel: (203) 238-0550

Heart Interface Corp.
811 1st Ave. S.
Kent, WA 98032
Tel: (206) 859-0640
Fax: (206) 859-3579
Heart inverters and battery
chargers

LaMarche Manufacturing
Co.
106 Bradrock Dr.
Des Plaines, IL 60018
Tel: (708) 299-1188
Fax: (708) 299-3061
Constavolt battery chargers

Newmar
P.O. Box 1306
Newport Beach, CA 92663
Tel: (800) 854-3906
  or (714) 751-0488
Fax: (714) 957-1621

Raritan Engineering
530 Orange St.
Millvillem, NJ 08332
Tel: (609) 825-4900
Fax: (609) 825-4409
Crown converter/charger

Real Goods
966 Mazzoni St.
Ukiah, CA 95482-3471
Tel: (800) 762-7325
Solar battery charger

Trace Engineering
5917 195th N.E.
Arlington, WA 98223
Tel: (206) 435-2229

Vetus - Den Ouden, Inc.
P.O. Box 8712
Baltimore, MD 21240-0712
Tel: Orders only: (800)
GO-VETUS
  or (410) 712-0740
Fax: (410) 712-0985

Battery Switches

Charles Industries
5600 Apollo Dr.
Rolling Meadows, IL 60008
Tel: (708) 806-6300
Fax: (708) 806-6231

Cole Hersee
20 Old Colony Ave.
S. Boston, MA 02127
Tel: (617) 268-2100
Fax: (617) 268-9490
Isolation switches

Guest
48 Elm St.
Meriden, CT 06450
Tel: (203) 238-0550
Isolation switches

Marinetics
P.O. Box 2676
Newport Beach, CA 92663
Tel: (800) 854-4601
  or (714) 646-8889
Fax: (714) 642-8627

Vetus - Den Ouden, Inc.
P.O. Box 8712
Baltimore, MD 21240-0712
Tel: Orders only: (800)
GO-VETUS
  or (410) 712-0740
Fax: (410) 712-0985

Battery Boxes

Glenwood Marine
1627 W. El Segundo Blvd.
Gardena, CA 90249
Tel: (213) 757-3141
Fax: (213) 779-8728

Sailing Specialties, Inc.
P.O. Box 99 Commerce Ave.
St. Mary's Industrial Park
Hollywood, MD 20636
Tel: (301) 373-2372
Fax: (301) 373-2734

Vetus - Den Ouden, Inc.
P.O. Box 8712
Baltimore, MD 21240-0712
Tel: Orders only: (800)
GO-VETUS
  or (410) 712-0740
Fax: (410) 712-0985

Battery Monitors

Ample Power Co.
1150 NW 52nd St.
Seattle, WA 98107
Tel: (206) 789-5758
Fax: (206) 789-9003

Balmar Products, Inc.
902 N.W. Ballard Way
Seattle, WA 98107
Tel: (206) 789-4970
Fax: (206) 784-0878

Cruising Equipment
6315 Seaview Ave. N.W.
Seattle, WA 98107
Tel: (206) 782-8100
Fax: (206) 789-1137

Vetus - Den Ouden, Inc.
P.O. Box 8712
Baltimore, MD 21240-0712
Tel: Orders only: (800)
GO-VETUS
or (410) 712-0740
Fax: (410) 712-0985

Inverters

Balmar Products, Inc.
902 N.W. Ballard Way
Seattle, WA 98107
Tel: (206) 789-4970
Fax: (206) 784-0878

Charles Industries
5600 Apollo Dr.
Rolling Meadows, IL 60008
Tel: (708) 806-6300
Fax: (708) 806-6231

Dynamote
1200 W. Nickerson
Seattle, WA 98119
Tel: (800) 426-2838
or (206) 282-1000
Fax: (206) 283-7714

Heart Interface Corp.
811 1st Avenue S.
Kent, WA 98032
Tel: (206) 859-0640
Fax: (206) 859-3579
Heart inverters and battery chargers.

Kenyon Galley Products
P.O. Box 308
New Whitfield St.
Guilford, CT 06437
Tel: (203) 453-4374
Fax: (203) 458-2998

Figure 2: Kenyon Galley Products make inverters for low power systems.

Newmar
P.O. Box 1306
Newport Beach, CA 92663
Tel: (800) 854-3906
or (714) 751-0488
Fax: (714) 957-1621

Converters and Voltage Conditioners

Cruising Equipment
6315 Seaview Ave. N.W.
Seattle, WA 98107
Tel: (206) 782-8100
Fax: (206) 789-1137

Marinetics
P.O. Box 2676
Newport Beach, CA 92663
Tel: (800) 854-4601
or (714) 646-8889
Fax: (714) 642-8627

Newmar
P.O. Box 1306
Newport Beach, CA 92663
Tel: (800) 854-3906
or (714) 751-0488
Fax: (714) 957-1621

Figure 3: This breaker box is available in many styles and sizes from Vetus-Den Ouden.

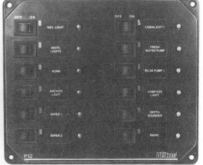

Lubricants, Polishes, Waxes, and Finishes

Greases and oils, polishes, and waxes, and finishes are still essential on boats, despite modern technology. Engines, winches, windlasses, generators, and almost every other moving part on a boat needs to be lubricated. Polishes and waxes are needed to prevent deterioration of the gelcoat and other exposed parts of the boat. Teak finishes are applied to wood surfaces to prevent deterioration and discoloring. But which ones are worth buying and which are not?

First, let me say that machinery manufacturers know their product best. Their recommendations should be followed when changing or oiling a mechanical part. If you do not know what the manufacturer recommends, look first at the compatibility of the oil or grease with seawater. Many greases, when exposed to seawater, become a gummy mess which seems to attract and hold sand and dirt. That sand and dirt is then carried into the gears and contributes mightily to wear and deterioration. Second, look to see how well the lubricant stays where it is put. If you oil your winches and the oil is washed out by rain or seawater, the winches won't stay lubricated for very long. Also, oil that gets washed out of gears tends to collect elsewhere and can cause problems in its new location. Third, check the compatibility of the lubicant with the piece of machinery. For instance, some gears have nylon bearing cages or other plastic parts, which can sometimes be harmed by exposure to inappropriate greases or oils.

If you have to lubricate parts that might carry electricity or are connected to electrical cables, make sure the oil or grease is not a conductor of electricity. This could give you a nasty shock, or cause the part to stop running.

Finally, set up a regular schedule for oiling or greasing mechanical parts, and try to maintain it. The parts will last longer and perform more efficiently than if the maintenance work is performed haphazardly.

POLISHES AND WAXES

While it may not seem like much, waxing the hull of your boat once a year can increase the life of the gelcoat and raise the boat's resale value. When looking for a wax for your boat, select one that is for use on fiberglass, has as much UV-resistance as possible, and is not degraded by exposure to saltwater.

To apply a wax, the hull should be washed clean of any fiberglass residues, saltwater, or dirt and carefully dried. Once the hull is dry, apply the wax by rubbing it on with a soft cloth. Make sure the cloth stays clean. Any dirt collected in the polishing cloth can make minute scratches on the hull, which may show up as sun reflects off the boat's shiny sides. Buff the hull using either a soft cloth or an electric drill with a buffing head. Again, change the buffing cloth frequently to ensure that dirt is not ground into the fiberglass.

TEAK FINISHES

There are a number of teak finishes on the market. The very best, but the one that requires the most work and constant maintenance, is varnish (see Paints and Varnishes section). Rather than varnishing their teak, many owners prefer simply to oil it or apply some other type of teak finish. When applying a teak finish, be aware that you don't do it once and forget it. Not if you want the teak to keep its warm woody patina. Most teak finishes have to be applied at least once a season, some more often. While many are teak oil with additives, some bear little resemblance to teak oil. I prefer teak oil, because the teak is being preserved with its own oil rather than a chemically derived equivalent.

When selecting a teak finish, make sure you get one that soaks into the wood quickly and doesn't puddle or turn sticky before soaking in. Check, too, that the finish will not stain the surounding fiberglass or woodwork. Finally, if you have already applied a teak finish and want to apply a different one, make sure the two are compatible.

Suppliers of Lubricants, Polishes, Waxes, and Finishes

Lubricants

Corrosion Block
2637 National Pl.
Garland, TX 75041
Tel: (214) 271-7361
Fax: (214) 278-9271

Liquid Glass Enterprises, Inc.
P.O. Box 1170
Teaneck, NJ 07666
Tel: (800) 548-5307
  or in NJ (201) 387-6755

Lubriplate Division/ Fiske Brothers Refining Co.
129 Lockwood St.
Newark, NJ 07105
Tel: (201) 589-9150
Fax: (201) 589-4432

PMS Products
285 James St.
Holland, MI 49424
Tel: (616) 786-9922
Fax: (616) 786-9130
Boeshield T.9 is marketed by this company

WD40 Company
P.O. Box 80607
San Diego, CA 92138-9021
Manufacturers of WD40

Polishes and Waxes

Boatlife Div. Life Industries
205 Sweet Hollow Rd.
Old Bethpage, NY 11804
Tel: (516) 454-0055
Fax: (516) 454-0452
Boatlife polishes and waxes

Star Brite
4041 S.W. 47 Ave.
Ft. Lauderdale, FL 33314
Tel: (800) 327-8583
  or (305) 587 6280
Fax: (305) 587-2813
Marine and RV polishes and waxes

Teak Finishes

All Guard Products
4934 Factory Dr.
Fairfield, OH 45014
Tel: (513) 829-8070
Teakguard teak finish

Boatek Ltd.
2038 Washington Ave.
Philadelphia, PA 19146
Tel: (215) 546-6110
Boatek teak preservative

Chemical-World
P.O. Box 376
Holtsville, NY 11742
Tel: (516) 654-9437
Environmentally friendly teak cleaner

Star Brite
4041 S.W. 47th Ave.
Ft. Lauderdale, FL 33314
Tel: (800) 327-8583
  or (305) 587 6280
Fax: (305) 587-2813
Gel Formula teak cleaner and Tropical teak sealer

Figure 1: Surface Safe teak cleaner from Rule Industries.

Figure 2: Stop metal deterioration with Corrosion Block from Corrosion Block.

Magazines and Newsletters

Before you send your hard-earned money to subscribe to a new magazine, ask yourself if it is the right magazine for you. Are you really interested in sport-fishing, or would you sooner fish inshore from a nearby seawall? Are you a closet racer or do you really like to cruise your sailboat?

A magazine that truly suits your interests is one that you are more likely to read. Before subscribing, pick up a copy at the newstand for a month or two. Then take advantage of any special offers to get your subscription as inexpensively as possible.

Publishers of Marine Magazines and Newsletters

Note: The magazines and newsletters listed here are nationally distibuted marine magazines to which anyone can subscribe.

Australian Sailing
Published monthly by Yaffa Publishing Group
Editorial offices:
GPO Box 606
Sydney, NSW 2001
AUSTRALIA
Tel: (+61) 02 281 2333
Fax: (+61) 02 281 2750
Subscription: $52 per year
Covers cruising and racing sailing in Australia

Big Boat Magazine
Editorial offices:
EPG, Le Theleme
Route des Dolines 06560
Sophia Antipolis
FRANCE
Tel: (+33) 92 96 09 44
Fax: (+33) 92 96 09 37
The magazine exclusively about large boats

Boatbuilder
Editorial offices:
P.O. Box 540638
Merrit Island, FL 32954
Tel: (407) 459-1558
Fax: (407) 459-3636
Subscription: $24 per year
Aimed exclusively at the amateur boat builder

Boating
Published monthly by Hatchette Magazines, Inc.
Editorial offices:
1633 Broadway
New York, NY 10001
Tel: (212) 767-5585
Fax: (212) 767-5618
Subscription: $24.00 per year
Circulation: 195,000
The largest and most informative powerboating magazine in the field

Coastal Cruising
Editorial offices:
108 Middle Ln.
Beaufort, NC 28516-2157
Tel: (919) 728-2157
Fax: (919) 728-6715

Cruising World
A New York Times publication
Editorial offices:
5 John Clarke Rd
Box 3400
Newport, RI 02840
Tel: (401) 847-1588
Fax: (401) 848-5048
Subscription: $23.94 per year
Circulation: 145,500
The magazine for cruising sailors

Motor Boating & Sailing

Published by The Hearst Corp.
Editorial offices:
250 West 55th Street
New York, NY 10019
Tel: (212) 649-4097
Fax: (212 489-9258
Subscription: $15.97 per year
Circulation: 145,500
Covers powerboating and some sailing

Power and MotorYacht

A Cahners Publication
Editorial offices:
1234 Summer St.
Stamford, CT 06905
Tel: (203) 323-3300
Fax: (203) 323-7039
Subscription: $29.97 per year
Circulation: 156,500
Covers power and motor yachts

Powerboat

Published by Nordskog
Publishing, Inc.
Editorial offices:
15917 Strathern St.
Van Nuys, CA 91406
Tel: (818) 989-1820
Subscription: $27.00 per year in USA
Circulation: 55,000
Bills itself as the world's leading powerboat performance magazine

Powerboat Reports

Published by Belvoir
Publications, Inc.
Editorial offices:
75 Holly Hill Ln.
Box 2626
Greenwich, CT 06836-2626
Tel: (203) 661-6111
Fax: (203) 661-4802
Subscription: $68 per year
A product analysis newsletter with no advertising

Practical Sailor

Published by Belvoir
Publications, Inc.
Editorial offices:
Box 819
Newport, RI 02840
Tel: (203) 661-6111
Subscription: $72 per year
A product analysis newsletter with no advertising

Professional Boatbuilder

Published by Woodenboat
Magazines
Editorial offices:
P. O. Box 78
Brooklin, ME 04616
Tel: (207) 359-4651
Fax: (207) 359-8920
Subscription: $35.95 per year
Circulation: 26,000
Aimed at the professional in the industry

Sail

A Cahners publication
Editorial offices:
275 Washington St.
Newton, MA 02158-1630
Tel: (617) 630-3710
Fax: (617) 964-8948
Subscription: $19.95 per year
Circulation: 178,000
Covers all facets of the sailing spectrum, from racing to cruising and everything in between

Sailing

Editorial offices:
125 E. Main St.
P. O. Box 249
Port Washington, WI 53074
Tel: (414) 284-3494
Fax: (414) 284-7764
Subscription: $24.75 per year
Circulation: 60,000
A large 10" x 12 1/2" format with terrific photography and easy to read stories

Sailing World

Published by the New York
Times
Editorial Offices:
5 John Clarke Road
Box 3400
Newport, RI 02840
Tel: (401) 847-1588
Fax: (401) 848-5048
Subscription: $23.94 per year
Circulation: 63,000
Covers the racing scene at both national and international levels

Saltwater Sportsman
A Times-Mirror publication
Editorial offices:
280 Summer St.
Boston, MA 02210
Tel: (617) 439-9977
Fax: (617) 439-9357
Subscription: $19.95 per year
Circulation: 142,000
The largest circulation
sport-fishing magazine

Scuba Times
Published bi-monthly by GBP,
Inc.
Editorial offices:
14110 Perdido Key Dr.
Suite 16
Pensacola, FL 32507
Tel: (904) 492-7805
Subscription: $15 per year
The active diver's magazine

Showboats International
Published bi-monthly by
Hachette Magazines, Inc.
Editorial offices:
1600 S.E. 17th St.
Ft. Lauderdale, FL 33316
Tel: (305) 525-8626
Fax: (305) 525-7954
Subscription: $24 per year
Showboats International
covers very large power yachts

Skin Diver
Published monthly by
Peterson Publishing Co.
Editorial offices:
8490 Sunset Blvd.
Los Angeles, CA 90069
Tel: (310) 854-2222
Fax: (310) 854-2121
Subscription: $21.94 per year
Bills itself as the world's
largest underwater magazine

Soundings
Published monthly by
Soundings Publications, Inc.
Editorial offices:
35 Pratt St.
Essex, CT 06426
Tel: (203) 767-3200
Fax: (203) 767-1048
Subscription: $18.97 per year
Circulation: 95,000 (not
audited)
Newspaper format covering
both sail and power and
containing regional inserts

Sport Fishing
Published nine times a year by
World Publications, Inc.
Editorial offices:
P.O. Box 2456
Winter Park, FL 32790
Tel: (407) 628-4802
Subscription: $18.97 per year
Circulation: 125,000
The magazine of offshore
fishing (See section on fishing
equipment)

Woodenboat
Published by Woodenboat
Magazines
Editorial offices:
P. O. Box 78
Naskeag Rd.
Brooklin, ME 04616
Tel: (207) 359-4651
Fax: (207) 359-8920
Circulation: 105,000
Covers wooden boats only

Yachting
A Times-Mirror publication
Editorial offices:
2 Park Avenue
New York, NY 10016
Tel: (212) 779-5000
Fax: (212) 725-1035
Subscription: $19.98 per year
Circulation: 132,000
Covers the big boat (over 40
feet) scene

Yachting Monthly
Editorial Offices:
Room 2209
King's Reach Tower
Stamford St.
London SE1 9LS
ENGLAND
Tel: (+44) 71 261 6040
Fax: (+44) 71 261 6704
A practical and technical
English sailing magazine

Mail Order Houses

Ordering equipment by mail can save time and money, but there are pitfalls. When buying gear by mail order, make sure you are dealing with a reputable vendor. If you have any doubts, call your local Better Business Bureau, or check with Dunn & Bradstreet.

If the item you are ordering is complex — for instance, it might be a piece of electronic equipment — after-sales support may be essential. Many mail order companies have an 800 number for after-sales support. You might use it if you need to ask questions after you have read the manual, or you may need to know how to upgrade the item. Ask if your mail order house has this support.

When ordering from a mail order house always use a credit card. That way, if anything goes wrong or the merchandise is defective, you can cancel the order and notify your credit card issuer. If the vendor refuses to return your money, the credit card issuer will often go to bat for you if you have a legitimate complaint.

When ordering, ask for the name of the person you are talking to and make a note of it. That way, if there's a problem, you'll be able to get back to the right person or to talk to that person's supervisor. Also, ask how long it will take for the item to be delivered. This will tell you when to expect it and if it has gone astray. Ask, too, for the total price and the invoice number. Find out how it will be delivered and how much the shipping charges are. You don't want to be surprised if a five dollar item costs twenty five dollars to ship. This is especially important if you are ordering a piece of gear from abroad. In many cases, when ordering from foreign companies, shipping by air freight is faster and less expensive than slower, more conventional routes. Plus, the item is less likely to be damaged in transit.

When you recieve a shipment from a mail order house, check the outside of the package for signs of damage. If damage is apparent, inform the carrier immediately, preferably before he leaves the premises. That way, you will be sure to get your money back if the item is, in fact, damaged.

If you have to return an item, make sure the company knows you are returning it. Many electronics and computer vendors request that you get a return authorization number (RAN) or a return merchandise authorization number (RMA). This is to protect you as well as them. If you simply mail an item and it goes astray, you have no way of knowing if they received it or whether it was lost en route. With a RAN, the company is expecting the item and will often call if it is not received within a certain time.

Addresses of Mail Order Houses

Baker, Lyman & Co.
3220 S. 110 Service Rd.
Metairie, LA 70001
Tel: (800) 535-6956
Navigation gear

Barris Marine
135 Dolphin Drive
P.O. Box 451
Woodmere, NY 11598
Tel: (516) 569-6878
Boating books and videos

Bennet Marine Video
730 Washington St.
Marina Del Rey, CA 90292
Tel: (310) 821-3329
Fax: (310) 306-3162
Marine videos

Boater's World
6711 Ritz Way
Beltville, MD 20705
Tel: Orders: (800) 826-BOAT
Marine discount centers

Bronze Star
812 Torrance St.
San Diego, CA 92103
Tel: (619) 291-7393
Fax: (619) 291-1031
*Bronze hardware for
traditional boats*

Cabela's
812 13th Ave.
Sidney, NE 69160-001
Fishing gear

Captain's Emporium
6600 N. Lincoln Ave.
Lincolnwood, IL 60645
Tel: (708) 675-5411
Fax: (708) 675-2635
Nautical trophies and gear

Celestaire
416 S. Pershing
Wichita, KS 67218
Tel: (316) 686-9785
Navigation equipment

Coast Navigation
116 Legion Ave.
Annapolis, MD 21401
Tel: (800) 638-0420
  or (410) 268-3120
Fax: (410) 268-0389
Marine electronics

**Consumers Marine
Electronics**
P.O. Box 1319
1771 Highway 34 S.
Wall, NJ 07719
Tel: (800) 332-2628
  or In Canada: (800)
626-4753

A.G.A. Correa
Wiscasset, ME 04578
Tel: (207) 882-7873
Marine jewelery

Crook & Crook
2795 S.W. 27th Ave.
Miami, FL 33133
Tel: (305) 854-0005
Fax: (305) 854-2474
*Accessories, electronics,
fishing, diving, and skiing
gear*

Cruising Equipment
6315 Seaview Ave. N.W.
Seattle, WA 98107
Tel: (206) 782-8100
Fax: (206) 789-1137

Cruising Gear
2751 S.W. 27th Ave.
Miami, FL 33133
Tel: (305) 854-7600
Fax: (305) 854-5984

Davis Instruments
3465 Diablo Ave.
Hayward, CA 94545
Tel: (510) 732-9229
Fax: (510) 732-9188

Defender Industries
255 Main St.
New Rochelle, NY 10801
Tel: (914) 632-3001
Fax: (914) 632-6544

E & B Marine Supply
201 Meadow Rd.
Edison, NY 08818
Tel: (201) 819-7400
Fax: (201) 819-4771
Marine equipment catalog

Freeport Marine Supply
47 West Merrick Rd.
Freeport, NY 11520
*256 page catalog of marine
equipment*

Goldberg's Marine
201 Meadow Rd.
Edison, NJ 08818
Tel: (800) BOATING

Hamilton Marine, Inc.
P.O. Box 227
Rt. 1
Searsport, ME 04974
Tel: (207) 548-6302
  or (207) 548-2985
Fax: (800) 969-6352
*Suppliers to the boat building
and fishing industries*

Hinckley Shipstore
Southwest Harbor, ME 04679
Tel: (207) 244-5531

H.M. Specialities
P.O. Box 1574
Radio City Station
New York, NY 10101
Tel: (800) 722-9999

InfoCenter, Inc.
P.O. Box 47175
Forestville, MD 20747
Tel: (301) 420-2468
Electronics

International Sailing Products
319 Main St.
P.O. Box 389
New Rochelle, NY 10802
Tel: (800) 645-7676
  or (914) 576-4050
Fax: (914) 632-2732
Clothes, sailing gear, and yacht equipment

International Watercraft
2389 S. E. Dixie Hwy.
Stuart, FL 34996
Tel: (800) 780-RAFT
Fax: (407) 283-0122
Inflatables boats and accessories

Jamestown Distributors
28 Narragansett Ave.
P.O. Box 348
Jamestown, RI 02835
Tel: (800) 423-0030
  or (401) 423-2520
Fax: (401) 423-0542
Fastener and fittings catalog

Johnson Marine
Industrial Park
East Haddam, CT 06423
Tel: (203) 873-8697
Rigging hardware catalog

JSI
3000 Gandy Blvd.
P.O. Box 20926
St. Petersburg, FL 33742
Tel: (813) 577-3220
Fax: (813) 576-1306
Sailboat and sailing supplies

Landfall Navigation
354 W. Putnam Ave.
Greenwich, CT 06830
Tel: (203) 661-3176
Fax: (203) 661-9613
Sextants and charts

Layline
P.O. Box 17467
Raleigh, NC 27619
Tel: (800) 542-5463
Fax: (919) 755-1539
Yacht racing equipment

M & E Marine Supply
P.O. Box 601
Camden, NJ 08101
Tel: (609) 858-1010
Fax: (609) 858-3117
Marine equipment catalog

Medof Marine
5330 Derry Ave.
Suite G
Agoura Hills, CA 91301
Tel: (818) 707-2991
Fax: (818) 707-9304
Marine equipment

Outer Banks Outfitters
Highway 70 E.
P.O. Drawer 500
Beaufort, NC 28516
Tel: to order: (800) 682-2225

Patagonia Mail Order
P.O. Box 8900
Bozeman, MT 59715
Tel: catalog: (800) 336-9090
  or to order: (800) 638-6464

R. C. Plath
5300 S.E. Johnson Creek Blvd.
Portland, OR 97222
Tel: (503) 777-2441
Fax: (503) 777-2450
Windlasses and marine hardware

Post Marine Supply, Inc.
111 Cedar St.
New Rochelle, NY 10801
Tel: (914) 235-9800
Fax: (914) 235-9008
Very large selection of marine equipment

Preston's
102 Main St.
Greenport, NY 11944
Tel: (516) 477-1990
Fax: (516) 477-0198

Quayside
59 Hawks Rd.
Kingston-upon-Thames,
Surrey KT1 3DS
ENGLAND
Tel: (+44) 81 541 5915
Fax: (+44) 81 541 5916
Marine equipmemt in the UK

The Rigging Co.
1 Maritime Dr.
Portsmouth, RI 02871
Tel: (800) 322-1525
  or (401) 683-1525
Fax: (401) 683-5442
Yacht rigging

Rostand
Box 737
Chepachet, RI O2814
Tel: (800) 635-0063

W C. Russell Moccasin
285 S. W. Franklin St.
Berlin, WI 54923
Tel: (414) 361-2252
Fax: (414) 361-3274
Moccasins and shoes

Sailrite Kits
305 W. Van Buren St.
Columbia City, IN 46725
Tel: (800) 348-2769
Fax: (2l9) 244-4148

Figure 1: Autopilots such as this Cetrek 727 are available from many mail order electronics suppliers.

Skipper Marine Electronics
3170 Commercial Ave.
Northbrook, IL 60062
Tel: (800) 621-2378
Fax: (708) 291-0244
Marine electronic equipment

Starboard Marine
3078 Lawson Blvd.
Oceanside, NY 11572
Tel: (516) 764-1224
Fax: (516) 536-0672
Wholesaler of marine electronics

Team One Newport
P.O. Box 1443
547 Thames St.
Newport, Rl 02840
Tel: (800) VIP-GEAR
Fax: (401) 849-8460

West Marine
P.O. Box 50050
Watsonville, CA 95077-5050
Tel: Customer Service: (800) 262-8042
  or (408) 728-5229
  or To Order: (800) 538-0775
  or (408) 728-4430
Fax: (408) 728-4360
Wide selection of marine equipment

Windsurfing by Mail
6043 N.W. 167 St.
Miami, FL 33015
Tel: (800) THE-SURF
Fax: (305) 822-2839
Windsurfing gear

Wintron Electronics
800 Rt. 71
Spring Lake Heights, NJ 07762
Tel: (908) 449-4850
Fax: (908) 449-4517
Wholesale electronics suppliers

WoodenBoat Catalog
P.O. Box 78
Brooklin, ME 04616
Tel: (800) 225-5205
Fax: (207) 359-8920

Modelmakers

Anyone who enjoys boats will almost certainly enjoy model boats. Some model boats are raced, some are used as toys, and others are kept as heirlooms. You can either buy a ready-made model or purchase a kit and build it yourself. While ready-made models are often of very high quality, kit-built boats will give you hours of building enjoyment, help hone your modeling skills, and give you even more pleasure sitting on a shelf in your home or office.

Ready-made models are usually commisioned from a modelmaker and can take up to six months to complete. If you want to have a model of your own yacht built, you will need to get all the plans together before approaching the modelmaker. Only by having all the drawings of your boat will you get an acccurate estimate of the cost and an accurate model. Expect to pay anywhere from $1,000 to $10,000 or even more if the model is particularly ornate.

If these prices are too high for your budget, you might think about building the model yourself. The easiest way to get experience is to start with a kit. Buy the best kit you can afford, preferably one that has the hull shape already cut out of a solid block of wood. Look for kits that are specifically designed for the beginner. This will get you started without spending a lot of money on an expensive kit that may be beyond your skills. Building models takes time, so you should be prepared to spend

two or three evenings a week for six or seven months on a reasonably complex kit. I usually build my models over the winter when the dark evenings force me to spend time indoors.

As your skills and range of tools increase, you can start building models from scratch. The most important part of scratch building is to do careful research. Quite often, researching the vessel will tell you how it was originally built and provide clues as to how to build your model. Be careful. Model research can often hook you as deeply as the actual model building.

Another type of model is the half hull. Years ago, few shipbuilders had the skills to sit down and draw a set of lines for a ship. Instead, they built a half hull and then cut up the half hull or measured it carefully to develop the lines of the full-size vessel. Many of these half hulls can be seen in antique shops and usually cost a pretty penny. But you can easily make your own using ordinary lumber, or if you want to try something a little fancier, use basswood. I get my basswood from Shipyard Supply, whose address is listed in the boat builder's supply section. The basswood is cut into lifts, each 1 inch thick. The lines of the boat are laid out using one lift at each waterline. Then the lifts are glued together to form a step shaped rough hull. From here on in it a matter of chiseling, planing, filing, and sanding until the hull shape emerges. Once the half hull has been fully sanded, it can be painted and mounted on a decorative board. The whole process should take about eight to ten hours.

If you keep at it, in a few years you'll have a very good collection. Then you'll have to figure out what to do with all those models. But that's a whole 'nother story.

Addresses of Modelmakers

American Marine Model Gallery
12-S Derby Sq.
Salem, MA 01970
Tel: (508) 745-5777
Ship model gallery

American Model Yachting Association
2793 Shellwick Ct.
Columbus, OH 43235
Tel: (614) 457-1185
Radio-controlled model yachts

Advanced Model Makers Ltd.
Unit 5A
Kemps Quay Industrial Park
Bitterne Manor
Southampton, Hampshire SO2 4AD
ENGLAND
Tel: 44-703 235126
Fax: 44-703 334271
Models made to order

Bluejacket Ship Crafters
P.O. Box 18
Main St.
Castine, ME 04421
Tel: (207) 567-3525
Models made to order and kits

Classic Marine Model Ships
5931 N.E. Terr.
Ft. Lauderdale, FL 33334
Tel: (305) 771-9002
Fax: (305) 945-1446
Ready-made models

David Air
8 Beach St.
New York, NY 10013
Tel: (212) 925-7867
Vintage ship and boat models

The Dromedary
6324 Belton Dr.
El Paso, TX 79912
Tel: (915) 584-2445
Ship modeler's supplies

Half Hull Classics
9214 15th Ave. N.W.
Seattle, WA 98117
Tel: (206) 789-3713
Half hull models

Bruce Hallet
US Rt. 2
R.F.D. Box 60
Sherman Mills, ME 04776
Models to order

Ken Gardiner Modelmaker
870 Production Pl.
Newport Beach, CA 92663
Tel: (714) 642-9127
Fax: (714) 642-5415
Models made to order

Lannan Ship Model Gallery
58 Thayer St.
Boston, MA 02118
Tel: (617) 451-2650
Museum quality ship models

Model Shipways, Inc.
P.O. Box 1000
Industrial Pk.
Mt. Pocono, PA 18344
Tel: (800) 821-0100
Ship model kits

North Star
1120 Lexington Ave.
New York, NY 10021
Tel: (212) 794-4277
Fax: (212) 794-5264
Model transport art gallery

The Scale Model Co.
1905 Poplar Ridge Road
Pasadena, MD 21122
Tel: (301) 255-8004
Models made to order

Seacraft Classics
6615 N. Scottsdale Rd.
Scottsdale, AZ 85260
Tel: (800) 356-1987
   or (602) 951-9518
Fax: (602) 998-2314
Hand-crafted models to order

Ship Model Gallery
P.O. Box 303
Hamilton, NY 13346
Tel: (315) 842-2462
Museum quality model ships

The Ship Model Shop
40 Deerfield Ln.
P.O. Box 536
Eastham, MA 0536
Tel: (508) 255-5375
Models of US navy warships

Southern Model Builders
104 Buena Vista Dr.
Daphne, AL 36526
Tel: (205) 626-0412
Models to order

Figure 1: This fine model of Ticonderoga is from Ken Gardiner.

Naval Architects and Designers

Many boat owners believe that having a boat designed specifically for them will be much more expensive than buying a good-quality production boat. But when everything is said and done, the custom boat is often only slightly more in price, plus the owner gets a boat that is exactly what he wants.

The first step in getting a custom designed boat is to pick a reputable designer. The designer will start by spending some time listening to your ideas. Then he'll sketch up an outboard profile and interior arrangement plan, or adapt existing plans to suit your wishes. The plans will probably go back and forth between you and the designer several times before you are both satisfied.

As soon as the design is reasonably solidified, the designer will make up a bid package. He'll take the profile and arrangement drawings and develop specifications from them. Then he'll add to the package some drawings of the hull shape and construction details. The bid package is sent to a number of builders, who estimate the cost of building the boat. At this stage, the designer may take you to meet with the builders who have submitted the best bids, to evaluate their work, and to discuss the payment schedule. When a builder is chosen, the owner signs a contract with him.

The builder will need a number of drawings from the designer. These are:

- The lines plan, which shows the shape of the hull. Instead of providing offsets, most designers now provide the builder with full-size computer-generated sections to reduce lofting time and expense.
- The arrangement plan, which shows how the interior of the boat is laid out.
- An outboard profile plan, which shows the exterior of the vessel. For a sailboat, the outboard profile shows the standing rigging, sail sizes, and spar information.
- The construction plan, which shows how the boat is to be constructed, including the laminate or plating schedule, all materials, the engine position and size, any special features, and a host of other details. Of all the drawings, this is probably the most important.
- Construction and joiner section drawings, if they are not included in other plans. These are essential if the construction and the interior are to fit accurately inside the boat.
- The deck plan, which shows how the deck is laid out, including each piece of equipment and its position on the boat.
- An engine arrangement drawing, which shows where everything is in the engine room or compartment. This is done for larger sailboats and all powerboats.
- Other drawings, depending upon the type of boat being designed. For instance, a sailboat might require a keel drawing, a rudder drawing, and details

of the rudder stock construction. Powerboats might require drawings showing the arrangement of fishbox plumbing and refrigeration systems.

- A wiring diagram and a plumbing diagram, which show the electrical and plumbing systems.
- Various detail plans, such as the mast layout for a sailboat, or a radar-arch drawing for a powerboat. These are often done by the builder.

Completing a set of plans for a yacht takes anywhere from two to five months, depending upon the boat's size and complexity. The designer's fee for this work will range between 8 and 12% of the cost of the finished boat, depending upon the size of the vessel.

While a boat is under construction, a good designer will visit the project on a regular schedule, but how often depends upon the distance involved. For instance, a designer living in Maine might visit a boat building in Australia only once, at the launching, but keep track of the project by mail, fax, and telephone. In contrast, if the boat is building a mile from the design office, somebody might check in every day.

Naval Architects and Designers

The A Group
Le Victoria Palace
13 Bd.
Princesse Charlotte MC 98000
MONACO
Tel: (+33) 93 25 89 18
Fax: (+33) 93 50 00 82

John G. Alden Naval Architects, Inc.
89 Commercial Wharf
Boston, MA 02110
Tel: (617) 227-9480
Fax: (617) 523-5465

David Allan Williams
21 Ambleside Rd.
Lymington, Hampshire
SO41 9QS
ENGLAND
Tel: (+44) 590 677903

Bob Ames Naval Architecture
8832 Stonebrook Lane
Columbia, MD 21045
Tel: (410) 596-7226

Ian Anderson MRINA
Newlands Farm
Broadclyst
Exeter, Devon EX5 3BZ
ENGLAND
Tel: (+44) 392 64887
Fax: (+44) 392 462878

Alan Andrews Yacht Design
241A Marina Dr.
Long Beach, CA 90803
Tel: (310) 594-9189
Fax: (310) 596-1859

Daniel Andrieu
41 Bis.
Quai de la Loire
75019 Paris
FRANCE
Tel: (+33) 1 42 49 29 05
Fax: (+33) 1 42 45 52 24

Jon Bannenberg
6 Burnstall St.
London SW3 3ST
ENGLAND
Tel: (+44) 71 352 4851

Barracuda Yacht Design
Vitruvio 12
28006 Madrid
SPAIN
Tel: (+34) 91 5644552
Fax: (+34) 91 5644553

Benford Design Group
P.O. Box 447
605 Talbot St.
St. Michaels, MD 21663
Tel: (410) 745-3235
Fax: (410) 745-9743

Jean Berret
Les Granges
St. Laurent de la Pree
1745C Fouras
FRANCE
Tel: (+33) 46 84 01 50
Fax: (+33) 46 84 08 72

Birger Kullman Design
Kongen
Frognerstranda 2
0271 Oslo
NORWAY
Tel: (+47) 2 44 05 26
Fax: (+47) 2 43 43 61

Philip Bolger
29 Ferry St.
Gloucester, MA 01930

Alan Boswell Designs
Filcombe Farm
Greenhead Lane
Sidbury, Nr. Sidmouth
Devon EX10 0QD
ENGLAND
Tel: (+44) 395 7646

Bouvet & Petit
5 Impasse du Moulin
06220 Vallauris
FRANCE
Tel: (+33) 93 64 99 90
Fax: (+33) 93 64 99 91

Luca Brenta & C.
V, Le Certosa
58 20155 Milano
ITALY
Tel: (+39) 02-3271725
Fax: (+39) 02-3271750

Ted Brewer Yacht Designs
117 Harbor Ln.
Anacortes, WA 98221
Tel: (206) 293-2282

Philippe Briand
41 Avenue Marillac
La Ville en Bois
17000 La Rochelle
FRANCE
Tel: (+33) 46 50 57 44
Fax: (+33) 46 50 57 94

Alan Buchanan C. Eng.
FRINA
La Ville au Bas
St. Lawrence, Jersey
CHANNEL ISLANDS
Tel: (+44) 534-865536
Fax: (+44) 534-864698

Francesco Budini Gattai
Via Dei Servi
51-50122 Firenze
ITALY
Tel: (+39) 055 284455
Fax: (+39) 055 212080

Chuck Burns
P.O. Box 1166
Kennebunkport, ME
04046-1166
Tel: (207) 967-8549

Tony Castro Ltd.
Rio House
76 Satchell Ln.
Hamble, Hampshire
SO23 5HL
ENGLAND
Tel: (+44) 703 454722
Fax: (+44) 703 456011

Chance & Co., Inc.
37 Pratt St.
Essex, CT 06426-0333
Tel: (203) 767-2161
Fax: (203) 767-2162

Coast Design
12837 - 76th Ave.
Unit 201
Surrey, British Columbia
V3W 2V3
CANADA
Tel: (604) 599-1278
Fax: (604) 599-1287

Cook Yacht Design
832 Main St.
Osterville, MA 02655
Tel: (508) 420-1180
Fax: (508) 420-1181

W I.B. Crealock
1401 Forest Ave.
Carlsbad, CA 92008
Tel: (619) 434-3253

Phil Curran Design
6 Parry St.
Fremantle
AUSTRALIA
Tel: (+61) 9 335 9966

Yarborough Davey
Unit 6A, Kemps Quay
Quayside Rd.
Bitterne Manor
Southampton, Hampshire
SO2 4AD
ENGLAND
Tel: (+44) 703 237149
Fax: (+44) 703 334271

De Groot Paterswolde BV
Boterdijk 39
9765 EB Paterswolde
HOLLAND
Tel: (+31) 5907 93818
Fax: (+31) 50 145668

Delta Marine
P.O. Box 828
Blue Hill, ME 04614
Tel: (207) 374-5404

Brendan Dobroth
123 Melba St.
Milford, CT 06460
Tel: (203) 877-5591
Fax: (203) 877-5591

Bill Dixon
Greydowns School Rd.
Old Burseldon
Southampton, Hampshire
SO3 8BX
ENGLAND
Tel: (+44) 703 405280
Fax: (+44) 703 406203

Dudley Dix Yacht Design
P.O. Box 26524
Hout Bay, 7872
SOUTH AFRICA
Tel: (+27) 21 790-2838

Dubois Naval Architects Ltd.
Solent House
Bath Rd.
Lymington, Hampshire
SO41 9RU
ENGLAND
Tel: (+44) 590 679333
Fax: (+44) 590 671496

Guy Ribadeau Dumas
Village Suisse 2
Av. Paul Deroulede
75015 Paris
FRANCE
Tel: (+33) 1 45 66 00 96
Fax: (+33) 1 45 66 02 93

Arthur Edmonds, Inc.
4310 Windemere Pl.
Sarasota, FL 34231
Tel: (813) 921-1553

Elliot Boat Design
P.O. Box 34-576
Birkenhead, Auckland
NEW ZEALAND
Tel: (+64) 9 483 7770
Fax: (+64) 9 483 4443

Mark Ellis Design
77 Bronte Rd.
Oakville, Ontario L6L 3B7
CANADA
Tel: (416) 825-0017
Fax: (416) 825-0051

Dieter Empacher
75 Evans Rd.
P.O Box 194
Marblehead, MA 01945
Tel: (617) 631-5705
Fax: (508) 744-2440

Bruce Farr & Associates, Inc.
613 Third St.
Suite 20
P.O. Box 4964
Annapolis, MD 21403-0964
Tel: (410) 267-0780
Fax: (410) 268-0553

Tom Fexus Yacht Design
333 Tressler Dr.
Suite B
Stuart, FL 34994
Tel: (407) 287-6558
Fax: (407) 287-6810

Figurehead
14 Rue Pasteur
06400 Cannes
FRANCE
Tel: (+33) 92 993 993
Fax: (+33) 92 993 999

Fontana-Maletto
Piazza Cacciatori delie Alp
1-22100 Como
ITALY
Tel: (+39) 031 209101

Formula Yachts
P.O. Box 9176
Noank, CT 06340
Tel: (203) 572-1110

Francis & Francis
BP 72
06902 Sophia Antipolis
Cedex
FRANCE
Tel: (+33) 93 95 85 10
Fax: (+33) 93 95 85 07

Fryco
Box 500-145
Houston, TX 77250
Tel: (713) 820-6617

German Frers
Via S. Paolo, 1
20121 Milano
ITALY
Tel: (+39) 2 86 46 54 17
Fax: (+39) 2 86 46 54

German Frers
Guido 1926 - 1 piso
1119 Buenos Aires
ARGENTINA
Tel: (+54) 802-0568
Fax: (+54) 801-0423`

Gerr Marine, Inc.
838 West End Ave.,
Suite BB
New York, NY 10025
Tel: (212) 864-7030
Fax: (212) 93Z-0872

Laurent Giles
The Station
Lymington, Hamshire
SO41 9AZ
ENGLAND
Tel: (+44) 590 673223

Groupe Finot
1, rue Pierre Vaudenay (Los
Metz)
78350 Jouy-en-Josas
FRANCE
Tel: (+33) 1 3 946 20 02

Ken Hankinson Associates
P.O. Box 2551
La Habra, CA 90631
Tel: (310) 947-1241

Robert B. Harris
2l2-1656 Duranleau St.
Granville Island
Vancouver, British Columbia
V6H 3S4
CANADA
Tel: (604) 683-6321
Fax: (604) 683-6321

**J.B. Hargrave Naval
Architects**
205 1/2 Sixth St.
W. Palm Beach, FL 33401
Tel: (407) 833-8567

Ray Harvey Design
12 Pamplyn Close
Lymington, Hampshire
SO4 9LD
ENGLAND
Tel: +44) 590 675242
Fax: (+44) 590 675243

Hoek Deign
Grote Kerkstraat 23
1135 BC Edam
HOLLAND
Tel: (+31) 2993 72853
Fax: (+31) 2993 71519

Ron Holland Design
Strand Farm House
Currabinny, County Cork
IRELAND
Tel: 353-21-378301
Fax: 353-21-378307

Holman & Pye
21 City Rd.
West Mersea
Colchester, Essex CO5 8NE
ENGLAND
Tel: (+44) 20638 2478

Ian Howlett
Chestnut Cottage
Beaulieu, Hampshire SO42
7YB
ENGLAND
Tel: (+44) 590 612589

Ted Hood Design Group
One Little Harbor Landing
Portsmouth, RI 02871
Tel: (401) 683-4400
Fax: (401) 683-3009

**Rob Humphreys Yacht
Design**
Lymington Marina
Bath Rd.
Lymington, Hampshire
SO41 9RW
ENGLAND

**C. Raymond Hunt &
Associates**
69 Long Wharf
Boston, MA 02110
Tel: (617) 742-5669
Fax: (617) 742-6354

Alastair Hunter
Provincial House
3 High St.
Ryde, Isle of Wight PO33 2PN
ENGLAND
Tel: (+44) 983 616578
Fax: (+44) 983 66559

Peter Ibold Designs
Eden Residence
Av. Francois de May
06320 - Cap-d Ail
FRANCE
Tel: (+33) 93 78 11 88
Fax: (+33) 93 78 04 85

Alain Jezequel
Via Cordrignano
60 40021- Borgo Tossignano
ITALY
Tel: (+39) 542 665070

Rodney S. Johnstone
68A Water St.
Stonington, CT 06378
Tel: (203) 535-2680
Fax: (203) 535-0291

Joubert-Nivelt
L Aubrecay
17138 Piullboreau
FRANCE
Tel: (+33) 461 37 40 58
Fax: (+33) 46 37 80 32

Judel-Vrolijk
Am Neuen Yacht Hafen 2000
Wedell
GERMANY
Tel: (+37) 04103 89890
Fax: (+37) 04103 89880

Scott Jutson Yacht Design P/L
34 Dudley St.
Balgowalh 2093
AUSTRALIA
Tel: (+61) 2 948 1512
Fax: (+61) 2 948 2392

Kaufman Design
222 Severn Ave.
P.O. Box 4219
Annapolis, MD 21403
Tel: (301) 263-8900
Fax: (301) 263-8923

Bruce Kelley Yacht Designers
2120 Grant St. #7
Berkeley, CA 94703
Tel: (415) 548-8614

Steve Killing Yacht Design
P.O. Box 755
Midland, Ontario L4R 4P4
CANADA
Tel: (705) 534-4016

Bruce King Yacht Design
Newcastle Square
Newcastle, ME 04553
Tel: (207) 563-1186
Fax: (207) 563-1189

Bruce Kirby, Inc.
213 Rowayton Ave.
Rowayton, CT 06853
Tel: (203) 853-1899

Kotzebue Marine Enterprises
24857 Pappas Rd.
Ramona, CA 92065
Tel: (619) 789-0622

C. William Lapworth
Providence
Cobbs Creek, VA 23035-0306
Tel: (804) 7Z5-9541

Bill Lee Yachts
3700 B Hilltop Rd.
Soquel, CA 95073
Tel: (408) 475-9627
Fax: (408) 475-0867

Marc Lombard
Le Sexton
Rue de la Trinquette
17000 La Rochelle
FRANCE
Tel: (+33) 46 45 30 30
Fax: (+33) 46 44 60 26

Nils Lucander
Box 7752
Tacoma, WA 98407
Tel: (206) 752-6528
Fax: (206) 635-0623

Lyons/Labreaux Yacht Design
P.O. Box 637
Spit Junction, New South Wales 2088
AUSTRALIA
Tel: (+61) 2 368 1280
Fax: (+61) 2 357 3080

Maclear & Harris, Inc.
117 E. 72nd St.
New York, NY 10021
Tel: (212) 472-1313
Fax: (212) 737-1970

Marine Engineering Design
M.E.D. 2208 Route de Grasse
06600 Antibes
FRANCE
Tel: (+33) 93 33 43 91
Fax: (+33) 93 33 18 95

Roger Marshall, Inc.
44 Fort Wetherill Rd.
Jamestown, Rl 02835
Tel: (401) 423-1400
Fax: (401) 423-2322

Rodger Martin Yacht Design
P.O. Box 242
Newport, Rl 02840
Tel: (401) 849-9850
Fax: (401) 848-0119

Massimo Paperini & Co.
Via l Crispi
82 00187 Rome
ITALY
Tel: (+39) 06 483958

McCurdy & Rhodes
P.O. Box 206
Cold Spring Harbor, NY 11724
Tel: (516) 692-4516

MRS Yacht Designers
Suite 8
Dockside Centre
8 Perry St.
Queensland
AUSTRALIA
Tel: (+61) 7 891 6868
Fax: (+61) 7 891 6865

Mulder Design
P.O. Box 444
4200AK Gorinchem
HOLLAND
Tel: (+31) 1830 35711
Fax: (+31) 1830 35315

Gary W. Mull, Naval Architects
6671 Gunn Dr.
Oakland, CA 94611-1438
Tel: (415) 339-9199
Fax: (415) 339-3219

Multiplast Composite Yachts
Parc du Golfe
56000 Vannes
FRANCE
Tel: (+33) 97 40 98 44
Fax: (+33) 97 46 03 58

Ian Murray & Assoc.
Suite 8
R.P.A.Y.C.
Mitala St.
Newport, NSW 2106
AUSTRALIA
Tel: (+61) 2 2979 6202
Fax: (+61) 2 979 6215

Navarte Boats Marine Design Studio
Suite 12/2 Charnwood Cres.
St. Kilda, Victoria 3182
AUSTRALIA
Tel: (+61) 3 525 5268
Fax: (+61) 3 525 5269

Nelson/Marek Yacht Design, Inc.
2820 Canon St.
San Diego, CA 92106
Tel: (619) 224-6347
Fax: (619) 224-5192

Charles Neville Associates, Inc.
P.O. Box 4805
2919 Wycombe Way
Palm Harbor, FL 34685
Tel: (813) 789-2689
Fax: (813) 789-5038

Richard C. Newick
5 Sheppards Way
Kittery Point, ME 03905
Tel: (207) 439-3768

C. W. Paine
P.O. Box 763
Camden, ME 04843
Tel: (207) 236-2166
Fax: (207) 236-2371

Harold H. Payson & Co.
Beach Rd.
S.Thomaston, ME 04858
Tel: (207) 594-7587

Parker Marine Enterprises
P.O. Box 3547
Fort Pierce, FL 34948
Tel: (407) 489-2191

Jay E. Paris
P.O. Box 459
Brunswick, ME 04011
Tel: (207) 443-9146

P B Design
Voorhaven 20-22
1135 BR Edam
HOLLAND
Tel: (+31) 2993 72739
Fax: (+31) 2993 71591

Pedrick Yacht Designs
Three Ann St.
Newport, RI 02840
Tel: (401) 846-8481
Fax: (401) 846-0657

Performance Design Corporation
610 Market St.
Suite 102
P.O. Box 2216
Kirkland, WA 98033
Tel: (206) 827-2643
Fax: (206) 822-1140

Robert H. Perry
6400 Seaview Ave. N.W.
Seattle, WA 98107
Tel: (206) 789-7212
Fax: (206) 789-7214

Reichel/Pugh Yacht Design
P.O. Box 6050
San Diego, CA 92106-0050
Tel: (619) 223-2299
Fax: (619) 224-1698

Bruce Roberts Intl.
P.O. Box 1086
Severna Park, MD 21146
Tel: (301) 544-4311

J.W. Sarin Naval Architects
Box 10151
Bainbridge Island, WA 98110
Tel: (206) 842-4651

Don Shead
The Old School
Funtley Court
Funtley
Fareham, Hampshire
ENGLAND
Tel: (+44) 329 285734

Schock Yacht Design
212 Via Lido Word
Newport Beach, CA 92663
Tel: (619) 434-4763

Carl Schumacher, N.A.
1815 Clement Ave.
Alameda, CA 94501
Tel: (415) 523-2580
Fax: (415)522-0870

Sciomachen Yacht Design
2330 Shelter Island Dr.
Suite 209
San Diego, CA 92106
Tel: (619) 223-9771
Fax: (619) 223-9792

Sparkman & Stephens
79 Madison Ave.
New York, NY 10016
Tel: (212) 689-3880
Fax: (212) 689-3884

Sponberg Yacht Design
P.O. Box 661
Newport, Rl 02840
Tel: (401) 849-7730
Fax: (401) 849-7898

Scott B. Sprague & Co.
1180 N.W. Finn Hill Rd.
Poulsbo, WA 987370
Tel: (206) 779-7797
Fax: (206) 697-6779

Studio Scanu
Via Cipriani 20
55049 Viareggio
ITALY
Tel: (+39) 584 960194
Fax: (+39) 584 31879

Structural Composites, Inc.
7705 Technology Ave.
W. Melbourne, FL 32904
Tel: (407) 951-9464
Fax: (407) 728-9071
Composite engineering and design

Takai International Yacht Design, Inc.
Wako Daiichi Bldg
1-39-2 Kanda Jinbocho
Chiyoda-ku
Tokyo
JAPAN
Tel: (+81) 03 3293-4681
Fax: (+81) 03 3293-4685

Tanton, Inc.
P.O. Box 270
America's Cup Ave.
Newport, Rl 02840
Tel: (401) 847-4112
Fax: (401) 849-8835

Jim Taylor Yacht Design
Tuckers Wharf
Marblehead, MA 01945
Tel: (617)631-6235

Georg K. Thomas P.E.
1303 Ponce De Leon Blvd.
Coral Gables, FL 33134
Tel: (305) 446-6257

Tripp Design
44 Post Rd. W.
Westport, CT 06880
Tel: (203) 221-0571
Fax: (203) 221-0575

Johan Valentijn, Inc.
80 Ayrault St.
Newport, Rl 02840
Tel: (401) 849-6926
Fax: (401) 849-6448

Van Dam Naval Architects
Helling 49
P.O. Box 33
NL-1430 AA Aalsmeer
HOLLAND
Tel: (+31) 2977 24517
Fax: (+31) 2977 23620

A. Vallicelli & C.
Via Vittoria 32
00187 Rome
ITALY
Tel: (+39) 6 6787634
Fax: (+39) 6 6795 931

E. G. Van de Stadt & Partners BV
Box 193
1520 AD Wormerveer
HOLLAND
Tel: (+31) 75 216581
Fax: (+31) 75 216742

Van de Stadt & Ohashi Ltd.
Nihonbashikabutocho
17-1-908 Chuo-Ku
Tokyo 103
JAPAN
Tel: (+81) 03-669 8140

Vismara Yacht Design
Via Trieste 24
55049 Viariggio
ITALY
Tel: (+39) 0584 388229
Fax: (+39) 0584 387949

Nestor Volker
Av. del Liberator 4902
23 B (1426)
Buenos Aires
ARGENTINA
Tel: (+54) 1 773-8547
Fax: (+54) 1 775-4374

F. de Voogt
Zonnelaan 12
2012 TC Haarlem
Haarlem
HOLLAND
Tel: (+31) 23 290352
Fax: (+31) 23 291629

W. de Vries Lentsch
Bureau Voor Scheepbouw B.V.
De Ruyterkade 143
1011 AC Amsterdam
HOLLAND
Tel: (+31) 20 6223608
Fax: (+31) 20 6204838

Charles W. Wittholz
100 Williamsburg Dr.
Silver Spring, MD 20901
Tel: (301) 593-7711
Fax: (301) 593-7711

Thomas Wylie Design Group
86 Ridgecrest Rd.
Canyon, CA 94516
Tel: (415) 376-7338
Fax: (415) 376-7982

Dick Zaal Yacht Design
Doelenkade 9
1621 BH Hoorn
HOLLAND
Tel: (+31) 22 9016 931
Fax: (+31) 22 9046 620

Interior Designers

Anita's Interiors
Lido Peninsula Marine Center
101 Shipyard Way
Berth D, Cabin G
Newport Beach, CA 92663
Tel: (714) 675-7198
Fax: (714) 675-8005

Dee Robinson
Custom Yacht Interiors, Inc.
2190 S.E. 17 St. Causeway
Suite 207
Ft. Lauderdale, FL 33316
Tel: (305) 523-9123
Fax: (305) 463-5617

Design Gallery, Inc.
Rt. 38 & Ark Rd.
Mt Holly, NJ 08088
Tel: (609) 778-0335
Fax: (609) 722-9011

Paola D. Smith & Associates
1600 S.E. 17th St.
Ft. Lauderdale, FL 33316
Tel: (305) 761-1800
Fax: (305) 761-3339

Robert Knack International
15233 Ventura Blvd.
Suite 1108
Los Angeles, CA 91403
Tel: (818) 981-1029
Fax: (818) 981-0150

Susan Pulleo
2101 S. Andrews Ave.
Suite 104
Ft. Lauderdale, FL 33316
Tel: (305) 522-0173

Terence Disdale Design Ltd.
3 Portland Terrace
The Green
Richmond, Surrey TW9 1QC
ENGLAND

Winch Design
The Old Power Station
121 Mortlake High St.
London, SW4 8SN
ENGLAND
Tel: (+44) 81 8788678

Yacht Interiors
1601 S.W. 20th St.
Ft. Lauderdale, FL 33315
Tel: (305) 522-1701

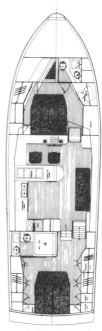

Figure 1: The interior layout of a 54 foot power yacht from the author's design studio.

Navigation and Sailing Performance Software

Rather than tediously working up sights, many sailors have opted to buy hand-held navigation computers, such as the Weems & Plath Galileo or the Tamaya NC99. Both of these machines have almanacs that can calculate the position of the sun, moon, planets, and a number of stars. They can reduce up to ten sights in a matter of minutes and can also predict the times of sunrise, sunset, and the sun's meridian passage. In addition, they can calculate great circle routes and can store variation, deviation, and time zones for any sailing area. While both machines are expensive (in the $600 to $1000 range, depending on where you buy them) they are well worth the money if you do not use any of the modern electronic navigation gizmos.

If you are the type of sailor who carries a computer onboard, there are several navigation programs designed to run on both Macintosh and IBM or compatible machines. However, many of these programs are quite expensive at this time. IBM, for example, has a computer-based system that displays a map showing where you are at any time, plus other navigational aids. This type of system is available from other vendors such as Maptech and C-Map.

If you are a performance sailor, you might want to make use of the RS 232 interface from your wind instruments and use performance analysis programs as a constant check on your yacht's performance. Such programs are made by Ockam Instruments and by Compusail. Armed with these programs, you can input data and eventually develop a polar diagram for your boat, or you can calculate the wind angle on the next leg of the course, along with many other functions. But once again, these programs are fairly expensive and are really only of use to the racing sailor or a real sailing buff.

Suppliers of Navigation and Sailing Performance Software

Programmable Computer Hardware

AUSCO
15 Goose Pond Rd.
Tabernacle, NJ 08088
Tel: (609) 268-3081
Hardware link between electronic instruments and computer

D.F. Crane Associates
2535 Ketner Blvd.
San Diego, CA 92101-7531
Tel: (619) 233-0223
Fax: (619) 233-1280

MariSys
P.O. Box 810414
Boca Raton, FL 33481
Tel: (407) 361-0598
Fax: (407) 361-0599

Navstar Electronics
1500 N. Washington Blvd.
Sarasota, FL 34236
Tel: (800) 486-6338
Fax: (813) 366-9335

Navigation Software

Accu-Weather
619 W. College Ave.
State College, PA 16801
Tel: (814) 234-9601
Weather database

Andren Software
P.O. Box 33117
Indialantic, FL 32903-0117
Tel: (407) 725-4115

Aqua Logic, Inc.
60 Woods Edge Ct.
Warrenton, VA 22186
Tel: (703) 347-1665

AUSCO
15 Goose Pond Rd.
Tabernacle, NJ 08088
Tel: (609) 268-3081
Software package for computer aided sailboat racing

Basic Marine
P.O. Box 3563
Annapolis, MD 21403
Tel: (410) 268-7517
Hand-held navigation computer

Celestaire
416 S. Pershing
Wichita, KS 67218
Tel: (800) 727-9785
  or (316) 686-9785
Fax: (316) 686-8926
Sextants, instruments, books, and videos

CompuSail
22120 Parthenia St.
Canoga Park, CA 91304
Tel: (818) 340-8851
Performance sailing software

D.F. Crane Associates
2535 Ketner Blvd.
San Diego, CA 92101-7531
Tel: (619) 233-0223
Fax: (619) 233-1280
MacWeather, PC HF fax, route planning, nav software

Fair Trade Technologies
18 Ray Ave.
Burlington, MA 01803
Tel: (617) 229-6409
Fax: (617) 229-2387
Software for charting

InfoCenter, Inc.
P.O. Box 47175
Forestville, MD 20747
Tel: (301) 420-2468

Maptech
2225 Sperry Ave.
Suite 1000
Ventura, CA 93003
Tel: (805) 654-8006
Fax: (805) 654-8147
Uses GPS or loran signal to track course

Micronautics
P.O. Box 1017
Rockport, ME 04856
Tel: (207) 236-0610
Tide and current information program

Nautasoft
P.O. Box 282
Rockland, DE 19732
Tel: (800) 999-5221
"MacTides" tidal prediction program for Macintosh

Ockam Instruments
26 Higgins Dr.
Milford, CT 06460
Tel: (203) 877-7453
Fax: (203) 878-0572
Performance prediction programs for PCs

Software Systems Consulting
150 Avenida Cabrillo
San Clemente, CA 92672
Tel: (714) 498-5784
Digital communication software

Zephyr Services
1900 Murray Ave.
Pittsburgh, PA 15217
Tel: (412) 422-6600

Figure 1: An HF weather fax satellite photo of North American weather is available by fax or computer from D.F. Crane Associates, Inc.

Plumbing Supplies

When looking for plumbing supplies, first check what you boat already has. For instance, if you are looking for a thru-hull or seacock fitting, you could cause yourself a problem if you installed an aluminum one when everything else on the boat is bronze. Galvanic corrosion could eat away the aluminum and sink your boat.

Plumbing systems divide themselves naturally into various components. They are: tanks, the marine head, showers, and intake and exhaust piping. Tanks are covered in the section dealing with tanks.

THE MARINE HEAD

The ideal marine head will never get blocked, never require dismantling on a Sunday afternoon, never backfill and flood the toilet compartment, and always work perfectly when required. Unfortunately, my three-year-old son can outsmart the designer of a marine head anytime. So selection of a marine head unit should be governed by Murphy's law. Assume whatever you buy will eventually give you at least some problems, but try to pick a unit that will minimize the number and severity of headaches. Here are some basic features to look for when choosing a marine head:

- Can the head be used at sea? Often head units installed at an angle are very hard to use when the boat is heeled. The easiest to use are those that are positioned at right angles to the centerline of the boat.
- Does the head need a power supply? Some of the more environmentally sound units need electrical power to macerate and fry the exhaust before disposal.
- How easy (or hard) is it to get spare parts? It might be difficult to get parts for a foreign built head unit.
- Does the head automatically stay dry or do you need to turn off the seacock after every use? The best kind are those that do not backfill and stay dry.
- Will the head exhaust line go to a holding tank, or is a Y valve to be fitted? If you sail on enclosed waters you must have a holding tank, but holding tanks are hard to pump out when you are offshore and a Y valve is usually used.

THE SHOWER UNIT

Shower units should be large enough to allow the occupant to turn around. That means they should be at least 20 inches (500 mm) on each side. The ideal shower unit is one that has solid closures, such as a glass door, not a flimsy curtain which always seems to allow water to escape. The shower head should be as high as possible in the compartment or should be a telephone style unit to enable it to be raised as needed. Remember, too, that the shower should have a place to put soap and shampoo.

I like to see at least a six-inch sill at the bottom of the shower unit to keep water inside. The shower should drain into a sump tank, not into the bilge, where the grease and soap can coat everything and smell. In my design work, I like to allow a minimum of ten gallons per person capacity in the sump tank, with a maximum of twenty gallons. The sump tank needs a pump to dispose of its contents.

INTAKE PIPING

Piping from the water tanks usually goes to the pressure water pump and then to the sink and shower units as a cold waterline. On the hot water side, it goes first to the pressure unit and then to the hot water heater. From there it goes to the hot faucet in the galley, heads, and showers. The actual piping should be at least half-inch diameter plastic line, fastened with double hose clamps.

EXHAUST PIPING

Exhaust piping is usually sized according to the outlet pipe on the unit. For instance, many marine heads have a two-inch diameter exhaust line, but some have two-and-a-half-inch line. Once again, all exhaust lines should be fastened with double hose clamps. Where an exhaust line goes to a thru-hull, it should have an anti-siphon fitting so that seawater cannot backflow up the pipe and fill the bilges.

Figure 1: This pump from Rule Industries can be used to pump out sump tanks or bilges.

Suppliers of Plumbing Equipment

Florida Flexibles, Inc.
3017 N.W. 25th Ave.
Pompano Beach, FL 33069
Tel: (305) 960-1313
Fax: (305) 960-1452
Flexible tubing

Genova Products
7034 East Court St.
P.O. Box 309
Davison, MI 48423-0309
Tel: (313) 744-4500
Tubing

Grohe America, Inc.
900 Lively Blvd.
Wood Dale, IL 60191
Tel: (708) 350-2600
Fax: (708) 350-2615
Marine faucets

Jered Brown Brothers
1608 Newcastle St.
Brunswick, GA 31250-6729
Tel: (912) 261-2732
Fax: (912) 261-2840
Vacuum toilets

Kracor
5625 W. Clinton Ave.
P.O. Box 23667
Milwaukee, WI 53223
Tel: (800) 255-6335
 or (414) 355-6335
Fax: (414) 355-8782
Marine tanks

Multiform Industries, Inc.
8000 Hub Parkway
Cleveland, OH 44125
Tel: (800) 321-9564
 or (216) 524-5170
Marine hose

PMC Parker Merrick Co.
245 S. W. 32nd St.
P.O. Drawer 22751
Ft. Lauderdale, FL 33335
Tel: (800) 432-3700
 or (305) 761-1677
AWAB hose clamps

Sealand Technology, Inc.
P.O. Box 38
Fourth St.
Bi Prarie, OH 44611
Tel: (216) 496-3211
Vacu-flush MSDs

Simpson-Lawrence
P.O. Box 11210
Bradenton, FL 34282-1210
Tel: (813) 746-7161
Blake toilets

Skandvik
2190 S.E. 17th St.
Ft. Lauderdale, FL 33316
Tel: (305) 524-7666
ABA hose clamps

Raritan Engineering Co., Inc.
1025 North High St.
Millville, NJ 08332
Tel: (609) 825-4900

Raske & van der Meijde bv
Nijverheidstraat 17
1135 GE Edam
HOLLAND
Tel: (+31) 02993-71100
Manual marine toilets

Shipyard Supply Co.
85 Water St.
So. Norwalk, CT 06426
Tel: (800) 442-2111
 or (800) BOAT-WIRE
Full line of plumbing supplies

Thetford Corp.
P.O. Box 1285
Ann Arbor, MI 48106
Makers of Porta-Potti and Aquamate

Vetus - Den Ouden, Inc.
P.O. Box 8712
Baltimore, MD 21240-0712
Tel: Orders only: (800) GO-VETUS
 or (410) 712-0740
Fax: (410) 712-0985
Flexible tanks, fittings, and toilets

Wilcox-Crittenden
699 Middle St.
Middletown, CT 06457
Tel: (203) 632-2600
Fax: (203) 632-2636
Plumbing supplies and pumps

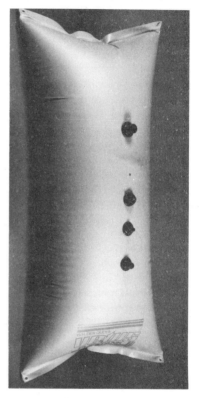

Figure 2: Flexible tanks are available from Vetus-Den Ouden.

Pre-Made Woodwork

We have all seen pre-made doors, storm windows, and other fittings for houses, so it should come as no surprise that some manufacturers make fittings for boats. These fittings may range from a simple teak toilet paper holder to a fully prefabricated interior joinerwork. If you are investigating pre-made items you should look at them before the surrounding area has been constructed, because premade fittings are usually made to a particular size and openings will need to be cut to fit them.

Manufacturers of Pre-Made Woodwork

**American Foreign
Industries**
2210 Gladstone
Pittsburg, CA 94565
Tel: (415) 427-2341
Fax: (415) 427-2342
Teak accessories

Cape Ann Marine Teakflex
Rear 1044 Washington St.
Gloucester, MA 01930
Tel: (508) 283-9276
*Teak furniture, cleaners, and
protectors*

H & L Marine Woodwork
2965 E. Harcourt
Rancho Dorninguez, CA 90221
Tel: (213) 636-1718

Marine Joinery
32 Water St.
Fairhaven, MA 02719
Tel: (508) 991-7407

Sea-Dog Line
P.O. Box 479
Everett, WA 98201
Tel: (206) 259-0194
Fax: (206) 339-1345

Figure 1: Cabinetry like this locker from Marine Joinery is often made in a workshop and installed as a complete unit in a boat.

Propulsion Systems

Selection of the right propeller can be critical to the enjoyment of your boat. A wrongly sized prop can cause vibration, over-revving or under powering of the engine, and a general lack of performance. You should talk to several propeller experts before selecting a new prop. Not all of them have the same ideas, and you may get better efficiency by getting several different opinions.

It used to be thought that propellers worked by screwing their way through the water, rather like a wood screw goes into wood. Current theory holds that props work by accelerating a column of water the diameter of the propeller. If you think about how a waterjet works — by exhausting a column of water from its orifice — this theory makes a lot of sense.

To work efficiently, the propeller's diameter and pitch need to to be matched to the engine rpms, the handedness of the propeller, the shape of the hull, the reduction gear, cavitation, ventilation, immersion, and the clearance between the hull and the propeller tips.

DIAMETER AND PITCH

While the meaning of a prop's diameter is obvious, it might not be so apparent what pitch is. Pitch is the distance the propeller moves in one revolution. In other words, a prop pitched at 18 inches will move 18 inches ahead in one complete revolution. In general, for boat speeds up to about 40 knots, prop diameters should be as large as possible, and should be run at low revolutions. Large-diameter props generally have low pitch and, consequently, low blade loadings. On faster boats, fully cavitating props should be used. These props are smaller, have higher pitch, and higher blade loadings. Note also that pitch is usually less at the boss or hub of the prop than at the tip, giving the blade a twisted look.

THE ENGINE SPEED

Most smaller marine engines run at around 2000 to 3500 revolutions per minute. This speed is much too fast for most propellers. It will cause cavitation, so a reduction gear must be used. Reduction gears go between the engine and the prop shaft and gear the engine rpms down. The amount of reduction is expressed as 2 to 1 where an engine running at 2000 rpms is stepped down to 1000 rpms. Reduction gears typically have ratios from 1.5 to one to as high as 3 to 1.

If engine weight is needed aft in order to trim the boat level, or if there simply isn't enough room for the engine to be further forward, a V-drive may be used. A V-drive may be a slightly more complicated reduction gear, where the engine faces forward instead of aft and the shaft leads forward into the V-drive, where it is turned aft.

THE HANDEDNESS OF THE PROPELLER

If you stand aft of a boat and look at the propeller, a right-handed prop rotates clockwise, and a left-handed prop rotates anti-clockwise. Most single-screw boats are standardized with right-handed props. Many twin-screw vessels also have right-handed props on both shafts. But having both props with the same handedness can cause bias when the boat is backing down, so the better installations have right-handed props on the starboard shaft and left-handed props on the port shaft. Both props are outward-turning. Inward-turning props can cause dangerous veering problems when the boat is operated in shallow water.

BIAS

According to several marine experts, bias — that is, the stern swinging to one side or the other — is due to the fullness or fineness of the stern. A full-sterned yacht will exhibit a greater bias than a fine-sterned one. Note also that bias can change as sternward speed accelerates.

CAVITATION

Cavitation arises when the propeller is run at too high a speed. Usually, the tips of the props exhibit the first signs of cavitation. Small pits start to show on the back faces near the tip. If the props continue to run at high speeds, this cavitation will eventually erode the entire back face of the blade, and could cause unbalancing and eventual disintegration of the entire prop.

Cavitation is caused by boundary layer separation. Consider the propeller blade in section as a wing similar to the wing of an aircraft. When the wing is operated at too high an angle of attack, it stalls, causing turbulence to flow over the upper edge. This turbulence destroys lift and the plane usually comes crashing to the ground. A propeller blade running at high rpms is in a similar situation. The water flow cannot reattach itself to the back of the blade, and a form of stall is created. Because the prop blade is operated in water, the bubble of turbulence collapses upon itself and recreates itself. This shows on the prop as a stream of bubbles flowing away from the blade tips, like the contrails on an airplane's wings. The continual collapsing and recreation of the turbulance (bubbling) causes shock loadings on the blade, which in turn causes pitting.

VENTILATION

If you have ever run an outboard motor behind a dinghy and been surprised to hear the outboard over rev, then settle down again, then over rev, you are probably witnessing ventilation. It happens when the prop operates too near the surface of the water and air is sucked from the surface into the revolving blades. It causes momentary loss of blade lift and power, but as the boat slows down, the prop resubmerges and ventilation stops. Often ventilation can be stopped by adding a flat plate above the prop blades to stop air being sucked downwards.

IMMERSION

A boat's propellers should be run as deeply immersed as possible. This will reduce the chances of ventilation and move the blades away from the hull. Except for high-speed surface piercing situations, props run best when they are fully covered by the hull. Note, too, that struts should be carefully faired and local discontinuities in the hull should be avoided near the propellers for best efficiency.

TIP CLEARANCE

Another annoying cause of vibration can be lack of clearance between the tip of the propeller and the hull of the vessel. When the prop is too close to the hull, the pressure wave accompanying each blade hits the hull as it passes and causes vibration. This can be eliminated by making sure the clearance between the prop tips and the hull is a minimum of 10% of the prop diameter. Some authorities use a slightly higher figure, up to 15%. Note that propellers that operate in a kort knozzle, or ring around the prop, have square-ended blades and do not have this problem. These ducted props are used where high towing power is required.

DIFFFERENT TYPES OF PROPELLERS

Propellers can vary dramatically. They can have just two blades or as many as twelve blades. The blades can stick straight out from the propeller boss (hub) or they can be skewed, that is, swept back. The blades can be fixed in place, adjusted by a control on the bridge (variable pitch), or they can align themselves with the water flow naturally (feathering). On some props, the blades can even fold into the hub for a more streamlined shape. High-speed props may have a completely different blade shape from low-speed props.

Skewed and Non-Skewed Blades

Most slower-speed blades stick straight out from the hub of the propeller. As speed increases, the blades are swept back to reduce tip loadings and the onset of cavitation. This sweepback is called skew. The blades of a modern submarine are highly skewed. This is done in part to reduce noise and vibration, as well as to maximize shaft horsepower.

Variable Pitch Propellers

Variable pitch propellers are used on sailboats and tugs, but they have different functions on each vessel. On sailboats, variable pitch props are used to align the blades with the flow of water when the boat is under sail. On tugs, the pitch is changed to maximize thrust when towing or to run the engines most efficiently when not towing.

Pitch, the angle of the blades relative to the flow of the water, is changed by gearing in the propeller hub. Some manufacturers adjust pitch by turning a shaft that runs down the center of the propeller shaft. Others do the same job electronically.

Feathering Propellers

Feathering props are used on sailboats and usually have flat blades that align themselves with the flow of water over the hull as soon as the engine stops and the boat begins to sail. When the engine is run, the blades turn to a preset pitch. Usually, efficiency is high both ahead and astern. Feathering props can be purchased with either two or three blades.

Folding Propellers

Folding props are also used on sailboats. These props fold the blades around the hub as the boat begins to sail. Usually, the blades have some twist to them and turn into a teardrop shape when folded. If you want a folding prop, get the type with geared blades so that both blades will stay closed. On types with non-geared blades, the prop must be aligned so that both blades are vertical when closed or one blade might fall open when sailing in lighter winds.

Supercavitating Propellers

Supercavitating props are used primarily on high-speed powerboats. In shape, the blades look like curved wedges, with the trailing edges only about a quarter inch thick. These props run at very high revolutions and usually have quite a small diameter. Fitting a supercavitating prop requires considerable experience and should be done by an expert.

Blade Shape and the Number of Blades

Blade shape affects the efficiency of a propeller. On slow-speed boats — for example, sailboats and low-speed powercraft — the blades of a propeller can be fairly wide. But on higher-speed vessels, props with wide tips absorb more power and are less efficient than medium-tipped blades. Narrow-tipped blades tend to lower the onset of cavitaion and therefore should be avoided if possible.

Yachts, especially racing yachts, tend to use two-bladed props for greater sailing efficiency, but three-bladed feathering props are better for cruising sailors. On powerboats, three- or four-bladed props are best. Props with more blades tend to be much more expensive, but give smoother performance. Blade loading is the primary factor affecting the number of blades. In general, fewer blades should be used when the thrust loading on the prop blades is high. Of secondary consideration is the vibration period of the hull. The number of blades should be chosen so that the prop vibrations do not coincide with the vibration period of the hull.

Manufacturers of Propulsion Systems

Bow Thrusters

American Bow Thrusters
(formerly Arcturus Marine
Systems)
517-A Martin Ave.
Rohnert Park, CA 94928
Tel: (800) 752 0661
  or (206) 835-7910
Fax: (206) 835-7878
*Manufacturers of electric and
hydraulic bow thrusters*

Bird-Johnson Co.
4451 Fourteenth Ave. N.W.
Seattle, WA 98107-4601
Tel: (800) 426-6526
Fax: (206) 782-9190

Jensen Marine
1145 Carey Rd.
Oakville, Ontario, L6J 2E1
CANADA
Tel: (416) 845-4837
Fax: (416) 338-6892
Electric bow thrusters

Keypower Equipment, Inc.
5-8091 Capstan Way
Richmond, British Columbia
V6X 1R4
CANADA
Tel: (604) 278-4836
Fax: (604) 278-4838
Bow thrusters

Michigan-Jastran
1501 Buchanan Ave. S.W.
Grand Rapids, MI 49507
Tel: (616) 452-6941
Fax: (616) 247-0227
Many sizes and styles

Omnithruster, Inc.
9515 Sorensen Ave.
Sant Fe Springs, CA 90670
Tel: (310) 802-1818
Units from 25hp to 3,000 hp

Richfield Bow Thrusters
IM/Lewmar Marine Ltd.
Southmoor Ln.
Havant, Hampshire PO9 1JJ
ENGLAND
Tel: (+44) 705 471841
Fax: (+44) 705 47603

Richfield Bow Thrusters
IM/Lewmar, Inc.
P.O. Box 308
New Whitfield St.
Guilford, CT 06437
Tel: (203) 458-6200

Vetus - Den Ouden, Inc.
P.O. Box 8712
Baltimore, MD 21240-0712
Tel: Orders only: (800)
GO-VETUS
  or (410) 712-0740
Fax: (410) 712-0985

**Vosper Thornycroft UK
Ltd.**
North American Sales and
Marketing
Coconut Grove Bank Building
Suite 605
2701 South Bayshore Drive
Miami, FL 33133
Tel: (305) 856 7710
Fax: (305) 856 7761

**Vosper Thornycroft UK
Ltd.**
Northarbour Rd.
Cosham, Hampshire PO6 3TL
ENGLAND
Tel: (+44) 705 383311
Fax: (+44) 705 3251384

Wesmar
18500 68th Ave. N.E.
Box 3001
Bothall, WA 98041-3001
Tel: (206) 481-2296
Fax: (206) 486-0909

Jet Propulsion Systems

American Hydro Jet
2033-F West McNab Rd.
Pompano Beach, FL 33069
Tel: (305) 978-8996
Fax: (305) 978-6597

**C.W.F. Hamilton and Co.
Ltd.**
P.O. Box 709
Christchurch
NEW ZEALAND
Tel: (+64) 9 488-849

KaMeWa
AB Karlstads Mekaniska
Werkstad
Kristinehamn Works
S-681 Kristinehamn
SWEDEN
Tel: (+46) 0550 152 00

**North American Marine
Jet, Inc.**
P.O. Box 1232
Benton, AR 72015
Tel: (501) 778-4151
Fax: (501) 778-6381

Propellers

Arneson Marine, Inc.
451 Mirror Ct. #103
Henderson, NV 89015
Tel: (702) 565-2205
Fax: (702) 565-6501
Surface-piercing drive systems

Alexander-Roberts
1851 Langley Ave.
Irvine, CA 92714
Tel: (714) 250-4571
Fax: (714) 250-1253
Austral folding and fixed props

Arneson Marine
29485 Airport Rd.
Eugene, OR 97042
Tel: (503) 461-2223
Fax: (503) 461-2224
Surface-piercing drive system

Bird-Johnson Co.
4451 Fourteenth Ave. N.W.
Seattle, WA 98107-4601
Tel: (800) 426-6526
Fax: (206) 782-9190

Cruising Design, Inc.
Mailing address:
P.O. Box 1457
Concord, MA 01742
Business address:
9 Old Sudbury Rd.
Maynard, MA 01754
Tel: (508) 897-5933
Fax: (508) 897-6038
*CD performance props for
sailboats*

Essex Machine Works
50 West Ave.
P.O. Box 39
Essex, CT 06426-0039
Tel: (203) 767-8285
*Suppliers of Michigan Wheel,
Brid-Johnson, and most other
props*

Federal Propellers
1521 Buchanan Ave. S.W.
Grand Rapids, MI 49507
Tel: (616) 452-49507
See also Michigan Wheel Corp.

Gori Marine
DK 6000 Kolding
DENMARK
Tel: (+45) 5 52 76 11
Geared-bladed folding props

Jensen Marine
1145 Carey Rd.
Oakville, Ontario L6J 2E1
CANADA
Tel: (416) 845-4837
Fax: (416) 338-6892
Propellers

Paul E. Luke
Box 816
E. Boothbay, ME 04544
Tel: (207) 633-4971
Fax: (207) 633-3388
Luke feathering prop

Martec Engineering Corp.
2257 Gaylord St.
Long Beach, CA 90813
Tel: (310) 435-4494
Fax: (310) 435-7846
Folding and feathering props

Michigan Wheel Corp.
1501 Buchanan Ave. S.W.
Grand Rapids, MI 49507
Tel: (616) 452-6941
Fax: (616) 247-0227
*Many sizes and styles of
Michigan and Federal props*

MPECO
Marine Propulsion Equipment
Co., Inc.
P.O. Box 1029
Harvey, LA 70059
Tel: (504) 392-6900

PYI, Inc.
P.O. Box 536
Edmonds, WA 98020
Tel: (206) 670-8915
Fax: (206) 670-8918
Max-Prop feathering propeller

Robiller's Boat Works
402 Fleitas
P.O. Box 6
Pass Christian, MS 39571
Tel: (601) 452-5459
*Importers of Prowell feathering
props*

Rolla SP Propellers SA
Via Silva 5
P.O. Box 251
6828 Balerna
SWITZERLAND
Tel: 091/439361
Fax: 091/430653

**Rolla SP Propellers USA,
Inc.**
4030 Mustang Rd.
Melbourne, FL 32943
Tel: (407) 242-7552
Fax: (407) 242-7771
Props for large power yachts

Sun Propeller, Inc.
308 N. Coden Hwy.
Bayou La Batre, AL 36509
Tel: (205) 824-4064
Rice props

Vetus Den Ouden, Inc.
P.O. Box 8712
Baltimore, MD 21240-0712
Tel: (410) 712-0740
Fax: (410) 712-0985
Shaft assemblies, stern gear, and props

VPF Propellers
10114 McDonald Park Rd.
Sidney, British Columbia
V8L 3X9
CANADA
Tel: (604) 655-3323
Variable pitch props

Volvo Penta North America, Inc.
1300 Volvo Penta Dr.
Chesapeake, VA 23320
Tel: (804) 436-2800
Sail-Drive props

Propeller and Bearing Pullers

Norseman Marine
516 West Olas Blvd.
Ft. Lauderdale, FL 33312
Tel: (305) 467-1407
Fax: (305) 462-3470

Walter Machine
P.O. Box 7700
84-89 Cambridge Ave.
Jersey City, NJ 07307
Tel: (201) 656-5654
Fax: (201) 656-0318

Propeller Glands and Bearings

Aqua Drive, Inc.
3340 Rt. 37 E.
Toms River, NJ 08753
Tel: (201) 929-1125
Aquadrive CVA bearing systems

The Evolution Co., Inc.
46 Washington St.
Camden, ME 04834
Tel: (207) 236-1008
Marine prop-shaft system

PYI, Inc.
P.O. Box 536
Edmonds, WA 98020
Tel: (206) 670-8915
Fax: (206) 670-8918
PSS packless sealing system

K.H. Allsop, Inc.
10131 N.W. 46th St.
Sunrise, Fl 33351
Tel: (305)742-3873
Fax: (305) 742-8322
Lasdrop stuffing box

Lucian Q. Moffit, Inc.
P.O. Box 1415
Akron, OH 44309
Tel: (216) 733-9955
BF Goodrich bearings

Soundown Corp.
23 Lime St.
Suite 1
Marblehead, MA 01945
Tel: (800) 359-1036
Shaft coupling

Svenska Uni-Carden AB
Box 42120
126 12 Stockholm
SWEDEN
Aquadrive CVA bearing systems

Trellex Morse
3588 Main St.
Keokuk, IA 52632
Tel: (800) 553-7036
Fax: (319) 524-7290
Trellcraft stuffing box

Propeller Shafts

ARMCO
Stainless Steel Division
Dept. LA-279
Box 600
Middletown, OH 45043
Aquamet shafts

Crucible Service Centers
5639 W. Genesee St.
Camillus, NY 13031-0991
Tel: (315) 487-0800
Fax: (315) 487-4028
Steel shafting

Figure 1: This three-bladed propeller is available from Vetus-Den Ouden.

Pumps

Yachts have had pumps since early times. The first pumps were crude wooden and leather devices that pump only the bilge. Today, pumps not only pump the bilge, they also empty holding tanks, pressurize water systems, are part of the watermaker, and are used for saltwater and freshwater washdowns. Most are power or electrically driven, even though purists may prefer hand-operated ones.

BILGE PUMPS

Every boat should have at least one bilge pump. In the case of a boat sitting at the dock, it is a good idea to have an automatic pump to keep the bilges dry while the owner is not aboard. Ideally, there will be another bilge pump driven off the engine and a hand-operated pump somewhere in the cockpit.

If the boat has watertight compartments, there should either be a bilge pump in each compartment or a single pump with piping from a master manifold leading to each compartment. This method makes most sense if the pump is driven by the main engine. Then each compartment can be pumped separately simply by opening and closing valves. Remember to close all the valves after use, and to have a vented loop in the exhaust line. One of my clients almost lost his boat because the person pumping the bilge forgot to close the manifold line and the exhaust line did not have a vented loop. Seawater was sucked back aboard.

If you lose engine power and do not have a manual bilge pump, you could be in real trouble. Therefore, I recommend to my clients that, in addition to power-driven pumps, they have a manual pump located somewhere near the cockpit. When buying a manual bilge pump, get the one with the largest through-put and with the least chance of clogging. The Edson Bone Dry is a good one. If your boat is sinking, you don't want to have to stop and unclog the pump.

THE PRESSURE FRESHWATER PUMP

All boats with a pressure water system will have a fresh-water pump to keep the system pressurized. These pumps are usually quite small and should be self-priming. Most of them operate by filling a bladder accumulator. As the water is used, the bladder deflates until it trips a microswitch, which turns the pump on again. The accumulator size varies but should be as large as possible for a given flow rate. The larger the accumulator, the fewer times the pump has to run, which reduces wear and tear.

THE SALTWATER WASHDOWN PUMP

While not essential, salt-water washdown pumps are extremely useful. A washdown faucet on the foredeck will enable you to rinse the anchor and chain as it comes aboard, rinse the foredeck when grubby shoes have left marks on it, and rinse dock lines and fenders after use. A faucet in the cockpit on a sport fishing boat will allow quick and easy washing of fish waste after chumming or bringing a fish aboard. Salt-water washdown pumps are similar to freshwater pressure pumps except that a strainer should be fitted at the intake.

SUMMING UP WHAT TO LOOK FOR

Pumps, then, need to be sized to suit the through-put of liquid. They should be self-priming, and as large as possible to reduce wear. If saltwater will be passing through the pump, make sure that it is constructed from materials that are compatible with other onboard materials. For instance, you may be asking for corrosion trouble if you install a pump with a bronze body on an aluminum hull.

Manufacturers of Pumps

Attwood Corp.
1016 N. Monroe St.
Lowell, MI 49331
Tel: (616) 897-9241
Electric pumps

Avon Seagull Marine
1851 McGaw Ave.
Irvine, CA 92714
Tel: (714) 250-0880
Whale pumps

Balmar Products, Inc.
1537 N.W. Ballard Way
Seattle, WA 98107
Tel: (206) 789-4970
Fax: (206) 784-0878
Bilge and pressure pumps

Beckson Marine, Inc.
165 Holland Ave.
Bridgeport, CT 06605
Tel: (203) 333-1412
Fax: (203) 384-6954
Thirsty-Mate bilge pumps

The Bosworth Co.
195 Anthony St.
E. Providence, RI 02914
Tel: (401) 438-8411
Seamaster pumps

Cleghorn Waring & Co. (Pumps) Ltd.
9-15 Hitchin St.
Baldock, Hertfordshire
SG7 6AH
ENGLAND
Tel: (+44) 462 893838
Pressure pumps

Henderson Pumps & Equipment Ltd.
38 Medina Rd.
Cowes, Isle of Wight
PO31 7BZ
ENGLAND
Tel: (+44) 983-29372
Bilge pumps

Imtra
30 Samuel Barnett Blvd.
New Bedford, MA 02745
Tel: (508) 995-7000
Fax: (508) 998-5359
Whale pumps

ITT Jabsco
ITT Fluid Technology Division
1485 Dale Way
P.O. Box 2158
Costa Mesa, CA 92628-2158
Jabsco and Par pumps,
Amazon hand diaphram
pumps

ITT Jabsco
Bingley Rd.
Hoddesdon, Hertfordshire
EN11 OBU
ENGLAND
Jabsco and Par pumps

Jamestown Distributors
28 Narragansett Ave.
P.O. Box 348
Jamestown, RI 02835
Tel: (800) 423-0030
   or   (401) 423-2520
Fax: (401) 423-0542
Rule, Jabsco, and Par pumps

Lovett Pumps
101 Shore Rd.
Somers Point, NJ 08244
Tel: (609) 927-4144
Submersible pumps

Nautalloy Products
140 Olive St.
Elmyria, OH 44035
Tel: (216) 323-3285
Fax: (216) 322-6388
Bilge pumps

Oberdorfer Pumps
6257 Thompson Rd.
Syracuse, NY 13206
Tel: (315) 437-0361
Electric pumps

Omnifac Corp.
1700 E. Whipp Rd.
Dayton, OH 45440
Tel: (513) 434-8400
Bilge pump

Rule Industries
70 Blanchard Rd.
Burlington, MA 01803
Tel: (617) 272-7400,
Fax: (617) 272-0920
Electric Pumps

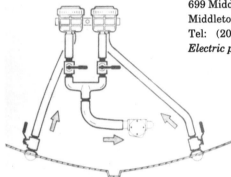

Vetus - Den Ouden, Inc.
P.O. Box 8712
Baltimore, MD 21240-0712
Tel: Orders only: (800)
GO-VETUS
   or   (410) 712-0740
Fax: (410) 712-0985
Cooling, circulating, water
pressure, deck wash, and bilge
pumps

Wilcox-Crittenden
699 Middle St.
Middletown, CT 06547
Tel: (203) 632-2600
Electric pumps and strainers

Figure 1: Every water intake system should have a strainer installed as shown in this diagram from Vetus-Den Ouden.

Figure 2: The strainer unit from Vetus-Den Ouden that should be installed in all intake lines.

Refrigeration

It used to be that a refrigeration system was comprised of three parts. Part one was the icebox, part two the blocks of ice, and part three the person who put the ice to the icebox. Today, refrigeration and freezer systems are a lot more sophisticated and are made up of many more parts. The ice box has given way to a dual-compartment refrigerator/freezer unit that is kept cool by a holding plate (the modern equivalent of the iceblock). The holding plate is cooled by a brine solution, which is cooled by a compressed gas. This gas is compressed and pumped through the system from the refrigeration unit, usually located in the engine compartment. The refrigeration unit replaces the person carrying the block of ice. Each part of the system is essential and must be considered carefully.

REFRIGERATION AND FREEZER BOXES

Most marine refrigerators hold food at a few degrees above freezing, and to keep the temperature low enough the unit must be well insulated. On production boats, the layer of insulating foam is usually about 2 to 3 inches (50 to 75mm) thick. Inside the foam is a liner, usually fiberglass, which is relatively easy to keep clean. Outside the foam is a layer of vapor barrier and the joinerwork that encloses the cabinet. In a nutshell, that construction covers most refrigeration systems. But, on custom boats, or vessel that must operate in warmer climates, refrigerators have much more insulation, often up to 6 inches (150mm) thick. Freezer units, too, have much more insulation. The thicker the insulation, the longer the inside of the unit will stay cool.

THE REFRIGERANT

The refrigerator/freezer is cooled by a gas. Up until 1989, that gas was H-12 or freon, but with the agreement known as the Montreal Protocols, signed in 1987, freon, which is a chlorofluorocarbon, was outlawed as an ozone-depleting gas. Freon is being replaced in new systems with a gas called HFC 134a, which affects the ozone layer to a very minor degree. However, systems already in use cannot use HFC 134a, because it requires a slightly different compressor and is incompatible with the oils and seals used with freon. So, as an interim measure, a mixture of freon and other gases are being used until the chemical companies can come up with a better alternative.

The refrigerant gas is compressed by a compressor in the engine compartment, whereupon it turns to liquid and gets very cold. The compressed liquid is piped to a holding plate inside the freezer or refrigerator box where it absorbs any heat in the holding plate, turning the liquid solution in the plate (a mixture of sodium chloride, water, and alcohol) into ice. The holding plate liquid is specially formulated to have minimal contraction or expansion qualities. As the refrigerant liquid absorbs the heat, it turns back into a gas and passes through a condenser. The condenser is really a heat exchanger cooled by seawater. After passing through the condenser, the gas is returned to the compresser and passes through the same cycle again.

THE COMPRESSOR/CONDENSER

When you want to select a refrigeration system for your boat, the manufacturer should figure out how often you will have to run the compressor to cool the unit. Running it more than an hour a day can be a nuisance. Ideally, you should be able to go two or three days before having to run the compressor again. This means that you should have an efficient system with plenty of insulation around the icebox.

POWER SUPPLIES

The compressor/condenser unit requires some form of power. It might be a 12-volt supply directly off the batteries, in which case the batteries will need to be very large

or under charge or it might be an engine-driven, water-cooled unit, or a 110 volt (in USA) unit driven by an auxiliary generator or shore supply. In most systems, a 12-volt supply is adequate provided that the refrigeration box is no larger than 3 or 4 cubic feet. This system can be charged at almost any time while the boat is under power, or via the battery charger and batteries when the boat is on shore supply. To make this system most efficient, the refrigerator should be opened as little as possible and should be extremely well insulated. This type of power supply is best for moderately sized sailing yachts.

Engine-driven units are also useful on sailing yachts that have small refrigeration boxes. Usually, the main engine is run when the yacht is leaving the harbor or upon entering the harbor. This will often be enough to keep the holding plate cold. However, if the yacht stays at anchor for several days, the engine will have to be run every day to keep the box cold.

On vessels with large freezers or refrigerators, a 110 volt system is by far the best. With this power supply, boxes up to 60 cubic feet can be cooled and kept cool. This type of system is best for trawler-type yachts or large powercraft.

Combination units, that can be driven off both the engine and the shore supply, have been developed. But they are very expensive and can be difficult to maintain.

Manufacturers of Refrigeration Systems

IM/Adler/Barbour
308 New Whitfield St.
Guilford, CT 06437
Tel: (203) 453-4374
Fax: (203) 453-6109

Cool Corp.
14170 23rd Ave. N.
Minneapolis, MN 55447
Tel: (612) 559-3317
Fax: (612) 559-9679

IMI/Crosby
308 New Whitfield St.
Guilford, CT 06437
Tel: (203) 453-4374
Fax: (203) 453-6109

Fleming Marine USA, Inc.
2302 Shelter Island Dr.
San Diego, CA 92106
Tel: (800) 638-9138
Fax: (619) 222-9124

Frigibar Industries, Inc.
6210 N.E. 4th Ct.
Miami, FL 33138
Tel: (800) 624-7175
  or in FL (305) 757-7697

Glacier Bay, Inc.
4053 Harlan St. #113
Emeryville, CA 94608
Tel: (510) 654-9333
Fax: (510) 658-3996

Grunert Refrigeration
A Marine Air Systems Co.
2000 N. Andrews Ave.
Pompano Beach, FL 33069
Tel: (800) 327-3137
  or (305) 973-2477
Fax: (305) 979-4414

Koolatron
27 Catharine Ave.
Brantford, Ontario N3T 1X5
CANADA
Tel: (519) 756-3725

Lunaire Marine
P.O. Box 3246
Williamsport, PA 17701
Tel: (800) 772-6777
  or (717) 326-1755
Fax: (717) 326-7304

**Marine Appliances
International**
2807 Antigua Dr.
Burbank, CA 91505
Tel: (800) 672-8297
  or (818) 842-0226
Fax: (818 953-9847

McDonnell Marine
8 East Newberry Rd.
Bloomfield, CT 06002
Tel: (203) 243-9114

Norcold
A Division of Stolle Corp.
600 Kuther Rd.
Sidney, OH 45365
Tel: (800) 752-8654

Ocean Master Marine
12 Park St.
Cranford, NJ 07016
Tel: (800) 443-4560
  or (908) 709-1777

Ocean Options, Inc.
50 Fort St.
Fairhaven, MA 02719
Tel: (508) 992-3644
Fax: (508) 999-5338

Origo
1121 Lewis Ave.
Sarasota, FL 34237
Tel: (813) 365-3660
Fax: (813) 955-2596

Rich Beers Marine
P.O. Box 14034
210 S.W. 7th Ave.
Ft. Lauderdale, FL 33302
Tel: (305) 764-6192
Fax: (305) 764-7259
*Technicold air conditioning
and refrigeration systems*

Sailing Specialties, Inc.
P.O. Box 99
Commerce Ave.
Hollywood, MD 20636
Tel: (301) 373-2372
Fax: (301) 373-2734
Coolers

Scan Marine Equipment
2144 Westlake Ave. N.
Suite D
Seattle, WA 98109
Tel: (206) 285-3675
Fax: (206) 285-9532

Sea Frost
C.F. Horton & Co, Inc.
Rt. 4
Barrington, NH 03825
Tel: (800) 435-6708
  or (603) 868-5720
Fax: (603) 868-1040

Technautics
120 Tustin Ave.
Newport Beach, CA 92663
Tel: (714) 645-3861

Rigging

All sailboats and some powerboats have rigging. On sailing craft, the rigging is of two types: standing rigging that supports the mast, and running rigging that is used to raise and lower the sails. On power craft, most rigging is standing rigging, such as the standing rigging that supports the tuna platform.

STANDING RIGGING

To determine the best standing rigging for a particular boat, the designer considers many factors. If the boat is a racing yacht, then weight, windage, elongation, and strength are primary considerations. On cruising boats, long-term corrosion resistance and flexibilty enter into the picture. While many boats simply use wire or rod rigging throughout, testing in many different applications is showing that a combination of materials may give the best overall performance.

For instance, when I sailed to Bermuda once on a 55 footer with rod rigging throughout, we encountered winds over 70 knots. We kept tension on the rig all through the storm, and only afterwards did we find compression hollows in the mast. I believe these hollows, which were the precursor of buckling and subsequent spar collapse, were caused by not allowing the rig to flex a little. Consequently, when I design

a cruising boat, I now specify that the lower shrouds be made of wire, rather than rod, to give the mast a little "give." I also recommend that the tension on the backstay, if the boat is fitted with a hydraulic tensioner, be backed off slightly in severe conditions.

Standing rigging is usually made of metal to reduce the amount of stretch. It may be 1 x 19 strand galvanized or stainless steel wire, or it may be MP35-N or nitronic 50 extruded rod. On top-notch racing boats titanium is often used, although it is very expensive. Some latest rigs have carbon fiber rigging, but carbon fiber standing rigging is still fairly expensive and difficult to attach fittings to. Kevlar rod is also used for standing rigging, especially on top-level racing yachts.

Shrouds and stays are usually referred to by numbers. Vertical lower shrouds are V1, diagonal lower shrouds are D1. The shrouds above the first spreader are known as V2 and D2, and above the second spreader as V3 and D3, and so forth. A backstay is called a running backstay if it can be adjusted (the tension can be let off completely to allow better sail tuning), or a permanent backstay if it is fixed (the stay can be adjusted by hydraulics, but remains fixed in place). At the front of the boat, the stay farthest forward is known as the fore or headstay, the next one aft as the midstay, and the stay nearest the mast is generally known as the babystay.

Galvanized 1 x 19 Wire

Galvanized 1 x 19 wire is reasonably inexpensive, fairly flexible, and end fittings can easily be attached to it. However, it corrodes fairly quickly, especially where the end fittings damage the galvanizing. For long term use, it should be coated with a mixture of tallow and white lead. This is a messy job, which can ruin the deck and the brightwork if the people applying the mixture are not very careful. Consequently, galvanized wire is rarely used as standing rigging today.

Stainless Steel 1 x 19 Wire

Where wire is used in the rig, 1 x 19 stainless steel is the material of choice. It is reasonably corrosion-resistant, although type 316, the most commonly used stainless, occasionally suffers from crevice corrosion and needs to be dye-tested once in a while. End fittings for stainless steel wire are easily obtainable; they are made in sizes to suit almost every wire diameter. Stainless steel wire rigging can be made up in any rigging shop, to any size. Its drawback is that it stretches more than rod rigging and is comparitively heavier in weight.

Rod Rigging

Rod rigging appears to be the most popular choice for both cruising and racing boats. One of the advantages of rod rigging is that it can be shaped into a streamlined shape to reduce windage.

When the first rod rigging was put on a boat, 316 stainless steel rod was used. But this often contained built-in crevice corrosion. Consequently, most rod rigging used today is an alloy. Nitronic 50 is a stainless steel alloy containing 22% copper, 13% nickel and 5% manganese, while MP35-N is a nickel/cobalt/molybdenum alloy. Of the two, Nitronic 50 is the less expensive, often by a factor of 50% or more. The price of MP35-N usually reserves it for use on extremely expensive racing boats where price is a secondary consideration. Titanium is usually reserved for end fittings where its properties of high strength and light weight make it ideal.

When specifying rod rigging always use discontinuous rod. That is, rigging that ends at the spreader is linked to another shroud by a plate at the spreader. Continuous rod can stretch more than discontinuous rod and can wear at the shroud tip. If you lose a V1 shroud with discontinuous rod, you lose only that shroud and may be able to save the rig. If you lose a V1 with continuous rod, you also lose the V2 and D3 and the rig. The disdvantage of discontinuous rod rigging is the slight increase in weight caused by the link plates at the spreader tips.

Carbon Fiber

While carbon fiber has been used as permanent backstays on America's Cup yachts, it still has some problems. The biggest one is that it can easily be damaged by sails or lines, resulting in a spectacular explosion when the shroud snaps. The next most serious problem is the attachement of end fittings. These need to be epoxied in place, and extreme care must be taken to ensure that the joint is made properly. No doubt these problems will be solved eventually, and carbon shrouds that offer a dramatic increase in strength-to-weight ratio (up to five times by some estimates) will become commonplace.

Kevlar

Kevlar once suffered from problems similar to carbon fiber, but these problems have been largely cured and kevlar rod is available for use as backstays and checkstays. If it is designed to be equivalent to steel in stretch it will be about 10% thicker, but over 60% lighter. Kevlar rod rigging should also have a UV inhibiting coating which adds to its diameter. The major problem with kevlar rigging is the difficulty of attaching terminals. This increases the expense of using it and becomes a potential failure point.

RUNNING RIGGING

Running rigging needs to be much more flexible than standing rigging. It has to bend around blocks and to be tied to sails. For that reason, dacron is the most popular choice, followed by kevlar and, on racing craft, 7 x 19 flexible steel or galvanized wire. The old style three-strand lines, made of natural materials, such as hemp and sisal, are rarely found today, except on character craft.

Dacron

Almost by default, cored dacron with a sixteen braid exterior cover has become the rope of choice for most sailors. It stretches a small amount under load (certain types have especially low stretch characteristics). It is easy to handle and remains flexible for a long period of time as long as it is washed in fresh water occasionally. It doesn't rot. It is made up of a core of low stretch dacron fibers and covered with a braided sheath to make it easy to handle. When the sheath becomes chafed or damaged, it is time to replace the line. Some of the latest ropes have a percentage of kevlar fibers in the core for even lower stretch.

It used to be that dacron tails were spliced to wire rope halyards, but with lower-stretch dacron available, totally dacron halyards are often used. This trend has been helped along by the fact that line stoppers are fitted on many boats and dacron rope can easily be locked off.

Nylon

Nylon line stretches terribly and has no place as running rigging on a boat. Its best use is for an anchor or dock line where it will absord much of the shock of the vessel.

Kevlar

Kevlar ropes have extremely low stretch characteristics and are becoming more common on both cruising and racing yachts. Most kevlar ropes are a combination of dacron and kevlar core materials with a dacron exterior sheath. The sheath reduces the abrasion problems that kevlar has and makes the rope easier to handle. Kevlar lines are lighter and stronger than similar sized dacron lines. But don't make the mistake of buying too small a diameter kevlar line. It may be hard to grip and you may have to put many more turns on a winch than with a dacron line. If you intend to use kevlar lines, remember that the rope requires specially shaped, larger diameter sheave blocks.

CARE OF RIGGING

Your rigging should be checked every time the rig is pulled from the boat. In the case of standing rigging, a visual inspection will often suffice, but every five years or so the end fittings should be ultrasonically or dye tested to ensure that they haven't corroded or been damaged. At the end of each season, running rigging should be soaked in fresh water to which a small amount of washing soap has been added. This will get the saltwater out of the lines. When you pull your halyards out of the mast, make sure you tie a messenger to each halyard so that you can easily reinstall it.

Suppliers of Rigging and Rigging Services

Rigging

EPI
Z.A. du Grand Pont
83360 Grimaud
FRANCE
Tel: (+33) 94 43 31 11
Fax: (+33) 94 43 34 87
Kevlar and carbon rigging

IM/Navtec
P.O. Box 308
New Whitfield St.
Guilford, CT 06437-0388
Tel: (203) 458-3163
Fax: (203) 458-9291
Rod rigging specialists

Joukema
Stad A/H Haringvliet
HOLLAND
Tel: (+31) 1871-2510
Fax: (+31) 1871-2543
Rigging

Monitor Marine International
17 Old St.
London EC1V 9HL
ENGLAND
Tel: (+44) 71 2537071
Fax: (+44) 71 251 4405
Load cells, turnbuckles, and kevlar rigging

Norseman Gibb Ltd.
Ollerton Rd.
Ordsall
Retford, Nottinghamshire
DN22 7TG
ENGLAND
Tel: (+44) 777 706465
Fax: (+44) 777 860346
Marina yacht ropes, wire rope, and rigging terminals

Norseman Marine, Inc.
516 West Olas Blvd.
Ft. Lauderdale, FL 33312
Tel: (305) 467-1407
Fax: (305) 462-3470
Wire rope, turnbuckles, terminals, and insulators; agents for Riggarna rigging

Riggarna UK Ltd.
Unit 3
Somerford Business Park
Wilverly Rd.
Christchurch, Dorset
BH23 3RU
ENGLAND
Tel: (+44) 202 480481
Fax: (+44) 202 479899
Rod rigging

Speciality Products Co.
Division of Macwhyte
2906-14th Ave.
Kenosha, WI 53141
Tel: (414) 654-5381
Fax: (414) 654-5339
Swageless rope terminals

Ropes and Lines

G & B Ropes
R.R. 4
Orillia, Ontario L3V 6H4
CANADA
Tel: (705) 327-7996

Gleason Sailmakers
P.O. Box 606
213 Ferry Ave.
Charlevoix, MI 49720
Tel: (616) 547-0095
Fax: (616) 547-6502
Makinac braid line

Imtra Corp.
30 Barnet Blvd.
New Bedford, MA 02745
Tel: (508) 990-7000
Fax: (508) 998-5359
Marlow ropes

Marlow West
Avon Seagull Marine
1851 McGaw Ave.
Irvine, CA 92714
Tel: (714) 250-0880

New England Ropes
Popes Island
New Bedford, MA 02740
Tel: (508) 999-2351

Norseman Marine, Inc.
516 West Olas Blvd.
Ft. Lauderdale, FL 33312
Tel: (305) 467-1407
Fax: (305) 462-3470
Wire rope

Norseman Gibb Ltd.
Ollerton Rd.
Ordsall
Retford, Nottinghamshire
DN22 7TG
ENGLAND
Tel: (+44) 777 706465
Fax: (+44) 777 860346
*Marina yacht ropes, wire rope,
and rigging terminals*

Penn Wire Rope
A Handy & Harman Co.
905 First St.
Williamsport, PA 17701
Tel: (717) 322-7832

Speciality Products Co.
Division of Macwhyte
2906-14th Ave.
Kenosha, WI 53141
Tel: (414) 654-5381
Fax: (414) 654-5339
Swageless rope terminals

Wellington Water Sports
Monticello Hwy.
Madison, GA 30650
Tel: (800) 221-5054
Water ski ropes

Yale Cordage, Inc.
Old Sparhawk Mill
Yarmouth, ME 04096
Tel: (207) 846-9048
Yale cordage

Rigging Services

Center Harbor Rigging
311 Jackson
Port Townsend, WA 98368
Tel: (206) 385-1080
Rigging, cordage, and books

Chesapeake Rigging Ltd
7310 Edgewood Rd.
Annapolis, MD 21403
Tel: (410) 268-0959
Fax: (410) 268-4914
Sailboat rigging and hardware

Diverse Yacht Services Ltd.
1A Birmingham Rd.
Cowes, Isle of Wight
PO31 7BH
ENGLAND
Tel: (+44) 983 29860
Fax: (+44) 983 295161

Hall Rigging
17 Peckham Dr.
Bristol, RI 02809
Tel: (401) 253-4858
Fax: (401) 253-2552

Hood Yacht Systems
1 Maritime Dr.
Portsmouth, RI 02871
Tel: (401) 683-2900
Fax: (401) 683-2410
Sailboat rigging and hardware

IMI/Navtec
P.O. Box 308
New Whitfield St.
Guilford, CT 06437-0388
Tel: (203) 458-3163
Fax: (203) 458-9291
Rod rigging specialists

Johnson Marine
Industrial Park
East Haddam, CT 06423
Tel: (203) 873-8697
Rigging hardware

Joukema
Stad A/H Haringvliet
HOLLAND
Tel: (+31) 1871-2510
Fax: (+31) 1871-2543
Rigging

Marinox, Inc.
403 N.E. 8th St.
Ft. Lauderdale, FL 33304
Tel: (305) 760-4702
Fax: (305) 763-8790
Dermac backstay adjusters,
and Macgrip mechanical
fittings

McDonald Yacht Rigging
Yacht Haven
Stamford, CT
Tel: (203) 323-5431

Monitor Marine
International
17 Old St.
London EC1V 9HL
ENGLAND
Tel: (+44) 71 2537071
Fax: (+44) 71 251 4405
Load cells, turnbuckles, and
kevlar rigging

Norseman Marine, Inc.
516 West Olas Blvd.
Ft. Lauderdale, FL 33312
Tel: (305) 467-1407
Fax: (305) 462-3470
Wire rope, turnbuckles,
terminals, and insulators;
agents for Riggarna rigging

Riggarna UK Ltd.
Unit 3
Somerford Business Park
Wilverly Rd.
Christchurch, Dorset
BH23 3RU
ENGLAND
Tel: (+44) 202 480481
Fax: (+44) 202 479899
Rod rigging

The Rigging Co.
1 Maritime Dr.
Portsmouth, RI 02871
Tel: (800) 322-1525
  or (401) 683-1525
Fax: (401) 683-5442

Rigging Only
P.O. Box P-100
S. Dartmouth, MA 02748
Tel: (508) 992-0434
Rigging equipment

Rigging Services, Inc.
P.O. Box 989
Chestertown, MD 21620
Tel: (301) 778-0970
Fax: (301) 778-5805
Agents for Riggarna rigging

The Rigging Shop
Unit 33
Gordleton Industrial Park
Sway Rd.
Lymington, Hampshire
SO41 8JD
ENGLAND

Speciality Products Co.
Division of Macwhyte
2906-14th Ave.
Kenosha, WI 53141
Tel: (414) 654-5381
Fax: (414) 654-5339
Swageless rope terminals

C. Sherman Johnson Co.
Rt 82, Industrial Park
East Haddam, CT 06423
Tel: (203) 873-8697
Fax: (203) 873-8589

U.S. Rigging Supply
4001 W. Carriage Dr.
Santa Ana, CA 92700
Tel: (714) 545-7444
Fax: (714) 545-3311

Rigging Tools

Loos & Co., Inc.
One Cable Rd.
Pomfret, CT 06258
Tel: (203) 928-7981
Fax: (203) 928-6167

Maritool, Division of
Huskin Tools
330 Windy Point Dr.
Glendale Heights, IL 60139
Tel: (708) 893-7755
Fax: (708) 790-2626

Norseman Marine, Inc.
516 West Olas Blvd.
Ft. Lauderdale, FL 33312
Tel: (305) 467-1407
Fax: (305) 462-3470
Hydraulic cutters and Wire
Teknik swaging machines

The Rigging Co.
1 Maritime Dr.
Portsmouth, RI 02871
Tel: (800) 322-1525
  or (401) 683-1525
Fax: (401) 683-5442
Tools

S & F Tool
1245 Logan Ave.
P.O. Box 1546
Costa Mesa, CA 92626
Tel: (714) 546-8073
Fax: (714) 546-9125

Speciality Products Co.
Division of Macwhyte
2906-14th Ave.
Kenosha, WI 53141
Tel: (414) 654-5381
Fax: (414) 654-5339

Figure 1: This Wichard adjustable backstay unit is available from Viscom International, Inc. (see address under deck gear.)

Sails

By Tom Whidden
Tom Whidden is the president of North Sails.
He is a life-long sailor, who has competed in
several America's Cups and has won numerous
offshore races.

When you make the decision to purchase a new sail, the first step is to find a sailmaker who will help you determine what is best for your boat. Talk to a number of lofts and find somebody who is simpatico to your ideas and type of sailing. Don't go with a loft just because they say they have the best fabric or sail shape if you and the sailmaker don't hit it off. Ideally, your relationship with your sailmaker should be long-term to ensure that your sails are taken care of during the life of your boat. For instance, at North we like to sail with our customers. We feel that this helps us establish a good rapport with the owner and enables us to help marry the rig to the sails. It should be remembered that the sails and rig should be carefully tuned to ensure the sails operate at their most efficient. Many of our sailmakers are rig specialists who can help tune the rig as well as set the sails up efficiently.

SAIL CLOTH

If you own a racing boat, your choice of sails will be very different than a cruising sailor's. Racing sailors also ask for a lot more help from their sailmaker to get the very best results. They need to find the best sails for their sailing conditions, which may vary from sailing area to area. The area in which they sail may also limit the type of sails. For instance, a boat that races in Long Island Sound will need mostly light-air sails, while a boat that races in San Francisco Bay will have an inventory dominated by heavy-air sails. The characteristics of the sails should also be matched to the boat's characteristics. For example, a heavy-displacement cruiser typically needs fuller sails than a lightweight offwind sled. Other restrictions may be imposed by the rating or racing rules in a particular area.

A cruising sailor, on the other hand, has longevity and durability in mind, as well as sail shape. Sails for cruising boats need to have fabric that is UV-inhibited to ensure a long life. The sailcloth should be flexible and soft rather than stiff and crinkly like heavily-sized racing sails may be.

You should also ask the sailmaker what is the best fabric for your purpose. Most cruising sails are made of dacron or dacron composite, but some are backed with a layer of mylar. The mylar is laminated to the sail to provide additional strength, but, while mylar-laminated sails retain their shape longer, they are relatively fragile and can be delaminated if care is not taken with them. They should not be overstretched by being set in heavy winds or by having excessive luff tension. Neither should the sail be allowed to flog unneccessarily. One of the latest developments in cruising sails is the composite sail. This is a sail where a layer of mylar is sandwiched between two lightly-woven dacron layers. This gives a soft sail with the shape retention of a mylar sail. Kevlar sail cloths are best reserved for the racing fraternity, but kevlar tape is often used to reinforce the edges of a cruising sail as well as areas of high stress. Flogging a kevlar sail should also be avoided because it can lead to degradation of the kevlar. Nylon sailcloth is used almost exclusively for spinnakers and gennakers. It is very light and stretches easily, and it can also be easily ripped. For its weight, nylon has a very high tensile strength, but it needs to be protected against sharp edges or snagging.

WHAT SAILS?

Sails for the cruising sailor can be categorized more easily than can sails for the racer, so we'll look at recommendations North would make for a typical range of cruising boats. Note that other sailmakers may suggest different cuts or sails.

For the cruising sailor who will stay within sight of land and owns a boat under 30 feet LOA, we would recommend a 6.5 ounce mainsail with full battens and two reef points. This sail would be made of our special UV-inhibited, tightly woven dacron sailcloth with a soft finish for longevity. For headsails, we would recommend a working jib made of 7 ounce dacron and a 4.5 ounce

all-purpose dacron 130% or 150% genoa which should be reefable. We would also suggest a 3/4-ounce medium cruising spinnaker for downwind sailing. This sail would be tacked to the headsail tack and sheeted on the transom corner. If another spinnaker were desired, we'd suggest a light 0.5 ounce nylon sail for downwind work in winds under 8 knots.

For a cruiser/racer with a medium displacement boat of around 34 to 37 feet, we would recommend a fully battened mainsail with three reefs, made of 7 ounce Dacron. For headsails, this boat would have a 7.5 ounce working jib, a 5.5 ounce 130% genoa, and a 3.8 ounce genoa for sailing in lighter winds. If the headsail is to be stored on a roller furling headstay, it should have a UV-limiting band sewn along the luff. For downwind work, the boat should have a general purpose 3/4-ounce spinnaker that sets on the pole, plus a 0.5 ounce downwind spinnaker for lighter airs. This is a slightly higher performance package then the smaller boat has. If the skipper is not comfortable with a spinnaker, then we'd use a gennaker tacked on the headstay tack fitting.

On a larger boat, one between 40 and 45 feet LOA, the inventory would vary depending upon the amount of performance the skipper desired. A top performing inventory, but one that is still below racing boat standards, would be an 8-ounce Kevlar fully battened mainsail, three genoas (a 150%, a 130%, and a 100% blade) and three spinnakers (a 0.5 ounce for light airs, a 0.75 ounce runner and a 1.5 ounce general-purpose sail which would both be set on the pole).

As you can see, the level of crew expertise, the level of performance desired, the area in which you sail, your style of sailing, and the size of your boat, all play a part in the selection of the right sails. A good sailmaker provides more than just sails. He will help tune the rig, set up the sails, show you how to flake sails, help optimize the boat for racing or cruising, and on occasion even suggest books to read, additional tips or features to help improve your sailing skills.

Suppliers of Sails and Sail Equipment

Sail Lofts

Amatti Sailmakers
The Loft
5 Torbet St.
Gourock, Renfrewshire PA19 1UP
SCOTLAND
Tel: (+44) 475-30943

American Sails USA
1669 Meeting St.
Charleston, SC 29405
Tel: (803) 853-0300

Anderson Sails
11 Garden Pl.
P.O. Box 9
Pelham, NY 10805
Tel: (914) 738-7087
Fax: (914) 738-1222

Anson Sailmakers, Inc.
319 Vaughan St.
Portsmouth, NH 03801
Tel: (603) 431-6676

Anson Sails
13 Dale St.
Brookvale, New South Wales 2100
AUSTRALIA
Tel: (+61) 2 905 6305
Fax: (+61) 2 905 7322

Atkinson Sails
Higher Mills Loft
Bridge St.
Bury, Lancaster BL9 6HH
ENGLAND
Tel: (+44) 61 764-5530

Bruce Banks Sail Lofts

Bruce Banks Sails Ltd.
372 Brook Ln.
Sarisbury, Southampton SO3 6ZA
ENGLAND
Tel: (+44) 489 582444
Fax: (+44) 489 589789

Banks Sails (USA)
P.O. Box 97
West End Ave.
Oyster Bay, NY 11771
Tel: (516) 922-3422
Fax: (516) 922-5178

Banks Sails (Caribbean)
P.O. Box 3527
Haulover Marina
St. Thomas, USVI 00803
Tel: (809) 776-5565
Fax: (809) 776-2169

Banks Sails (Italy)
Veleria Semeraro S.r.l.
Seda Logale
Via De Nicolo 48
70121 Bari
ITALY
Tel: (+39) 080 670508

Brewer Sailmakers
2/39 Sydenham Rd.
Brookvale, New South Wales 2100
AUSTRALIA
Tel: (+61) 2 905 4103

Cameron Sails
3222 Nasa Rd. 1
Seabrook, TX 77586
Tel: (713) 326-5566
Fax: (713) 326-5567

Clark Sailmakers
37 Pratt St.
Essex, CT 06426
Tel: (203) 767-8278

Classic Sails
7 Duke Place
Balmain, New South Wales
2041
AUSTRALIA
Tel: (+61) 2 555 7450

Cressy Sails
16 Lincoln Ave.
Marblehead, MA 01945
Tel: (617) 631-4735

D & D Sailmakers
P.O. Box 737
Smithtown, NY 11787
Tel: (516) 543-0350
Fax: (516) 543-1728

Diamond Sail Lofts

Diamond Sailmakers
Sundkrogskai 8
DK2100
Copenhagen
DENMARK
Tel: (+45) 31 20 40 90
Fax: (+45) 31 20 44 12

Diamond Sailmakers
Espana SA
A Ran-Cuntis
36670 Pontevedra
SPAIN
Tel: (+34) 86-548132
Fax: (+34) 86-548259

Diamond Sailmakers Italy
SAS
Piazza die Lenan
13
57123 Livorno
ITALY
Tel: (+39) 586-894009
Fax: (+39) 586-895141

Diamond Sailmakers Japan
Ltd.
2-15-37 Dai Kamakura 247
JAPAN
Tel: (+81) 467 45-3666
Fax: (+81) 467 44-6777

Diamond Sailmakers
France SA
Port du Croesty
56640 Arzon
FRANCE
Tel: (+33) 97 53 78 58
Fax: (+33) 97 53 86 74

Diamond Sailmakers
UK representative:
Richard Bagnall
6 Quay St.
Lymington, Hampshire SO41
9AS
ENGLAND
Tel: (+44) 590 678039
Fax: (+44) 590 670321

Diamond Sailmakers
Atalanta Marine
Kassandras Str. 9
18533 Piraeus
GREECE
Tel: (+30) 1 4174669
Fax: (+30) 1 4112951

Dolphin Sails
400 Main Rd.
Harwich, Essex CO12 4DN
ENGLAND
Tel: (+44) 255 243366
Fax: (+44) 255 240920

Doyle Sail Lofts

Doyle Sailmakers
89 Front St.
Marblehead, MA 01945
Tel: (617) 639-1490
Fax: (617) 639-1497

Doyle Annapolis
108 Severn Ave.
Annapolis, MD 21403
Tel: (410) 268-1175
Fax: (410) 268-2071

Doyle Sailmakers Bermuda
P.O. Box GE72
St. Georges GEBX
BERMUDA
Tel: (809) 297-1008
Fax: (809) 297-8330

Doyle Botts
3059 Jarrow Ave.
Missassauga, Ontario L4X 2C6
CANADA
Tel: (416) 602-9111
Fax: (416) 602-1938

Boston/Sarnia
120 Michigan Ave.
Point Edward, Ontario N7V
1E6
CANADA
Tel: (519) 344-5236
Fax: (519) 344-5237

Doyle Sailmakers BVI
P.O. Box 8309
Cruz Bay, USVI 00831
Tel: (809) 494-2569
Fax: (809) 494-2034

Doyle Sailmakers Florida East
503 N. Andrews Blvd.
Ft. Lauderdale, FL 33301
Tel: (305) 462-3695
Fax: (305) 767-0076

Doyle France
Z.I. du Capitou
83600 Frejus
FRANCE
Tel: (+33) 94 40 84 84
Fax: (+33) 94 40 75 46

Doyle Halifax
5558 Bilby St.
Halifax, Nova Scotia B3K 1V3
CANADA
Tel: (902) 455-5411
Fax: 453-0657

Doyle Italia
Via F. Orlando, 22
90246 Palermo
ITALY
Tel: (+39) 91 685-0285
Fax: (+39) 91 685-0282

Doyle Japan
264 Tsukui
Yokosuka-shi
Kanagawa
JAPAN 239
Tel: (+81) 46-848-2665

Doyle Long Island
40 Matinicock Ave.
Port Washington, NY 11050
Tel: (516) 944-5660
Fax: (516) 944-5715

Doyle Mt. Clemens
P.O. Box 126
Mt. Clemens, MI 48046
Tel: (313) 468-1488
Fax: (313) 468-9732

Doyle Newport Beach
512 29th St.
Newport Beach, CA 92663
Tel: (714) 675-0982

Northwind
Fiskatra Marin Center
133 00 Saltsjobaden
SWEDEN
Tel: (+46) 87 170-546
Fax: (+46) 87 174-004

Doyle Norway
481- Lyngor
NORWAY
Tel: (+47) 41 66- 542
Fax: (+47) 41 66-705

Doyle Offshore Sails Ltd.
6 Crossroads
St. Phillips
Barbados
WEST INDIES
Tel: (809) 423-4600
Fax: (809) 423-4499

Doyle Rhode Island
62 Maritime Dr.
Portsmouth, RI 02871
Tel: (401) 683-6899

Doyle South Africa
P.O. Box 270
Salt River
7924 Cape
SOUTH AFRICA
Tel: (+27) 21 477-512
Fax: (+27) 21 478-090

Doyle South Africa
253 Albert Rd. Woodstock
Capetown
SOUTH AFRICA
Tel: (+27) 21 471-971
Fax: (+27) 31 305-2504

Doyle South Shore
Marine Service Bldg.
Unit C
2 Shipyard Dr.
Hingham, MA 02403
Tel: (617) 740
Fax: (617) 740-4664

Doyle Stearns
2243 North Elston Ave.
Chicago, IL 60614
Tel: (312) 384-2828
Fax: (312) 384-2830

Southwind
3 Lockwood Blvd.
Charleston City
Charleston, SC 29401
Tel: (803) 722-0823

Doyle UK
The Loft
Shamrock Quay
William St., Southampton SO1
1QL
ENGLAND
Tel: (+44) 703 332622
Fax: (+44) 703 232905

Windjammer
1182 Akron St.
San Diego, CA 92106
Tel: (619) 226-2131
Fax: (619) 222-6314

Doyle Service Center
283 Derby St.
Salem, MA 01970
Tel: (508) 741-8732
Fax: (617) 639-1497

Eastern Sailmakers
52 Marion Rd.
Mattpoisett, MA 02739
Tel: (508) 758-3741

Fairclough Sailmakers
108 W. Main St.
Milford, CT 06460
Tel: (203) 882-8433

Genco Sails Ltd.
544 King St. W.
Toronto, Ontario M5V 1M3
CANADA
Tel: (416) 364-2891
Fax: (416) 364-6635

Haarstick Sail Lofts

Haarstick Sailmakers, Inc.
1415 North Clinton Ave.
Rochester, NY 14621
Tel: (800) 342-5033
  or (716) 342-5200

Haarstick Chesapeake
910 Commerce Rd.
Annapolis, MD 21401
Tel: (800) 3560
  or (301) 266-3666

Haarstick New England
P.O. Box 295
606 Ten Rod Rd.
Wickford, RI 02852
Tel: (401) 294-3826

**Haarstick Lake
Champlain/Montreal**
P.O. Box 537
Rt. 22 and Burke Rd.
Plattsburgh, NY 12901
Tel: (800) 562-7245
  or (518) 563-7128

Haarstick/Bay Sails
469 Bay St. N.
Hamilton, Ontario
CANADA
Tel: (416) 529-7245

Haarstick Service Lofts

**Haarstick Hudson/Western
L.I. Sound**
P.O. Box 990
Westerly Rd.
Ossining, NY 10562
Tel: (914) 762-1595

Haarstick/J.C. Sails
178 Railway St.
Kingston, Ontario
CANADA
Tel: (613) 531-9373

Haarstick Carolina
P.O. Box 878
705 Broad St.
Oriental, NC 28571
Tel: (919) 249-3001

Haarstick/Doug Fowler
1182 East Shore Dr.
Ithaca, NY 14850
Tel: (607) 277-0041

Halsey Sailmakers
P.O. Box 205
Rt. 184
Old Mystic, CT 06372
Tel: (203) 536-4235
Fax: (203) 536-6952

**Hathaway, Reiser &
Raymond**
184 Selleck St.
Stamford, CT 06902
Tel: (203) 324-9581
Fax: (203) 348-3057

Hild Sails, Inc.
Box 207
225 Fordham St.
City Island, NY 10464
Tel: (718) 885-2255
Fax: (718) 885-0813

Hild Sails Connecticut
314 Boston Post Rd.
Westbrook, CT 06498
Tel: (203) 399-4911
Fax: (203) 399-4911

Hood Sail Lofts

Hood US
200 High Point Ave.
Portsmouth, RI 02871
Tel: (401) 683-4660
Fax: (401) 683-4791

Hood UK
Bath Rd.
Lymington, Hampshire SO41
9RW
ENGLAND
Tel: 0590-675011
Fax: 0590-673797

Hood Textiles
McCurtain Hill
Clonakilly, County Cork
IRELAND
Tel: (+353) 23-33406

Hood Argentina
1636 Olivos
Buenos Aires
ARGENTINA
Tel: (+54) 1 799-6960
Fax: (+54) 1 799-0767

Hood Adelaid
43 Carlisle St.
Ethelton, South Australia
5015
AUSTRALIA
Tel: (+61) 8 49-4000

Hood Brisbane
124 Glenora St.
Wynnum, Queensland 4178
AUSTRALIA

Hood Costa Mesa
981.B West 18th St.
Costa Mesa, CA 92627
Tel: (714) 548-3464
Fax: (714) 548-9268

Hood Gippsland Lakes
P.O. Box 5
Faynesville, Victoria 3880
AUSTRALIA
Tel: (+61) 51 56-6077

Hood Italy
Via G. Matteotti, 12
20080 Zibido S. Giacomo
Milano
ITALY
Tel: (+39) 2 9000-2661
Fax: (+39) 2 9000-2234

Hood Japan
3-33-8 Nagai
Yokosuka-Shi
Kanagawa-Ken
JAPAN
Tel: (+81) 4 68 57-2345
Fax: (+81) 4 68 57-2333

Hood Lake Macquarie
34 Brougham St.
Fennell Bay, New South Wales
2283
AUSTRALIA
Tel: (+61) 49 50-4485

Hood Maryland
616 Third St.
Annapolis, MD 21403
Tel: (410) 268-4663
Fax: (410) 626-0733

Hood Melbourne
105 Nott St.
P.O. Box 385
Port Melbourne, Victoria 3207
AUSTRALIA
Tel: (+61) 3 646-5273
Fax: (+61) 3 646-4798

Hood New Zealand
P.O. Box 31-330
Milford
Auckland 9
NEW ZEALAND
Tel: (+64) 9 444 0055
Fax: (+64) 9 443-2605

Hood North Queensland
113 Perkins St.
South Townsville, Queensland
4810
AUSTRALIA
Tel: (+61) 77 71-5429

Hood San Francisco
466 Coloma
Sausalito, CA 94965
Tel: (415) 332-4104
Fax: (415) 332-0943

Hood Spain
P.O. Box 35
Avenida del Puerto s/n
30740 San Pedro
Del Pinatar
Murcia
SPAIN
Fax: (+34) 68 18 40 91

Hood St. Petersburg
107 Fifteenth Ave., S.E.
St. Petersburg, FL 33701
Tel: (813) 823-3392
Fax: (813) 823-3309

Hood Sweden
P.O. Box 62
S-450 43 Smogen
SWEDEN
Tel: (+46) 523-38015
Fax: (+46) 523-31628

Hood Sydney
P.O. Box 217
19 West St.
Brookvale, NSW 2100
AUSTRALIA
Tel: (+61) 2 905-0800
Fax: (+61) 2 905-0900

Hood Tasmania
76 Regent St.
Sandy Bay 7005
AUSTRALIA
Tel: (+61) 02 23-5660
Fax: (+61) 02 23-7664

Hood Toronto Canada
3289 Lenworth Dr.
Mississauga, Ontario L4X 2H1
CANADA
Tel: (416) 625-1789
Fax: (416) 624-1383

Hood Victoria Canada
533 Chatham St.
Victoria, British Columbia
V8T 1E1
CANADA
Tel: (604) 385-9022
Fax: (604) 385-9012

Hood Agents

Eldridge Yard
Marsh Rd.
Noank, CT 06340
Tel: (203) 572-9547
Fax: (203) 572-0778

MacDougalls
Cape Cod Marine Service, Inc.
145 Falmouth Heights Rd.
Falmouth, MA 02540
Tel: (508) 548-3164
Fax: (508) 548-7262

North Carolina
Hodges St.
P.O. Box 768
Oriental, NC 28571
Tel: (919) 249-2093

Portland Sail & Rigging
58 Fore St.
Portland, ME 04102
Tel: (207) 828-0003
Fax: (207) 774-7035

Hood Peru
Leonidas Yerovi
225 - San Isidro
Lima 27
PERU
Tel: (+51) 14 41 84 71
Fax: (+51) 14 40 24 25

Hood Vertiebs Gmbh
Hasselbinnen 28
D-2000 Schenefeld Bz.
Hamburg
GERMANY
Tel: (+49) 40 830-0087
Fax: (+49) 40 830-4279

Van Vliet Zeilen
Westhavendijk 8
3241 LP Middleharnis
NETHERLANDS
Tel: (+31) 1870-83790
Fax: (+31) 1870-86810

Hong Kong Sailmakers
Rm 1001-3 Mongkok
Commercial Centre
16 Argyle St.
Kowloon
HONG KONG
Tel: (+852) 789 1938
Fax: (+852) 789 3155

Ian Short Sails
11/141 Taren Point Rd.
Taren Point, New South Wales
2229
AUSTRALIA
Tel: (+61) 2 525 9779

Jasper & Bailey Sailmakers
64 Halsey St. #11
Newport, RI 02840
Tel: (401) 847-8796

Bob Johnson Sailmakers
1903 Douglas Ave.
Clearwater, FL 34615
Tel: (813) 446-6211

JSI/Johnson Sails
P.O. Box 20926
St. Petersburg, FL 33742
Tel: (800) 234-3220
Fax: (813) 577-3220

KA Sails
27 Byre Ave.
Somerton Pk., South Australia
AUSTRALIA
Tel: (+61) 8 294 6211
Fax: (+61) 8 294 9599

Kerr Sailmakers
8417 East 41st St.
Tulsa, OK 74145
Tel: (918) 665-1467

Lam Sails
P.O. Box 76798
Station S
Vancouver, British Columbia
V5R 5S7
CANADA
Tel: (604) 931-3777

Lee Sail Distibutors

Lee Sails
112 E. Woodside Ave.
North Patchogue, NY 11772
Tel: (516) 654-8008
Fax: (516) 654-8117

Lee Sails
1553 Bayville St.
Norfolk, VA 23503
Tel: (804) 480-3676
Fax: (804) 587-1507

Lee Sails
2094 Marina Bay Dr.
Kemah, TX 77565
Tel: (713) 334-2727
Fax: (713) 759-9151

Lee Sails
Box 513
Cruz Bay
St. Johns, USVI 00830
Tel: (809) 767-7127

Lee Sails
647 Pacific Ave.
Alameda, CA 94501
Tel: (415) 523-9011

Lee Sails
1214 S.E. Malden
Portland, OR 97202
Tel: (503) 232-8031

Lee Sails Canada
R.R. #3
London, Ontario N6A 4B7
CANADA
Tel: (519) 657-9972

Lee Sails
P.O. Box 24774
Vancouver, British Columbia
V5T 4E9
CANADA
Tel: (604) 266-8388

W.G. Lucas & Son Ltd.
Broad St.
Old Portsmouth, Hampshire
PO1 2JF
ENGLAND
Tel: (+44) 705 826629
Fax: (+44) 705 861741

Manchester Sailmakers
278 Elm St.
P.O. Box P-203
S. Dartmouth, MA 02748
Tel: (508) 992-6322

McWilliam Sailmakers Ltd.
Crosshaven
County Cork
IRELAND
Tel: (+353) 21 831505
Fax: (+353) 21 831700

McWilliam Sailmakers Ltd.
Ancasta Marina
Cowes, Isle of Wight PO31
7AY
ENGLAND
Tel: (+44) 983 281100
Fax: (+44) 983 281101

Neil Pryde Sail Lofts

Bootsbau W. Schmalzl
Oss See - Suduferstrasse 34
9523 Landskron
9220 Velden
Seecorso 13
AUSTRIA
Tel: (+43) 4274-2284
Fax: (+43) 4242-41960

C.B. Sails
5308 East Business Hwy. 38
Panama City, FL 32404
Tel: (904) 871-6221
Fax: (904) 871-1921

Caledonian Yacht Services
Ardfruoch
Glemosston Rd.
Kilmacolm, Renfrewshire
SCOTLAND
Tel: (+44) 50 5874383

Cameron Sails, Inc.
3222 NASA Rd. #1
Seabrook, TX 77586
Tel: (713) 326-5566
Fax: (713) 326-1607

Charters Marine, Inc.
P.O. Box 22
Ste-Anne de Bellevue, Quebec
H9X 3L4
CANADA
Tel: (514) 457-3929

Dan Winter Sailmakers Ltd.
34 East Queens Way
Hampton, VA 23669
Tel: (804) 722-5711
Fax: (804) 723-8079

Fairweather Marine
P.O. Box 2723
Sausalito, CA 94966
Tel: (415) 332-6167
Fax: (415) 332 6169

Fowler Sails, Inc.
2210 N.W. 14th St.
Bay # 10
Miami, FL 33125
Tel: (305) 638-8885
Fax: (305) 636-2620

G.T. Sails
5401 N. Marginal Rd.
Cleveland, OH 44114
Tel: (216) 391-4823
Fax: (216) 361-0996

Hurricane Canvas
19 Polson St.
Toronto, Ontario M5A 1A4
CANADA
Tel: (416) 466-7000
Fax: (416) 463-5871

Leading Edge Sailmakers
502 Meeting St.
West Columbia, SC 29169
Tel: (803) 794-7139

Moana SAS di V. Malingri
Via Broletto, 37
20121 Milano
ITALY
Tel: (+39) 075 920-251
Fax: (+39) 075 920-069

Neil Pryde Holland
Deltahoek 1A
Postbus 12
4510 AA Breskens
HOLLAND
Tel: (+31) 1172-2101
Fax: (+31) 1172-3284

Neil Pryde Ltd.
16/Fl. Tins Centre, Stage 3
3 Hung Cheung Rd.
Tuen Mun
HONG KONG
Tel: (+852) 4633216
Fax: (+852) 4626944

Neil Pryde Sails, Inc.
P.O. Box 50
50 Broad St.
Milford, CT 06460
Tel: (203) 874-6984
Fax: (203) 877-7014

Quantum Marine Services Ltd.
45/2 Moo 9
Chaofa Rd.
Ao Chalong Area
Phuket 83130
THAILAND
Tel: (+66) 076 381-322

Ralph DiMattia Sailmakers, Inc.
735 East Squantum St.
Quincy, MA 02171
Tel: (617) 328-1100
Fax: (617) 328 1102

Rush Sails
2222 North Pacific
Seattle, WA 98103
Tel: (206) 545-7245
Fax: (206) 547-8038

Sail Consultants, Inc.
613 Third St.
Suite 12
Annapolis, MD 21403
Tel: (410) 263-5846
Fax: (410) 280-3985

Sailing System, Inc.
2-22-6-201 Ikego
Zushi City
Kanagawa
JAPAN
Tel: (+81) 468 71-4727
Fax: (+81) 468 71-4727

Savage Sails
2 Maclaren
Suite F
Irvine, CA 92718
Tel: (714) 588-9994

Savage Sails
2841 Canon St.
San Diego, CA 92106
Tel: (619) 222-1210
Fax: (619) 222-1036

Spanier & Bourne
Sailmakers
P.O. Box 1840
111 Hana Hwy.
Kahului, HI 96732
Tel: (808) 877-7443
Fax: (808) 877-2149

The Sail Specialist
Mailing address:
P.O. Box 1265
Golden, CO 80402-1265
Loft Address:
8845 North I-70
Frontage Rd. #390
Arvada, CO 80002
Tel: (303) 279-3718
Fax: (303) 239-8978

Wah Lee Industrial Corp.
235 Chung Chen Rd.
10/fl.
Kaohsiung
TAIWAN, R.O.C.
Tel: (+866) 07 231-4117
Fax: (+866) 07 251 2208

Zammit & Cachia Ltd.
Cachia Building
Canon Rd.
Qormi
MALTA
Tel: (+356) 227179

North Sail Lofts

North Sails Group, Inc.
66 Quirk Rd.
Milford, CT 06460
Tel: (203) 877-8234
Fax: (203) 877-1575

North Cloth
189 Pepe's Farm Rd.
Milford, CT 04640
Tel: (203) 877-7638
Fax: (203) 878-9045

North Sails Argentina
CNEL F Uzal 3245
1636 Olivos
Buenos Aires
ARGENTINA
Tel: (+54) 1 7905375
Fax: (+54) 1 112350

North Sails Australia
P.O. Box 511
12 Polo Ave.
Mona Vale, NSW 2103
AUSTRALIA
Tel: (+61) 2 9975966
Fax: (+61) 2 9974805

North Sails Belgium
Middelmolenlaan 117-119
B-2100
Deurne
BELGIUM
Tel: (+32) 3 325720
Fax: (+32) 3 3256719

North Sails Brazil
Velas Brasileiras Commercial
Ltda
Rua Trona Constanzo, 10
05516 Sao Paulo, SP
BRAZIL
Tel: (+55) 11-8139244
Fax: (+55) 11-8430408

North Sails Chesapeake
317 Chester Ave.
Annapolis, MD 21403
Tel: (410) 269-5662
Fax: (410) 268-8155

North Sails Detroit
20010 E. Nine Mile Rd.
St. Clair Shores, MI 48080
Tel: (313) 776-1330
Fax: (313) 776-2762

North Sails East
189 Pepe's Farm Rd.
Milford, CT 06460
Tel: (203) 877-7621
Fax: (203) 874-6059

North Sails Finland
Purjeneulomo Niiniranta Oy
Purjetie 5
20360 Turku
FINLAND
Tel: (+358) 21-471000
Fax: (+358) 21-471022

North Sails Fogh
2242 Lakeshore Blvd. W.
Toronto, Ontario M8V 1A5
CANADA
Tel: (416) 259-9644
Fax: (416) 259-0825

North Sails France
Z. A. de Kermarquer
56470 La Trinite Sur Mer
FRANCE
Tel: (+33) 97 55 78 08
Fax: (+33) 97 55 81 11

North Sails Germany
N.S. O.D.-und Yacht-Segel
Gmbh
Seeshaupter Str. 60
D-8122 Penzberg
GERMANY
Tel: (+49) 8856-9150
Fax: (+49) 8856-1601

North Sails Greece
16, Aeginis & Pontou Str.
173 42 Agios Dimitrios
Athens
GREECE
Tel: (+30) 1-983-4065
Fax: (+30) 1-983-2216

**North Sails Huntington
Beach**
15221 Transistor Ln.
Huntington Beach, CA 92649
Tel: (714) 898-1234
Fax: (714) 898-8197

North Sails Italy
Via Ponte Vecchio 42
16042 Carasco GE
Genova
ITALY
Tel: (+39) 185-350955
Fax: (+39) 185-350481

North Sails Japan
3-23-26 Nagai
Yokosuka
Kanagawa-Ken
JAPAN
Tel: (+81) 468-571262
Fax: (+81) 468-570370

**North Sails Lanka (Pvt)
Ltd.**
Ring Road 3
K.I.P.Z. 11
Katunayake
SRI LANKA
Tel: (+94) 1-452378
Fax: (+94) 1-452470

North Sails Marblehead
16 Lincoln Ave.
Marblehead, MA 01945
Tel: (617) 631-5147
Fax: (617) 639-2461

**North Sails (Vic)
Melbourne Pty**
2 Vale St.
St. Kilda, Victoria 3182
AUSTRALIA
Tel: (+61) 3-5340363
Fax: (+61) 3-5253095

North Sails Midwest
P.O. Box 1
1253 East Wisconsin Ave.
Pewaukee, WI 53072
Tel: (414) 691-3050
Fax: (414) 691-3218

North Sails New Orleans
1716 Lake Ave.
Metairie, LA 70005
Tel: (504) 831-1775
Fax: (504) 831-1776

North Sails New Zealand
Street Address:
27 Mackelvie St.
Ponsonby
Mailing Address:
P.O. Box 37-419
Parnell, Auckland
NEW ZEALAND
Tel: (+64) 9 378-1320
Fax: (+64) 9 378-1565

**North Sails One Design
Central**
330 W. Spring St.
Columbus, OH 43215
Tel: (614) 221-2410
Fax: (614) 221-1228

**North Sails One Design
East**
189 Pepe's Farm Rd.
Milford, CT 06460
Tel: (203) 877-7621
Fax: (203) 874-6059

**North Sails One Design
West**
1111 Anchorage Ln.
San Diego, CA 92106
Tel: (619) 226-1415
Fax: (619) 224-7018

North Sails San Diego
1111 Anchorage Ln.
San Diego, CA 92106
Tel: (619) 224-2424
Fax: (619) 224-7018

North Sails San Francisco
2415 Mariner Sq.
Alameda, CA 94501
Tel: (510) 522-5373
Fax: (510) 522-0597

North Sails Scandinavia
Vaerebrovej 25
4040 Jyllinge
DENMARK
Tel: (+45) 46-731429
Fax: (+45) 46-730076

North Sails Capetown
First Floor, Island Centre
Industry Rd.
Paarden Eiland 7520
SOUTH AFRICA
Tel: (+27) 21-5112154
Fax: (+27) 21-5101266

North Sails Espana SA
Muell viejo Espigon exterion
s/n
07012 Palma de Mallorca
SPAIN
Tel: (+34) 71-715752
Fax: (+34) 71-718374

North Sails Scandinavia
Sweden AB
Filaregatan 23
442 34 Kungelv
SWEDEN
Tel: (+46) 303-10508
Fax: (+46) 303-17661

North Sails (U.K.) Ltd.
Newgate Ln.
Fareham, Hampshire PO14
1BP
ENGLAND
Tel: (+44) 329-231525
Fax: (+44) 329-220442

North Sails (Canada) Ltd.
#5 - 11911 Machrina Way
Richmond, British Columbia
V7A 4V3
CANADA
Tel: (604) 271-2111
Fax: (604) 271-4742

North Service Lofts

North Sails France Antibes
1900 Route de Grasse
06600 Antibes
FRANCE
Tel: (+33) 93 339697
Fax: (+33) 93 334794

North Sails Atlanta
3017 Peachtree Industrial
Blvd.
Buford, GA 3051
Tel: (404) 945-2800

North Sails Atlantic
150 Pelham
P.O. Box 850
Lunenburg, Nova Scotia BOJ
2CO
CANADA
Tel: (902) 634-3343
Fax: (902) 634-3306

North Sails Austin
4415 Hudson Bend Rd.
Austin, TX 78734
Tel: (512) 266-1895

North Sails Baltimore
2501 Boston St.
Baltimore, MD 21224
Tel: (301) 276-0988

North Sails Berlin
Salzburger Str. 4
D-1000 Berlin 62
GERMANY
Tel: (+49) 30 7815615
Fax: (+49) 30 4911139

North Sails Bodensee
Argenwag 60/V
7994 Langenaren
GERMANY
Tel: (+49) 7543-1689
Fax: (+49) 7543-4537

North Sails Buffalo
1884 Niagara St.
Buffalo, NY 14207
Tel: (716) 877-3267
Fax: (716) 877-6895

North Sails Cape Cod
80 Mid Tech Dr. #10
West Yarmouth, MA 02673
Tel: (508) 778-6550
Fax: (508) 778-9332

North Sails Carolina
121 Turner St.
Beaufort, NC 28516
Tel: (919) 728-7481

North Sails Channel
Islands
3615 Victoria Ave.
Oxnard, CA 93035
Tel: (805) 984-8100
Fax: (805) 985-3117

North Sails Chicago
Chicago Yachting &
Navigation
1661 North Elston Ave.
Chicago, IL 60622
Tel: (312) 227-0285
Fax: (312) 227-8655

North Sails Chiemsee
Eschenweg 15
8210 Prien
GERMANY
Tel: (+49) 8051-1433
Fax: (+49) 8051-1273

North Sails Chile
Gonzalez/Zuazola
Condell 1190 OF135
Valparaiso
CHILE
Tel: (+56) 32-216076
Fax: (+56) 32-976246

North Sails Cleveland (Ohio)
19106 Detroit Rd.
Rocky River, OH 44116
Tel: (216) 333-0766
Fax: (216) 333-9087

North Sails Colorado
11234 E. Caley Ave. #D
Englewood, CO 80111
Tel: (303) 790-8033
Fax: (303) 790-8021

North Sails Corfu
Nikos Mousouros
Corfu 491 00
GREECE
Tel: (+30) 0661-33597

North Sails Cyprus
22, Paliados Str.
Ayios Ionnis Quartier P.S. 212
Limassol
CYPRUS
Tel: (+357) 05-364815
Fax: (+357) 05-365444

North Sails Durban
38 Vitoria Embankment
Durban 4001
SOUTH AFRICA
Tel: (+27) 31-323624
Fax: (+27) 31-321606

North Sails Florida
3703A 131st Ave. N.
Clearwater, FL 34622
Tel: (813) 573-7730
Fax: (813) 573-2518

North Sails Ft. Lauderdale
1900 S.E. 15th St.
Ft. Lauderdale, FL 33316
Tel: (305) 522-8840
Fax: (305) 522-8841

North Sails Geneva
Voiles Phi S.A.
5CH Pre-Bouvier
CH 1217 Meyrin
SWITZERLAND
Tel: (+41) 22-782-3222
Fax: (+41) 22-785-2431

North Sails Hamburg
Leverkusenstrasse 25
D-2000 Hamburg 50
GERMANY
Tel: (+49) 40-8512338
Fax: (+49) 40-859724

North Sails Hampton, Inc.
The Yachting Center
523 Bridge St.
Hampton, VA 23669
Tel: (804) 722-4000
Fax: (804) 722-2420

North Sails Hawaii
1125 Ala Moana Blvd.
Honolulu, HI 96814
Tel: (808) 523-1092
Fax: (808) 536-8159

North Sails Kalamata
Klias Verginades
Kanari 60
Kalameta 241 00
GREECE
Tel: (+30) 0721-85382

North Sails Kiel
Dorf 15
D-2300 Kiel 17
GERMANY
Tel: (+49) 431-393489
Fax: (+49) 431-392387

North Sails Kobe
Sumanoura Building
4-4-6 Sumanoura
Sumaku
Kobe
JAPAN
Tel: (+81) 757-323215

North Sails Long Island
313 Center Island
Oyster Bay, NY 11771
Tel: (516) 624-9070
Fax: (516) 624-9071

North Sails Marina Del Rey
13106 W. Washington Blvd.
Los Angeles, CA 90066
Tel: (213) 827-8888

North Sails New Hampshire
P.O. Box 146
Rt. 114
North Sutton, NH 03208
Tel: (603) 927-4367

North Sails Newport Beach
2000 Newport Blvd.
Costa Mesa, CA 92627
Tel: (714) 642-7238
Fax: (714) 642-7835

North Sails Scandinavia Norway
Sarbuvollveien 2B
1322 Sarbuvollen
NORWAY
Tel: (+47) 2 537729
Fax: (+47) 2 550838

North Sails Oregon
26 S.W. Boundary St.
Portland, OR 97201
Tel: (503) 222-9121
Fax: (503) 286-5896

North Sails Pastra
Thomas Pouliasis
Amerikis 40
Patra 264 41
GREECE
Tel: (+30) 061 420515

North Sails Portland
P.O. Box 6147
215 Foreside Rd.
Falmouth, ME 04105
Tel: (207) 781-7070

North Sails Puerto Rico
Fajardo Canvas
P.O. Box 185
Puerto Real
Fajardo 00738
PUETRO RICO
Tel: (809) 863-3761
Fax: (809) 860-3760

North Sails Rhode Island
20 Perry Mill Wharf, #40
Newport, RI 02840
Tel: (401) 849-8733
Fax: (401) 848-2817

North Sailing Products
3514 Delaware Ave.
Suite 202
Buffalo, NY 14217
Tel: (716) 876-5917

North Sails Seattle
6317 Seaview Ave. N. W.
Seattle, WA 98107
Tel: (206) 789-4950
Fax: (206) 789-4952

North Sails Service West
Albert-Hahn-Strasse 29
D-4100 Duisburg 29
GERMANY
Tel: (+49) 203 760800
Fax: (+49) 203 765070

North Sails Nynashamn
Box 278
S-149 23 Nynashamn
SWEDEN
Tel: (+46) 8 752-20676

**North Sails
Deutchsprachige Schweiz**
Rico Gregorini AG
Tannackerstrasse 5
CH 3653 Oberhofen
SWITZERLAND
Tel: (+41) 33 432-045
Fax: (+41) 33 432-014

North Sails Texas
P.O. Box 1205
Kemah, TX 77565
Tel: (713) 334-7223
Fax: (713) 334-7226

North Sails Thessaloniki
68, Themistokli Sofouli Str.
Thessaloniki 546 55
GREECE
Tel: (+30) 031 423-495

North Sails Turkey
4 Gazeteciler Sitesi CP
Blok Da: 6 Levent
Istanbul
TURKEY
Tel: (+90) 1 1695136

North Sails Turkey South
Tahsin Oge
35220 Ataturk Cad. No.
386/511
Izmir
TURKEY
Tel: (+90) 51 682650
Fax: (+90) 51 631147

North Sails Vermilion
653 1/2 Main St.
Vermilion, OH 44089
Tel: (216) 967-9576

North Sails Vermont
266 Pine St.
Burlington, VT 05401
Tel: (802) 862-6554
Fax: (802) 860-1935

**North Sails French West
Indies**
Porte de la Marina
Bas du Fort
97110 Pointe-a-Pitre
GUADELOUPE
Tel: (+590) 908044
Fax: (+590) 908976

Olympic Sails
224 Harbord Rd.
Brookvale, New South Wales
2100
AUSTRALIA
Tel: (+61) 2 938 2474
Fax: (+61) 2 905 5896

**Parker & Kay Sailmakers
(East)**
Suffolk Yacht Harbour
Levington
Ipswich, Suffolk 1P10 OLN
ENGLAND
Tel: (+44) 473 659878

**Parker & Kay Sailmakers
(South)**
Port Hamble
Satchell Ln.
Hamble, Southampton SO3
5QD
ENGLAND
Tel: (+44) 703 458213

Ray Blackmore Sails
Fareham Marina
Lower Quay
Fareham, Hampshire
PO16 ORW
ENGLAND
Tel: (+44) 329 825566

Relling Sails
Unit 7c
Titchfield Industries
Titchfield, Hampshire
PO14 4AR
ENGLAND
Tel: (+44) 329 46816
Fax: (+44) 329 46641

Saturn Sails
11 Montgomery Place
Harborside
Irvine KA12 8PN
ENGLAND
Tel: (+44) 294 311627
Fax: (+44) 294 72328

Scott Sailmakers
7416 Edgewood Rd.
Annapolis, MD 21403
Tel: (410) 268-2268
Fax: (410) 268-4273

Shore Sail Lofts

Shore International
7 Merton Rd.
Newport, RI 02840
Tel: (401) 849-2971
Fax: (401) 849-7952

Shore Sails RI
1 Maritime Dr.
Portsmouth, RI 02871
Tel: (401) 683-7997
Fax: (401) 683-9121

Shore Sails Long Island
1345 New York Ave.
Huntington Station, NY 11746
Tel: (516) 673-5055
Fax: (516) 673-6736

Shore Sails Vermont
P.O. Box 4187
Marble Ave.
Burlington, VT 05406
Tel: (802) 863-6266

Shore Sails New Jersey
2422 Rt. 34 N.
Manasquan, NJ 08736
Tel: (908) 528-8899
Fax: (908) 528-6565

Shore Sails Maine
P.O. Box 634
Yarmouth, ME 04096-0634
Tel: (207) 846-6400
Fax: (207) 846-6088

Shore Sails Miami
615 S. W. 2nd Ave.
Miami, FL 33130
Tel: (305) 858-3000
Fax: (305) 858-1209

Shore Sails Connecticut
18 Marshall St.
S. Norwalk, CT 06854
Tel: (203) 854-1616

Shore Sails Houston
P.O. Box 940
602 West Dr.
Kemah, TX 77565
Tel: (713) 334-7559
Fax: (713) 334-1081

Shore Sails Cleveland
8506-A Lake Ave.
Cleveland, OH 44102
Tel: (216) 281-5111

Shore Sails Great Lakes
10321 E. Cherry Bend Rd.
Traverse City, MI 49684
Tel: (616) 941-1222
Fax: (616) 941-7770

Shore Sails Puget Sound
1607 Dexter Ave. N.
Seattle, WA 98109
Tel: (206) 284-3730
Fax: (206) 284-2932

Shore Sails San Francisco
1 Harbor Way S.
Richmond, CA 94804
Tel: (510) 234-9047
Fax: (510) 234-0048

Shore Sails Hawaii
438 Kamakee St.
Honolulu, HI 96814
Tel: (808) 591-0168

Shore Sails Japan
1-22 Chikusa-2-Chome
Nagoya
Aichi 464
JAPAN
Tel: (+81) 52 741-771
Fax: (+81) 52 732-1666

Shore Sails Italy
Piazza Zagora, 39
16155 Genova GE
ITALY
Fax: (+39) 35-214246

Shore Sails Brazil
R. Juari, 900
CEP 04446 Sao Paulo SP
BRAZIL
Fax: (+55) 11 52 27626

Skelley Sails, Inc.
750 N. Adams St.
Havre de Grace, MD 21078
Tel: (410) 939-9261
Fax: (410) 9399364

Sobstad Sail Lofts

Sobstad Chesapeake
951 Bay Ridge Rd.
Annapolis, MD 21403
Tel: (410) 268-1161
Fax: (410) 263-5779

Sobstad Sails
1230 Brickyard Cove Rd.
Point Richmond, CA 94801
Tel: (415) 234-8192

Sobstad Sails
951 Bay Ridge Rd.
Annapolis, MD 21403
Tel: (301) 263-1161
Fax: (301) 263-5779

Sobstad Sails
790 Boston Post Rd.
Westbrook, CT 06498
Tel: (203) 399-0077
Fax: (203) 399-5128

Sobstad Sails
24030 Frampton Ave.
Harbor City, CA 90710
Tel: (213) 539-4911
Fax: (213) 539-2707

Sobstad Sails
1900 N. Northlake Way
Seattle, WA 98103
Tel: (206) 634-0636

Sobstad Sails
100 Southwest 15th St.
Ft. Lauderdale, FL 33315
Tel: (305) 522-6767

Sobstad Sails
2832 Canon St.
San Diego, CA 92106
Tel: (619) 226-2422
Fax: (619) 226-0687

Sobstad Sails
404 S. Roadway Dr.
New Orleans, LA 70124
Tel: (504) 283-4058

Sobstad Sails
23766 Greater Mack
St. Claire Shores, MI 48080
Tel: (313) 778-1501
Fax: (313) 886-5294

Sobstad Sails
Roslagsvagen 101
10405 Stockholm
SWEDEN
Tel: (+46) 816 6276
Fax: (+46) 816 6149

Sobstad Sails
Box 35
Landsdowne, Cape Province
7764
SOUTH AFRICA
Tel: (+27) 21 719103
Fax: (+27) 21 7974773

Sobstad Sails
246 Harbor Rd.
Brookvale, NSW 2199
AUSTRALIA
Tel: (+61) 029 050681
Fax: (+61) 029 050624

Sobstad Sails
Dalveien 4
1396 Bjerkas
Asker
NORWAY
Tel: (+47) 279 8914
Fax: (+47) 279 7483

Sobstad Sails
Via Tangone 12
16030 Casarza Ligure (GE)
ITALY
Tel: (+39) 18 54 65 31
Fax: (+39) 18 54 65 32

Sobstad Sails
Hipolito Yrigoyen 942
1640 Martinez
Buenos Aires
ARGENTINA
Tel: (+54) 17980146
Fax: (+54) 1112206

Sobstad Sails
Mercury Marina
Satchell Ln.
Hamble, Southampton
SO3 5HO
ENGLAND
Tel: (+44) 703 456205
Fax: (+44) 703 452465

Sobstad Sails
18 Eden St.
Box 9168
New Market
Auckland
NEW ZEALAND
Tel: (+64) 9 505 697
Fax: (+64) 9 548 699

Sobstad Sails
Rte des Juenes 59
CH 1227 Garouge (Geneva)
SWITZERLAND
Tel: (+41) 22 430 900
Fax: (+41) 22 430 276

Sobstad Sails
Ionisfil 400 Industrial Park
Thornton, Ontario LOL ZN
CANADA
Tel: (705) 436-5550
Fax: (705) 726 2286

Sobstad Sails
10 Afxentiou Str.
Kalamaki
Athens
GREECE
Tel: (+30) 4125092
Fax: (+30) 9810211

Sobstad Sails
Kanagawa
JAPAN
Tel: (+81) 4688 25451
Fax: (+81) 4688 24319

Sobstad Sails
Les Terriers
06600 Antibes
FRANCE
Tel: (+33) 93 74 67 66
Fax: (+30) 93 22 28 087

Stearns Sailmakers
2243 N. Elston Ave.
Chicago, IL 60614
Tel: (312) 384-2828
Fax: (312) 384-2830

Thomas Clark Sailmakers
37 Pratt St.
Essex, CT 06426
Tel: (203) 767-8278

Thurston Sail Lofts

Thurston Sails, Inc.
112 Tupelo St.
Bristol, RI 02809
Tel: (401) 254-0970
Fax: (401) 253-6830

Thurston Sails, West Bay, Inc.
1 Division St.
East Greenwich, RI 02818
Tel: (401) 885-3667
Fax: (401) 885-6150

John Walker
1041 South Pershing Ave.
Stockton, CA 95206
Tel: (209) 464-3974

Nantucket Sail
71 Milestone Rd.
Nantucket, MA 02554

Leonard's Loft
14375 Oak
Orchard-on-the-Lake
Waterport, NY 14571
Tel: (716) 682-4292

UK Sail Lofts

UK Sailmakers Argentina
Av. Tiscornia 917
(1642) San Isidro
Buenos Aires
ARGENTINA
Tel: (+54) 1 747-9366

UK Sailmakers Australia
21 Higginbotham Rd.
Gladesville, NSW 2111
AUSTRALIA
Tel: (+61) 2 809-5784
Fax: (+61) 2 809-7729

UK Sailmakers Florida
1211 N. Betty Ln.
Clearwater, FL 34615
Tel: (813) 461-0022
Fax: (813) 461-6670

UK Sailmakers Hong Kong
14th Floor
Agincourt Industrial Building
428 Cha Kwo Ling Rd.
Yau Tong
Kowloon
HONG KONG
Mailing address:
P.O. Box No. 62535
Kwun Tong Post Office
Kowloon
HONG KONG
Tel: (+852) 775-7711
Fax: (+852) 775-7722

UK Sailmakers Illinois
2323 S. Michigan Ave.
Chicago, IL 60616
Tel: (312) 326-1053
Fax: (312) 791-1473

UK International
175 City Island Ave.
City Island, NY 10464
Tel: (718) 885-2287
Fax: (718) 885-1726

UK Sailmakers Italy
Veleria Marco Holm
Via Dei Confini 285
50010 Capalle Firenze
ITALY
Tel: (+39) 55 895-1219
Fax: (+39) 55 895-2634

UK Sailmakers Japan
166 Sajima
Yokosuka-City
Kanagwa-Pre
JAPAN 240-01
Tel: (+81) 468-57-2655
Fax: (+81) 468-57-2656

UK Sailmakers Michigan
24541 N. River Rd.
Mt. Clemens, MI 48043
Tel: (313) 468-4110
Fax: (313) 468-5254

UK Sailmakers New York
175 City Island Ave.
City Island, NY 10464
Tel: (718) 885-1700
Fax: (718) 885-1726

**UK Sailmakers So.
California**
112 North Catalina
Redondo Beach, CA 90277
Tel: (310) 379-9611
Fax: (310) 379-8254

UK Sailmakers Sweden
Skogsovagen
133 00 Saltjobaden
SWEDEN
Tel: (+46) 8 717-5070
Fax: (+46) 8 717-1270

UK Sailmakers Texas
1606 First St.
Seabrook, TX 77586
Tel: (713) 474-4168
Fax: (713) 474-3256

Ullman Sail Lofts

Ullman Sails, Inc.
410 29th St.
Newport Beach, CA 92663
Tel: (714) 675-6970
Fax: (714) 675-6276

Ullman Sails Argentina
Espanana 997
1642 San Isidro
Buenos Aires
ARGENTINA
Tel: (+54) 1 747-8197
Fax: (+54) 1 743-6461

Ullman Sails Atlanta
Weathermark
6087 Holiday Rd.
Buford, GA 30518
Tel: (404) 945-0788
Fax: (404) 932-0622

Ullman Sails Florida
957 Lime St.
Sarasota, FL 34237
Tel: (813) 951-0189
Fax: (813) 955-4758
or
2201 1st. Ave. S.
St. Petersburg, FL 33712
Tel: (813) 327-5361

**Ullman Sails by Sergio
Fabbi**
Via S. Pietro, 38F
16035 Rapallo (GE)
ITALY
Tel: (+39) 185 261720
Fax: (+39) 185 261730

Ullman Sails by Giorgio Zuccoli
Viale Repubblica 12
25049 Iseo (BS)
ITALY
Tel: (+39) 30 307966
Fax: (+39) 30 9822178

Ullman Sails By Roberto Vencato & Co.
Androna Campo Marzio 9/c
34123
Trieste
ITALY
Tel: (+39) 40 306309
Fax: (+39) 40 302690

Ullman Sails Japan
630 Fujisawa
Fujisawa SHI
Kanagawa 251
JAPAN
Tel: (+81) 466 26-6310
Fax: (+81) 466 26-6324

Ullman Sails Long Beach
6400 Marina Dr.
Long Beach, CA 90803
Tel: (310 598-9441

Velerisa, Ullman de Mexico
Av. Manuel Avila Camacho
131
Col. Lomas de Chapultepec
Mexico D.F. 11000
MEXICO
Tel: (+52) 5 540-3047
Fax: (+52) 5 520-9808

Ullman Sails Norge
P.B. 696
Havnegaten 97
3040 Drammen
NORWAY
Tel: (+47) 3 818-495
Fax: (+47) 3 818-402

Ullman Sails San Diego
2805 Canon St.
San Diego, CA 92106
Tel: (619) 226-1133
Fax: (619) 226-3244

Ullman Sails Seattle
6507 6th Ave.
Seattle, WA 98117
Tel: (206) 789-7628

Ullman Sails Southwest
309 N. Oakland
Dallas, TX 75226
Tel: (214) 741-2364
Fax: (214) 748-3159

Ullman Sails UK
The Sail Loft
Port Hamble, Hamble S03 5NN
ENGLAND
Tel: (+44) 703 454254
Fax: (+44) 703) 455971

Ullman Sails Ventura
3639 E. Harbor Blvd.
Ventura, CA 93001
Tel: (805) 644-9579
Fax: (805) 644-8643

Sail Cloth

Allied Fibers
1411 Broadway
New York, NY 10018
Tel: (212) 391-5131

Bainbridge/Aquabatten
252 Revere St.
Canton, MA 02021
Tel: (800) 422-5684
or (508) 821-2600
Fax: (617) 821-2609

Dimension/Polyant Sailcloth, Inc.
78 Highland Dr.
P.O. Box 922
Putnam, CT 06260
Tel: (800) 441-2424
or (203) 963-7413
Fax: (203) 928-0161

Hood Textiles
McCurtain Hill
Clonakilly
County Cork
IRELAND
Tel: (+353) 23-33406

North Cloth
189 Pepe's Farm Rd.
Milford, CT 04640
Tel: (203) 877-7638
Fax: (203) 878-9045

Shore Cloth
7 Merton Rd.
Newport, RI 02840
Tel: (401) 849-2971
Fax: (401) 849-7952

Sail Brokerages

Atlantic Sail Traders
P.O. Box 12313
2062 Harvard
Sarasota, FL 34278
Tel: (813) 351-6023
Fax: (813) 957-1391

Bacon & Associates
112 West St.
P.O. Box 3150
Annapolis, MD 21403
Tel: (410) 263-4880

Sail Hardware

Bete Fleming
Box 906
44 Marion Rd.
Mattapoisett, MA 02739
Tel: (508) 758-4996

Lord & Hodge, Inc.
P.O. Box 737
Middletown, CT 06457
Tel: (203) 632-7006
Fax: (203) 632-2192
Grommet suppliers

Master Tool
6115 N.W. 3rd St.
Miami Lakes, FL 33014
Tel: (305) 557-1020
Fax: (305) 556-0908

Nicro Marine
2065 W. 140th Ave.
San Leandro, CA 94577
Tel: (415) 357-8332

Viscom
507 Hopmeadow St.
Simsbury, CT 06070
Tel: (203) 658-2201
Fax: (203) 651-8408

**Battslide Full Batten Sail
Hardware**
Sailpower Systems, Inc.
112 Bond Ct.
Los Gatos, CA 95032
Tel: (408) 356-3392
Fax: (408) 356-3234
Full-batten sail hardware

Sail Repair Kits

Sailrite Kits
305 W. Van Buren St.
Columbia City, IN 46725
Tel: (800) 348-2769
Fax: (219) 244-4184

Hayden/Schreiber
57 Crompton Ave.
E. Greenwich, RI 02818
Tel: (401) 885-4565

Sail Brite Midwest
2886 Archer Ave.
Chicago, IL 60608
Tel: (312) 523-0206

SailCare
410 Ninth St.
Ford City, PA 16226
Tel: (800) 433-7245
Repairs

Spartan International
1845 S. Cedar
Holt, MI 48842
Tel: (517) 694-3911
Fax: (517) 694-7952
Repair tape

Schools

There are several different kinds of schools related to boats and boating. For instance, the family with children that is sailing around the world must get the children educated. The best method of doing this is by correspondence with a school back home. For the person who wants to learn about boatbuilding, there are boatbuilding schools. Usually, these are residential and seek to train novice builders to a level that will enable them to get a job building boats. By far the largest category of schools are sailing schools. In the source list that follows, I have selected some of the better ones.

When checking out a sailing school, ask questions. How long have the instruc-

tors been teaching sailing? Do they have US Sailing accreditation? What type of boats do they teach in? Ideally, you should learn to sail in boats that you intend to continue sailing. How long does the course take? At what level will you be at the end of the course? Will you be able to skipper your own boat in a strong breeze? How much will the course cost? Does the course include lectures and reading on sailing theory or just sailing lessons? Understanding the theory will help you sail better and make it easier to see why you are doing something. What about insurance? Who pays if you have an accident? These are all questions you should ask before you sign up for classes.

Addresses of Schools

Boatbuilding Schools

Bates/The Job School
2201 South 78th
Tacoma, WA 98409
Tel: (206) 596-1705

Landing School of Boat Building & Design
P.O. Box 1490
Kennebunkport, ME 04046
Tel: (207) 985-7976
Fax: (207) 985-7942

Woodenboat School
P.O. Box 78
Brooklin, ME 04616
Tel: (207) 359-4651
Fax: (207) 359-8920

Correspondence Schools for Sailing Children

Calvert School
105 Tuscany Rd.
Baltimore, MD 21210
Tel: (410) 243-6030
Fax: (410) 366-0674

Design Schools

Westlawn School of Yacht Design
733 Summer St.
Stamford, CT 06901
Tel: (203) 359-0500

Sailing Schools

Annapolis Sailing School
P.O. Box 3334
601 Sixth St.
Annapolis, MD 21405
Tel: (800) 638-9192

Chesapeake Sailing School
7074 Bembe Beach Rd.
Annapolis, MD 21403
Tel: (800) 966-0032
  or (410) 269-1594
Fax: (410) 269-5856

**Corpus Christi
International School of
Sailing**
Cooper's Alley
Corpus Christi, TX 78403
Tel: (512) 881-8503

**Havre de Grace Sailing
Services, Inc.**
P.O. Box 441
Tidewater Marina
Havre de Grace, MD 21078
Tel: (800) 526-1528

J World
Key West and Newport
Tel: (800) 343-2255
  or (401) 849-5492
San Diego
Tel: (800) 666-1050
  or (619) 259-3836

Offshore Sailing School
16731 McGregor Blvd.
Ft. Myers, FL 33908
Tel: (800) 221-4326
Fax: (813) 454-1191

Oyster Bay Sailing School
P.O. Box 447
West End Ave.
Oyster Bay, NY 11771
Tel: (516) 624-7900
Fax: (516) 922-4502

**Philadelphia Sailing
School**
Reserve Ave.
P.O. Box 611
Riverside, NJ 08075
Tel: (800) 669-3992
Fax: (609) 461-9415

Sea School N.E.
29 Audrey Ave.
Oyster Bay, NY 11771
Tel: (516) 624-9768
Fax: (516) 624-6029

Texas Sailing Academy
P.O. Box 5700
Austin, TX 78763
Tel: (512) 261-6193

Womanship
The Boat House
410 Severn Ave.
Annapolis, MD 21403
Tel: (800) 342-9295
  or (410) 269-0784

Figure 1: Learning to sail the Womanship Way.

Spars

By Jonathan D. Young

Jonathan D. Young is a graduate of Yacht Design Institute and former spar designer at Hood Yacht Systems. He is now running his own composite spar shop at Nautika Teknik A.S. / Composite Spars.

There are several familiar choices to be made when selecting a new rig: fractional or masthead, sloop or cutter, furling or full-batten, and so on. Today, however, technology has added a new wrinkle, the choice of material. Should you stay with tried-and-true aluminum or go with one of the new high-tech carbon fiber sections? The following brief discussion of the merits of each material will help you to make this decision.

ALUMINUM

The majority of today's yachts are equipped with 6061-T6 grade aluminum alloy masts. Aluminum's principal advantages are relatively low cost due to the efficiency of producing extruded mast sections, and a high strength-to-weight ratio compared with traditional alternatives such as wood or steel. In addition, a wide assortment of extrusion shapes and sizes are available, and the material is easy to work. If necessary, it can be cut, drilled, and tapped with hand tools.

Some disadvantages of the 6061-T6 alloy are relatively low fatigue strength and poor corrosion resistance. Special care must be taken when welding, as this destroys the metal's temper, reducing its strength in the area of the weld by one half. Corrosion can also be a problem. The widespread use of stainless steel fittings can cause unsightly "bubbling" and make the removal and replacement of fasteners a chore. Highly loaded fittings, such as tangs or goosenecks, may cause stress cracking in aluminum, exposing it to extra corrosion.

In general, though, the aluminum spar has proved to be a solid, predictable performer that will see continued service for the foreseeable future. The fact that several racing rules specifically mandate the use of aluminum masts helps guarantee their continued use.

CARBON FIBER

A standard grade (T-300 style) carbon fiber/epoxy mast laminate, at 60 percent fiber by weight, approaches half the density per unit volume of 6061 aluminum, and has approximately five times the ultimate strength. This means that, for the same strength, a carbon spar can be much lighter, which translates into improved performance or draft reduction.

If carbon spars are designed to meet the required moments of inertia, their compressive strength will be much higher than that of a comparable aluminum spar. In itself, this factor has saved a few masts. It has been said by more than one single-handed BOC racer that his composite mast has survived a topmast shroud failure that would have proved fatal to an aluminum spar.

Other benefits are less immediate but equally valuable. Carbon/epoxy laminates do not corrode in the presence of electrolytic solutions such as seawater — an on-going problem with aluminum — and composites also show a marked improvement in long-term fatigue strength over alloy (i.e., in the $10\neg6$ to $10\neg8$ cycles range). These factors increase the life of the spar tremendously. The longevity of the unstayed composite Freedom Yacht spars over a fifteen-year period will atttest to this.

Carbon spars are made either by hand layup, or by machines. Hand layup requires little investment in capital equipment, but it pays a penalty in labor cost. Machine layup provides uniformity in fiber tension and orientation, with less labor. The process used is of interest to designers and builders, because it gives an indication of the how consistent the laminate will be from part to part. Typically, the builder of hand laid up spars uses fibers that have been pre-impregnated with a specific proportion of resin, while machine processes, such as filament-winding or braiding, incorporate a controlled resin-impregnating system. Both methods result in a uniform resin distribution that cannot be achieved with simple hand application. Resin cure is completed by heating either under vacuum pressure or with the assistance of an autoclave, which raises the cure pressure to 5 atmospheres or more. Most standard hardware can be employed for fitting out, and the spar is finished with an appropriate primer, followed by a marine two-part polyurethane.

A carbon fiber mast outperforms an aluminum one by virtually every meaningful measure. However, the engineering and manufacturing of a carbon spar is technically more complex, which increases its cost. Prices do vary, though, since a number of different production processes are employed. The buyer may therefore wish to establish some fundamental benchmarks, such as relative stiffness and weight, with which to compare the value of competing products.

Suppliers of Spars and Spar Components

Boom Brakes

Martinus Van Breems, Inc.
571 Riversdie Ave.
Westport, CT 06880
Tel: (203) 454-0222
Dutchman

Walder
2 Rue Turgot
06110 Le Cannet
MONACO
Tel: (+33) 93 46 07 64
Fax: (+33) 93 45 26 06
Walder system

Backstay Adjusters

IM/Navtec
P.O. Box 308
New Whitfield St.
Guilford, CT 06437-0388
Tel: (203) 458-3163
Fax: (203) 458-9291

Riggarna UK Ltd.
Unit 3
Somerford Business Park
Wilverly Rd.
Christchurch, Dorset BH23
3RU
ENGLAND
Tel: (+44) 202 480481
Fax: (+44) 202 479899

SAILTEC, Inc.
1712 Graber St.
Oshkosh, WI 54901
Tel: (414) 233-4242
Hydraulics

Seaway Products Ltd.
The Hydraulic Centre
Tregonniggle Industrial Estate
Falmouth, Cornwall TR11 4SN
ENGLAND
Tel: (+44) 326-74008
Hydraulic vangs

Masts and Spars

Allyacht Spars P/L
1853 Lytton Rd. Lytton,
Queensland AUSTRALIA
Tel: (+61) 7 893 2233
Fax: (+61) 7 893 2478

Amco Marine Co.
5420 Manthei
Petoskey, MI 49770-9744
Tel: (616) 347-7222
Fax: (616) 347-7220
*Whisker poles, spinnaker poles,
and downwind systems*

Annapolis Spars
7416 Edgewood Rd.
Annapolis, MD 21403
Tel: (301) 269-0771
Alloy spars

Carbospars Ltd.
Hamble Point Quay
School Ln.
Hamble, Southampton SO3
5NB
ENGLAND
Tel: (+44) 703 456736
Fax: (+44) 703 455361
Carbon spars

Dwyer Aluminum Mast Co.
21 Commerce Dr.
North Branford, CT 06471
Tel: (203) 484-0419
Fax: (203) 484-2014
Alloy spars

Forespar
22322 Gilberto
Rancho Santa Margarita, CA
Tel: (714) 858-8820
Fax: (714) 858-0505
Composite and alloy spars

Francespar/Sparcraft
Zone Industrielle
Rue Blaise Pascal
17185 Perigny
FRANCE
Tel: (+33) 46 44 16 65
Fax: (+33) 46 45 36 59
Alloy spars

Geotz Marine Technology
14 Broad Common Rd.
Bristol, RI 02809
Tel: (401) 253-8802
Fax: (401) 253-9359
Composite spars

Hall Spars
17 Peckham Dr.
Bristol, RI 02809
Tel: (401) 253-4858
Fax: (401) 253-2552
Composite and alloy spars

Hood Yacht Systems
Maritime Dr.
Portsmouth, RI 02871
Tel: (401) 683-2900
Fax: (401) 683-2410
Alloy spars

IM/Isomat
Route de La Hogue
50550 St. Vaast La Hogue
FRANCE
Tel: (+33) 33 54 43 19
Fax: (+33) 33 54 55 19
Alloy spars

IM/Isomat
1031 Amble Dr.
Charlotte, NC 28206
Tel: (704) 596-9449
Fax: (704) 597-7503
Alloy spars

Figure 1: This masthead spar is available from IM/Kenyon.

IM/Kenyon Spars
1031 Amble Dr.
Charlotte, NC 28206
Tel: (704) 596-9449
Fax: (704) 597-7503
Alloy spars

IM/Sparcraft
1031 Amble Dr.
Charlotte, NC 28206
Tel: (704) 596-9449
Fax: (704) 597-7503
Alloy and carbon spars

Figure 2: This three-quarter rig spar is available from IM/Sparcraft.

IM/Sparcraft (Europe) Ltd
Waterloo Rd.
Lymington, Hampshire SO41 9DB
ENGLAND
Tel: (+44) 590 677714
Fax: (+44) 590 679932

Kemp Masts Ltd.
St. Margaret's Ln.
Titchfield, Hampshire PO14 4BG
ENGLAND
Tel: (+44) 329 41900
Fax: (+44) 329 47052

LeFiell Marine Products
13700 Firestone Blvd.
Santa Fe Springs, CA 90670
Tel: (213) 921-3411
Fax: (213) 926-1714
Alloy spars

Metalmast Marine
55 Providence St.
Putnam, CT 06260
Tel: (203) 928-2776
Fax: (203) 928-7312
Alloy spars

Nautika Teknik A.S. / Composite Spars
Tersanler Cad.
G50 No.3 81700
Tuzla - Istambul
TURKEY
Tel: (+90) 1-395-7340/1/2/3
Fax: (+90)-1-395-0531
Composite spars

Norseman Marine
711 N.W. 1st St.
Ft. Lauderdale, FL 33312
Tel: (305) 524-1750
Alloy spars

Offshore Spar Co.
50200 E. Russell Schmidt
Chesterfield, MI 48051
Tel: (313) 598-4700
Fax: (313) 598-4705
Composite spars

Peelgrane Marine Pty. Ltd.
14 Erskine St.
Taren Point, New South Wales 2229
AUSTRALIA
Tel: (+61) 2 525 0821
Fax: (+61) 2 540 1982
Proctor yacht masts

Proctor Masts
Duncan Rd.
Swanwick, Southampton SO3 7ZQ
ENGLAND
Tel: (+44) 489 583111
Fax: (+44) 489 577889
Alloy spars

R.C. Marine Products Co. Ltd.
6-10 Parkway Dr.
Mairangi Bay
Auckland
NEW ZEALAND
Tel: (+64) 478-9185

Reckman Mast Systems
Port Hamble Marina
Satchell Ln.
Hamble, Southampton SO3 5NN
ENGLAND
Tel: (+44) 703 454280
Fax: (+44) 703 456047

Rondal bv
P.O. Box 52
8325 ZH
Vollenhove
NETHERLANDS
Tel: (+31) 0 5274 3500
Fax: (+31) 0 5274 3900
Spars for larger craft

Selden Mast AB
Redegaten 11
S-421 Vastra Frolunda
SWEDEN
Tel: (+46) 031-29 21 90
Fax: (+46) 31 29 71 37

W.V. Manufacturing Pty. Ltd.
41 Winbourne Rd.
Brookvale, New South Wales 2100
AUSTRALIA
Tel: (+61) 2 938 4722
Sheerline spars

Southern Spars Ltd.
Corner Gaunt and Daldy Sts.
P.O. Box 90238
Auckland
NEW ZEALAND
Tel: (+64) 9 358 3315
Fax: (+64) 9 359 6309
*Custom racing and cruising
spars*

Spartech
P.O. Box 4988
Emerald Isle, NC 28594
Tel: (919) 354-6288
Fax: (919) 326-6113
*Carbon fiber spars and rigging
components*

Viscom
507 Hopmeadow St.
Simsury, CT 06070
Tel: (203) 658-2200
Fax: (203) 651-8404

Vangs

Euro Marine Trading, Inc.
64 Halsey St.
Newport, RI 02840
Tel: (401) 849-0060
Fax: (401) 849-3230
Antal vangs

Forespar
22322 Gilberto
Rancho Santa Margarita, CA
Tel: (714) 858-8820
Fax: (714) 858-0505
Rod vang

Hall Spars
17 Peckham Dr.
Bristol, RI 02809
Tel: (401) 253-4858
Quik vang

Harken Yacht Equipment
1251 E. Wisconsin Ave.
Pewaukee, WI 53072
Tel: (414) 691-3320
Fax: (414) 691-3008
Rope vangs

IM/Isomat
Route de La Hogue
50550 St. Vaast La Hogue
FRANCE
Tel: (+33) 33 54 43 19
Fax: (+33) 33 54 55 19
Isovang

IM/Isomat
1031 Amble Dr.
Charlotte, NC 28206
Tel: (704) 596-9449
Fax: (704) 597-7503
Isovang

IM/Lewmar, Inc.
P.O. Box 308
New Whitfield St.
Guilford, CT 06437
Tel: (203) 458-6200
Fax: (203) 453-5669
Rope vangs

IM/Navtec
P.O. Box 308
New Whitfield St.
Guilford, CT 06437-0388
Tel: (203) 458-3163
Fax: (203) 458-9291
Navtec vang

Imtra Corp.
30 Barnet Blvd.
New Bedford, MA 02745
Tel: (508) 990-7000
Fax: (508) 998-5359
Spinlock Index vang

Kemp Masts Ltd.
St. Margaret's Ln.
Titchfield, Hampshire PO14
4BG
ENGLAND
Tel: (+44) 329 41900
Fax: (+44) 329 47052
Gas Rodkicker vang

Larsen Marketing
P.O. Box 968
16 Old Boston Rd.
Westbrook, CT 06498
Tel: (203) 399-9522
Pfeiffer vang

Lefiell Marine Products
13700 Firestone Blvd.
Santa Fe Springs, CA 90670
Tel: (213) 921-3411
Vari-vang

Norseman Marine, Inc.
516 West Olas Blvd.
Ft. Lauderdale, FL 33312
Tel: (305) 467-1407
Fax: (305) 462-3470
Rondal vang

Offshore Spar Co.
50200 E. Russell Schmidt
Chesterfield, MI 48051
Tel: (313) 598-4700
Fax: (313) 598-4705
Offshore vang

**Performance Marine
Technologies**
P.O. Box 6843
Beaverton, OR 97007
Tel: (800) 526-2119
  or (503) 645-9200
Performance vangs

Rondal bv
P.O. Box 52
8325 ZH
Vollenhove
NETHERLANDS
Tel: (+31) 0 5274 3500
Fax: (+31) 0 5274 3900
Vangs for larger craft

Sail Systems, Inc.
P.O. Box 1218
Marblehead, MA 01945
Tel: (617) 639-0440
Fax: (617) 631-7517
Furlex Rodkicker

SAILTEC, Inc.
1712 Graber St.
Oshkosh, WI 54901
Tel: (414) 233-4242
Hydraulic vangs

Schaeffer Marine
12 Industrial Park
New Bedford, MA 02745
Tel: (508) 995-9511
Rope vangs

Seaway Products Ltd.
The Hydraulic Centre
Tregonniggle Industrial Estate
Falmouth, Cornwall TR11 4SN
ENGLAND
Tel: (+44) 326-74008
Hydraulic vangs

Spinlock USA
20 Barnett Blvd.
New Bedford, MA 02745
Tel: (508) 995-7000
Fax: (508) 994-4919

Welborn Marine
805 Court St.
Clearwater, FL 34616
Tel: (813) 443-7661
Fax: (813) 447-0867
Ronstan vangs

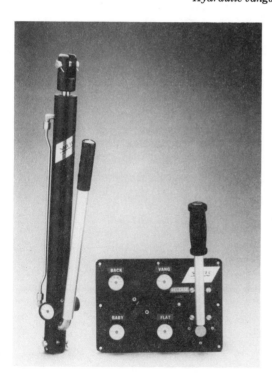

Figure 3: Hydraulic mast and rig adjustment can be made with this SAILTEC ram and pump.

Stabilizers and Trim Tabs

STABILIZERS

Stabilization is the reduction of rolling by means of various devices either attached to the hull or onboard the vessel. In general, most stabilizing devices work better when the boat is underway. The only type that works well when the ship is at rest is the flume tank. But flume tanks — tanks on either side of the ship connected by a large-diameter pipe — do not prevent the onset of rolling; they only dampen rolling.

Stabilizers are not for everybody. But with more windage aloft and a greater tendency to roll, many modern power yachts are being fitted with stabilizers before they leave the builder's yard. For long, lean, older vessels that tend to roll in a seaway, a stabilizer may be the best solution. Not only will the stabilizer reduce the rolling of the vessel, it will also probably help reduce yaw and the associated strains on the steering.

There are two major groups of stabilizing devices: passive and active. Selection of the best type depends upon the function of the vessel, the amount of damping required, and the speed at which the vessel moves through the water.

Passive Devices

Passive devices include bilge keels and flume tanks. They are generally custom-designed for a particular vessel and fitted by the builder.

Bilge Keels

On a round-bottomed boat, the most usual stabilizing device is the bilge keel. Bilge keels are often designed as part of the structural members of the boat and run down either side of the hull at the turn of the bilge. However, because bilge keels have a very low aspect ratio, their effectiveness is reduced. If the keel were to be broken up into shorter, higher aspect ratio sections, it would be more efficient, but the structural benefits would be reduced or eliminated.

Bilge keels are ineffective at very low speeds or at a mooring, when they only offer slight resistance to rolling. They work best when the vessel is at cruising speed, when the keels act like miniature wings.

Flume Tanks

Flume tanks are large tanks on either side of the vessel connected by a large-diameter pipe. The tanks can be full of fuel or water, but note that their effectiveness goes down as the liquid is used up. At their most effective, the tanks are about half full. The anti-rolling action can be adjusted by raising or lowering the height of the liquid in the tank.

The idea behind a flume tank is that the liquid moves across the vessel out of sync with the vessel's roll. For instance, if the vessel is heeled to port, the liquid flows to port. As the vessel rolls back to starboard, the liquid is restrained slightly by the connecting pipe. Eventually, it starts to flow to starboard, but only after the boat has rolled to starboard.

Ideally, the motion of the liquid should follow the boat's roll about one quarter period behind it. If the tank is designed properly and the liquid flows correctly, the roll can be damped in one or two cycles. It should be understood, though, that the liquid flow cannot stop the rolling; it can only dampen it. But because the boat need not be underway for dampening to start, this method of stabilization can be used effectively on stationary or slow-speed vessels.

Note also that flume tanks have a large area of free surface. That is, the water surface is not controlled. This reduces stability somewhat, which means that this type of stabilization can only be installed on a vessel with high initial stability.

Active Stabilizers

Active stabilizing devices include stabilizing fins, gyroscopes, and forced-transfer tanks. Active types use power and input from the vessel to achieve stabilization.

Stabilizing Fins
Stabilizing fins are the most popular solution to rolling problems. They can easily be retrofitted and their operation is fully automatic. They can be thought of, in their simplest form, as rudders sticking out at an angle to the hull. Rather than controlling the port and starboard direction of the boat, they act in sync to control the up and down motion of each side of the boat. In the simplest of terms, when the boat is underway and rolling, the fin on the side heading downwards is adjusted so that it is creating lift and trying to raise that side upwards. As the boat rolls back the other way, the fin on the other side of the boat performs the same function, and the fin on the side going up is reset to create lift as it rises, which tries to drive its side of the boat downwards.

Most active fins are driven by hydraulic pressure and are fixed on the outside of the hull. For yacht use, there are several retractable stabilizers, which make it easier to bring the boat alongside a dock. In general, only one pair of fins is fitted, and both fins have a maximum rotation of about 30 degrees.

Gyroscopes
Gyroscopic stabilizers are rarely seen on vessels under 100 feet LOA. They tend to be heavy (up to 2% of the boat's displacement) and often are not too satisfactory in certain sea conditions.

Forced-Transfer Tanks
These tanks operate in a manner similar to flume tanks, in that liquid is moved from one tank to another. But the liquid in forced-transfer tanks is pumped back and forth. This gives much greater control over the damping speed, although a considerable amount of power is needed to move large volumes of water quickly.

TRIM TABS

A number of respected experimenters, among them Korvin-Kroukosky, Savitsky, Shoemaker, and Diehl, have hypothesized based on towing tank data that the optimum trim angle for a planing powerboat is between 4 1/2 and 6 1/2 degrees. These angles give the best tradeoff between angle of incidence, lift, and drag. But many powerboats do not run between those angles. Some trim up to eight degrees as they are climbing over the "hump" of the power curve, and then they settle back to a two or three degree trim angle. In general, boats with a high angle of trim are less efficient and take longer to get on a plane than boats with a lesser angle. Visibility over the bow is also reduced until the boat levels out at its normal planing trim.

In order to optimize the trim angles and get on a plane quickly, then run at the most efficient angle of incidence, trim tabs are often built into the planing surface of the vessel. These trim tabs are raised and lowered by an electric or hydraulic arm. The size of the tabs depends upon the speed of the powerboat, the area of planing surface, and the angle at which the boat is expected to trim out at.

Trim tabs should be sized by an expert, as the wrong size tab can make trim problems worse. When using trim tabs, adjust them in small increments at set engine speeds until you get a feel for the effect on the boat. You may find that a small amount of tab at a higher speed will get you on a plane quicker than using a large tab angle at a low speed.

Manufacturers of Stabilizers and Trim Tabs

Stabilizers

Gyro-Gale, Inc.
P.O. Box 2650
Stuart, FL 34995
Tel: (407) 283-1711
Quadra Fin stabilizers

Van Dusen and Meyer, Inc.
P.O. Box 558
Shelton, CT 06484
Tel: (203) 929-6355
Fax: (203) 929-3594
Naiad stabilizers

Wilcox Marine Products
262 S.W. 33rd St.
Ft. Lauderdale, FL 33315
Tel: (305) 527-1471
Seabrace stabilizers

Trim Tabs

Bennet Marine, Inc.
550 N.W. 12th Ave.
Deerfield Beech, FL 33316
Tel: (305) 427-1400
Fax: (305) 480-2897

Boat Leveler Co. Division of Kercheval Industries
7305 Natural Bridge Rd.
St. Louis, MO 63121
Tel: (314) 385-7470
Fax: (314) 385-9173

Lenco, Div. of L. Saraga, Inc.
15 E. Mall Dr.
Plainview, NY 11803
Tel: (516) 752-3800
Fax: (516) 752-3803

Trim Master Trim Tabs
3081 Mercantile Industrial Dr.
St. Charles, MO 63301
Tel: (314) 949-8746
Fax: (314) 949-5363

Steering Gear

By Will Keene

Will Keene and his brother Hank have messed around in boats almost all their lives. After college, Hank and Will worked in the marine industry for five years and then joined the Edson Corporation on a full-time basis. In 1989, Will and Hank purchased the Edson Corporation from their family and are now guiding it into the next century. The company's 150th anniversary is in the year 2009.

Which steering system best suits your boat depends upon several things. These include hull configuration, rudder location, how much deadwood is in front of the rudder, the ease of taking a linkage between the rudder stock and the helm, and the size and style of the cockpit arrangement. All should be considered in selecting steering gear.

There are three major parts in a steering system: the rudder, the linkage, and the helm position. Each performs a specific function and each part can vary tremendously.

THE RUDDER

For the purposes of selecting a steering system, rudders can be divided into three groups: balanced rudders, rudders with a skeg or deadwood in front of them, and transom-hung rudders. Balanced rudders are usually seen on boats with higher performance. They make the boat easy to steer, but can stall fairly easily when turned at large angles. Rudders with a skeg or deadwood in front of them tend to stall less easily, but they may also operate in an area of dead water, which limits the degree of sensitivity that may be obtained. Transom-hung rudders are, as the name implies, hung off the transom and generally do not have a rudder post on which a quadrant can be mounted. Most transom-hung rudders are steered with a tiller or, like many catboats, some form of rack and pinion system.

THE LINKAGE

The linkage is basically the system by which the rudder is linked to the wheel, steering arm, or tiller. Linkages may be a solid bar with universal joints at each corner, chain and wire, pull/pull systems, push/pull systems, worm gear, rack and pinion, or hydraulic.

The solid linkage in which the rudder stock is connected to the helm station by solid bars or tubes, with a universal joint at each turn of the linkage, rather like the transmission system of a truck or car, has largely dropped out of favor today. It had a tendency to bind up at inopportune moments, to be fairly heavy, and to take up a lot of space. But with carbon fiber tubing and some of the more sophisticated universal joints, they may eventually make a comeback.

Chain and wire linkage is the most popular system found on auxiliary sailboats today. This type of linkage has gained its popularity because it is easily repaired at sea or in any port. It is extremely simple, which makes it easy for nontechnical boat owners to understand, and it can be easily and fully adjusted so that all play can be tensioned out for maximum responsiveness and feel. With a chain and wire linkage, the boat owner can increase or decrease the steering loads by changing the diameter of the steering wheel, sprocket, or quadrant. The reliability of chain and wire is excellent. If failures occur, typically, they do so after the first two to three months, as a result of misaligned sheaves leading the steering cables in a way that chafes the cable. As with any system, proper installation is the key to optimum performance. When installed properly, chain and wire linkages are the most versatile and economical linkages that can be installed on a sailboat.

The pull/pull steering linkage is, in effect, another way of routing the cables of a chain and wire system. The advantage of the pull/pull linkage is that it allows you to route the steering cables through a jacketed, flexible conduit rather than around sheaves. This saves the installer time because he does not have to align the sheaves. The disadvantage of the pull/pull linkage can be felt in the increased friction of the system and general lack of feel if not carefully installed. Pull/pull systems are usually found on midship cockpit sailboats

and powerboats where the routing needs to be simplified as much as possible.

Push/pull steering linkages are single cables that push the rudder or outboard in one direction and pull it in the other direction. These systems are generally inexpensive because there are few moving parts. They work best on small sailboats and powerboats due to their ease of installation and low cost.

Worm gear linkages were developed in the mid 1800s to steer Gloucester fishing schooners out to the George's Banks fishing grounds. These sailing vessels were long-keeled good tracking boats that would maintain course as long as the sails were balanced and the rudder was kept in one place. The worm gear is perfect for this duty because it is a nonreversing system. This means that pressure on the rudder will not feedback and move the helm position. As a result, the crew could easily work the fishing lines. Today, a worm gear linkage works well on long-keeled cruising boats with attached rudders. However, it is not recommended for today's contemporary spade rudder designs.

Rack and pinion steering linkages are reversing gear-driven steerers, which allow the helmsman to feel the pressure on the rudder blade. They work best when the rudder stock is close to the wheel position. One drawback to a rack and pinion system is that it uses 30% of the gears 80% of the time. This leads to wear on the middle section of the rack or quadrant, which cannot be alleviated without causing the pinion to bind at the extreme end of the quadrant. This drawback, plus the fact that all spare parts must come from the original equipment manfacturer, can be a problem if you intend to sail in remote areas.

Hydraulic steering systems are the method of choice for most powerboats. The responsiveness of the sytem should be geared to the speed of the vessel. The faster the boat, the slower and less responsive the sytems should be. One factor that makes hydraulic steering systems attractive for powerboats is that they usually have twice as many turns hard over to hard over as a comparable wire system. Plus, with a hydraulic system, multiple helm stations for the tower, bridge, and cockpit can be easily added.

THE HELM POSITION

The helm position can be anywhere on the boat, but on sailboats most are near the stern to simplify the installation of the steering linkage. On power yachts, the helm position is either on the bridge, flybridge, tower, or in the cockpit. The primary requirements for the helm position are visibility and shelter. As long as the helmsman can see where the vessel is going, the helm position may be anywhere. However, helming the boat from a location near the bow can be disorienting to some people and can make visibility aft somewhat of a problem. Most helm positions are developed to suit the style of the boat. For instance, a sport fishing boat may have a steering position on the tower for spotting fish, and another in the cockpit for fighting the fish. Sailboats may have a steering position aft or in the mid cockpit, or the helm may be below deck in the cabin house.

Manufacturers of Steering Components and Systems

Helm Seats and Gas Spring Supports

Bomar
South West St.
P.O. Box W
Charlestown, NH 03603
Tel: (603) 826-5791
Fax: (603) 826-4125
Helm seats and bases

Spring Lift Corp.
113 Commerce Dr.
Monticello, AR 71655
Tel: (501) 367-2404
Fax: (501) 367-6839
Gas springs

D. B. Follansbee, Inc.
12 Alice Ct.
Pawcatuck, CT 06379
Tel: (203) 599-1849
Fax: (203) 599-2316
Gas springs and seats

Swivl-eze Marine Products
1504 South Beckley Rd.
Lancaster, TX 75146
Tel: (214) 223-5533
Fax: (214) 223-4795
Chair pedestals and posts, ski pylons

Zwaardvis bv
Postbus 115
5480 AC Schijndel
NETHERLANDS
Tel: (+31) 04104-92074
Gas springs and chairs

Steering Systems

Edson International
460 Industrial Park Rd.
New Bedford, MA 02745
Tel: (508) 995-9711
Fax: (800) 338-5021
Complete steering systems, service work, and new installation

Figure 1: An oversized wheel and pedestal as supplied by Edson International.

D. B. Follansbee, Inc.
12 Alice Ct.
Pawcatuck, CT 06379
Tel: (203) 599-1849
Fax: (203) 599-2316

Galley Maid Marine Products
P.O. Box 10417
Riviera Beach, FL 33419
Tel: (407) 848-8696
Fax: (407) 848-8872
Wheels and pedestals

Goiot S.A.
28 rue du Frere-Loius
44062 Nantes Cedex 02
FRANCE
Tel: (+33) 40 75 68 39
Fax: (+33) 40 75 43 56
Goiot systems

HyDrive America Corp.
432 E. 91st St.
New York, NY 10028
Tel: (212) 831-0317
Hydraulic steering

Hynautic
P.O. Box 908
Osprey, FL 34229
Tel: (813) 966-2151
Hydraulic systems

Jastran Engineering Ltd.
485 Mountain Hwy.
N.Vancouver V7J 2L3
CANADA
Tel: (604) 986-0714
Fax: (604) 986-0334
Electric and manual helm pumps; custom steering gear

Lunenburg Foundry & Engineering
P.O. Box 1240
Lunenburg, N.S. B0J 2C0
CANADA
Tel: (902) 634-8827
Fax: (902) 634-8886
Wire and worm steering systems

Teleflex Marine
Division of Teleflex, Inc.
640 North Lewis Rd.
Limerick, PA 19468
Tel: (800) TEC PLUS
    or (215) 495-7011
Steering systems

Vetus - Den Ouden, Inc.
P.O. Box 8712
Baltimore, MD 21240-0712
Tel: Orders only: (800) GO-VETUS
    or (410) 712-0740
Fax: (410) 712-0985
Hydraulic and power-assisted steering

Steering Hardware

Buck Algonquin Marine Hardware
370 N. Main Street
Smyrna, NJ 19977-1011
Tel: (302) 659-6900
Fax: (302) 659-6909
Rudder caps, tiller straps, and rudder collars

Davis Instruments
3465 Diablo Ave.
Hayward, CA 94545-2746
Tel: (415) 732-9229
Fax: (415) 732-9188
Wheels, rudder indicator, and outboard extension

Dwyer Aluminum Mast
21 Commerce Dr. N.
Branford, CT 06471
Tel: (203) 484-0419
Fax: (203) 484-2014
Pintles and gudgeon pins

Edson International
460 Industrial Park Rd.
New Bedford, MA 02745
Tel: (508) 995-9711
Fax: (800) 338-5021
Complete line of parts

Harken Yacht Equipment
1251 E. Wisconsin Ave.
Pewaukee, WI 53072
Tel: (414) 691-3320
Fax: (414) 691-3008
Rudder bearings and blocks

Loos & Co., Inc.
One Cable Rd.
Pomfret, CT 06258
Tel: (203) 928-7981
Fax: (203) 928-6167
Cable and wire

Macwhyte Wire Rope
2606 14th Ave.
Kenosha, WI 53141
Tel: (414) 654-5381
Fax: (414) 654-5384
Cable and wire

New Found Metals
240 Airport Rd.
Pt. Townsend, WA 98368
Tel: (206) 385-3315
Fax: (206) 385-6097
Bronze rudder fittings

Nicro Marine Corp.
2065 W. 140th Ave.
San Leandro, CA 94577
Tel: (415) 357-8332

Omnifac Corp.
1700 E. Whipp Rd.
Dayton, OH 45440
Tel: (513) 434-8400
Rudder indicator

Sanlo
P.O. Box 242
Michigan City, IN 46360
Tel: (219) 879-0241
Cable and wire

Schaefer Marine
12 Industrial Pk.
New Bedford, MA 02745
Tel: (508) 995-9511
Fax: (508) 995-4882
*Pintles and gudgeons, blocks,
rudder heads, and sheaves*

Spartan Marine
Robinhood Marine Center
Robinhood, ME 04530
Tel: (207) 371-2542
Fax: (207) 371-2024
Cast bronze tiller heads

Van der Staay
Veersedijk 83
P.O. Box 151
3340 AD H.I Ambacht
HOLLAND
Tel: (+31) 1858 1 66 11
Steering wheels

W.H. Autopilots
655 N.E. Northlake Pl.
Seattle, WA 98105
Tel: (206) 633-1830
Quadrants

Wilcox-Crittenden
A Gulf & Western Mfg. Co.
Middletown, CT 06457
Tel: (203) 632-2600
Wheels and blocks

Tillers, Extensions, and Hiking Sticks

Davis Instruments
3465 Diablo Ave.
Hayward, CA 94545-2746
Tel: (415) 732-9229
Fax: (415) 732-9188
Outboard motor extension

H & L Marine Woodwork
2965 E. Harcourt
Rancho Dominguez, CA 90221
Tel: (213) 636-1718
Pre-made laminated tillers

Offshore Instruments Ltd.
41 Birmingham Rd.
Cowes, Isle of Wight PO31
7BH
ENGLAND
Tel: (+44) 983 295555
Fax: (+44) 983 295542
*Spinlock hiking sticks and
tiller extensions*

**Simpson Lawrence USA.,
Inc.**
3004 29th Ave. E.
Bradenton, FL 34208
Tel: (813) 746-7161
Fax: (813) 746-7166
Tiller extensions

Imtra
30 Sam Barnet Blvd.
New Bedford, MA 02745
Tel: (508) 994-4919
*Spinlock tiller extensions and
hiking sticks*

Nicro Marine Corp.
2065 W. 140th Ave.
San Leandro, CA 94577
Tel: (415) 357-8332
Tiller extensions

**Welborn Marine &
Industrial Products**
805 Court St.
Clearwater, FL 34616
Tel: (813) 443-7661
Fax: (813) 447-0867
Ronstan tiller extensions

Figure 2: This pedestal and
cockpit table were supplied by
Edson International.

Stoves and Grills

Purchasing a new stove requires many decisions. What fuel will you use? How many burners do you need? Do you need an oven or a grill? Should it be gimballed or fixed?

FUEL

The most common and most explosive fuel for stoves is LPG or liquified propane gas. It may be comprised of propane, butanes, or butylenes. As LPG gas is odorless, colorless, non-toxic, and heavier than air, it can be dangerous. Should you have a leak in the system, the gas will collect in the bottom of the boat. The moment you create a spark, the gas/air mixture could explode, and that will make your ears ring! On the plus side, the heat value of LPG is much higher than for any other fuel, which is one of the reasons people prefer it.

Many precautions have been developed to detect gas leaks. Commercial producers of LPG add an odorant to enable you to detect it, and companies such as Xintex make detection systems that set off an alarm if there is a leak. Several organizations recommend standards for installing and using LPG to which the marine industry adheres. They are: the U.S. Coast Guard, the National Fire Protection Association (NFPA), and the American Boat and Yacht Council (ABYC). Their addresses can be found in the associations and organizations section of this book.

Compressed natural gas or CNG does not have the heat value of LPG but it is much safer. It is colorless and odorless, and it is lighter than air, so it will vent itself out of a boat if allowed to do so. Another factor in its favor is that it takes a much larger concentration of gas in the air to create an explosion. The biggest drawback of CNG is its limited availability around the world, although this situation is steadily improving.

Kerosene (paraffin) is a very safe fuel, but its heat value is quite low. Most kerosene stoves work by vaporizing the liquid, and lighting them can be quite tricky. If you decide this is the stove for you, be sure to get a self-priming model.

Diesel oil can be used as a stove fuel, but it does have a few drawbacks. If you don't have a good draft through the stove, it may burn with a smoky flame, which gives your food an interesting flavor. Also, I have been told that a diesel stove should have a blower, or a back draft can fill the cabin with smoke. Another point against diesel stoves is that the few that are available are not gimballed because of the vent pipe that needs to go through the cabin top.

Electric stoves are an option, too, but short of taking along your own generating plant, they are not viable for the small boat sailor who wants to spend some time at sea.

If your boat has a generator, a small burner uses about 750 watts of power, so if you want a four-burner electric stove, you'll have to generate at least 3 kw. The cheapest and most efficient electric stove to have aboard is the microwave. It uses about 750 watts on full power and can be run with an inverter if desired.

The only other types of fuel that might be considered for a boat stove would be wood or coal. Neither are practical if you intend to sail in the tropics. A wood or coal stove takes a while to get hot and needs to be kept stoked. Plus hot coals can fall out of the stove, causing a fire hazard. Even worse, the stove in a tightly closed boat could use up all the oxygen, leaving none for the crew.

OTHER STOVE FEATURES

Having decided upon the fuel for the stove, the next step is to determine a variety of other features, such as how many burners, whether to have an oven or broiler, and whether the stove will be gimballed. Most of these decisions can easily be made by the cook, unless you want a diesel- or wood-burning stove. In this case, a flue is required and the stove will be almost impossible to gimball.

No matter what type of stove you select, it should have certain safety features. They are:

1. A safety bar should be fitted in front of the stove to prevent anybody from falling onto the stove.

2. Gas stoves should have a turn-off valve at the cylinder and another turn-off valve at the stove. The gas cylinders should be installed in their own locker, which is vented over the side. There should be no other gear in the gas cylinder locker.

3. A gas stove should be fitted with leak-detecting equipment. The leak detector controls should be well away from the stove. Ideally, they should be located so that the cook has to go past them to get to the stove.

4. The stove should be fitted with a guard rail about 2 inches high all around it. Stoves with more than two burners should also have clamps to secure pots on them.

5. All burner controls should be on the front of the stove so that the cook does not have to reach over the unit to turn anything off.

6. Gimballed stoves should be securely fastened in place. There should be a locking mechanism so that when the stove is not gimballed, it can be secured. A gimballed stove should also be able to rotate 180 degrees without falling out of its gimbals.

7. Gimballed stoves should be able to swing through an arc of at least 70 degrees, plus the stove should have some form of damping mechanism to slow down the swing.

8. The tanks on alcohol stoves should be removable to minimize the risk of fire when the stove is being refueled.

9. The area around the stove should be ventilated.

10. The surfaces of furniture near the stove should be protected from heat. The ABYC recommends that surfaces near the stove should not be raised more than 90 degrees above the temperature of the galley.

Manufacturers of Stoves and Gas Detectors

Stoves

Balmar Products, Inc.
1537 N.W. Ballard Way
Seattle, WA 98107
Tel: (206) 789-4970
Fax: (206) 784-0878
Stoves and cabin heaters

The Dickinson Mfg. Co. Ltd.
407-204 Caver St.
Coquitlam, British Columbia
V3K 5B1
CANADA
Tel: (604) 525-6444
Fax: (604) 525-6417
Stoves and cabin heaters

Dickinson USA, Inc.
11324 Mukilteo Speedway
Mukilteo, WA 98275
Tel: (206) 347-4028
Fax: (206) 347-8502
Stoves and cabin heaters

ERC
(Formerly the stove division of GSI Gas Sytems, Inc.)
2970 E. Maria St.
Rancho Dominguez, CA 90221
Tel: (800) 323-8924
  or (310) 603-2970
Fax: (310) 603-0165
Natural gas stoves

Fab-All Marine Manufacturing. Ltd.
#2 3005 Murray St.
Port Moody, British Columbia
V3H 1X3
CANADA
Tel: (604) 461-8522
Fax: (604) 461-2518
Stoves, cabin heaters, and barbeques

Force 10 Marine
23080 Hamilton Rd.
Richmond, British Columbia
V6V 1C9
CANADA
Tel: (604) 522-0233
Fax: (604) 522-9608
Barbeques and stoves

IM/Kenyon Galley Products
P.O. Box 308
New Whitfield St.
Guilford, CT 06437-0388
Tel: (203) 453-4374
Fax: (203) 453-6109
Stoves, inverters, and other galley equipment

Magma Products, Inc.
1201 E. Hill St.
Long Beach, CA 90806
Tel: (800) 866-2462
  or (310) 427-7050
Fax: (310) 424-9091
Yacht barbeques

Origo
1121 Lewis Ave.
Sarasota, FL 34237
Tel: (813) 365-3660
Fax: (813) 955-2596
Alcohol heaters and stoves

Figure 1: The Seacook Offshore cooking stove from Sterling Engineeering.

Sterling Engineering Corp.
P.O. Box 358
Barre, VT 05641
Tel: (802) 476-4149
Seacook Offshore cooking stove

Shipmate Stove Division
Richmond Ring Co.
Souderton, PA 18964
Tel: (215) 855-2609
Stoves and ranges

Tasco Marine
490 Somerset Ave.
N. Dighton, MA 02764
Tel: (508) 823-0786
Stoves and grills

Gas Detectors and Monitors

Brisson Development
13845 Nine Mile Rd.
Warren, MI 48089
Tel: (313) 778-3038
Fax: (313)778-0780
CO2 and fume detectors

Figure 2: This specially designed tank is from Margas Manufacturing in California.

Figure 3: Every gas system should have a control panel like this one from Margas Manufacturing.

Margas Mfg.
399 Harbor Dr.
Sausalito, CA 94965
Tel: (415) 332-8302
Fax: (415) 332-3780
Control panels and regulators

Xintex
A Fireboy Company
P.O. Box 152
Grand Rapids, MI 49501-0152
Tel: (616) 235-2360
Fax: (616) 454-8256
Gas detectors

Gas System Components

GSI Gas Systems, Inc.
5361 Production Dr.
Huntington Beach, CA 92649
Tel: (714) 891-2411
Fax: (714) 895-4079
CNG fuel manufacturers

Margas Mfg.
399 Harbor Dr.
Sausalito, CA 94965
Tel: (415) 332-8302
Fax: (415) 332-3780
Tanks, regulators, and control panels

Simpson-Lawrence USA., Inc.
3004 29th Ave. E.
Bradenton, FL 34208
Tel: (813) 746-7161
Fax: (813) 746-7166
Taylor's marine stoves

Surveyors

I would like to thank certified marine surveyor Paul Coble for assistance in the preparation of this section.

Buying a used boat can get you out sailing for a lot less money than buying a brand new one. But when you buy a used boat, how do you know what you are getting? Unlike automobiles, used boats are usually bought from the previous owner, not from a used boat salesman's yard. This means that you have no guarantee that everything is in good condition.

To get information about the condition of a boat, you can make use of an expert, a surveyor. A good surveyor will report on the condition of every item on board. Every used boat should be surveyed before the closing! The usual procedure is for the seller and buyer to reach an agreement "subject to survey," and the buyer then hires a surveyor. The term "subject to survey" is accepted as meaning that should any defect be uncovered by the survey, the terms of the sales agreement will be renegotiated or rejected. In Paul Coble's experience, there is usually a reduction in price that more than pays for the repairs, and often covers the surveyor's fee as well.

Until now, I have never seen a list of surveyors. When one of my clients needed a surveyor, I did what everybody else did and called people I knew. The list in this book is culled from the directories of the two main surveyor organizations. They are the National Association of Marine Surveyors (NAMS) and the Society of Accredited Marine Surveyors (SAMS). Members of either association must complete a written and/or an oral exam. I have listed only certified surveyors in the case of NAMS members and accredited surveyors from the SAMS membership rosters.

When looking for a surveyor, first check through the list to find one in the state where the boat is. Then ask people about that surveyor. Check the surveyor out carefully or, as Paul puts it, survey the surveyor. Note that choosing a surveyor from a list provided by the broker selling the boat might not always be desirable. The broker's recommendation may be influenced by his desire to make the sale. When checking out the surveyor, talk to other boat owners, insurance companies, and local boatyards.

If the survey of the surveyor is good, the next step is to call the surveyor. Ask about the cost of getting your boat surveyed. Ask for references from previous clients, or, if you can talk to previous clients, ask if you can have a report from a previous survey that the surveyor has done. Reading the report should tell you how detailed your survey is likely to be. For instance, if the report says "the water heater is ok," I would want to know what is meant by ok. Is the water heater operational? Was it in the boat or on the dock? If it is an electric heater, what is its wattage? Does the exterior show signs of rust or does it have dents that might lead to leakage later? Is it fixed properly in place with strong retaining straps or does it just sit on chocks? Does the piping show signs of corrosion or has it been kept bright and shiny? In my opinion, unless I trusted the surveyor's opinion totally, the report should clearly specify the condition of every accessible item of gear on the boat.

Note that not every piece of gear can be inspected properly without ripping the boat apart. For instance, a surveyor who looks at the engine cannot tell the condition of the valves or pistons. All the surveyor can do is check the engine exterior for signs of oil leakage, exhaust soot, and general condition. If you have any doubt about the condition of the engine, you should hire a specialist engine surveyor to check it over. This surveyor should have a good feel for any problems that engines from that particular manufacturer have had and can look for signs of those problems. Sometimes engines in the same line of boats have similar problems. For instance, on one line of boats, the exhausts were located in such a way that back pressure built up in the engine and eventually blew seals. A good engine surveyor will be familiar with such problems, and may be able to recommend solutions.

A surveyor works for you, is paid by you, and reports to you. The survey report serves not only as an excellent negotiating tool, but also as a document to obtain financing, to get insurance, and as the start of a prioritized work list. A good surveyor will save you money in the long run, so it is important not to select one on price alone. A poor report benefits nobody.

To survey a moderately sized boat properly can take up to ten hours; for a good job on a large boat up to three days may be needed. That is if the surveyor is allowed to work undisturbed. Interruptions add to the time taken and increase the cost. Then the surveyor has to write a report. This can add another eight to twelve hours. Paul Coble prefers a narrative style report which describes everything he has observed, the defects that exist, the priority of the repairs and the best procedures to carry them out. Other surveyors list each item of gear and give its condition, then specify the priority of repairs and repair procedures. The report format does not matter as long as it is thorough and accurate. The cost of a full survey can range from 3/4 to 1.5% of the cost of the boat.

Most surveyors make use of modern instruments and do a good job. If you are in doubt as to what something in the report means, ask. A good surveyor will explain what he has seen and why his report says what it does.

Addresses of Marine Surveyors

Note: Marine surveyors are listed by state to make it easier to find one near you.

Alaska

Edwin E. Lindbeck
4007 Borland Dr.
Anchorage, AK 99517
Tel: (907) 272-7724

Rocky Point Enterprises, Inc.
Box 1047
Homer, AK 99603
Tel: (907) 235-8967
Fax: (907) 235-2108

Alabama

Port City Marine Services
P.O. Box 190321
Mobile, AL 36619
Tel: (205) 443-8413
Yachts, cargo, and small craft

John H. Van Aken Company, Inc.
P.O. Box 1738
Daphne, AL 36526
Tel: (205) 626-9309
Fax: (205) 626-9050

Capt. J. Paul Wright & Associates
P.O. Box 662
Bayou La Batre, AL 36509
Tel: (205)873-4382

Arkansas

Angus Rankin
P.O. Box 264
Maynard, AR 72444
Tel: (501) 892-8300
Yachts and small craft

British Columbia

Aegis Marine Surveyors Ltd.
745 Clark Dr.
Vancouver, British Columbia
V5L 3J3
CANADA
Tel: (604) 251-2210
Fax: (604) 254-0515

Total Boat Marine Surveyors, Ltd.
P.O. Box 2185
Sidney, British Columbia V8L 3S8
CANADA
Tel: (604) 656-5826
Fax: (604) 656-6752

F. I. Hopkinson Marine Surveyors, Ltd.
1256 West Pender St.
Suite 201
Vancouver, British Columbia
V6E 2S8
CANADA
Tel: (604) 688-9233
Fax: (604) 687-7127

Meadows Marine Surveyors, Ltd.
302-1095 McKenzie Ave.
Victoria, British Columbia
V8P 2L5
CANADA
Tel: (604) 727-2161
Fax: (604) 727-2869

Sechelt Marine Surveys Ltd
P.O. Box 3
Sechelt, British Columbia
V0N-3A0
CANADA
Tel: (604) 885-3643

Chris Small Marine Surveyors Ltd.
15219 Royal Ave.
White Rock, British Columbia
V4B 1M4
CANADA
Tel: (604) 531-8127

Barry D. Smith & Company Ltd.
159 Riverside Dr.
North Vancouver, British Columbia V7H 1T6
CANADA
Tel: (604) 924-1123
Fax: (604) 929-0273

California

Advance Marine Surveyors
4009 Pacific Coast Hwy.
Torrance, CA 90505
Tel: (213) 541-4263

Anderson International Marine Surveyor
433 North H St.
Suite G
Lompoc, CA 93436
Tel: (805) 737-3770
Fax: (805) 737-3773
Yachts, fishing vessels, and small craft

Ray A. Arceneaux
3467 Verano Way
Cameron Park, CA 95682
Tel: (916) 676-0203
Fax: (916) 676-0203

American Marine Surveyors, Inc.
3639 E. Harbor Blvd.
Suite 203-B
Ventura, CA 93001
Tel: (805) 644-9330
Fax: (805) 644-9385

Clark Barthol Marine Surveyors
27 Buccaneer St.
Marina Del Rey, CA 90292
Tel: (213) 823-3350

Thomas Bell & Associates
1323 Berkley St.
Santa Monica, CA 90404
Tel: (310) 393-4321
  or (310) 828-5329
Yachts, cargo, and small craft

John Bradshaw Marine Surveyor
1621 W. 25th St.
Suite 313
San Pedro, CA 90732
Tel: (310) 547-5400
Fax: (310) 547-5641

Brandmeyer International
2447 Sparta Dr.
Rancho Palo Verdes, CA 90274-6538
Tel: (310) 519-1979
Fax: (310) 519-9551

Harry G. Braun
2814 Van Buren St.
Alameda, CA 94501
Tel: (510) 522-1561
Fax: (510) 522-1561

H. F. Brennan & Associates
P. O. Box 1182
Oakley, CA 94561
Tel: (510) 757-1600

Peter K. Britton
16678 Mount Baxter Circle
Fountain Valley, CA 92708
Tel: (714) 531-2444

William L. Butler, III
P.O. Box 11914
Marina del Rey, CA 90295
Tel: (310) 396-1791
Yachts, fishing vessels, and small craft

Campbell's Marine Survey
340 Countryside Dr.
Santa Rosa, CA 95401
Tel: (800) 640-4344
Fax: (707) 542-8812
Yachts and small craft

Richard Christopher
14705 Watsonville Rd.
Morgan Hill, CA 95037
Tel: (408) 778-5143
Yachts and small craft

Stu Clark Marine Surveyors
5326 Dupont Dr.
Santa Rosa, CA 95409
Tel: (707) 538-1217
Yachts and small craft

Cullen Maritime Services, Inc.
465 Forty Sixth St.
Richmond, CA 94805
Tel: (510) 232-6700
Fax: (510) 632-6766

Warren R. Cushman, CMS
518 Acadia Dr.
Petaluma, CA 94954
Tel: (707) 765-9558

DONRU Marine Surveyors
32 Cannery Row
Monterey, CA 93940
Tel: (408) 372-8604
Fax: (408) 373-2294

William R. Falkenberg
803 N. Figueroa St.
Wilmington, CA 90744-2307
Tel: (310) 834-3413

Captain Franke Marine Surveyors
P. O. Box 1230
Del Mar, CA 92014
Tel: (619) 259-6970

Peter H. Finie
P.O. Box 1686
Camarillo, CA 93011
Tel: (805) 484-8202

Lorne Gould Marine Surveying
351 Embarcadero
Oakland, CA 94606
Tel: (510) 465-2527
Fax: (510) 465-7014

Ernest L. Grosskopf, CMS
Hull & Cargo Surveyors, Inc.
1891 N. Gaffey St.
Suite 244
San Pedro, CA 90731
Tel: (310) 548-8552
Fax: (310) 831-3087

**Pierre Helia Marine
Surveyors**
2554 Lincoln Blvd.
Suite 365
Marina del Rey, CA 90291
Tel: (310) 821-4350
Fax: (310) 821-4350
Yachts and small craft

**Marvin Henderson Marine
Surveyors, Inc**
2727 Shelter Island Dr.
Suite C
San Diego, CA 92106
Tel: (619) 224-3164

Kelly & Associates
P.O. Box 1031
Napa, CA 94581
Tel: (707) 641-1061

James C. Jessie
351 Embarcadero
Oakland, CA 94606
Tel: (510) 465-2527
Fax: (510) 465-7014

**Christopher A. Kiefer,
Marine Surveyors, Inc**
1310 Rosecrans St.
Suite K
San Diego, CA 92106
Tel: (619) 224-2944
  or (619) 224-0167

Milton Lane
Tower Bridge Marine
P.O. Box 703
West Sacramento, CA 95691
Tel: (916) 372-0833
Yachts and small craft

**Lester & Lester Marine
Survey, Inc.**
1310 Rosecrans St.
Suite K
San Diego, CA 92106
Tel: (619) 224-2944
Fax: (619) 224-0167
*Yachts, fishing vessels, large
ships, and small craft*

J. Mackinnon, Inc.
P.O. Box 335
San Lorenzo, CA 94580-0335
Tel: (510) 276-4351
Yachts and small craft

M & D Offshore
1310 Rosecrans St.
Suite K
San Diego, CA 92106
Tel: (619) 224-2944
Fax: (619) 224-0167
*Yachts, fishing vessels, and
small craft*

Malin Marine Surveyors
6461 Harmony Cir.
Huntington Beach, CA 92674
Tel: (714) 897-6769
*Yachts, fishing vessels and
small craft*

**Marine Appraisal Survey
Service**
4888 Sherman Church Ave.,
S.W.
Canton, OH 44706-3966
Tel: (216) 484-0144
Yachts and small craft

**Rex Michel Marine
Surveyors**
3007 Washington Blvd.
Suite 210
Marina del Rey, CA 90292
Tel: (310) 393-4493
Fax: (310) 393-3401

**Michel & Christen Marine
Surveyors**
5732 E. Second St.
Long Beach, CA 90803
Tel: (310) 433-7260
Fax: (310) 439-8789
*Yachts, fishing vessels, cargo,
and small craft*

K.D. Moore Associates
582 Market St.
Suite 1604
San Francisco, CA 94104
Tel: (415) 433-0691
Fax: (415) 788-4013

Moore Marine Services
520 Washington Blvd.
Suite 345
Marina del Rey, CA 90292
Tel: (310) 823-1184
Fax: (310) 827-4756
Nicholas W. Moore

**John J. Norrie &
Associates, Inc.**
3335 Fithian Ave.
Los Angeles, CA 90032
Tel: (213) 255-8006
Fax: (213) 255-0785

**Ocean Marine Consultants,
Inc.**
664 Santana Rd.
Novato, CA 94945
Tel: (415) 892-7922
Fax: (415) 892-4389

Arturo Oliva
2506 20th St.
Santa Monica, CA 90405
Tel: (310) 823-4581

Pacific Marine Surveyors
P.O. Box 3111
Long Beach, CA 90803
Tel: (310) 434-5711

Don Parish
4140 Oceanside Blvd.,
#159-320
Oceanside, CA 92056
Tel: (619) 721-9410

James Pelot
17271 Julip Ln.
Huntington Beach, CA 92647
Tel: (714) 847-0672
Fax: (813) 797-1309

Stuart E. Riddell, CMS
53 Waldo Point, B Dock
Sausalito, CA 94965-1356
Tel: (415) 332-9036
Fax: (415) 332-8122

**Skip Riley Maritime
Surveyors**
3203 S. Victoria Ave.
Suite B
Oxnard, CA 93035
Tel: (805) 984-8889
Fax: (805) 984-4418
Yachts and small craft

Rodgers & Associates
2695 E. Cliff Dr. -Yacht
Harbor
Santa Cruz, CA 95062
Tel: (408) 475-4468
Fax: (408) 476-4306

Rosenberger & Co.
400 S. Gramercy Pl.
Suite 321
Los Angeles, CA 90020
Tel: (213) 738-5327

Seacraft Marine Surveyors
3600 S. Harbor Blvd.
Suite 229
Oxnard, Ca 93035
Yachts and small craft

**Doug Shotton Marine
Surveyor**
P.O. Box 121
El Cerrito, CA 94530
Tel: (510) 235-6679

A. N. Tillet & Associates
663 Switzer St.
San Diego, CA 92101
Tel: (619) 235-0766

Todd & Associates, Inc.
2390 Shelter Island Dr.
Suite 22
San Diego, CA 92106
Tel: (619) 226-1895
Fax: (619) 223-8942

**Robert A.Viel Marine
Surveyor**
P.O. Box 113
Walnut Grove, CA 95690
Tel: (916) 776-1094

R.J. Whitfield & Associates
7011 Bridgeport Cir.
Stockton, CA 95207
Tel: (209) 956-8488
Fax: (209) 956-8490

Stan Wild & Associates
1912 Stanford St.
Alameda, CA 94501
Tel: (510) 521-8527
Fax: (510) 521-8196

**Frank K. Wyatt, Marine
Surveyor, Inc.**
1067 Shafter St.
San Diego, CA 92106
Tel: (619) 223-8167

Connecticut

W. T. Bedient
48 Donald Rd.
Guilford, CT 06437
Tel: (203) 457-0457

James Curry
62 Kelseytown Rd.
Clinton, CT 06413
Tel: (203) 669-3119

The Curtis Co.
P.O. Box 2035
Salem, CT 06415
Tel: (203) 859-6466

Greaves Yacht Service Ltd.
30 Toby Hill Rd.
Westbrook, CT 06498
Tel: (203) 399-6966
Yachts and small craft

Clifford A. Gustafson
1080 Portland-Cobalt Rd.
Portland, CT 06480
Tel: (203) 342-2868

Dexter A. Holaday & Co.
P.O. Box 9201
Noank, CT 06340
Tel: (203) 536-8573

Roger F. Hughes
88 Eastwood Rd.
Groton, CT 06340
Tel: (203) 446-9473

Robert Keaney, Jr.
7 Candlewood Heights
New Milford, CT 06776
Tel: (203) 354-1372

**Denis M. Leahy &
Co./Williams & Ross, Inc.**
P. O. Box 8271
New Fairfield, CT 06812
Tel: (203) 746-2050

**New England Marine
Surveyors**
19 Commerce St.
P.O. Box 533
Clinton, CT 06413
Tel: (203) 669-4018
Fax: (203) 669-7742

**Professional Marine
Surveys**
125 Sraagr St.
Waterbury, CT 06708
Tel: (800) 982-6466

**Doran M. Podoloff Marine
Surveyor Inc.**
161 Peddlers Dr.
Branford, CT 06405
Tel: (203) 481-4404
Fax: (203) 488-6191

**Robotham Marine
Surveyors & Consultants**
P.O. Box 2143
Westport, CT 06880
Tel: (203) 227-9640
Fax: (203) 255-4918

William Stadel
1088 Shippan Ave.
Stamford, CT 06902
Tel: (203) 324-2610
Yachts and small craft

George Stafford
244 Bear Rock Rd.
Durham, CT 06422
Tel: (203) 297-6459

Truslow Marine Surveying
P.O. Box 9185
Forestville, CT 06011-9815
Tel: (203) 583-6503
Yachts and small craft

**Welles Worthen Marine
Surveyors, Inc.**
102 Milford Point Rd.
Milford, CT 06460
Tel: (203) 874-2445
Fax: (203) 874-8002

Delaware

**Technical Marine Ship
Services Ltd, Inc.**
501 Silverside Rd.
Wilmington, DE 19809
Tel: (302) 791-0670
Fax: (302) 791-0673

Ron Smith
132 Rockrose Dr.
Newark, DE 19711
Tel: (302) 737-0752

Florida

AA Boat & Yacht Surveyors
4906 Clinton Blvd.
West Palm Beach, FL
33463-2269
Tel: (407) 731-2966
Yachts and small craft

Dewey Acker
551 61st St. Gulf
Marathon, FL 33050
Tel: (305) 743-2397
Yachts and small craft

**Charles Akers Marine
Surveyors**
2816 Ahern Dr.
Orlando, FL 32817
Tel: (407) 658-0622

Allen's Boat Surveying
638 North U.S. Hwy. 1
Suite 207
Tequesta, FL 33469
Tel: (407) 746-2317
Yachts and small craft

**Alp's Marine Surveying,
Inc.**
281 N.W. 42nd Ave.
Coconut Creek, FL 33066
Tel: (305) 973-1135
Yachts and small craft

Dave Alter & Associates
6500 S.W. 129th Terr.
Miami, FL 33156
Tel: (305) 667-0326
Yachts and small craft

**American Yacht Services,
Inc.**
P.O. Box 561047
Miami, FL 33256-1047
Tel: (305) 274-4133
Fax: (305) 598-4992
Yachts and small craft

Andrews Marine Surveying
P.O. Box 316
Ellenton, FL 34222-0316
Tel: (813) 723-2913
Fax: (813) 723-1861

Paul R. Anstey, Inc.
1008 S.E. 5th Court
Ft. Lauderdale, FL 33301
Tel: (305) 763-8276

B & S Marine
1002 N.E. 105th St.
Miami Shores, FL 33138
Tel: (305) 891-0445
Yachts and small craft

Ballard & Associates, Inc.
18845 S.W. 93rd Ave.
Miami, FL 33157
Tel: (305) 252-8008
Fax: (305) 255-4681

Roger Bass & Associates, Inc.
10536 Inverness Dr.
Jacksonville, Fl 32257
Tel: (904) 262-4015
Yachts and small craft

Raymond Bernard
P.O. Box 353586
Palm Coast, FL 32135-3586
Tel: (904) 445-1409
Yachts and small craft

Gene Briggs and Associates, Inc.
505 Decatur Ave.
Pensacola, FL 32507
Tel: (904) 456-4986
Yachts and small craft

Michael M. Bullock
820 S.E. 11th Court
Fort Lauderdale, FL 33316
Tel: (305) 524-5951

Canaveral Marine Consultants
677 George King Blvd.
Suite 112
Cape Canaveral, FL 32920
Tel: (407) 783-1771
Fax: (407) 783-1772

C & J Marine Surveyors, Inc.
4163 Frances Dr.
Delray Beach, FL 33445
Tel: (407) 495-4920
Fax: (407) 495-8701
Yachts and small craft

Cardic Marine Services, Inc.
567 Imperial Dr.
Largo, FL 34641
Tel: (813) 581-3113
Fax: (813) 586-3951

Edward Cook
422 Big Pine Rd.
Key Largo, FL 33037
Yachts and small craft

Continental Marine Consultants, Inc
700 North U.S. Hwy. #1
North Palm Beach, FL 33408
Tel: (305) 844-6111

Captain Tom Corley & Son
6308 N. Lagoon Dr.
Panama City, FL 32408
Tel: (904) 784-9939
Yachts and small craft

CTS And Associates
11320 S.W. 108th Ct.
Miami, FL 33176
Tel: (305) 238-0202

D & G Marine, Inc.
58 Ocean Blvd.
Naples, FL 33942
Tel: (813) 643-0028

Edward H. Davis
2943 Grouper Dr., Box 2342
Marathon Shores, FL 33052
Tel: (305) 743-5330

Despres & Associates
332 Pine St.
West Palm Beach, FL 33407
Tel: (800) 755-2628
  or   (407) 820-9290
Yachts and small craft

Allister A. Dredge
170 N.W. 147th St.
Miami, FL 33168
Tel: (305) 687-7389

Larry Dukehart
P.O. Box 1172
Islamorada, FL 33036-1172
Tel: (305) 664-9452
Yachts and small craft

Richard Everett, III
P.O. Box 13512
Pensacola, FL 32591
Tel: (904) 435-9026
Yachts and small craft

Fortson Marine Surveyors, Inc.
3386 Lakeshore Blvd.
Jacksonville, FL 32210
Tel: (904) 389-0904

Jerry Fuller Marine Survey Co.
RR 1, Box 511-F
Big Pine Key, FL 33043-9998
Tel: (305) 872-2179

Garlington Marine Services
1083 S.E. St. Lucie Blvd.
Stuart, FL 34996
Tel: (407) 283-5102
Yachts and small craft

Guin Marine Service, Inc.
2908 Riverview Dr.
Melbourne, FL 32901-7348
Tel: (407) 984-7616

**Gulfstream Marine
Surveyors & Consultants**
1456 Keene Rd. South
Clearwater, FL 34616
Tel: (813) 442-5210
Fax: (813) 442-0428

**Captain E. Bay Hansen,
Inc.**
1302 N. 19th St.
Suite 101
Tampa, FL 33605
Tel: (813) 248-6897
Fax: (813) 247-5373

Charles Harden
P.O. Box 13256
Tampa, FL 33681
Tel: (813) 254-4273
Fax: (813) 251-5438
*Yachts, fishing vessels, and
small craft*

**Independent Marine
Surveyors**
P.O. Box 6203
Ft. Myers Beach, FL 33931
Tel: (813) 466-4544

Intramarine, Inc.
P. O. Box 53043
Jacksonville, FL 32201
Tel: (904) 353-0828

JGB Corp.
8716 54th Ave. West
Bradenton, FL 34210
Tel: (813) 794-6303

**Key West Marine Services,
Inc.**
P. O. Box 4854
Key West, FL 33040
Tel: (305) 872-9073

Arthur T. Kyle
6428 Heather Way
West Palm Beach, FL 33406
Tel: (407) 964-6189
Yachts and small craft

**Veronica M. Lawson &
Associates**
P.O. Box 1201
Naples, FL 33939
Tel: (813) 434-6960

Stanley F. Lowe
6531 Peacock Rd.
Sarasota, FL 34242
Tel: (813) 349-2050

Marine Evaluation Service
1323 S.E. 17th St.
Suite 119
Ft. Lauderdale, FL 33316
Tel: (305) 763-9562

The Marine Surveyors, Inc.
P.O. Box 100145
Ft. Lauderdale, FL 33310
Tel: (800) 522-5119
  or (305) 566-6806
Yachts and small craft

McCrory & Associates
5224 S. W. 89th Ave.
Miami, FL 33165
Tel: (305) 274-2242
Fax: (305) 371-7301

**Merolla Marine Surveyor,
Inc.**
4761 N.E. 29th Ave.
Ft. Lauderdale, FL 33308
Tel: (305) 772-8090
Fax: (305) 772-7976
Yachts and small craft

**Marty Merolla Marine
Surveyor, Inc.**
4300 S. E. St. Lucie Blvd.-128
Stuart, FL 34997
Tel: (407) 286-4880
Fax: (407) 221-9408
Yachts and small craft

Alexander Milligan
170 N.W. 139th St.
P.O. Box 680-126 Gratigny
Station
Miami, FL 33168-0126
Tel: (305) 681-4368
Fax: (305) 681-7193

McCulley Marine Services
101 Sea Way Dr.
Suite A
Ft. Pierce, FL 34950
Tel: (407) 489-6069
Fax: (407) 595-0395
Yachts and small craft

**Nautical Services
Technologies**
424 Production Blvd., #70
Naples, FL 33940
Tel: (813) 434-7445
Fax: (813) 947-5175
Yachts and small craft

**North Florida Marine
Services**
3360 Lakeshore Blvd.
Jacksonville, FL 32210
Tel: (904) 384-4356
Fax: (904) 388-8321
Yachts and small craft

Mark Perkins
901 Fleming St.
Key West, FL 33040
Tel: (305) 294-7635
Yachts and small craft

Porpoise Marine Services, Inc.
3626 Corsair Ct.
Newport Richey, FL 34652
Tel: (813) 843-0989
Yachts and small craft

Professional Marine Surveys, Inc.
7491-C5 North Federal Hwy.
Suite 232
Boca Raton, FL 33486
Tel: (800) 329-1053
  or (407) 272-1053

Rhodes Marine Surveyors
3650 N. Federal Hwy.
Suite 212 Lighthouse Point,
FL 33064
Tel: (305) 946-6779
Fax: (305) 783-0057
Yachts, large vessels, and small craft

James B. Robbins
7701 Pine Lake Dr.
Merrit Island, FL 32953
Tel: (407) 459-1196
Fax: (407) 459-1238
Yachts and small craft

Harold W. Roberts
10 Edgemont Dr.
Pensacola, FL 32506
Tel: (904) 455-1981

Ed Rowe and Associates
1821 S.W. 22nd Ave.
Ft. Lauderdale, FL 33312
Tel: (305) 792-6062
Yachts and small craft

Norman L. Schreiber II
P.O. Box 350247
Ft. Lauderdale, FL 33335
Tel: (305) 537-1423
Fax: (305) 761-9087

Russell M. Thomas
737 Bywood N.E.
Palm Bay, FL 32905
Tel: (407) 768-0634

Sea-Masters Ltd.
502 N. Orlando Ave.
Suite 313-01
Winter Park, FL 32789
Tel: (405) 728-800
Fax: (405) 722-2628
Yachts and small craft

R.E. Silvera & Associates
1904 S.W. 86th Ave.
N. Lauderdale, FL 33068
Tel: (305) 720-8660
Fax: (305) 720-8964
Yachts and small craft

Gerald Slakoff & Associates
1524 S. Andrews Ave.
Ft. Lauderdale, FL 33316
Tel: (305) 535-7930
Yachts and small craft

Southern Yacht Surveyors
2895 Del Rio Dr.
Belleair Bluffs, FL 34640
Tel: (813) 585-8949
Fax: (813) 581-0395

Stevens & Stevens Ltd.
3250 Candice Ave. #132
Jensen Beach, FL 34957
Tel: (407) 229-6394
Yachts and small craft

Stiocchi & Co.
P.O. Box 16541
Jacksonville, FL 32245-6541
Tel: (904) 398-1862
Fax: (904) 398-1868
Yachts, fishing vessels, and small craft

George Stuck
P.O. Box 5481
Key West, FL 33045
Tel: (305) 294-4959
Yachts, fishing vessels, and small craft

Summerlin's Marine Survey
200 Naco Rd.
Suite C
Ft. Pierce, FL 34946
Tel: (407) 464-6090
Fax: (407) 464-7470
Yachts and small craft

Sunset Harbor Marine
1928 Purdy Ave.
Miami Beach, FL 33139
Tel: (305) 673-0044

Surfside Harbor Associates, Inc.
6201 S.E. Monticello Terr.
Hobe Sound, FL 33455-7383
Tel: (407) 545-0011
Yachts and small craft

Gene Thornton Diesel Survey
4564 N.E. 11th Ave.
Ft. Lauderdale, FL 33334
Tel: (305) 776-7242
Engines

Treffer Marine Surveyor, Inc.
2865 S. Tropical Dr.
Merrit Island, FL 32952
Tel: (407) 453-6064
Fax: (407) 459-3816
Yachts and small craft

Roger Trottier
775 J. Ringling Blvd.
Suite G-25
Sarasota, FL 34236
Tel: (813) 746-4106

Thomas Van Dorn
P.O. Box 21843
South Side Station
Ft. Lauderdale, FL 33335
Tel: (305) 463-0142
Yachts and small craft

Adrian J. Volney & Co.
5086 Whistlewood Cir.
Sarasota, FL 34232
Tel: (813) 371-8781
Yachts and small craft

W.F. Willien Associates
15 Crossroads
Suite 250
Sarasota, FL 34239
Tel: (813) 951-6138
Fax: (813) 951-1038
Yachts and small craft

Willis Marine Services, Inc.
861 Rafael Blvd. N.E.
St. Petersburg, FL 33704
Tel: (813) 823-7333

Georgia

Ronald E. Collins
26 North End Dr.
Brunswick, GA 31525
Tel: (912) 262-0448
Yachts and small craft

Bolling F. Douglas Marine Associates, Inc.
6654 Johnson Circle
Flowery Branch, GA 30542
Tel: (404) 967-4175
Fax: (404) 967-0749

Southeastern Marine Surveying Company
P.O. Box 9854
Savannah, GA 31412
Tel: (912) 233-4157

Toplis & Harding, Inc.
5901-B Peachtree Dunwoody Rd.
Suite 300
Atlanta, GA 30328
Tel: (404) 396-3030
Fax: (404) 396-3536

Woodside Surveys
15 Howell Mill Plantation
Atlanta, GA 30327
Tel: (404) 314-6300
Yachts and small craft

Hawaii

All Ship & Cargo Surveys, Inc.
965-A2 Nimitz Hwy.
Honolulu, HI 96817
Tel: (808) 538-3260

Mike Doyle, Ltd.
606 Fort St., Rm. 300
Honolulu, HI 96813
Tel: (808) 521-9881
Fax: (808) 537-9329

Dennis Smith 677
Ala Moana Blvd., Suite 812
Honolulu, HI 95813
Tel: (808) 545-1333
Yachts and small craft

Iowa

U.S. Inland Marine Surveying, Inc.
1599 Vail Ave.
Muscatine, IA 52761
Tel: (310) 263-6235

Illinois

A3Pi Services, Inc.
8695 S. Archer Ave., Unit 111
Willow Springs, IL 60480
Tel: (708) 839-1494
Fax: (708) 839-1506

Lee H. Ashbridge
480 McClurg Ct.
Apt. #1002
Chicago, IL 60611
Tel: (312) 464-9640
Yachts and small craft

Davis & Company, Ltd.
P.O.Box 359
Lisle, IL 60532
Tel: (312) 852-7944

Hunt, Leithner & Company, Inc.
1020 Milwaukee Ave.
Deerfield, IL 60015
Tel: (708) 459-7171
Fax: (708) 459-7857

Inland Surveyors, Inc.
307 North Michigan Ave.
Suite 1008
Chicago, IL 60601
Tel: (312) 329-9881

James Slinger
1854 York Ln.
Highland Park, IL 60035
Tel: (708) 831-9157
Fax: (708) 831-9155
Yachts, cargo, and small craft

Kentucky

Riverlands Marine Surveyors & Consultants, Inc.
817 Huntington Rd.
Louisville, KY 40207
Tel: (502) 897-9900

Louisiana

A & B Marine Consulting, Inc.
Box 256, Rte. 4
Morgan City, LA 70380
Tugs and barges

Bachrach &Wood/Maritime Surveyors
P.O. Box 7415
Metairie, LA 70010-7415
Tel: (504) 454-0001
Fax: (504) 454-3257

Perry H. Beebe & Associates
352 Fairfield Ave.
Gretna, LA 70056
Tel: (504) 368-1718
Fax: (504) 366-1362
Yachts, fishing vessels, and small craft

Breit Marine Surveying, Inc.
1311 Leonidas St.
New Orleans, LA 70118
Tel: (504) 866-1814

Chauvin & Associates, Inc.
P.O. Box 788
Morgan City, LA 70381
Tel: (504) 385-1043

Deep-Sea Marine Surveyors, & Consultants Inc.
1500 Fourth St.
Suite Y
Harvey, LA 70058
Tel: (504) 367-5623

Entach & Associates, Inc.
P.O. Box 1470
Houma, LA 70361
Tel: (504) 868-5524
Yachts and small craft

Arthur A. Grant & Son, Inc.
1100 Pere Marquette Bldg.
New Orleans, LA 70125
Tel: (504) 524-5436

Capt. Kaare G. Fjeldso, Inc.
43420 N. Pine Crest St.
Gonzales, LA 70737
Tel: (504) 622-1975
Cargo and ocean-going shipping

Fredricks Marine Corp.
230 26th St.
New Orleans, LA 70124
Tel: (504) 482-0474
Fax: (504) 891-3775

Hale Associates
207 Clayton Dr.
Houma, LA 70360
Tel: (504) 876-5450

Matthews, Matson & Kelley, Inc.
3525 N. Causeway Blvd., #106
Metairie, LA 70002
Tel: (504) 831-2678
Fax: (504) 831-2445

Rivers & Gulf Marine Surveyors, Inc.
P.O. Box 783
Marrero, LA 70073
Tel: (504) 347-4637

Shearer & Associates, Inc.
P.O. Box 9576
Metairie, LA 70055
Tel: (504) 836-6009
Fax: (504) 831-8431

Southern Surveying, Inc.
P.O. Box 1157
Morgan City, LA 70381
Tel: (504) 385-4220
Fax: (504) 385-4222

Stickney, Dufour & Associates, Inc.
P.O. Box 15650
New Orleans, LA 70175-5650
Tel: (504) 891-3764
Fax: (504) 891-3775

**Arthur H. Terry &
Company**
101 W. Robert E. Lee Blvd.
Suite 200
New Orleans, LA 70124-2459
Tel: (504) 283-1514
Fax: (504) 283-1520

**United Marine Surveying,
Inc.**
P.O. Box 609
Destrehan, LA 70047-0609
Tel: (504) 764-8321

Verner Marine Ltd.
P.O. Box 6287
Metairie, LA 70003
Tel: (504) 454-2056

**Albert B. Westerman &
Company**
2800 Sells St.
Metairie, LA 70003-3543
Tel: (504) 888-8865
Fax: (504) 455-7960

Si Williams
101 W. Robert E. Lee Blvd.
Suite S-200
New Orleans, LA 70124
Tel: (504) 283-1514
Fax: (504) 283-1520
Yachts and small craft

Massachussets

David W. Bemis
14 Linda Ln.
Plymouth, MA 02360
Tel: (508) 224-2270

Certified Marine Surveyors
44 19th St.
Lowell, MA 01850-1308
Tel: (508) 454-1688
Yachts and small craft

Desmond Connolly
P.O. Box 621
Buzzards Bay, MA 02532
Tel: (508) 759-8338
Fax: (508) 759-8333

D & G Marine, Inc.
P.O. Box 635
N. Eastham, MA 02651
Tel: (508) 255-2406
Yachts and small craft

Friedline & Carter, Inc.
436 Main St.
P.O. Box 338
Hyannis, MA 02601
Tel: (508) 771-3232

**Capt. G.W. Full &
Associates**
46 Cedar St.
Marblehead, MA 01945
Tel: (617) 631-4902

**Hull and Cargo Surveyors,
Inc.**
P.O. Box 268
Milton, MA 02186-0268
Tel: (617) 472-8603
Fax: (617) 786-8607
Yachts and small craft

**Independent Marine
Surveyors & Adjusters, Inc.**
18 Sandra Rd.
East Walpole, MA 02032
Tel: (508) 668-8416
Fax: (508) 660-8351

Morris Johnson
P.O. Box 531
West Yarmouth, MA 02673
Tel: (508) 771-8054
Yachts and small craft

Ray Kershaw Company
P.O. Box 104
Manchester, MA 01944
Tel: (508) 526-4488
Fax: (508) 526-8191

Robt. N. Kershaw, Inc.
25 Garden Pk.
P.O. Box 285
Braintree, MA 02184
Tel: (617) 843-4550
Yachts and small craft

Capt. Norman LeBlanc
P.O. Box 185
Beverly, MA 01915
Tel: (508) 921-1151
Fax: (508) 741-4365
Yachts and small craft

Manchester Yacht Survey
P.O. Box 1576
Manchester, MA 01944
Yachts and small craft

H. C. Mustin Company
P.O. Box 167
Marblehead, MA 01945
Tel: (617) 631-4146

James T. Simonitsch
P.O. Box 1214
West Chatham, MA 02669
Tel: (508) 945-2531
Fax: (508) 945-3122

Maryland

**Anchor Marine
Enterprises, Inc.**
208 Dorchester Ave.
Cambridge, MD 21613
Tel: (410) 228-2105

Atlantic Marine Surveyors, Inc.
1107 A Talbot St.
P.O. Box 299
St. Michaels, MD 21663
Tel: (410) 745-3080
Fax: (410) 228-1321

Beacon Marine Surveys
2916 Cox Neck Rd. E.
Chester, MD 20690
Tel: (301) 994-1508
Yachts and small craft

Thomas P. Brittain
8809 Thomas Lea Terrace
Gaithersburg, MD 20879
Tel: (301) 948-0015

Chesapeake Marine Surveyors
P.O. Box 322
Mayo, MD 21106-0322
Tel: (301) 798-5077

John R. Griffiths, Inc.
785 Knight Island Rd.
Earleville, MD 21919
Tel: (410) 275-8750
Fax: (410) 275-8750

Frederick E. Hecklinger, Inc.
17 Hull Ave.
Annapolis, MD 21403
Tel: (410) 268-3018

Horan/Russell & Associates, Inc.
P.O. Box 3566
Annapolis, MD 21403
Tel: (410) 626-1855
Fax: (410) 263-3422

Kaufman Design, Inc.
222 Severn Ave.
P.O. Box 4219
Annapolis, MD 21403
Tel: (410) 263-8900
Fax: (410) 263-8923

The Marine Surveyors, Inc.
410 Severn Ave.
Suite 311/312
Annapolis, MD 21403
Tel: (410) 268-6588
Fax: (410) 268-7247

Oxford Marine Survey
4383 Holly Harbor Rd.
Oxford, MD 21645
Tel: (410) 226-5616
Fax: (410) 226-5611
Yachts and small craft

Skord & Co., Inc.
400 Forest Beach Rd.
Annapolis, MD 21401
Tel: (410) 757-7454
Fax: (410) 757-4804
Yachts and small craft

R.M. Stimson & Assoc.
7074 Bembe Beach Rd.,#102
Annapolis, MD 21403
Tel: (410) 268-0080

Whittaker Marine Consultants
381 Tourmaline Dr.
Hebron, MD 21830
Tel: (410) 749-1890
Yachts and small craft

Maine

Associated Marine Surveyors, Inc.
Lower Falls Landing
38 Lafayette St., Rt.88
Yarmouth, ME 04096
Tel: (207) 846-4900
Fax: (207) 846-4700

Casco Marine Consultants, Inc.
5 Ledgeview Ln., RFD #5
Brunswick, ME 04011
Tel: (207) 729-6711
Fax: (207) 729-6547
Yachts, fishing vessels, cargo, and small craft

Delta Marine, Inc.
P.O. Box 828
Blue Hill, ME 04614
Tel: (207) 374-5404

Samuel E. Slaymaker Marine Surveying Inc.
P.O. Box 252
Rockport, ME 04856
Tel: (207) 785-4975

Wilbur L. Turner
P. O. Box 353
Eliot, ME 03903
Tel: (207) 439-9403

Michigan

Barnhardt Marine Surveys
1228 6th St., Suite 1
Port Huron, MI 48060
Tel: (313) 984-2400
Fax: (313) 984-8768

Davis & Company (Mich.) Ltd.
339 E. 16th St.
Suite 220
Holland, MI 49423
Tel: (616) 396-6996
Fax: (616) 396-9523

Great Lakes Marine Surveyors, Inc.
P.O. Box 466
Spring Lake, MI 49546
Tel: (616) 842-9400
Yachts and small craft

Personal Marine Services
52671 CR 388
Grand Junction, MI 49056
Tel: (616) 434-6396
Yachts and small craft

Missouri

Merrill Marine Services, Inc.
12231 Manchester Rd.
Saint Louis, MO 63131
Tel: (314) 822-8002
Fax: (314) 822-1232

Mississippi

R. Andre Marine Surveyor
414 McGuire Cir.
Gulfport, MS 39507
Tel: (601) 863-5962
Fax: (601) 865-9776
Yachts and small craft

Marine Management, Inc.
P.O. Box 1803
Ocean Springs, MS 39564
Tel: (601) 872-2846
Fax: (601) 872-2846

North Carolina

Robert M. Chiles
P.O. Box 3496
417-A Broad St.
New Bern, NC 28560
Tel: (919) 637-4702

James C. Harper & Associates
P.O.Box 494
Wrightsville Beach, NC 28480
Tel: (919) 452-0768
Fax: (919) 392-5600

Maritime Services Inc.
P.O. Box 3549
Morehead City, NC 28557
Tel: (919) 726-8365

Quay Carolina Yacht Surveys
P.O. Box 809
Oriental, NC 28571
Tel: (919(249-2275
Yachts and small craft

Smith International Maritime Consultants, Inc.
214 McGinnis Dr.
Pine Knoll Shores, NC 28512
Tel: (919) 247-4658

W. Thomas Suggs Marine Surveyor
P.O. Box 400
502 North St.
Oriental, NC 28571
Tel: (919) 249-0374
Fax: (919) 249-0374
Yachts and small craft

M.B. Ward & Son, Inc.
P.O. Box 3632
Wilmington, NC 28406
Tel: (919) 392-1425
Fax: (919) 392-3367

Newfoundland

Wilfred K. Blackmore
104 Freshwater Rd.
St. Johns, Newfoundland A1C 2N7
CANADA
Tel: (709) 579-0567

New Hampshire

Julian Hatch
210 Bay Rd.
Newmarket, NH 03857
Tel: (603) 659-3452

Independent Marine Surveyors & Adjusters, Inc.
819 Second St.
Suite B281
Manchester, NH 03102
Tel: (603) 644-4545
Fax: (603) 644-7886
Yachts, fishing vessels, and small craft

New Jersey

W. J. Campbell
9 Gate Rd.
Tabernacle, NJ 08088
Tel: (609) 268-8239

Robert Gibble, Inc.
25 Black Oak Dr.
Ocean View, NJ 08230
Tel: (609) 390-3708
Fax: (609) 390-8857
Yachts and small craft

**Henry C. Halboth &
Company, Inc.**
51 Bingham Ave.
Rumson, NJ 07760
Tel: (908) 758-8990
Fax: (908) 842-4557

**Mid Atlantic Marine
Consulting**
RD #5, Box 1556
Franklinville, NJ 08322
Tel: (609) 694-3340
Yachts and small craft

**National Marine
Consultants, Inc.**
25 Clover Leaf Dr.
Marlboro, NJ 07746
Tel: (908) 780-9523

**Rebel Marine Surveyors,
Ltd.**
Caspar Ln.
Fort Lee, NJ 07024
Tel: (201) 944-5378
Fax: (201) 944-4855

**R.T. Marine Associates,
Damage Survey**
275 Shepherd Ave.
Bound Brook, NJ 08805
Tel: (908) 563-0615
Yachts and small craft

Stephen Sperlak
310 Third St.
Rio Grande, NJ 08242
Tel: (609) 465-9258
Fax: (609) 465-5161

Nova Scotia

**Universal Marine
Consultants(Maritimes)Ltd.**
5 Carriageway Ct.
Bedford, Nova Scotia B4A 3V4
CANADA
Tel: (902) 835-2283
Fax: (902) 835-1493

Nevada

**Mudgett Marine Surveying
& Air Safety Investigators,
Inc.**
107 Slott Peak Court
P.O. Box 6213
Incline Village, NV
89450-6213
Tel: (702) 832-2113
Fax: (702) 832-2113

New York

**Bartnett Marine Services,
Inc.**
52 Ontario St.
Honeoye Falls, NY 14472
Tel: (716) 624-1380

**Continental Survey Bureau
Inc.**
80 Maiden Ln. 22nd Floor
New York, NY 10038
Tel: (212) 509-2518
Fax: (212) 344-5257

Charles B. Darcy
R.R. #3
Cliff Rd.
Wading River, NY 11792
Tel: (516) 929-3059

**George P. Farrell, Marine
Surveyors, Inc.**
220 Longstreet Ave.
Bronx, NY 10465
Tel: (212) 409-4098

Garvey Marine Surveyors
143 W. Montauk Hwy.
Hampton Bays, NY 11946
Tel: (516) 728-5429
Yachts and small craft

**Gay & Taylor Marine
Division**
327 51st St.
Lindenhurst, NY 11757
Tel: (516) 957-8625
Fax: (516) 957-3856

**Great Lakes Marine
Consultants**
R.D. #1, Box 354J
Clayton, NY 13624
Tel: (315) 686-2368
Yachts and small craft

Frederick Hamburg
65 Buckley St.
City Island, NY 10464
Tel: (212) 885-1866

**LaMarque Marine Services,
Inc.**
6 Red Oak Dr.
Rye, NY 10580
Tel: (914) 967-7731

**Jerry Masters Professional
Marine Surveys**
P.O. Box 727
Poughkeepsie, NY 12602
Tel: (800) 272-8258
Yachts and small craft

Marine Surveyors Bureau
221 Central Ave.
White Plains, NY 10606
Tel: (914) 684-9889
Fax: (914) 684-9870
Yachts and small craft

Marine Surveyors Inc.
220 Longstreet Ave.
Bronx, NY 10465
Tel: (212) 409-4098

McGroder Marine Surveyors
P.O. Box 405
228 Central Ave.
Silver Creek, NY 14136
Tel: (716) 934-7848
Fax: (716) 934-7849

Morris Gumpel, Yacht Surveys
20 Old Mamaroneck Rd.
White Plains, NY 10605
Tel: (914) 761-4949

Newcombe & Company
672 10th St.
Brooklyn, NY 11215
Tel: (718) 768-0110
Fax: (718) 499-8268

Ocean Bay Marine Services
P.O. Box 668
Yaphank, NY 11980
Tel: (516) 924-4362
Yachts and small craft

Stanley Ray Marine Surveyor & Consultant
55 Centre St.
City Island, NY 10464
Tel: (212) 885-1059

Edward J. Viola
P.O. Box 430
Mattituck, NY 11952
Tel: (516) 298-9518

Albert A. Young, Inc.
P.O. Box 312
Centerport, NY 11721
Tel: (516) 757-1558
Fax: (516) 757-1558

Ohio

Blue Water Surveys
511 Crestland Ave. N.W.
N. Canton, OH 44720
Tel: (216) 497-3501
Yachts and small craft

Botten Adjustors & Surveyors
P.O. Box 114
Avon Lake
Cleveland, OH 44012-0114
Tel: (216) 696-2092

Davis & Company, Ltd.
3178 Republic Blvd. N.
Suite 9
Toledo, OH 43615
Tel: (419) 841-8606
Fax: (419) 841-8817

Great Lakes Marine Service Co., Inc.
P. O. Box 449
Mentor, OH 44061-0449
Tel: (216) 946-1111

Lake Erie Marine Survey Co.
3931 Kings Mill Run
Rocky River, OH 44116
Tel: (216) 333-9292
Fax: (216) 331-2999

Marine Survey Professionals
14532 Pearl Rd.
Suite 102
Strongsville, OH 44136
Tel: (216) 572-0866
Yachts and small craft

Mobile Marine Associates, Inc.
110 Ottawa St.
Suite 500
Toledo, OH 43602
Tel: (419) 244-8292
Fax: (419) 244-9505

E.J. Mulaney
P.O. Box 533
Huron, OH 44839
Tel: (419) 433-2720

Neare, Gibbs & Co.
151 West Fourth St.
Suite 602
Cincinnati, OH 45202-2733
Tel: (513) 621-1415

West Sister Marine Surveys
12513 Lagoon Dr.
Curtice, OH 43412
Tel: (419) 836-8264
Yachts and small craft

Oklahoma

Sea-Masters Ltd.
5909 N.W. Expwy.
Suite 230
Oklahoma City, OK 73132-5102
Tel: (405) 728-8000
Fax: (405) 722-2628
Yachts and small craft

Ontario

Intermar Surveys, Ltd.
2 Lansing Sq.
Suite 901
Willowdale, Ontario M2J 4P8
CANADA
Tel: (416) 495-0458
Fax: (416) 495-7274

**International Marine
Surveyors Ltd.**
P.O. Box 214
Postal STN Clarkson
Mississauga, Ontario L5J 3Y1
CANADA
Tel: (416) 822-5040

Marine Surveys, Inc.
136 John St.
Gananoque, Ontario K7G 1A5
CANADA
Tel: (613) 382-5211
Fax: (613) 382-8388

**McKie Marine Surveys,
Ltd.**
2263 Marine Dr., Unit 1201
Oakville, Ontario L6L 5K1
CANADA
Tel: (416) 827-6322
Fax: (416) 338-0498

**Nisbet Marine Surveyors,
Ltd.**
345 Lakeshore Rd. E., #301
Oakville, Ontario L6J 1J5
CANADA
Tel: (416) 844-6670
Fax: (416) 844-6833

Oregon

Associated Marine Systems
P.O. Box 152
Corbett, OR 97019
Tel: (503) 695-5385

**Parker C. Emerson &
Associates**
17935 Cardinal Dr.
Lake Oswego, OR 97034
Tel: (503) 638-7286
Fax: (503) 638-7286

**Marine Surveyors
Northwest, Inc.**
7776 S. W. Barnard Dr.
Beaverton, OR 97007
Tel: (503) 641-4604
Fax: (503) 641-4604

**Raymond O. Nulf &
Associates, Inc.**
P.O. Box 308
Coquille, OR 97423
Tel: (503) 396-3928

Charles Thompson
450 W. Lexington Ave.
Astoria, OR 97103
Tel: (503) 325-4062
Fax: (503) 325-9649
Fishing vessels

Toplis and Harding, Inc.
700 N. Hayden Island Dr.
Suite 270
Portland, OR 97217
Tel: (503) 283-0024
Fax: (503) 283-0027

Pennsylvania

**John P. Colletti &
Associates**
373 Vanadium
Pittsburgh, PA 15243
Tel: (412) 276-2200

**Davis Marine Surveyors,
Inc.**
147 William Circle
McKees Rocks, PA 15136
Tel: (412) 771-0609

F. Michael Simone
3561 Stafore Dr.
Bethlehem, PA 18017
Tel: (215) 882-0146

Puerto Rico

**John S. Lipuscek Marine
Consultants, Inc.**
P.O. Box 2081
San Juan, PR 00903
Tel: (809) 724-7634

Quebec

**Trident Marine
Consultants, Inc.**
6955 Taschereau Blvd.
Suite 207
Brossard, Quebec J4Z 1A7
CANADA
Tel: (514) 443-8122
Fax: (514) 443-8123

Rhode Island

Paul V. Coble, CMS
Surveyacht, Marine Architects
& Surveyors
P.O. Box 35
Newport, RI 02840-0001
Tel: (401) 846-0700

**Jerry Masters Professional
Marine Surveys**
65 Laurel St.
Ashaway, RI 02804
Tel: (800) 982-6466
Yachts and small craft

South Carolina

Lucas & Brown
P.O. Box 536
Charleston, SC 29402
Tel: (803) 577-5782

Tennessee

Patterson Marine Services
549 East Main St.,
Suite#F-93
Hendersonville, TN
37075-2630
Tel: (615) 824-7240
Fax: (615) 451-0352

Texas

Diers & Associates, Inc.
8705 Katy Freeway
Suite #202
Houston, TX 77024
Tel: (713) 932-9717
Fax: (713) 932-0598

E.M. Glover Associates, Inc.
P.O. Box 1239
Fulton, TX 78358
Tel: (512) 729-7853

**John L. Kingston &
Associates, Inc.**
14425 Torrey Chase Blvd.
Suite 240
Houston, TX 77014
Tel: (713) 537-7770
Fax: (713) 537-7810

Guy Mathews
45 Pebble Brook
Wimberley, TX 78676
Tel: (713) 847-3673

**McAllister Marine
Surveying Co.**
P.O. Box 6375
Corpus Christi, TX 78466-6375
Tel: (512) 855-2172
Fax: (512) 852-3776

**James Moon Marine
Associates**
839 Pinewood Ln.
Seabrook, TX 77586-4408
Tel: (713) 236-7155

**Capt. Trevor O'Brien &
Associates, Inc.**
11821 East Fwy.
Suite 510
Houston, TX 77029
Tel: (713) 453-0906

John B.Oliveros
127 Marlin St.
Galveston, TX 77550
Tel: (409) 763-3123

Reiter Marine Service
11723 Perry Ave.
Houston, TX 77071
Tel: (713) 723-5815

Sabine Surveyors
9509 Hwy. 69
Port Arthur, TX 77640
Tel: (409) 724-6969
Fax: (409) 724-7761

R.E. Summers & Associates
2900 Dickinson Ave.
Suite 3
Dickinson, TX 77539
Tel: (713) 333-5553

Duane E.Tucker
2802 Pilgrims Point Dr.
Webster, TX 77598-3313
Tel: (713) 332-1077

World Marine Associates
13301 East Freeway
Suite 201
Houston, TX 77015
Tel: (713) 453-3131
Fax: (713) 453-0788

Virginia

Frederick A. Edwards, JR.
P.O. Box 4616
Virginia Beach, VA 23454
Tel: (804) 486-8357

**Horan/Russell &
Associates, Inc.**
7319 Pinecastle Rd.
Falls Church, VA 22043
Tel: (703) 573-5705
Fax: (703) 207-9106

Knox Marine Consultants
Tidewater Yacht Marina
10 Crawford Pkwy.
Portsmouth, VA 23704
Tel: (804) 393-9788
Fax: (804) 393-9789

Virgin Islands

R.E. Shank
P.O. Box 3078
Christiansted, USVI 00820
Tel: (809) 773-3320
Fax: (809) 773-0413

Vermont

William Talbott
RD Box 2450
N. Ferrisburg, VT 05473
Tel: (802) 425-2973

Washington

**Capt. Harold E. Aune &
Associates, Inc.**
P.O. Box 504
Ilwaco, WA 98624
Tel: (206) 642-4178

**Blomquist Marine Surveys,
Inc.**
24021 Crystal Lake Rd.
Woodinville, WA 98072
Tel: (206) 485-7373
Fax: (206) 485-4471

**Coastal Marine Surveying
and Consulting, Inc.**
815 Chehalis St. N.
Montesano, WA 98563-1307
Tel: (206) 249-5698
Fax: (206) 249-3715

**Ian T. Coffer & Associates,
Inc.**
P. O. Box 1397
Mercer Island, WA 98040
Tel: (206) 232-2288
Fax: (206) 236-1278

**Commercial Marine
Service**
P.O. Box 33836
Seattle, WA 98133-0836
Tel: (206) 670-0366
Fax: (206) 672-395

Alexander Gow, Inc.
221 First Ave. West
Suite 115
Seattle, WA 98119
Tel: (206) 285-0520

Mathew L. Harris
1333 Lincoln St., #323
Bellingham, WA 98226
Tel: (206) 647-6966

**Herbert O. Johnson Marine
Surveyors, Inc.**
202 N. W. 56th St.
Seattle, WA 98107-2025
Tel: (206) 783-0694
Fax: (206) 789-1189

**Maritime Services
International**
14816 Bothell Way N.E. #436
Seattle, WA 98155
Tel: (206))362-0859

**Maritime Survey
Associates, Inc.**
P.O. Box 16328
Seattle, WA 98116-0328
Tel: (206) 932-9004
Fax: (206) 937-1378

Michael K. McGlenn Inc.
#9 Harbor Mall
Bellingham, WA 98225
Tel: (206) 734-0527
Fax: (206) 647-9538

**Montgomery Maritime
Survey, Inc.**
P.O. Box 185
Port Townsend, WA
98368-0185
Tel: (800) 626-7061
or (206) 385-5067
Fax: (206) 385-5914

M.H. Munsey, Inc.
628 Bell St., Apt. C
Edmonds, WA 98020
Tel: (206) 771-4027

**Ocean Marine Surveyors,
Inc.**
17801 Fremont Ave.
N. Seattle, WA 98133
Tel: (206) 546-2100
Fax: (206)546-2244

Western Marine Surveyors
P.O. Box 8585
Port Orchard, WA 98366
Tel: (206) 876-9181

Figure 1: All boats should be
surveyed before purchase.

Tanks

Suppose your fuel tank has sprung a leak and you have to buy a new one. What do you look for? A number of features should be carefully checked:

1. Make sure the tank has been constructed in accordance with ABYC and ABS specifications. That means that all the materials are resistant to deterioration by fuel and other compounds that might get into the tank, such as oil or water in a fuel tank.
2. The materials must be compatible on the galvanic scale to prevent corrosion.
3. Check that the tank has been pressure tested. According to the ABYC, it should be tested to a minimum pressure of 100 psi to check for porosity, and after being fitted with pipes and vents it should be tested to a minimum of 3 psi. ABS says that the tank should be tested to a head of pressure not less than the top of the overflow or to 2/3 the distance to the point of maximum freeboard, whichever is greater.
4. The tank materials should be steel sheet, aluminized steel, or galvanized steel (galvanized steel should not be used for fuel oil tanks as the fuel can react with the zinc coating), aluminum, copper, or some plastics (generally used for fresh water tanks).
5. All joints on metal tanks should be welded. The ABYC recommends specific methods of welding for different tank materials.
6. There should be no holes in the tank sides, ends, or bottom, only in the top.
7. A tank should have large removeable plates in the top for cleaning it.
8. Tanks should have plenty of baffles inside to prevent water sloshing around. The ABYC recommends that the baffle area be no more than 2/3 of the area of the tank in the same plane as the baffle.
9. Every tank should be permantently installed and strapped in place. You don't want a full fuel tank crashing around inside the hull if the boat were to capsize.
10. All tanks should have a vent line led either to the upper deck or, in the case of fresh water tanks, to the galley sink.
11. The amount of fuel in the tank should be easily measured. Provision should be made for a dipstick to be lowered into the tank, in case the fuel meter jams or reads incorrectly.
12. Fuel fills should be capable of being secured tightly so that water cannot get into the tank, and they should be clearly labeled with the type of fuel.
13. Ideally, a fuel strainer should be fitted between the fuel fill and the tank to keep the fuel clean.
14. If two tanks on either side of the boat are cross-connected, they should have

a shut-off valve between them to prevent the liquid inside from draining to the lowest tank when the boat is heeled. Note that all piping coming out of a tank should have shut-off valves to enable that line to be closed should it break.

BLADDER TANKS

If they are handled with care, bladder tanks can be used as temporary water or waste tanks. I prefer not to use them as a permanent built-in tank because they can break and all the contents descend into the bilge. If this happens to be the holding tanks you'll be in for a messy, smelly time. If you are making a long trip and need additional fuel or water stored in a sport fishing boat's cockpit or on deck, bladder tanks may be the ideal solution. But make sure they are properly secured and try them first to make sure there are no leaks.

Manufacturers of Tanks and Tank Measuring Devices

Fab-All Marine Mfg. Ltd.
#2 3005 Murray St.
Port Moody, British Columbia
V3H 1X3
CANADA
Tel: (604) 461-8522
Fax: (604) 461-2518
Stainless steel tanks

Kracor
5625 W. Clinton Ave.
P.O. Box 23667
Milwaukee, WI 53223
Tel: (800) 255-6335
 or (414) 355-6335
Fax: (414) 355-8782
Marine tanks

Imtra
30 Barnet Blvd.
New Bedford, MA 02745
Tel: (508) 995-7000
 Nauta inflatable tanks

Avon Seagull Marine
1851 McGaw Ave.
Irvine, CA 92714
Tel: (714) 250-0880
Nauta inflatable tanks

Vetus - Den Ouden, Inc.
P.O. Box 8712
Baltimore, MD 21240-0712
Tel: Orders only: (800)
GO-VETUS
 or (410) 712-0740
Fax: (410) 712-0985
Flexible tanks

Tank Measuring Devices

Hart Systems, Inc.
1695 1st Interstate Plaza
Tacoma, WA 98402
Tel: (206) 383-3399
The Tank Tender

Marcra
1530 East Edinger Ave.
Santa Ana, CA 92705
Tel: (714) 953-9319
Liquid level gauge system

Small Marine, Inc.
P.O. Box 5278
Lighthouse Point, FL 33064
Tanksight

Small Marine, Inc.
2700 N.E. 7th Ave.
Pompano Beach, FL 33064
Tel: (305) 943-4265

Figure 1: Nauta flexible tanks are available from Imtra. The top one is folded and the lower one is filled.

Towers and Pipework

Tuna towers, half towers, bridge enclosures, and radar arches are all relatively inexpensive methods of increasing the space available on a boat. The pipeworker takes aluminum tubes and turns them into structures that expand the horizons of the vessel upwards.

A full tower is one that raises the helmsman above the boat. This enables him to see where fish are likely to be, to watch over the action in the cockpit, and to control the boat's speed and direction. A full tower usually has a simple bimini top to shade the helmsman. Up in the tower with the helmsman are dulicate sets of controls, and often a duplicate set of instruments including radar and sonar.

Towers should be strongly made and strongly fastened. If the top is canvas and poorly made, it could tear off in very strong winds. Canvas tops should be of heavyweight material and have good stitching. Some towers have a fiberglass top, but this adds additional weight aloft and reduces stability. Note also that at high speeds the tower top can act as a lifting surface and affect control of the boat.

A half tower is lower than a full tower. The helmsman is also lower in that he is on the flybridge rather than another level above it. A half tower may have a rigid or canvas top, and it can be fully enclosed with side flaps that can be rolled down in bad weather. If the top is rigid (fiberglass),

it may have an electronics box installed. Except in very bad conditions, most of the steering will be done from the half tower where visibility is better.

Even sailboats are having radar arches installed as basic equipment. Whereas once the radar antenna was installed on front of the mainmast (where it was battered by the genoa everytime the boat tacked), it is now placed on its own arch at the aft end of the boat. This gives the antenna better range, and also enables other antennae to be placed in a high position where they will not be battered by sails or people. In addition to supporting the radar, this arch has davits to carry the dinghy.

Putting the radar too high can cause other problems. As Will Keene of the Edson Corporation points out, "sailors typically think that mounting radar as high as possible on their boats will enable them to see further. A mast-mounted radar can pick up an object 24 miles away, and for a sailboat moving at 8 knots, that is three hours away. But putting the radar antenna high up on the boat can cause it to overlook nearby targets. Typically, it will miss cans and nuns or other channel markers, and the longer cable run will reduce the resolution of the picture on the screen, making it harder to see close objects. Plus, the annual maintenance cost will be higher because of the difficulty of accessing the radar. Ideally, the radar should be mounted about eight or nine feet off the deck on a radar arch or stern post, many of which are available as 'off the shelf' items."

Other pipework onboard boats are bow and stern pulpits, handrails, and grabrails. All rails, stanchions, and other pipework should be strongly bolted down and at least 1 inch in diameter. The materials usually used are stainless steel or aluminum. Both are suitable and strong.

Manufacturers of Towers and Pipework

Towers

Atkinson Marine
235 S.W. 32nd Ct.
Ft. Lauderdale, FL 33315
Tel: (305) 763-1652
Fax: (305) 763-7605

Atlantic Marine Stainless Corp.
7176 S.W. 47th St.
Miami, FL 33155
Tel: (305) 665-9900
Towers

Birdsall Marine Design
530 Nottingham Blvd.
West Palm Beach, FL 33403
Tel: (407) 832-7879
Fax: (407) 832-3762
T-Tops and towers

Bluewater Towers
1240 W. Industrial Ave.
Boynton Beach, FL 33426
Tel: (407) 369-0686
Fax: (407) 369-0890
T-Tops, towers, radar arches, and leaning posts

Certified Marine Welding
146 B Nassau Ave.
Islip, NY 11751
Tel: (516) 277-7073

E-Tec Marine Products
7555 Garden Rd.
Riviera Beach, FL 33404
Tel: (407) 848-8351
Fax: (407) 848-8354
Tower fittings

Innovative Fabrication
1837 Opa Locka Blvd.
Opalocka, FL 33054
Tel: (305) 681-9223
Fax: (305) 681-7242
Tower parts

Pipewelders Marine
2965 W. State Rd. 84
Ft. Lauderdale, FL 33312-4867
Tel: (305) 587-8400
Fax: (305) 587-3007
Towers, outriggers, and davits

South Shore Custom Towers
270 Rt. 109
East Farmingdale, NY 11735
Tel: (516) 752-7994
Towers

Thurston Towers
125 Steamboat Ave.
Wickford, RI 02852
Tel: (401) 294-3340
Tuna towers, leaning posts, radar arches, and half towers

Tower Power
5144D W. Hurley Pond Rd.
Farmingdale, NJ 07757
Tel: (908) 938-3953
Fax: (516) 938-7320

Pipework

Aluminum Marine Products, Inc.
1890 Griffin Rd.
Dania, FL 33004
Tel: (305) 923-1955
Fax: (305) 923-1842
Outboard brackets

Trailers

If you buy a boat that is small enough to tow behind a vehicle, your sailing horizions can expand dramatically. But towing a boat is not as easy as it seems. You'll need to check the size and weight of your boat before you try to tow it.

If the boat is wider than 8 feet 6 inches, theoretically you should carry a wide-load sticker. But many boats that are only a few inches wider than the limit are routinely towed. With everything onboard, the boat should be no higher than 13 feet 6 inches. This limit is reasonably high and seldom creates a problem.

Weight is a different matter. While there are no legal weight limits for small boats, weight affects the size of the towing vehicle. You need a bigger van or truck to tow a big boat. For instance, a sailing friend tows his J24 weighing around 3100 pounds with a Chevy Surburban van. The van has a V8 350hp engine, and is fitted out with a full towing package: a transmission cooler, heavy duty shocks, an oversized radiator and weight distibuting hitch. This makes for easier towing. Double-axle trailers also make the towing job easier and more stable. And the longer the wheelbase of the towing vehicle, the more stable the rig will be.

Some states require that trailers have surge-brakes, which operate entirely separately to the towing vehicle's brakes. Surge brakes are best used when the towing vehicle is much smaller than the load being towed. When the towing vehicle decelerates, surge-brakes slow the trailer. Unfortunately, surge-brakes can operate if the driver of the towing vehicle changes gear or slows down when going downhill. Sometimes they lock on and get very hot. Different states have different weight limits for loads on trailers with surge-brakes. Check with the Department of Transportation in any states you intend to cross.

The alternative to surge-brakes are solenoid-operated brakes. These work at the same time as the towing vehicle's brakes. They are best when the towing vehicle is the same size by weight as the load being towed.

When launching your boat off a trailer, a few tips will make your life easier:

- Let the trailer cool for about half an hour before backing it into the water. This will prevent inadvertant cooling and possibly distorting hot spots.
- Paint the trailer's brake light seals with clear nail polish to seal them against water ingress. Always unplug trailer lights before backing the trailer into the water. This will prevent blowing the light fuses.
- Make sure the trailer bearings are well packed with a grease that will not react with seawater.
- Rinse off the trailer with fresh water as soon as possible to reduce corrosion.

- Get extra-wide rear-view mirrors.
- Practice backing up before trying it on a narrow launching ramp.
- Try not to back your towing vehicle into the water. If you do, your brakes may not work.

Manufacturers of Trailers

B & M
P.O. Box 499
Camdenton, MO 65020
Tel: (314) 346-7246
Haulrite trailers

Boyer Industries
460 W. 12th St.
Erie, PA 16501
Tel: (814) 453-7176
Trailers

Calkins Trailers
P.O. Box 14527
Spokane, WA 99214
Tel: (509) 928-7420
Trailers

Con-O-Lift Hydraulic Trailers
R.R. 2
Parry Sound, Ontario P2A 2W8
CANADA
Tel: (705) 366-2210
Fax: (705) 378-3814
Hydraulic trailers and stands

Eagle Loadrite Trailers
4624 13th St.
Wyandotte, MI 48192
Tel: (313) 284-2310
Trailers

E-Z Loader Trailers, Inc.
P.O. Box 3263
Spokane, WA 99220
Tel: (509) 489-0181
Trailers

Float-On Boat Trailers
3001 Industrial Ave., No. 3
Ft. Pierce, FL 34946
Tel: (407) 465-7420
Trailers

Freedom Wheels
1401 Commercial Dr.
Litchfield, IL 62056
Tel: (217) 324-0390
Trailers

Heritage Custom Trailers
R.R. 4, Box 91
Benton, IL 62812
Tel: (618) 439-9626
Trailers

Hostar Marine Transport Systems
1 William Gould Way
Kingston, MA 02364
Tel: (800) 783-9303
  or (617) 585-9300
Fax: (617) 585-6131
Hydraulic trailers, dollies, and stands

Load Rite Trailers, Inc.
265 Lincoln Hwy.
Fairless Hills, PA 19030
Tel: (215) 949-0500
Trailers

Long Trailer
Rt. 2, Box 1
Tarboro, NC 27886
Tel: (919) 823-8104
Fax: (919) 641-0412
Trailers

Magic Tilt Trailers
2161 Lions Club Rd.
Clearwater, FL 34624
Tel: (813) 535-5561
Fax: (813) 539-8472
Magic Loader trailers

Midwest Industries, Inc.
P.O. Box 235
Ida Grove, IA 51445
Tel: (712) 364-3365
Trailers

Price Designs, Inc.
Rt. 1, Box 87
Grifton, NC 28530
Tel: (919) 524-5790
Fax: (919) 524-4446
Trailers and sailboat cradles

Sea Lion Metal Fabricators
1916 S. Bancroft St.
Philadelphia, PA 19145
Tel: (215) 467-8797
Sealion trailers

Shoreline Products, Inc.
P.O. Box 848
Arlington, TX 76010
Tel: (817) 465-1351
Fax: (817) 472-9638
Trailers

Trail-Rite Boat Trailers
3100 W. Central Ave.
Santa Ana, CA 92704

Trailex
60 Industrial Dr.
P.O. Box 553
Canfield, OH 44406
Tel: (216) 533-6814

Triad Trailers
90 Danbury Rd.
New Milford, CT 06776
Tel: (203) 354-1146
*Maker of J Boat trailers and
custom trailers*

Wallstrong Trailers
1400 W. 260th St.
Harbor City, CA 90710
Tel: (213) 530-2740
Trailers

Figure 1: This trailer was built by Triad Trailers of Connecticut.

Vane Steering Gear

Somebody once said that every blue water cruising boat should have vane steering gear. But which one is right for you? To some extent, your options are controlled by the type of vessel you sail. If the boat is small and reasonably light, the vane can be fairly simple. A vane that turns a large diameter drum that is wired to the tiller is often all that is needed. As the boat gets larger and the forces required to operate the rudder increase, the vane must be larger to be able to turn the rudder. Usually, this also means that the vane mechanism increases in complexity. And as complexity increases, so sensitivity is lost. In order to improve sensitivity, wedge-shaped or finned vanes were tried. Depending upon the size of the fins or angle of the wedge, the sensitivity could be finely tuned. But still not enough force was generated to turn the rudder of a large yacht.

The earliest type of vane steering system linked the vane directly to the rudder. But this meant that the vane had to be very large even on moderately sized boats. Sir Francis Chichester referred to the vane on Gypsy Moth as a spare mizzen, it was so large. In order to reduce the size of the vane, a small trim tab on the back of the rudder blade was tried. It was turned by the vane via a complex linkage, which kicked the rudder over. The system had problems, however, because of friction, complexity, and the fact that the tab could easily catch weeds or ocean debris, requiring a trip over the side to clear it. The next evolutionary step was to try a servo pendulum rudder.

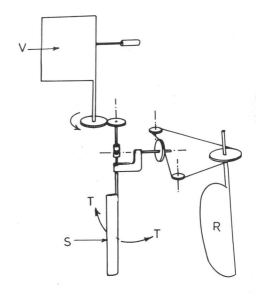

Figure 1: Most modern vane steering gears work in the following manner. When the wind turns the vane (V) it turns the pendulum rudder (S). The pendulum rudder tilts (T) and exerts a force which turns the yacht's main rudder (R).

Most of the current generation of wind vanes use a servo pendulum to generate the forces required to turn the rudder. The pendulum rudder hangs in the water astern of the yacht, and is turned by direct gearing to the vane. When the pendulum is turned, it is kicked up out of the water by the turning action. As the pendulum comes up out of the water, it creates a turning moment which turns the rudder via a linkage. The principle is illustrated in Figure 1.

Manufacturers of Vane Steering Gear

Cape Horn Marine Products
314 Girovard St.
P.O. Box 699
Oka, Quebec J0N 1E0
CANADA
Tel: (514) 479-6314
Fax: (514) 479-1895

Cruising Gear
2751 S.W. 27th Ave.
Miami, FL 33133
Tel: (305) 854-7600
Fax: (305) 854-5984

Cruising Yacht Systems
P.O. Box 38
Merritt, NC 28556
Tel: (919) 745-5959

Fleming Marine USA, Inc.
2302 Shelter Island Dr.
San Diego, CA 92106
Tel: (800) 638-9138
Fax: (619) 222-9124

International Marine Mfg.
8895 S.W. 129th St.
Miami, FL 33176
Tel: (305) 255-3939
"RVG" vanes

Sailomat International
Box 10 123, S-100
Stockholm
SWEDEN
Tel: 46-(8)-23-00-00

Sailomat USA
P.O. Box 2077
La Jolla, CA 92038-2077
Tel: (619) 454-6191
Fax: (619) 454-3512

Scanmar Marine Products
298 Harbor Dr.
Sausalito, CA 94957
Tel: (415) 332-3233
Fax: (415) 332-0957
Self-steering wind vane

Windpilot
1-1000 Bishop St.
Cambridge, Ontario N3H 4Y7
CANADA
Tel: (519) 653-9261
Fax: (519) 653-3414
Self steering wind vane

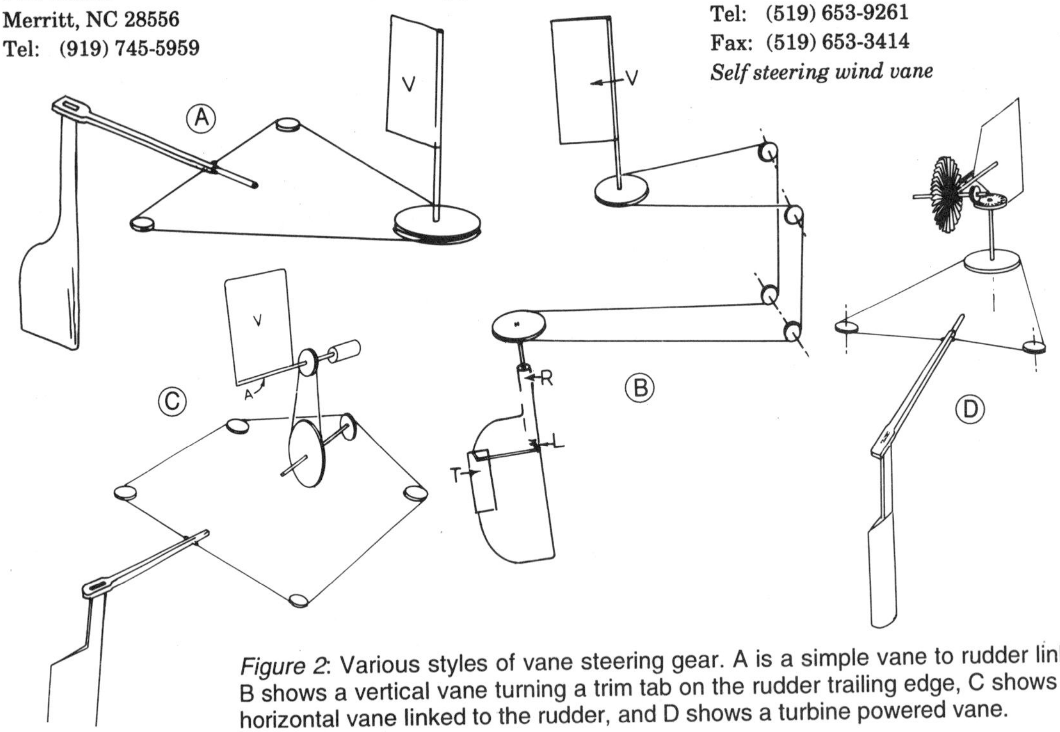

Figure 2: Various styles of vane steering gear. A is a simple vane to rudder link, B shows a vertical vane turning a trim tab on the rudder trailing edge, C shows a horizontal vane linked to the rudder, and D shows a turbine powered vane.

Watermakers

I would like to thank Diwan Nesicolaci of Universal Aqua Technologies, Inc. for help with this introduction.

With water supplies all over the world becoming more expensive and subject to chemical, bacterial, or parasitic contamination, a watermaker is rapidly becoming the norm aboard larger cruising yachts. A watermaker is not, as its name implies, a machine that makes water. It is a machine that removes the salt from seawater to make it drinkable. In other words, it is a desalinator, similar in function to the larger desalinators used on commercial ships. On commercial ships, fresh water is obtained by condensing it from the steam made in the boilers. On smaller craft, without boilers, fresh water is obtained by forcing seawater through a membrane. The membrane holds back the larger salt molecules but allows the tiny water molecules to pass through.

What do you look for in a watermaker? First, you look for a unit with the right capacity for your needs. To determine the right capacity, you must estimate the amount of water you use on a daily basis, for showering, drinking, cooking, dishwashing, washing clothes, and so forth. Then divide this total by the number of hours per day you want your generator to run. (The generator is needed to generate power for the watermaker.) This will give

you the desired output in gallons per hour. Note that many watermaker outputs are listed in gallons per day.

Having decided upon the capacity of your unit, you should look at the power requirements. A few watermakers run on 12 volts, but usually the amperage draw at 12 volts has to be quite high to give the unit enough muscle to force water through the membrane. The better units run at 110 volts or 220 volts. Note, too, that the ship's generator should be large enough to run the watermaker and all the other electrical equipment. Watermakers use between 7 and 18 amps depending upon the size of the unit. At 220 volts, that translates into 1500 watts to 4000 watts. On larger vessels, as an additional backup, you might want to have a power take-off from the engine to drive the watermaker. This will enable you to run the watermaker without running the generator.

Physical size and weight are other factors that must be taken into account when selecting a watermaker. It is no use settling upon a 200 gallon per day unit driven by 110 volts only to find that it does not fit in the engine compartment, or that it is too heavy to put where you want it.

Next, the ease of servicing must be considered. All watermakers need some servicing, but the design of some units makes it easier to tell when servicing is required. For instance, some units come with an electronic diagnostic display, which gives an immediate readout of the watermaker's status.

This readout indicates whether the prefilters need cleaning, whether the oil in the high-pressure pumps needs changing, and most importantly, when to clean the membranes. Without a diagnostic display, you will have to log the readings from the gauges and flowmeters and then decide what needs to be done. Ideally, the diagnostic display panel should be mounted in the navigation area so that it can be checked often. If it is in the engine room, there is a good chance it will be looked at only when the main engine is checked.

Finally, a few more features should be included in your watermaking system:

1. The watermaking unit should be ordered with an oil/water separator and a booster pump, especially if it is to be used in harbor or near the coast. If oil is allowed to contact the membrane it will deteriorate it, and a deteriorated membrane will allow saltwater through.

2. Ideally, the boat should be set up with two freshwater tanks. Then, if the membrane or the shore water supply is contaminated, at least one tank will not be affected. Also, the unit should have an automatic diverter valve. Then, if the membrane allows contaminated water through, that water will be automatically diverted over the side.

3. Because the unit has seawater and electrical current passing through parts of it, it should have a sacrificial zinc to prevent stray electrical current from causing electrolysis of the high-pressure pump.

4. Ideally, the unit should be self-cleaning to ensure that the water made stays pure. Some units do this by flushing the system on a regular basis. To make it easy, the watermaker should have a built-in cleaning system. In some units, this system can be activated simply by turning one valve and adding the right amount of cleaning powder. To flush the unit, simply return the valve to its original position. Other systems have a much more cumbersome cleaning system, which makes it likely that the unit will not be cleaned as often as it should.

5. Cleaning the membranes is the most important maintenance task and should be done regularly. Choose a unit on which the membrane is easy to clean.

6. If you want to be sure that your fresh water stays pure, incorporate an ultraviolet sterilizer and carbon filter into the system. These will reduce bacterial contamination of your water supply.

7. If you intend to sail overseas, pick a unit that is sold and serviced worldwide.

8. The seawater intakes for the watermaker should be well forward of any bilge or engine room exhaust outlets. This will limit the possibility of oil getting into the system.

9. Ideally, the high-pressure fittings in the watermaker should be 316 stainless steel to prevent corrosion in a saltwater environment.

Manufacturers of Watermakers and Purifiers

Aqua-Chem, Inc.
Water Technologies Division
P.O. Box 421
Milwaukee, WI 53210
Tel: (414) 962-0100
300 to 1500 gallons per day

Astro-Pure Water Purifiers
3025 S.W. 2nd Ave.
Ft. Lauderdale, FL
33315-3309
Tel: (305) 832-0630
Fax: (305) 832-0729
Water purifiers

Balmar Products, Inc.
1537 N.W. Ballard Way
Seattle, WA 98107
Tel: (206) 789-4970
Fax: (206) 784-0878
Aqua-Master desalinator

**Galley Maid Marine
Products**
4348 West Roads Dr.
West Palm Beach, FL 33407
Tel: (407) 848-8696
Fax: (407) 848-8872

General Ecology, Inc.
151 Sheree Blvd.
Exton, PA 19431
Tel: (215) 363-7900
Fax: (215) 363-0412
Water purification systems

HRO Systems
A Division of Standard
Communications
P.O. Box 92151
Los Angeles, CA 90009-2151
Tel: (800) 366-4476
  or   (310) 532-5300
Fax: (310) 769-5917

Lifesteam
P.O. Box 92408
Long Beach, CA 90809-2408
Tel: (800) 468-5426
  or   (213) 426-3260
Fax: (213) 595-0274

**Maritime Services (Div. of
Triton Holdings)**
3440 Bridgeway St.
Vancouver, British Columbia
V5K 1B6
CANADA
Tel: (604) 294-4444

McDonnell Marine
8 East Newberry Rd.
Bloomfield, CT 06002
Tel: (203) 243-9114

Ocean Options, Inc.
50 Fort St.
Fairhaven, MA 02719
Tel: (508) 992-3644
Fax: (508) 999-5338

**PUR, Division of Recovery
Engineering, Inc.**
2229 Edgewood Ave. S.
Minneapolis, MN 55426
Tel: (800) 845-PURE
  or   (612) 541-1313
Fax: (612) 541-1230
*12 Volt watermakers up to 86
gallons per day*

Sea Recovery
P.O. Box 2560
Gardena, CA 90247-0560
Tel: (800) 354-2000
  or   (310) 327-4000
Fax: (310) 327-4350
*Systems ranging from 8 to
1000 gallons per day*

**Universal Aqua
Technologies, Inc.**
12207 Los Nietos Rd.
Plant C
Santa Fe Springs, CA 90670
Tel: (310) 944-4121
Fax: (310) 941-9633

Vetus Den Ouden, Inc.
P.O. Box 8712
Baltimore, MD 21240-0712
Tel: (410) 712-0740
Fax: (410) 712-0985

Village Marine Tec
Gardena, CA 90247
Tel: (800) 421-4503

Figure 1: This watermaker unit
is available from Universal Aqua
Technologies. Note how all the
parts can easily be removed for
maintenance.

Winches

By Dick Rath

Dick Rath is the national sales manager for International Marine, Lewmar Division. He has been associated with the winch market for the last nineteen years. He cruises and races regularly in northeastern waters.

HOW MANY WINCHES?

A winch allows a person to exert force beyond what the average person can exert by hand. For most vessels, a winch is the simplest and most logical answer to providing any additional power or mechanical advantage that is required. There might be as many as fifteen different applications for winches on a modern racing or cruising sloop, and the number might go even higher for a ketch, yawl, or cutter rig. Some common applications are:

- Genoa/jib sheets
- Spinnaker sheets
- Staysail sheets
- Mainsheet
- Mizzen sheet
- Genoa/jib halyard
- Spinnaker halyard
- Staysail halyard
- Main halyard
- Mizzen halyard
- Mainsail outhaul
- Mizzen outhaul
- Spinnaker staysail halyard
- Spinnaker pole topping lift
- Spinnaker pole butt lift
- Boom vang
- Running backstays
- Permanent backstays
- Furling line
- Mainsail reef/cunningham line

Prior to the development of rope clutches (or sheet stoppers, as they are often called), it was not uncommon to see vessels equipped with one or two winches for each of these applications. But today, as better rope clutches have become available, we often find a single winch being used for two, three, four, or even more applications. The exact number of winches on a particular boat depends on the vessel's size, purpose, design, and displacement, as well as the owner/skipper's desires, abilities, wants, needs, and budget.

The average performance cruising/racing yacht today generally has six winches on deck, with rope clutches set up in front of most, if not all, of them. With the number of winches decreasing, and with most being relied upon to tension a wider variety of lines, extreme care must be taken to precisely match the winch to the task. The required power, speed, and strength or safe working load of the winch for each application should be determined to begin selecting the winch model that most closely meets the requirements. If self-tailing winches are specified, the line diameter for each application must meet the self-tailing specification for each winch.

WINCH CHARACTERISTICS

Every winch has certain characteristics. In order of importance they are: strength, power, speed, and weight.

Strength

A winch's strength is generally expressed as its "safe working load." Safe working load is usually 1/2 of the load at which the winch fails in any number of ways, but typically some internal component bends or distorts so that the winch will no longer function as designed. Since most winches have enormous strength, it is extremely rare to see a failure related to overloading. But winch failures, although rare, do occur, and the cause is most commonly improper or nonexistent maintenance rather than overloading. It is thus crucial to follow your winch manufacturer's recommendations for service and maintenance to assure a long and trouble-free life expectancy. For a variety of reasons, winch manufacturers rarely publish safe working loads. However, this information is easily obtained by contacting the manufacturer's home office or regional office.

Power

A winch's power, or more accurately, its pulling power, is today commonly stated in terms of power ratio. Power ratio is a theoretical expression derived through a universally accepted formula:

$$\frac{2 \times \text{handle length} \times \text{gear ratio}}{\text{drum diameter}} = \text{power ratio}$$

The standard handle length used in this calculation is 10 inches. Thus, to determine a winch's power ratio, you need its gear ratio in each speed and its drum diameter at the point where the first wrap of line encircles the drum. Both figures are supplied in the manufacturer's catalog. For example, using the data in the current Lewmar catalog, the calculations for the power ratios of the Lewmar model 44 two-speed winch would be:

1st speed:
$$\frac{20 \times 5.83 \times 2.4}{3.43} = 13.99$$

2nd speed:
$$\frac{20 \times 5.83 \times 7.6}{3.43} = 44.31$$

Where
Handle length x 2 = 20
Gear ratio = 2.4 for 1st speed
Gear ratio = 7.6 for 2nd speed
Drum Diameter = 3.43

This means that in second speed, with 100 pounds of pressure applied to a 10 inch winch handle, the winch should theoretically pull or lift 4,431 pounds.

Keep in mind that the term power ratio is theoretical in the sense that the formula does not take into account a winch's efficiciency. Efficiency can only be measured in a pull test which, to be accurate, would have to be performed on each individual winch. Tests on a wide variety of winch models reveal that efficiency varies between 65% and 90%. In larger winches, which generally include more roller bearings, efficiency averages about 85%. Small winches that only include roller bearings on the drum bore average about 75% efficiency. Since your winch must operate in a rather hostile saltwater/salt air environment, in a wide range of temperatures, and since it consists of a number of different materials and is rarely serviced on a daily basis, it is manufactured to tolerances that accept these factors and allow it to be operated easily despite them.

However, winches must be serviced on a regular basis if they are to perform to their designed specifications. The loss of efficiency due to lack of a regularly scheduled maintenance program can be dramatic; in extreme cases, efficiency may be reduced by 50%. The general rule is that winches undergo a complete servicing once each year if the vessel sails in saltwater. If there is a winter layup period, the servicing should be done in the fall to rid the winches of corrosive salts during the period when they would do most damage.

Speed

The question of winch speed is really a question of tradeoffs between speed, power, weight, and cost. For racing boats, speed is paramount. Racing sailors try to optimize speed and still retain power by choosing three-speed winches. This allows the sails to be trimmed very fast utilizing a very high first speed gear ratio (usually between 1.0 to 1 and 2.3 to 1), a moderately fast second speed (usually between 4.0 to 1 and 8.0 to 1), and a slow but very powerful

third speed for final trim. As a rule, during a fast tack, about 90% of the sheet should be brought in before dropping to third speed. Not only is speed a requirement for the sheet winches on a racing boat; the halyard winches must be fast as well.

In addition to the faster gearing, racers will also opt for wide diameter drums, which contribute to faster line speeds and minimize the number of wraps required on the drum. Fewer wraps mean that castoffs are quicker and easier. Wide drum winches also have a very shallow radius to the flair at the top of the drum, further easing the castoff procedure.

Those at the upper echelon of sailboat racing often forego all the benfits self-tailing winches offer, fearing that even one snag on the stripper arm could blow a tack and slow the boat down. But the more relaxed performance cruiser will generally select self-tailers for every application. Performance cruisers generally use two-speed models for primaries on boats under 45 feet. For larger boats, the low-speed power requirement becomes so great that three speeds become necessary to achieve an acceptable power/speed curve.

Flat-out cruisers pay scant attention to speed. All they want is to get the sails up and trimmed with as little effort as possible. They will usually select one- or two-speed self-tailers with slow but powerful gearing.

Weight

The rule of thumb is that the more performance-oriented the vessel, the more concious its designer or owner becomes of weight. At one end of the spectrum, every effort is made to cut weight out of each winch on deck. Extensive use of aluminum, titanium, carbon fiber, torlon, and very high-grade stainless-steel in the design of racing winches can cut weights in half. Weight savings generally come at a very high cost, however, since these are low-volume products, essentially custom made, with expensive materials that are difficult to machine or fabricate. Additionally, because many dissimilar metals and materials are used in their construction, lightweight winches require far more attention and servicing than their counterparts on cruising boats.

In between the heavy but extremely durable bronze or stainless steel winches that can go for longer intervals between servicing, are the middle-weight, aluminum-drum, racer/cruiser winches. These are usually identical to their chrome or stainless counterparts, but have heavy drums replaced with lightweight aluminum. This minor change can mean big savings in weight. An average 40 foot racer/cruiser can save perhaps 50 pounds on deck simply by selecting aluminum-drum winches. But again, there is a tradeoff. Aluminum is not as durable as bronze or stainless steel, and it is prone to electrolysis and corrosion in a saltwater environment, particularly so because of the dissimilar metals in its works. Another reason for the more frequent service intervals with aluminum winch drums is that black anodizing is used on them because of its superior hardness. As the sun beats down on these winches, they get quite hot inside, causing rapid evaporation of the seawater that normally washes through a winch in heeled conditions. As the seawater evaporates, salt deposits are left. These mix with the winch's grease, further increasing electrolysis and corrosion. Chrome or stainless winches reflect the heat rather than absorb it. They stay cool and are more tolerant to reasonable neglect. Again, the tradeoff.

CHOOSING YOUR WINCHES

Each manufacturer publishes a selection guide for its winches based on calculations of loads and power requirements for a wide variety of applications on most modern sailing yachts. While it is generally safe to make your winch selections using these guides, it is always best to consult the manufacturer's agents to confirm your choices.

Self-Tailing or Standard?

In addition to the model selection, you have to decide whether you want self-tailing or standard winches. There is no application on a modern sailing yacht that cannot benefit from self-tailing winches. They turn a two-person job into a job easily handled by one; they allow two hands to be used (on a double grip handle); they eliminate the need for expensive cleats, creating more comfortable seating. Generally, they pay for themselves in increased enjoyment and dimished effort. About the only serious argument against self-tailers is the Grand Prix racer's concern regarding snags in super-fast tacking situations. Also, in a few applications, the extra expense may not be worth it. For example, halyards on furling sails that are used only twice a year when the sail goes up or comes down, may not be considered appropriate candidates for self-tailing winches. Perhaps the only real decision you'll have to make regarding self-tailers is whether you want ones that automatically adjust to a wide range of line diameters, such as Lewmar's Ocean series. These winches incorporate a spring-loaded jaw mechanism in their design. Alternatively, you can opt for a self-tailer that you adjust manually to suit different line diameters.

Electric or Hydraulic?

For those considering power winches, there is yet another decision to be made: will electric or hydraulic drive winches best suit your needs? In many instances, the size of the vessel and the owner's budget will determine the choice.

Hydraulic winches require a large, somewhat complicated, and initially quite expensive external power source — the D.C. motor-driven pump, the fluid reservoir tank, and the manifold containing the flow controls. This unit is usually referred to as the Commander system or power pack. As the number of winch functions increases, the Commander is called upon to deliver more, and the cost per function goes down in comparison to electric winches. Thus, the owner of a 45 footer, whose powered winch requirements include only a pair of primaries, would find electric winches the best choice. They would be less

expensive, since the hydraulic Commander unit would be very costly to install for only two winches. Moreover, the space the Commander would have taken up could be utilized for the interior design. The external power required for the two electric winches would simply be the yacht's standard batteries.

On larger vessels it becomes desirable, perhaps even necessary, to power things other than winches, such as furlers, travellers, windlasses, centerboard lifts, or transom doors. Since all these can be driven from the same Commander power source, the cost to drive each item drops as more functions are added.

While both electric and hydraulic systems are considered extremely reliable, each is always designed with the ability to be driven manually in the event of a failure. The difference, though, is that if a hydraulic power pack fails, all the powered functions fail. With electric winches, a failure is generally confined to a specific winch, and that failure can often be temporarily overcome through cross-sheeting to a functioning winch. Although, you must be sure that the load direction is adequately reinforced.

Whatever you choose — electric or hydraulic, powered or manual, self-tailing or standard, racing or cruising models — the right winches, carefully selected and properly installed and maintained will prove to be one of the best investments you'll ever make on your boat. They'll add greatly to both your sailing performance and pleasure.

Manufacturers of Winches

Antal SRL
Via del Progresso, 10
35020 Padova
ITALY
Tel: (+39) 49 870 2655
Fax: (+39) 49 760 906
Antal winches

ABI Industries, Inc.
1261 Anderson Dr.
Suite C
San Rafael, CA 94901
Tel: (415) 258-9300
Fax: (415) 258-9461
Centerboard winches

Euro Marine Trading, Inc.
64 Halsey St.
Newport, RI 02840
Tel: (401) 849-0060
Fax: (401) 849-3230
*Antal winches and deck gear;
manual and self-tailing
winches*

Goiot SA
28 rue du Frere-Loius
44062 Nantes Cedex 02
FRANCE
Tel: (+33) 40 75 68 39
Fax: (+33) 40 75 43 56
Winches and deck gear

Figure 2: IM/Lewmar manufacture a large line of winches.

Harken, Inc.
1251 E. Wisconsin Ave.
Pewaukee, WI 53072
Tel: (414) 691-3320
Fax: (414) 691-3008
Winches

IM/Barient
P.O. Box 308
New Whitfield St.
Guilford, CT 06437
Tel: (203) 458-6200
Fax: (203) 453-5669
Winches

IM/Lewmar Marine, Inc.
P.O. Box 308
New Whitfield St.
Guilford, CT 06437
Tel: (203) 458-6200
Fax: (203) 453-5669
*Winches, capstans, hatches,
and deck gear*

Maxwell Marine, Inc.
629 Terminal Way
Suite #1
Costa Mesa, CA 92627
Tel: (714) 631-2634
Fax: (714) 631-2846
Winches and capstans

Maxwell Winches Ltd.
P.O. Box 100-703
North Shore Mail Center
Auckland 9
NEW ZEALAND
Tel: (+64) 9 444-7396
Fax: (+64) 9 444-0090
Winches and capstans

Meissner Engineering bv
Stationsplien 3
3224 AT Hellevoetsluis
HOLLAND
Tel: (+31) 0 1883-22835
Fax: (+31) 0 1883-23838
Winches

Scanvik, Inc.
980 36th Ct. S.W.
Vero Beach, FL 32968
Tel: (407) 567-2877
Fax: (407) 567-9113
Andersen winches

Figure 1: This self-tailing winch from Harken can be easily disassembled for maintenance.

Windlasses

You are lying at anchor in a peaceful cove, ready to head home. You go forward to begin the process of raising anchor. The line comes in a few fathoms and then stops. You stand on the windlass button again, but nothing happens to the line. You signal to the helmsman to come forward until the anchor line is vertical and some line comes in, but the windlass cuts out. This means a trip aft to the electrical panel to reset the windlass breaker, then forward again to start getting line in once more. The line comes in a few feet and stops. Again the windlass cuts out. Eventually, after cutting out three more times, you resort to hand-cranking the windlass to get the anchor line up. Unusual scenario? Not if you anchor a lot. But it tells you a lot about problems in your anchor handling system. First, either your windlass is too small or the breaker may be set too low when full load is needed. Second, its a long way back and forth to the breaker panel every time it must be reset.

Finding the ideal windlass is not easy. It should be light in weight, easy to turn, have a high torque, not consume too much power (check how much power it takes to stall the drum before determining size), and be easily operated by electricity or by hand. It should have a small footprint — that is, it shouldn't take up much room on the foredeck. The gypsy should be suited to the chain being used and the capstan should be of large enough diameter to allow at least three turns of the anchor rode to fit comfortably. The body of the windlass should be well protected against corrosion, and the entire electrical unit should be sealed against water ingress. Check, too, the maintenance schedule of the windlass. If it needs oiling everytime it gets wet, you should look at another model.

If a hawshole is fitted, make sure that it drains to the bilge. Also make sure that the chain locker and any anchor wells have good sized drains. Make sure that the chain, anchor line, and any splices or shackles fit through the hawse hole.

Boats under 35 feet LOA will probably have a manual windlass. This should be a double-action type, in that the drum or gypsy is turned on both strokes of the lever. Larger vessels have the battery or engine power to drive an electric or hydraulic windlass. You might also need a saltwater washdown pump at the bow to rinse off the chain and anchor. All these items must be considered before you go out and purchase a windlass.

Manufacturers of Windlasses

ABI Industries, Inc.
1261 Anderson Dr.
Suite C
San Rafael, CA 94901
Tel: (415) 258-9300
Fax: (415) 258-9461

Avon Seagull Marine
1851 McGaw Ave.
Irvine, CA 92714
Tel: (714) 250-0880

Balmar
1537 N.W. Ballard Way
Seattle, WA 98107
Tel: (206) 789-4970
Fax: (206) 784-0878
Manual, hydraulic, and electric windlasses

Benson Marine
8160 Spire Ct.
Colorado Springs, CO 80919
Tel: (800) 828-2343
Fax: (719) 260-7388

Bomar
South West St.
P.O. Box W
Charlestown, NH 03603
Tel: (603) 826-5791
Fax: (603) 826-4125
Manual and electric models

Dorchester Industries, Inc.
Dorchester, NJ 08316
Tel: (609) 785-1242
Hytec Concepts hydraulic anchor winch

Goiot SA
28 rue du Frere-Loius
44062 Nantes Cedex 02
FRANCE
Tel: (+33) 40 75 68 39
Fax: (+33) 40 75 43 56

Ideal Windlass Co.
P.O. Box 430
5810 Post Rd.
E. Greenwich, RI 02818
Tel: (401) 884-2550
Fax: (401) 884-1260
Electric windlasses and capstans

Imtra Corp.
30 Barnet Blvd.
New Bedford, MA 02745
Tel: (508) 990-2700
Fax: (508) 994-4919

Figure 1: The 3500 series gypsy capstan from IM/Lewmar.

IM/Lewmar Marine, Inc.
P.O. Box 308
New Whitfield St.
Guilford, CT 06437
Tel: (203) 458-6200
Fax: (203) 453-5669

Johnson Fishing, Inc.
1531 Madison Ave.
Mankato, MN 56001
Deck Hand electric anchor windlass

Lunenburg Foundry & Engineering
P.O. Box 1240
Lunenburg, Nova Scotia BOJ 2CO
CANADA
Tel: (902) 634-8827

Lofrans Windlasses
South Pacific Assoc.
4918 Leary Ave.
N.W. Seattle, WA 98107
Tel: (800) 22-SOPAC

Marinox, Inc.
403 N.E. 8th St.
Ft. Lauderdale, FL 33304
Tel: (305) 760-4702
Fax: (305) 763-8790
GDI Windlasses

Maxwell Marine, Inc.
629 Terminal Way
Suite #1
Costa Mesa, CA 92627
Tel: (714) 631-2634
Fax: (714) 631-2846
Maxwell-Nilsson Winches

Maxwell Winches Ltd.
P.O. Box 100-703
North Shore Mail Center
Auckland 9
NEW ZEALAND
Tel: (+64) 9 444-7396
Fax: (+64) 9 444-0090

Nilsson Winches Ltd.
69 Hillside Rd.
Takapuna
Auckland 10
NEW ZEALAND
Tel: (+64) 9 444-9329

R. C. Plath
5300 S.E. Johnson Creek Blvd.
Portland, OR 97222
Tel: (503) 777-2441
Fax: (503) 777-2450

Powerwinch
810 Union Ave.
Bridgeport, CT 06607
Tel: (203) 384-8000
Windlasses and boat hauling winches

Scanvik Inc.
980 36th Court S.W.
Vero Beach, FL 32968
Tel: (407) 567-2877
Fax: (407) 567-9113

Scott & Felzer Power Winch Division
100 Production Dr.
Harrison, OH 45030
Tel: (513) 243-3097

Simpson-Lawrence Ltd.
218/228 Edmiston Dr.
Glasgow G51 2YT
SCOTLAND
Tel: (+44) 41-4275331
Fax: (+44) 41-4275419

Simpson-Lawrence USA, Inc.
3004 29th Ave. E.
Bradenton, FL 34208
Tel: (813) 746-7161
Fax: (813) 746-7166

So-Pac
4918 Leary Ave.
Seattle, WA 98107
Tel: (800) 22-SOPAC
  or (206) 782-7700
Fax: (206) 782-4531
Muir and Lofrans windlasses

Vetus - Den Ouden, Inc.
P.O. Box 8712
Baltimore, MD 21240-0712
Tel: Orders only: (800)
GO-VETUS
  or (410) 712-0740
Fax: (410) 712-0985
Manual and electric windlasses

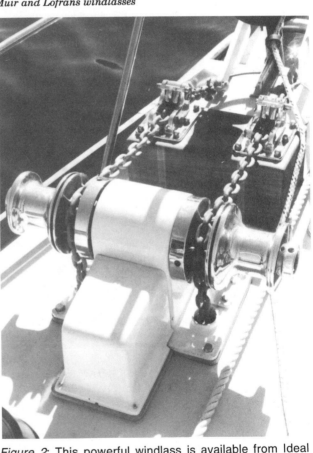

Figure 2: This powerful windlass is available from Ideal Windlass Company.

Yacht Brokers

By Jeffrey C. Foster

Jeffery C. Foster is vice president of Northrup and Johnson, Newport, Rhode Island. He has been a yacht broker for twenty years and is a former vice president of the Yacht Architects and Brokers Association. He has sailed on many Bermuda races and has frequently navigated the maxi yacht "Matador."

Brokers are the agents who list boats for sale or help a buyer find the right boat. For instance, if you are about to buy a boat, you might ask a broker to determine if your estimate of what you can get for your money is accurate. (It usually isn't.) Or if you are selling a boat, you would ask a broker to list it. Nowadays, many boats for sale are put on a master list that is circulated to other brokers, usually nationwide.

You'll get your best service by working with a single yacht broker. If you go to several brokers, they will know they are competing with each other and are unlikely to work hard on your behalf since the sale is likely to go to someone else. In contrast, if you use a single broker, and have a good rapport with that person, he'll probably work hard because he knows he'll eventually make the sale.

BUYING A BOAT

When buying a boat, here's what you can reasonably expect of a yacht broker.

1. *Find out what you are looking for.* In broker's terminology, he will find out your needs and uses. This means that you can help the broker by writing down what you intend using the boat for and the features you want in a new boat. For a powerboat, your list of features should include the type of engines you desire, the steering position, the number of bunks, the number of heads, the speed, the tankage, and the power, which will affect the boat's range, and your price limit. For a sailboat, you should include the approximate size, the number of bunks, the price you can afford, the rig type, the engine style (inboard or outboard), and other features, such as an enclosed head, showers, and so forth. When you have listed all the features you want, make another list showing the ones you are willing to compromise on. That way, the broker will get a better feel for which boats to show you and which ones to skip over.

2. *Research the market to find the boat that is nearest to your desires and your budget.* The broker will then present to you a number of boats and their specifications. Usually, he will look at the boats before offering it to a client. This is to avoid arriving at a boat that may be listed in fabulous condition, but in real life is an unsellable mess.

3. *Arrange times and places for you to view prospective boats.* Quite often a boat is listed by one broker, called the listing broker, and another broker brings a client to see it. In this case, it is likely that both the listing broker and your broker will lead you through the inspection.

4. *Prepare all the necessary paperwork for you to make an offer.* At the time of making an offer, you will be asked to pay a deposit, which the broker will put in an escrow account. This deposit can range from 2 to 20% of the price of the boat, depending upon the vessel's size and complexity.

5. *Present your offer, subject to survey, to the seller.* The broker will also assist in negotiating the boat's inventory as well as the purchase price.

6. *Help you find a good surveyor in the area where the boat is located.* Before you purchase any used boat, have it surveyed. There are no exceptions to this rule. If problems are found, the broker will help you renegotiate the deal.

7. *Inventory everything that comes with the boat and ensure that it matches the inventory you signed when the bill of sale went through.*

8. *Prepare the paperwork for the closing and ensure that there are no liens on the boat.* The broker may also set up any insurance or other documents that need to be obtained before you take possession of the boat.

9. *Attend the closing to make sure the deal goes through smoothly.* Hopefully, you will now have the boat you want.

The broker has a different set of responsibilities when a client has a boat to sell and is hoping to get as much money as possible for it. In this case, the broker will:

1. *Make a thorough inspection.* At that time, the broker will itemize the yacht's inventory and discuss with the client what is to be sold with the boat. Normally, the boat is sold as is, except for the owner's personal belongings.

2. *Advise the seller of the current market value of similar boats.* This may be very easy if the boat is one of a production run. In that case, the base price is reasonably well established and only the extras need to be estimated. If the boat is a custom vessel, the job becomes harder. But an experienced broker will have a feel for the market and will be able to give the client a good indication of the price that should be asked.

3. *Advise the seller of similar vessels that are on the market and their price.* This will help the seller set a suitable price.

4. *Write up a complete listing for the boat.* This listing is then sent out to other brokers. The broker might also suggest an advertising campaign to sell the yacht as soon as possible.

5. *Answer all the inquiries on the boat.*

6. *Ensure that any offers received are legitimate and that the potential buyer has money on deposit before forwarding the offer to the seller.*

7. *Ensure that other potential buyers know that the boat is under offer.*

8. *When an offer is accepted, get all the paperwork together so that the sale can proceed quickly.* The broker will make

sure the seller's rights are protected, and get everything ready for the closing.

9. *Attend the closing to ensure that everything goes smoothly and the paperwork is completed in a timely fashion.*

For doing all this work the broker receives a commission which can vary between 5% and 12% of the selling or purchase price of the boat. Where one broker has listed the boat and another broker has brought the client in, the commission is split between the brokers in a previously negotiated proportion.

Brokers can make selling or buying a boat a much easier task for the average client. But when you decide to use a broker, make sure that he or she is associated with a nationally recognized company and is a member of the Yacht Architects and Brokers Association.

Addresses of Yacht Brokers

American Yacht Brokers

A & M Yacht Sales, Inc.
5004 Dauphin Island Pkwy.
Mobile, AL 36605
Tel: (800) 548- 9193
  or (205) 471-6949
Fax: (205) 479-4625

Able Yacht Brokerage
P.O. Box 8055
Bar Harbor Airport Rd.
Trenton, ME 04605
Tel: (800) 847-4717
  or (207) 667-6235
Fax: (207) 667-3986

Able Yacht Brokerage
Little Harbor Boat Yard
42 Doaks Ln.
P.O. Box 584
Marblehead, MA 01945
Tel: (617) 639-4280
Fax: (617) 639-4233

Active MarineYacht Brokerage
31785 South River Rd.
Mt. Clemens, MI 48045
Tel: (800) 682-9975
  or (313) 463-7441
Fax: (313) 468-7071

Active Marine Yacht Brokerage
1111 N. Elston
Chicago, IL 60622
Tel: (800) 769-2871
  or (312) 862-5665
Fax: (312) 862-5784

Active Marine Yacht Brokerage
20 N. Van Brunt
Englewood, NJ 07631
Tel: (201) 567-8952
Fax: (201) 567-8953

Admiral Yachts
326 First St.
Annapolis, MD 21403
Tel: (410) 267-0367
Fax: (410) 280-5258

Aggressive Marine
32393 S. River Rd.
Mt. Clemens, MI 48045
Tel: (313) 463-1234
Fax: (313) 465-1954

Alden Yacht Brokerage
89 Commercial Wharf
Boston, MA 02110
Tel: (617) 227-9480
Fax: (617) 523-5465

Alden Yacht Brokerage
1909 Alden Landing
Portsmouth, RI 02781
Tel: (401) 683-4285
Fax: (401) 683-3668

Hank Aldrich Yacht Sales, Inc.
Brewer Dauntless Shipyard
37 Pratt St.
Essex, CT 06426
Tel: (203) 767-4988
Fax: (203) 767-4998

Alexander Yachts, Inc.
2150 S.E. 17th St.
Suite 121
Ft. Lauderdale, FL 33316
Tel: (305) 763-7676
Fax: (305) 763-7758

Allied Marine Yacht Division
401 S.W. First Ave.
Ft. Lauderdale, FL 33301
Tel: (305) 462-7424
Fax: (305) 462-0756

Altech Yachts, Inc.
1500 Cordova Rd.
Ft. Lauderdale, FL 33316
Tel: (305) 462-0400
Fax: (305) 462-4968

American Yacht/Mainsail
2144 Westlake Ave.
Seattle, WA 98109
Tel: (206) 284-6354
 or (206) 285-5380
Fax: (206) 285-1772

Anacortes Yacht Sales
24151 T Ave.
Suite 120
Anacortes, WA 98221
Tel: (206) 293-0631
Fax: (206) 293-0633

Anchor Bay Yacht Sales, Inc.
202 Nanticoke Rd.
Essex, MD 21221
Tel: (800) 666-3386
 or (410) 574-0777
Fax: (410) 574-8364

Anchor Marine, Inc.
10967 N. Bayshore Dr.
Sister Bay, WI 54234
Tel: (414) 854-2124

Anchor Yacht Brokerage
At Anchor Point Marina
10905 Corduroy Rd.
Curtice, OH 43412
Tel: (419) 836-8985

Annapolis Motor Yachts
P.O. Box 2193
Annapolis, MD 21404
Tel: (800) 777-7187
 or (301) 268-7171
Fax: (301) 268-6921

Annapolis Yacht Sales
7416 Edgewood Road
Annapolis, MD 21403
Tel: (410) 267-8181
 or (410) 626-1781
Fax: (410) 267-7409

Bob Anslow Yacht Sales
400 B. Flagler Dr.
W. Palm Beach, FL
Tel: (407) 832-6005
Fax: (407) 832-9149

Ardell Yacht and Ship Brokers
2101 West Coast Hwy.
Newport Beach, CA 92663
Tel: (714) 642-9884
Fax: (714) 642-5735

Ardell Yacht and Ship Brokers
1550 S.E.17th St.
Ft. Lauderdale, FL 33316
Tel: (305) 527-1292
Fax: (305) 527-7637

Atlantic-Pacific Sailing Yachts
2244 S.E. 17th St.
Ft. Lauderdale, FL 33316
Tel: (305) 463-7651
Fax: (305) 779-3316

Atlantic Yacht & Ship, Inc.
Harbor Town Marina
850 N.E. 3rd St.
Dania, FL
Tel: (305) 921-1500
Fax: (305) 921-1518

The Atlantic Yacht Market
Cape Ann's Marina
75 Essex Ave.
Gloucester, MA 01930
Tel: (508) 283-2161
Fax: (508) 281-4905

Atlantic Yacht Sales, Inc.
1717 N. Bayshore Dr.
Suite 114
Miami, FL 33132
Tel: (305) 374-7447
Fax: (305) 374-7448

Browns Bridge Marine Brokerage, Inc.
6930 Holiday Rd.
Buford, GA 30518
Tel: (404) 945-2166

Bruce A. Bales & Co.
1635 S. Miami Rd.
Suite 2
Ft. Lauderdale, FL 33316
Tel: (305) 522-3760
Fax: (305) 522-4364

Bartram & Brakenhoff
2 Marina Plaza
Goat Island
Newport, RI 02840-1560
Tel: (401) 846-7355
Fax: (401) 837-6329

Bass Harbor Marine
Bass Harbor, ME 04653
Tel: (207) 244-7534
Fax: (207) 244-7535

Bass Harbor Marine
49 America's Cup Ave.
Newport, RI 02840
Tel: (401) 849-0240
Fax: (401) 849-0620

Bayport Yachts
Mears Point Marina
Rt. 50 and Kent Narrows
Grasonville, MD 21683
Tel: (410) 827-5500
Fax: (410) 827-5481

Bay Yacht Agency
326 First St.
Annapolis, MD 21403
Tel: (800) 922-4820
  or (410) 236-2311
Fax: (410) 236-2711

Bay Yacht Brokerage
26 Tanglewood Ln.
Salem, MA 01970
Tel: (508) 741-1477

Bay Yacht Traders
7310 Edgewood
Annapolis, MD 21403
Tel: (410) 268-4930

Beaufort Yacht Sales
328 Front St.
Beaufort, NC 28516
Tel: (919) 728-3155
Fax: (919) 728-6715

Ron Berger Yachts, Inc.
Yacht Haven
Stamford, CT
Tel: (203) 323-4522
Fax: (203) 323-2313

Berry-Boger Yachts Sales
P.O. Box 36
North Myrtle Beach, SC 29597
Tel: (803) 249-6167
Fax: (803) 249-0105

Carl Bettano Yacht Brokerage
550 Pleasant St.
Winthrop, MA 02152
Tel: (617) 846-5354
Fax: (617) 846-8154

Jay Bettis & Co.
2509 NASA Rd. #1
Seabrook, TX 77586
Tel: (713) 474-4101
Fax: (713) 532-1305

Martin Bird & Associates
326 First St.
Annapolis, MD 21403
Tel: (301) 268-1086
Fax: (301) 268-0942

Bluewater Yacht Sales, Inc.
25 Marina Rd.
Hampton, VA 23669
Tel: (804) 723-0793
Fax: (804) 723-3320

Boatworks Yacht Sales
Brewer Dauntless Shipyard
37 Pratt St.
Essex, CT 06426
Tel: (203) 767-3013
Fax: (203) 767-7178

Bollman Yachts
2064 SE 17th St.
Ft. Lauderdale, FL 33316
Tel: (305) 761-1122
Fax: (305) 463-9878

Bonnie Castle Marine
Sands Hotel & Marina
101 North Riverside Dr.
Pompano Beach, FL 33062
Tel: (305) 782-3806
Fax: (305) 782-3844

Boston Yacht Sales Inc.
275 River St.
N. Weymouth, MA 02191
Tel: (617) 331-2400
Fax: (617) 331-8215

Bradford International Yacht Sales, Inc.
3151 State Rd. 84
Ft. Lauderdale, FL 33312
Tel: (800) 327-9719
  or (305) 791-2600
Fax: (305) 791-2655

Brennan Marine Sales
1809 S. Water St.
Bay City, MI 48207
Tel: (517) 894-4181
Fax: (517) 894-0371

Brewer Yacht Sales
Brewer Yacht Yard
500 Beach Rd.
Greenport, NY 11944
Tel: (516) 477-0770

Brewer Yacht Sales
Cove Haven Marina
101 Narragansett Ave.
Barrington, RI 02806

Brewer Yacht Sales
Cowesett
100 Folly Landing
Warwick, RI 02887
Tel: (401) 884-1690

Brewer Yacht Sales
Pilot's Point Marina N.
Westbrook, CT
Tel: (203) 399-6213
Fax: (203) 399-4379

Brewer Yacht Sales
Plymouth Marine
14 Union St.
Plymouth, MA 02630
Tel: (508) 746-4500

Brewer Yacht Sales
Sakonnet Marina
222 Naragansett Blvd.
Portsmouth, RI 02871
Tel: (401) 683-3977

Brewer Yacht Sales
Wickford Cove
P.O. Box 436
N. Kingstown, RI 02852

Brigadoon Yacht Sales
1500 Westlake Ave. N.
#114
Seattle, WA 98109
Tel: (206) 282-6500
Fax: (206) 282-2410

Bristol Yacht Sales
623 Sixth St.
Annapolis, MD 21403
Tel: (410) 280-6611
Fax: (410) 280-0170

Broward Yacht Sales
1535 SE 17th St.
Suite 202
17th St. Quay
Ft. Lauderdale, FL 33316
Tel: (305) 763-8201
Fax: (305) 763-9079

Luke Brown & Assoc.
1500 Cordova Road
Suite 200
Ft. Lauderdale, FL 33316
Tel: (305) 525-6617
Fax: (305) 525-6626

Brunell's Marina
One Alvord St.
S. Hadley, MA 01075
Tel: (413) 536-3132
Fax: (413) 532-6595

Bullock Cove Marina
254 Riverside Dr.
Riverside, RI 02915
Tel: (401) 433-3010

Burr Yacht Sales, Inc.
1106 Turkey Pt. Rd.
Edgewater, MD 21037
Tel: (410) 798-5900
Fax: (410) 798-5911

Buzzard's Bay Yacht Sales, Inc.
P.O. Box 369
Westport Pt., MA 02971
Tel: (508) 636-4010
Fax: (508) 636-5929

Cabo Rico Yachts, Inc.
17th St.
Ft. Lauderdale, FL 33316
Tel: (305) 462-6699
Fax: (305) 522-1317

Camden Harbor Yachts
Sea St.
P.O. Box 880
Camden, ME 04843
Tel: (207) 236-7112
Fax: (207) 236-7113

Camper & Nicholsons
450 Royal Palm Way
Palm Beach, FL 33480
Tel: (407) 655-2121
Fax: (407) 655-2202

Cannell, Payne & Page
American Boathouse
Atlantic Ave.
P.O. Box 1208
Camden, ME 04843
Tel: (207) 236-2383
Fax: (207) 236-2711

Cape Yacht Brokerage
800 Scallop Dr.
Port Canaveral, FL 32920
Tel: (407) 799-4724
Fax: (407) 799-0096

Capt. Jack's Yacht Brokerage
101 16th Ave. S.
St. Petersburg, FL 33701
Tel: (813) 825-0757
Fax: (813) 822-6415

Carolina Wind Yachting Center, Inc.
P.O. Box 967
Washington, NC 27889
Tel: (800) 334-7671
  or (919) 944-4653
Fax: (919) 946-8841

Carson Yacht Brokerage
1035 Riverside Dr.
Palmetto, FL 34221
Tel: (813) 723-1825
Fax: (813)729-8254

Casco Bay Yacht Exchange
Rt 1.
Freeport, ME 04032
Tel: (207) 865-4016
Fax: (207) 865-0759

Castlemain International Yacht Brokers
New River Ct.
Suite 4
300 S.W. 2nd Street
Ft. Lauderdale, FL 33312
Tel: (305) 760-4730
Fax: (305) 760-4737

Cedar Island Marina, Inc.
P.O. Box 181
Riverside Dr.
Clinton, CT 06413
Tel: (203) 669-8681
Fax: (203) 669-4157

Certified Sales, Inc.
19 Uxbridge Rd.
Mendon, MA 01756
Tel: (508) 478-0200
Fax: (508) 473-2021

Certified Sales, Inc.
New River Marina
3001 State Rd. 84
Ft. Lauderdale, FL 33312
Tel: (305) 584-2500
Fax: (305) 791-7522

Charleston Yacht Sales
Charleston Municipal Marina
P.O. Box 477
Charleston, SC 29402
Tel: (803) 577-5050
Fax: (803) 723-9829

Cherry Yachts
Oak Grove Marine Center
2830 Solomons Island
Edgewater, MD 21037
Tel: (410) 266-3801
 or (410) 841-2686
Fax: (410) 266-3805

Cherry Yachts
424 E. Queen St.
Hampton, VA 23669
Tel: (804) 728-BOAT
Fax: (804) 728-0130

Chrisholm Marina
226 Rt. 154
Chester, CT 06412
Tel: (203) 526-5147
Fax: (203) 526-1473

Clarks Landing Marinas
1224 U.S. Hwy. 109
P.O. Box 2170
Cape May, NJ 08204
Tel: (609) 898-9889
Fax: (609) 898-1633

Classic Yacht Sales
2945 State Rd. 84
Ft. Lauderdale, FL 33312
Tel: (305) 584-3440
Fax: (305) 583-3083

Class Sea Yachts, Inc.
207 N. Hager
Barrington, IL 60010
Tel: (708) 382-2100
Fax: (708) 381-1265

Clipper Bay Yachts, Inc.
P.O. Box 16
Tracys Landing, MD 20779
Tel: (301) 261-5775
Fax: (301) 261-5775

Coastal Marine
P.O. Box 228
143 River Rd.
Cos Cob, CT 06807
Tel: (203) 661-5765
Fax: (203) 661-6040

Colonial Yachts
901 S.E. 17th St.
Suite 203
Ft. Lauderdale, FL 3316
Tel: (305) 463-0555
Fax: (305) 463-8621

Compass Point Marine, Inc.
2381 Post Rd.
Warwick, RI 02866
Tel: (401) 738-8778

Concordia Yacht Sales, Inc.
South Wharf
South Dartmouth, MA 02748
Tel: (508) 993-9100
Fax: (508) 992-4682

Coneys Marine
32 New York Ave.
Rt. 110
Huntington, NY 11743
Tel: (516) 421-3366

Coveside Marine
Christmas Cove
HC 64, Box 150
S. Bristol, ME 04586
Tel: (207) 644-8282
Fax: (207) 644-8204

Cozy Cove Marina, Inc.
300 N. Federal Hwy.
Dania, FL 33004
Tel: (305) 921-8800
Fax: (305) 922-0173

Crusader Yacht Sales
Port Annapolis Marina
Annapolis, MD 21401
Tel: (410) 269-0939
 or (301) 858-6868

Damar Ltd.
Midway Marina
Haddam Dock Rd.
Haddam, CT 06483
Tel: (800) 498-6838
  or (203) 345-4330

Dave D Onfrio Yacht Sales, Inc.
1875 S.E. 17th St.
Ft. Lauderdale, FL 33316
Tel: (800) 771-4848
  or (305) 527-4848
Fax: (305) 462-6817

Ian Day Yacht Sales
726 2nd St.
Annapolis, MD 21403
Tel: (410) 267-6762
Fax: (410) 267-7482

Daytona Marina & Boatworks
645 S. Beach St.
Daytona Beach, FL 32114
Tel: (904) 253-6266
Fax: (904) 253-8174

Duffy & Duffy
Box 383
Brooklin, ME 04616
Tel: (207) 359-4658
Fax: (207) 359-8948

East Coast Yacht Sales
Lower Falls Landing
Yarmouth, ME 04096
Tel: (207) 846-4545
Fax (207) 846-6088

Eastern Yacht Sales
349 Lincoln St.
Hingham, MA 02043
Tel: (617) 749-8600
Fax: (617) 740-4149

Eastern Yacht Sales
1177 Ave. C
Riviera Beach, FL 33404
Tel: (407) 844-1100
Fax: (407) 844-8946

Eastern Yacht Sales
2550 S. Bayshore Dr.
Miami, FL 33133
Tel: (305) 854-2700
Fax: (305) 854-9017

Eastern Yacht Sales
One Lagoon Rd.
Portsmouth, RI 02871
Tel: (401) 683-2200
Fax: (401) 683-0961

Eastland Yachts, Inc.
33 Pratt St.
Essex, CT 06426
Tel: (203) 767-8224
Fax: (203) 767-9094

E & H Yacht Sales, Inc.
2180 Idlewild Rd.
Palm Beach Gardens, FL 33410
Tel: (407) 622-8550
Fax: (407) 622-5092

Emerald Yacht Brokers
759 N. Milwaukee St.
Suite 522
Milwaukee, WI 53202
Tel: (800) 343-3551
  or (414) 271-2595
Fax: (414) 271-4743

Emerald Yacht and Ship
3300 Irvine Ave
Suite 308
Newport Beach, CA 92660
Tel: (714) 553-0695
Fax: (714) 752-0462

Emerald Yacht and Ship
801 Seabreeze Blvd.
Bahia Mar Yachting Center
Ft. Lauderdale, FL 33316
Tel: (800) 938-9938
  or (305) 522-0556
Fax: (305) 522-3194

Emerald Yacht and Ship
8 Vine Yard
London SE1 1QN
ENGLAND
Tel: (+44) 71 378-0014
Fax: (+44) 71 357-6070

Essex Island Yachts Ltd.
P.O. Box 219
Essex, CT 06426
Tel: (203) 767-8645
Fax: (203) 767-0075

Everglades Marina, Inc.
1801 S.E. 17th St.
Ft. Lauderdale, FL 33316
Tel: (305) 763-3030
Fax: (305) 763-3167

Fair Harbor Marina, Inc.
831 N. Section St.
Fairhope, AL 36532
Tel: (205) 928-3417
Fax: (205) 928-6439

Fay's Boat Yard
71 Varney Pt. Rd.
Gilford, NH 03246
Tel: (603) 293-0700

Florida Yacht Charter and Sales
Miami Beach Marina
1290 5th St.
Miami Beach, FL 33139
Tel: (800) 537-0050
  or (305) 532-7600
Fax: (305) 672-2039

**Fort Lauderdale Yacht &
Ship Brokers, Inc.**
2248 S.E. 17th St.
Ft. Lauderdale, FL 33316
Tel: (305) 524-5815
Fax: (305) 524-5818

**Four Points Yacht &
Shipbrokers**
101 N. Riverside Dr.
Suite 214
Pompano Beach, FL 33062
Tel: (305) 941-5500
Fax: (305) 941-5521

Flaherty Yachts, Inc.
Rt. 14, P.O. Box 288
Sodus Pt., NY 14555
Tel: (315) 483-9171

Fraser Yachts
1205 Westlake Ave. N.
Seattle, WA 98109
Tel: (206) 282-4943
Fax: (206) 285-4956

Fraser Yachts
320 Harbor Dr.
Sausalito, CA 94965
Tel: (415) 332-5311
Fax: (415) 332-7036

Fraser Yachts
3471 Vialido
Box 2268
Newport Beach, CA 92663
Tel: (714) 673-5252
Fax: (714) 673-8975

Fraser Yachts
2160 Southeast 17th St.
Ft. Lauderdale, FL 33316
Tel: (305) 463-0600
Fax: (305) 463-1053

Fraser Yachts
Newport, RI 02840
Tel: (401) 841-5710
Fax: (401) 683-4141

Freeman Eckley
P.O. Box 135
Vermilion, OH 44089
Tel: (216) 967-0260

**Free Spirit Marine Corp. of
Florida**
533 Boston Post Rd.
Westbrook, CT 06489
Tel: (203) 399-6462
Fax: (203) 399-5752

Free State Yachts, Inc.
P.O. Box 6529
Annapolis, MD 21401
Tel: (301) 266-9060
Fax: (301) 266-8309

Arnold Gay Yacht Yards
#1 Shipwright St.
Annapolis, MD 21404
Tel: (800) 822-1033

Gemini Marine Group
326 First St.
Annapolis, MD 21403
Tel: (800) 525-5105
Fax: (410) 267-6127

**The George Nicholson
Group**
Solidmark
North Cove Yacht Sales
393 South End Ave.
New York, NY 10280
Tel: (212) 938-9000
Fax: (212) 839-0901

Gibson-Weaver Yacht Sales
2511-B Nasa Rd. 1
Suite 100
Seabrook, TX 77586
Tel: (713) 326-1574
Fax: (713) 532-1173

Gilman Yachts
1212-A U.S. Hwy. 1
N. Palm Beach, FL 33480
Tel: (407) 626-1790
Fax: (407) 626-5870

**Global Boat & Yacht Sales,
Inc.**
1310 N.W. 18th Ave.
Miami, FL 33125
Tel: (305) 545-6699
Fax: (305) 545-0609

**Frank Gordon Yacht Sales,
Inc.**
801 Seabreeze Blvd.
Bahia Mar Yachting Center
Marina Building, 2nd Floor
Ft. Lauderdale, FL 33316
Tel: (305) 525-8476
Fax: (305) 525-6024

Gratitude Boat Sales, Inc.
Upper Bay Lawton Ave.
Rock Hall, MD 21661
Tel: (410) 639-7111

Gratitude Boat Sales, Inc.
Lower Bay Rt. 33
Deltaville, VA 23043
Tel: (804) 776-7056

Gratitude Boat Sales, Inc.
6100 Red Hook Qtr.
Suite 4
St. Thomas, USVI 00802
Tel: (809) 777-7654

Great Lakes Marine Services, Inc.
2133 County Hwy. W.
Grafton, WI 53204
Tel: (414) 375-3033
Fax: (414) 375-0004

Handy Boat Service
215 Foreside Rd.
Falmouth, ME 04105
Tel: (207) 781-5110
Fax: (207) 781-7534

Harbor Yachts
1611 Bayville St.
Norfolk, VA 23503
Tel: (800) 359-YACHT
  or (804) 722-0011

Hatteras of Lauderdale
401 S.W. First Ave.
Ft. Lauderdale, FL 33301
Tel: (305) 462-5557
Fax: (305) 462-5563

Hatteras in Miami
2550 S. Bayshore Dr.
Coconut Grove, FL 33133
Tel: (305) 854-1100
Fax: (305) 854-1186

Hatteras in Palm Beach
2401 PGA Blvd.
Suite 155
Palm Beach Gardens, FL 33410
Tel: (407) 775-3531
Fax: (305) 775-8790

Hatteras in Stuart
110 North Federal Hwy.
Stuart, FL 34994
Tel: (407) 692-1122
Fax: (407) 692-1341

Harrison Yacht Sales, Inc.
Rt. 50, Exit 42
S. Kent Narrows Bridge
P.O. Box 98
Grasonville, MD 21683
Tel: (410) 827-6600

Havre de Grace Yacht Sales
723 Water St.
Havre de Grace, MD 21078
Tel: (410) 939-2161
Fax: (410) 939-0220

Hellier Yacht Sales, Inc.
128 Howard St.
New London, CT 06320
Tel: (203) 442-1154
Fax: (203) 442-3622

Bruce Hill Yacht Sales
219 Harbor Rd.
Shelburne, VT 05482
Tel: (802) 985-3336
Fax: (802) 985-3337

Hinckley Yacht Brokerage
Shore Rd.
South West Harbor, ME 04679
Tel: (207) 244-5531
Fax: (207) 244-9833

The Hinckley Co.
49 America's Cup Ave.
Newport, RI 02840
Tel: (401) 849-0120

HMY Yacht Sales, Inc.
850 N.E. 3rd St.
Dania, FL 33004
Tel: (305) 926-0400
Fax: (305) 921-2543

HMY Yacht Sales
Crows Nest Marina
Atlantic Beach, NC
Tel: (919) 247-6900

Howell Yachts
326 First St.
Annapolis, MD 21403
Tel: (410) 269-0353

Hyannis Yacht Sales
157 Pleasant St.
Hyannis, MA 02601
Tel: (508) 790-2628
Fax: (508) 790-0996

Integrity Marine, Inc.
1263 Lafayette St.
P.O. Box 541
Cape May, NJ
Tel: (609) 898-0801
Fax: (609) 898-0785

Interyacht
318G Sixth St.
Annapolis, MD 21403
Tel: (410) 269-5200
Fax: (410) 269-0571

Irish Boat Shop
Stover Rd.
Charlevoix, MI 49720
Tel: (616) 547-9967
Fax: (616) 547-4129

Chas. P. Irwin Yacht Brokerage
Bahia Mar Yachting Center
801 Seabreeze Blvd.
Ft. Lauderdale, FL 33316
Tel: (305) 463-6302
Fax: (305) 523-0056

Sam Israeloff
711 N.E. 205 Terr.
North Miami Beach, FL 33179

Jet Sea Yacht Brokers
1650 SE 17th St.
204
Ft. Lauderdale, FL 33316
Tel: (305) 766-2600
Fax: (305) 766-2611

Hal Jones & Co.
1900 S.E. 15th St.
Ft. Lauderdale, FL 33316
Tel: (305) 527-1778
Fax: (305) 523-5153

Kingman Yacht Brokerage
at Kingman Marine
1 Shipyard Ln.
Cataumet, MA 02534
Tel: (508) 563-7136
Fax: (508) 563-6493

Tom Klein Yacht
P.O. Box 39853
Ft. Lauderdale, FL
33339-9853
Tel: (305) 772-7070
Fax: (305) 772-7086

Lakeside Marine, Inc.
Lakeside, OH 43440
Tel: (419) 798-4406

Lake Union Yacht Sales, Inc.
3245 Fairview Ave. E.
Seattle, WA 98102
Tel: (206) 323-3505
Fax: (206) 323-4751

Larsen Marine Service
Grebe Shipyard
3250 N. Washtenaw Ave.
Chicago, IL 60618
Tel: (312) 993-7711
Fax: (312) 993-7769

Larsen Marine Service
625 Seahorse Dr.
Waukegan, IL 60085
Tel: (708) 336-5456
Fax: (708) 336-5530

Latitude 26 Yacht Sales
2150 S. E. 17th St.
Ft. Lauderdale, FL 33316
Tel: (305) 462-7406
Fax: (305) 462-7407

Lawson Yachts, Inc.
349 Lincoln St.
Building 34
Hingham, MA 02043
Tel: (617) 749-1645
Fax: (617) 749-0332

Liberty Yacht Sales and Charter, Inc.
Royal Palm Yacht Basin
629 N.E. 3rd St.
Dania, FL 33004
Tel: (305) 920-0117
Fax: (305) 920-1122

Lippincott Marine
Rts. 301/50
Grasonville, MD 21638
Tel: (410) 827-9300
Fax: (410) 827-9303

Lippincott Yacht Brokers
3028 Kent Narrows Way S.
Grasonville, MD 21638
Tel: (800) 827-8089
Fax: (410) 827-5380

Little Harbor Yacht Sales
1 Little Harbor Landing
Portsmouth, RI 02871
Tel: (401) 683-5600
Fax: (401) 683-3009

Lurssen Yachts America
2247 N.E. 20th St.
Ft. Lauderdale, FL 33305
Tel: (305) 561-7400
Fax: (305) 563-5480

Luxury Yacht Corp.
1635 S. Miami Rd.
Ft. Lauderdale, FL 33316
Tel: (305) 764-3388
Fax: (305) 763-8852

William Magness Yacht Brokers
207 Tackle Circle
Chester, MD 21619
Tel: (410) 643-8434
Fax: (410) 643-8437

Dave Maples Yacht Broker, Inc.
1530 Westlake Ave. N. # 100
Seattle, WA 98109
Tel: (206) 284-0880
Fax: (206) 285-7903

Marina Yacht Sales
315 Victory Rd.
Quincy, MA 02172
Tel: (617) 471-2181
Fax: (617) 328-9226

The Marine Group
Orange Beach Marina
P.O. Box 650
Orange Beach, AL 36561
Tel: (205) 981-9200
Fax: (205) 981-9137

The Marine Group
Soverel Harbor
2401 PGA Blvd.
Suite 104
Palm Beach Gardens, FL
33410
Tel: (407) 627-9500
Fax: (407) 627-9503

Marine Unlimited
232 Basin Dr.
Lauderdale-by-the-Sea, FL
33308
Tel: (305) 491-0430
Fax: (305) 771-6122

Maritime Yacht Brokerage
1994 Eastwood Rd.
Wilmington, NC 28403
Tel: (919) 256-8004
Fax: (919) 256-8253

Maryland Yachts
301 Tilghman St.
Oxford, MD 21654
Tel: (410) 226-5571

**Massey Yacht Sales &
Service**
1015 Riverside Dr.
Palmetto, FL
Tel: (800) 375-0130
 or (813) 723-1610
Fax: (813) 729-7520

Maynard Yacht Brokers
Rt. 50, Saratoga Rd.
Burnt Hills, NY 12027
Tel: (518) 399-3062
Fax: (518) 399-4241

**McMichael Yacht Brokers
Ltd.**
447 E. Boston Post Rd.
Mamaroneck, NY 10543
Tel: (914) 381-5900
Fax: (914) 381-5060

Med-Sale U.S.A., Inc.
201 S.E. 15th Terr.
Suite 210
Deerfield Beach, FL 33441
Tel: (305) 481-1790
Fax: (305) 481-2433

Megayachts International
918 North East 20th Ave.
Ft. Lauderdale, FL 33304
Tel: (305) 527-1988
Fax: (305) 728-9027

Merlewood & Associates
1535 Southeast 17st.
Suite 206
Ft. Lauderdale, FL 33316
Tel: (305) 525-5111
Fax: (305) 525-5165

Merrill-Stevens Yacht Sales
1270 N.W. 11th St.
Miami, FL 33125
Tel: (305) 324-5211
Fax: (305) 326-8911

Merrill-Stevens Yacht Sales
2701 South Bayshore Dr.
Suite 605
Miami, FL 33133
Tel: (305) 858-5911
Fax: (305) 858-5919

Merrit Yacht Brokers, Inc.
2040 S.E. 17th St.
Ft. Lauderdale, FL 33316
Tel: (800) 446-6695
 or (305) 761-1300
Fax: (305) 463-8617

**Merrit Boat & Engine
Works Brokerage, Inc.**
2931 N.E. 16th St.
Pompano Beach, FL 33062
Tel: (305) 943-6250
Fax: (305) 943-6251

Metnic Yacht Brokers
Seal Cove Boatyard
Box 99
Harborside, ME 04642
Tel: (207) 326-4411

Midcoast Yacht Sales
P.O. Box 221
Wiscasset, ME 04578
Tel: (207) 882-6445
Fax: (207) 882-4250

Milford Boatworks
1 High St.
Milford, CT 06460
Tel: (203) 874-3667

Minnesott Yacht Sales
P.O. Box 128
Arapahoe, NC 28510
Tel: (919) 249-1424
Fax: (919) 249-0504

**The Moorings Yacht
Brokerage**
19345 U.S. 19 N.
Suite 402
Clearwater, FL 34624
Tel: (800) 521-1126
 or (813) 530-5651

**Robert J.W. Moran Yacht &
Ship, Inc.**
1300 S.E. 17th St.
Suite 204
Ft. Lauderdale, FL 33316
Tel: (305) 768-0707
Fax: (305) 768-0057

Nanny Cay Yacht Sales Ltd.
Box 638 Road Town
Tortola, BVI
Tel: (809) 494-3260
Fax: (809) 494-3535

Naples Yacht Brokerage
774- 12th Ave. S.
Naples, FL 33940
Tel: (813) 434-8338
Fax: (813) 434-6848

Nashville Yacht Brokers, Inc.
1 Vantage Way
Suite B
Nashville, TN 37228
Tel: (800) 959-9444
  or (615) 259-9444
Fax: (615) 259-9481

Nautilus Yacht Sales
Skipjack Cove
Georgetown, MD 21930
Tel: (301) 275-1100
Fax: (301) 275-1133

Nautor Swan
USA East Coast
55 America's Cup Ave.
Newport, RI 02840
Tel: (401) 846-8404

Nautor Swan
USA East Coast
300 Alton Rd.
Miami Beach, FL 33139
Tel: (305) 673-4600
Fax: (305) 673-2560

Nautor Swan
USA West Coast
Swan Pacific, Inc.
2505 West Coast Hwy.
Suite 202
Newport Beach, CA 92663
Tel: (714) 645-4600

Nautor Swan
USA Northwest
McKee And Mooney, Inc.
1530 Westlake Ave. N. Suite 300
Seattle, WA 98109
Tel: (206) 284-0144

Nautor Swan
USA Gulf Coast
P.O. Box 891386
Houston, TX 77289-1386
Tel: (713) 334-7926

Nelson Yacht Sales
103 Hill Str.
P.O. Box 1129
Beaufort, NC 28516
Tel: (919) 728-3663
Fax: (919) 728-5333

New Wave Yachts
6A Cliff St.
Marblehead, MA 01945
Tel: (617) 639-0206
Fax: (617) 639-1488

New York Yacht Corp.
102 Woodcleft Ave.
Freeport, NY 11520
Tel: (516) 546-3377

Northrop & Johnson Yachts-Ships, Inc.
3575 N.E. 207th St.
Suite B16
Aventura, FL 33180
Tel: (305) 933-3344
  or (305) 522-3344
Fax: (305) 933-3523

Northrup & Johnson Sales Corp. of Mass.
256 Marginal St.
E. Boston, MA 02128
Tel: (617) 569-6900
Fax: (617) 569-9247

Northrup & Johnson
19 Brown & Howard Wharf
Newport, RI 02840
Tel: (401) 848-5500
Fax: (401) 848-0120

Norwalk Cove Marina, Inc.
Beach Rd.
East Norwalk, CT 06855
Tel: (203) 838-2326
Fax: (203) 838-9258

Norwood Marine, Inc.
R-24 Ericsson St.
Boston, MA 02122
Tel: (617) 288-1000
Fax: (617) 282-5728

Odyssey III Ltd.
1650 S.E. 17th St.
Suite 300
Ft. Lauderdale, FL 33316
Tel: (305) 463-3646
Fax: (305) 463-3648

Offer & Associates
2945 State Rd. 84
Suite A-1
Ft. Lauderdale, FL 33312
Tel: (305) 587-0935
Fax: (305) 587-8272

Old Port Yacht Sales
Long Wharf
Portland, ME 04101
Tel: (207) 772-1132
Fax: (207) 772-3601

Olson/Weidman International Yacht Brokers
34th & Intercoastal Waterway
Ocean City, NJ 08226
Tel: (609) 390-2288
Fax: (609) 390-1260

Onset Bay Yacht Sales
R.F.D. #3
Green St.
Buzzards Bay, MA 02532
Tel: (508) 295-2300
Fax: (508) 295-8873

Onset Yachts
2830 Solomom's Island Rd.
Edgewater, MD 21037
Tel: (410) 266-3898

Owens Yacht Sales
371 Canal Park Dr.
Duluth, MN 55802
Tel: (218) 722-9212
Fax: (218) 722-4730

Oxford Boatyard
402 East Strand
P.O. Box 340
Oxford, MD 21654
Tel: (410) 226-5101
Fax: (410) 226-5116

The Oxford Yacht Agency
317 S. Morris St.
Oxford, MD 21645
Tel: (410) 226-5454
Fax: (410) 226-5244

Oyster Harbors Marine, Inc.
122 Bridge St.
Osterville, MA 02655
Tel: (508) 428-2017
Fax: (508) 420-5398

Palm Beach Yacht Center
7848 S. Federal Hwy. (US 1)
Hypoluxo, FL 33462
Tel: (407) 588-9911
Fax: (407) 585-9933

Palm Beach Yacht Club - Marina & Brokerage
800 N. Flagler Hwy.
West Palm Beach, FL 33401
Tel: (407) 833-8633
Fax: (407) 833-8639

Palmer Johnson Yacht Sales and Brokerage
61 Michigan St.
Sturgeon Bay, WI 54235
Tel: (414) 743-4412
Fax: (414) 743-3444

Parrot and Herst Yacht & Ship Brokerage, Inc.
1515 S.W. 20th St.
Ft. Lauderdale, FL 33315
Tel: (800) 466-7497
or   (305) 523-9700
Fax: (305) 523-0937

Parrot, Parrot, Elfenbein, & O Brien, Inc.
1600 S.E. 17th St.
Suite 405
Ft. Lauderdale, FL 33316
Tel: (305) 524-6434
Fax: (305) 524-6439

Performance Yacht Sales
1495 Old Griffin Rd.
Ft. Lauderdale, FL 33044
Tel: (305) 920-3531

P.G.A. Yachts of Palm Beach
2401 PGA Blvd.
Palm Beach Gardens, FL 33410
Tel: (407) 627-0100
Fax: (407) 627-0262

Herb Phillips Yacht Sales
1535 S.E. 17th St.
Suite 117-B
Ft. Lauderdale, FL 33316
Tel: (305) 523-8600
Fax: (305) 523-8609

Pier 33
250 Anchors Way
St. Joseph, MI 49085
Tel: (616) 983-0677
Fax: (616) 983-3847

Pilot Yacht Sales
3 Lockwood Dr.
Charleston, SC 29401
Tel: (803) 723-8356
Fax: (803) 723-2102

Portland Boat Works, Inc.
1 Grove St.
Portland, CT 06480
Tel: (203) 342-1085
Fax: (203) 342-0544

Preferred Yacht & Ship Brokers, Inc.
535 Dock St.
Suite 112
Tacoma, WA 98402
Tel: (206) 272-4550
Fax: (206) 272-4804

Premiere Yachts
757 S.E. 17th St.
Ft. Lauderdale, FL 33316
Tel: (305) 456-1466
Fax: (305) 359-9448

Prestige Yacht Sales
84 Southfield Ave.
Stamford, CT 06902
Tel: (203) 353-0373
Fax: (203) 359-0026

Pugh's on Erie Yacht Sales
950 Erie St.
Racine, WI 53402
Tel: (414) 636-8020
Fax: (414) 636-8002

Quay & Associates Yacht Sales
Box 563
Oriental, NC 28571
Tel: (919) 249-1825
Fax: (919) 249-2240

Randall Yacht Sales
145 S. Montowese St.
Branford, CT 06405
Tel: (203) 481-3866
Fax: (203) 481-8699

Rex Yacht Sales
2152 S.E. 17th St.
Ft. Lauderdale, FL 3316
Tel: (305) 463-8810
Fax: (305) 462-3640

Rex Yacht Sales
308 Harbor Dr.
Sausalito, CA 94965
Tel: (415) 331-0533
Fax: (415) 331-1642

Rhodes Yacht Brokers, Inc.
2901 N. E. 28th Ct.
Lighthouse Point, FL 33064
Tel: (305) 941-2404
Fax: (305) 941-2507

Robinhood Marine Center, Inc.
Robinhood, ME 04530
Tel: (800) 255-5206
  or (207) 371-2343
Fax: (207) 371-2899

Rose Yacht Sales
Box 923/240 Wareham Rd.
Marion, MA 02738
Tel: (508) 748-2211
Fax: (508) 748-3773

Ross Yacht Service, Inc.
Windward Passage
Clearwater, FL 34630
Tel: (813) 446-8191
Fax: (813) 443-0076

Royce Yacht & Ship Brokers
1600 S.E. 17th St.
Ft. Lauderdale, FL 33316
Tel: (305) 764-0100
Fax: (305) 764-0192

Rybovich Spencer
4200 N. Dixie
West Palm Beach, FL 33407
Tel: (407) 844-0340
Fax: (407) 845-8774

Sailaway Yachts
5006 Dauphin Island Pkwy.
Mobile, AL 36605
Tel: (800) 476-9295
Fax: (205) 476-2132

Sailaway Yachts
400-D N. Flagler Dr.
West Palm Beach, FL 33401
Tel: (800) 369-2445
Fax: (407) 655-2669

Sailboats, Inc.
400 E. Randolph St.
Chicago, IL
Tel: (312) 861-1757
Fax: (312) 861-9520

Sailboats Northeast
Box 924
20 Doaks Ln.
Marblehead, MA 01945
Tel: (617) 631-4910
Fax: (617) 631-3279

Sailboat Sales Co.
2500 S. Corbett
Chicago, IL 60608
Tel: (312) 225-2046
Fax: (312) 225-6354

Sail Yard, Inc.
326 First St.
Suite 18
Annapolis, MD 21403
Tel: (800) 394-7245
  or (410) 268-4100

Sandy Hook Yacht Sales
1246 Ocean Ave.
Sea Bright, NJ 07760
Tel: (908) 530-5500
Fax: (908) 530-1323

D.M. Savage Yacht & Ship Brokerage, Inc.
4326 Central Ave.
St. Petersburg, FL 33711
Tel: (813) 327-1288
Fax: (813) 321-0491

Bob Saxon Associates
1500 Cordova Rd.
Suite 214
Ft. Lauderdale, FL 33316

Scituate Yacht Co.
70 Crescent Ave.
Scituate, MA 02066
Tel: (617) 545-1900
Fax: (617) 545-5088

Sea Yachts, Inc.
837 N.E. 20th St.
Ft. Lauderdale, FL 33304
Tel: (305) 522-0993
Fax: (305) 768-9027

S.G.K. Yacht Sales
901 N.E. 25th Ave.
Pompano Beach, FL 33062
Tel: (305) 781-8721
Fax: (305) 781-7630

Shelter Island Yacht Sales
2330 Shelter Island Dr. # 200
San Diego, CA 92106
Tel: (619) 222-0515
Fax: (619) 222-5283

John B. Slaven, Inc.
Box 864
31300 N. River Rd.
Mt. Clemens, MI 48046

Sloane Yacht Sales, Inc.
421 Atlantic Ave.
Stamford, CT 06904
Tel: (914) 273-3211

SOLIDMARK North America
Gateway Plaza
385 South End Ave.
Suite 4-F
New York, NY 10280-1040
Tel: (212) 321-9300
Fax: (212) 321-9808

SOLIDMARK France
Residence du Grand Hotel
45 La Croisette
06400 Cannes
FRANCE
Tel: (+33) 93 39 84 19
Fax: (+33) 93 99 17 04

SOLIDMARK Spain
Club de Mar
Palma de Mallorca
SPAIN
Tel: (+34) 71 40 57 11
Fax: (+34) 71 40 58 57

Solomons Yacht Brokerage & Services
Town Center Marina
Solomons, MD 20688
Tel: (301) 326-6748
Fax: (301) 326-2149

Southeast Florida Yacht Sales, Inc.
3565 S.E. St. Lucie Blvd.
Stuart, FL 34997
Tel: (407) 220-6822
Fax: (407) 220-6811

Southern Trades Yacht & Ship Brokers, Inc.
P.O. Box 6647
St. Thomas, USVI 00804
Tel: (809) 774-7174
Fax: (809) 774-7174

Sparkman & Stephens
79 Madison Ave.
New York, NY 10016
Tel: (212) 689-3880
  or (212) 689-9292
Fax: (212) 689-3884

Spinnaker Key Yacht Sales & Charters
1500 Cordova Rd.
Suite 300
Ft. Lauderdale, FL 3316
Tel: (305) 525-6379
Fax: (305) 525-6385

St. Barts Yachts
2 Harbor Place N.
Myrtle Beach, SC 29582
Tel: (803) 249-8807
Fax: (803) 249-6571

St. Barts Yachts
4607 Oleander Dr.
Wilmington, NC 28403
Tel: (919) 350-0714

Sterling Yacht Sales
P.O. Box 652
Mystic, CT
Tel: (203) 572-8810
Fax: (203) 572-0036

Sunset Marine
3701 N. Main
E. Peoria, IL
Tel: (309) 678-2370
Fax: (309) 694-2764

Taber Yacht Sales, Inc.
Stirling Harbor Marina
340 Manhasset Ave.
Greenport, NY 11944
Tel: (516) 477-8938
Fax: (516) 477-8940

Taber Yacht Sales, Inc.
Pirates Cove Marina
P.O. Box 1687
Port Salerno, FL 34992
Tel: (407) 288-7466
Fax: (407) 288-7476

Bruce Tait Yacht Sales
Waterfront Marina
Bay St.
P.O. Box 1928
Sag Harbor, NY 11963
Tel: (516) 725-4222
Fax: (516) 725-9886

Torresen Marine, Inc.
3126 Lakeshore Dr.
Muskegon, MI 49441
Tel: (616) 759-8596

United/Director Gunnell
1316 SE 17th St.
Ft. Lauderdale, FL 33316
Tel: (305) 524-4616
  or (305) 949-3415
Fax: (305) 524-4621

Virginia Yacht Brokers, Inc.
4503 Ericson Dr.
Hampton, VA 23669
Tel: (804) 722-3500
Fax: (804) 722-7909

Waldock Yacht Sales, Inc.
117 E. Washington Row
Sandusky, OH 44870
Tel: (800) 537-4648

Michael Waters Yacht Broker
112 Beech St.
Rockland, ME 04841
Tel: (207) 594-4234

West Coast Yachts
1800 Westlake Ave. N.
Suite 301
Seattle, WA 98109
Tel: (206) 298-3724
Fax: (206) 298-0227

Wells Yachts of Marblehead
91 Front St.
Marblehead, MA 01945
Tel: (800) 688-6072 in MA
(617) 631-3003

Western Yacht Sales
1220 Westlake N.
Seattle, WA 98109
Tel: (206) 282-0052
Fax: (206) 283-2297

Steve Winn Yacht & Ship Brokers, Inc.
2150 S.E. 17th St.
Suite 155
Ft. Lauderdale, FL 33316
Tel: (305) 779-7447
Fax: (305) 779-3735

Woods & Oviatt
Pier 66 Resort & Marina
2301 S.E. 17th St.
Ft. Lauderdale, FL 33316
Tel: (800) 327-1799
  or (305) 463-5606
Fax: (305) 522-5156

Yacht & Ship Brokers, Inc.
2501 S. Federal Hwy.
Ft. Lauderdale, FL 33316
Tel: (305) 779-7447
Fax: (305) 779-3735

Yacht Brokerage USA
16521 San Carlos Blvd.
Ft. Myers, FL 33908
Tel: (813) 466-9344

Yacht Brokerage USA
1700 E. Las Olas
Ft. Lauderdale, FL 33301
Tel: (305) 463-1255

Yacht-Eng.
13601 McGregor Blvd.
Suite 16
Ft. Myers, FL 33919
Tel: (813) 481-3511
Fax: (813) 481-3064

Yacht Registry
Brandy Marina/Marker 1
343 Causeway Blvd.
Dunedin, FL 34698
Tel: (813) 733-0334
Fax: (813) 733-6754

ZK Marine, Inc.
Harbour Towne Marina
801 N.E. 3rd St.
Dania, FL 33004
Tel: (305) 923-7441
Fax: (305) 923-7477

European Yacht Brokers

Nigel Burgess Ltd.
16/17 Pall Mall
London SW1Y 5LU
ENGLAND
Tel: (+44) 71 8394366
Fax: (+44) 71 8394329

Nigel Burgess Ltd.
Le Panorama
57 rue Grimaldi
MONACO
Tel: (+33) 93 50 22 64
Fax: (+33) 93 25 15 89

Camper & Nicholsons
31 Berkeley St.
London W1X 5FA
ENGLAND
Tel: (+44) 71 4912950
Fax: (+44) 71 6292068

Camper & Nicholsons
Port Pierre Canto
06407 Cannes
FRANCE
Tel: (+33) 93 43 16 75
Fax: (+33) 93 94 13 48

Camper & Nicholsons
12 Avenue de la Liberation
06600 Antibes
FRANCE
Tel: (+33) 9291 29 12
Fax: (+33) 92 91 29 00

Camper & Nicholsons
Club de Mar
07015 Palma de Mallorca
SPAIN
Tel: (+34) 71 40 33 11
Fax: (+34) 71 40 14 12

Lurssen Yachts America
Club de Mar
07015 Palma de Mallorca
SPAIN
Tel: (+34) 71 70 04 45
Fax: (+34) 71 70 05 51

Solidmark France
Residences du Grand Hotel
45 La Croisette
06400 Cannes
FRANCE
Tel: (+33) 93 39 84 19
Fax: (+33) 93 99 17 04

Solidmark UK
250A Brompton Rd.
London SW3 2AS
ENGLAND
Tel: (+44) 71 225 2769
Fax: (+44) 71 225 2523

United Yachting, Monaco
Port de Fontvieille
8, Quai des Sanbarbani
MC 98000
MONACO
Tel: (+33) 92 05 67 00
Fax: (+33) 92 05 67 65

Note: I have tried to list as many brokers as possible. If I have missed your company, please send a current advertisement showing all the above details, and you will be included in the next edition of Marshall's Marine Source Book and in *Marshall's Monthly Review.*

Figure 1: Quality boats like this Swan 40 are available from many brokers.

Yacht Charter Brokers

By Missy Johnston

Missy Johnston is the manager of the yacht charter department at Northrup & Johnson in Newport, Rhode Island. She has been in the charter business for nine years, first as a charter chef and for the last five years as a broker. She attends all the major charter shows and has cruised most of the major charter grounds.

Rather than having the expense of owning a boat, many people charter one for a summer or a winter cruise. Businesses also charter yachts for company parties or special events.

To charter a boat, you should find a charter broker who knows the area in which you want to sail. Some brokers know about and charter in only their immediate area. A broker in Newport, Rhode Island, for instance, might not necessarily be helpful if you want to cruise the British Virgin Islands. The best broker to work with is the full-service broker who usually has contacts all over the world, has sailed in many chartering grounds, and can book charters almost anwhere. Because every reputable broker has access to all boats listed for charter, calling several different brokers usually only results in getting the same brochures offering the same boats. Consequently, if you find a broker you like, stay with that person as long as you are getting good service.

Few states require yacht charter brokers to be licensed, so your best approach, if you haven't chartered before, is to go to one of the established houses. Do not go to a travel agent to charter a yacht. As soon as your vacation moves from land to sea, a whole new set of rules apply, rules which very few travel agents know. To complicate matters even more, these rules change from country to country. If you have a travel agent you like to work with, have that agent contact a yacht broker on your behalf. Many brokers work with travel agents to put together a hassle-free vacation for their clients.

When booking a charter, you need to find out several things. First, is the location served by a major airline? The broker should know. If you have to make several flight changes, you may not arrive until late in the evening. In this case, you will probably spend the first night in a shoreside hotel. The cost of the hotel should be figured in. Fortunately, for people who charter in the Caribbean, most flights from the US arrive around midday, and the charter can be timed to start upon arrival. This is also true of overnight flights to European destinations, such as Greece.

Second, when booking a charter you need to find out if it will begin and end at the same location. Quite often, a charter might begin at one island and end at another. If this happens, you should have accommodations available at the destination island, plus your airline flight should leave from there rather than from your starting point. If you have to get the boat back to your starting point, allow plenty of time. Disasters can be caused by pushing schedules to get back on time. Your charter broker should be able to advise you if a particular itinerary can be accomplished. Keep in mind that you'll want to spend time swimming, snorkeling, and just unwinding. This will reduce the number of miles you can cover.

Third, you should make sure the boat is provisioned before you start. There may not be a supermarket in the area where the boat is going, or food may be very expensive. Many charter brokers will spend extra time advising you where to get the boat provisioned with food that you and your crew like. On a fully crewed charter, you will probably be asked what types of food and drink you prefer. This will enable the chef to customize the menu especially for you.

The area that offers the greatest choice of charters is the Caribbean, and the choice there is widest in winter. The next most popular areas are New England in the summer, Florida/Bahamas, and the Mediterranean. Other options include Mexico, Australia and New Zealand, the South Sea Islands, and Alaska (in the summer). If you hanker for little known destinations, ask a broker. There are boats located in odd places, but be prepared for a limited choice.

While there are charters in some locations in the spring and fall, many of the boats are changing cruising locations during this time and availability is not as good.

In addition, weather can be a problem in many charter locations in the fall.

Besides choosing your season and destination, you must also decide whether you want a fully crewed or a bareboat charter. All charter brokers book crewed charters, but not all of them book bareboat ones. In general, bareboat charters are offered by a particular company that has a number of boats in one location. Charters can be booked directly through the fleet owner or through a broker. There is no price difference. Working with a broker has an advantage in that the broker has information on all the various bareboat fleets and can answer your questions with one phone call. The broker will also know the reputation of the different fleet operators. In an area like the Caribbean, where there are many bareboat fleets sailing, a good broker will be very helpful in getting you the best vacation. If you want to charter a fully crewed boat, you will have to work through a broker.

When choosing a crewed yacht, not only are the boat and accommodations important, so is the crew that you will be spending your time with. A qualified charter broker will attend the industry shows in each major charter location at the start of each season. During the shows, the various boats are presented in charter-ready condition and the brokers have the opportunity to review the boats and talk with the crews. Your broker should be able to discuss with you each boat and its crew.

Note also that the crew members on a fully crewed boat in the Caribbean are generally tipped 10 to 20% of the charter fee. In Europe, most Europeans will tip only up to

5%. This has often led European crews to expect 5%, rather than the higher rate which American crews expect.

Some of the best charter boats are often booked months in advance, so begin your enquiries early if you can. If you intend to book around Christmas and the New Year vacations in the Caribbean, or during spring break, you should book well in advance. In the Mediterranean, book early for charters in August when most of Europe goes on vacation.

Yacht Charter Operators

Abaco Bahamas Charters
10905 Cowgill Pl.
Louisville, KY 40243
Tel: (800) 626-5690
  or (502) 245-9428
Fax: (502) 245-1537
Area of charter: Abaco, Bahamas

ABC Yacht Charter
1903 Skyline Way
Anacortes, WA 98221
Tel: (800) 426-2313
  or (206) 293-9533
Area of charter: Pacific and northwest coast

A-B-Sea Sailing Charters
4995 U.S. Hwy. 19
New Port Richey, FL 34652
Tel: (800) 227-5127
  or (813) 845-1726
Area of charter: West coast Florida and Keys

Alaskan Wilderness Safaris
P.O. Box 1313
Valdez, AK 99686
Tel: (907) 835-5175
Fax: (907) 835-5679
Area of charter: South coast of Alaska

American Bahamas Charters
Box 331072
Coconut Grove, FL 33133
Tel: (305) 443-8310
Area of charter: South Florida, Bahamas

Adventure Plus Yacht Charters
Sandusky Harbor Marina
1 Hurin St.
Sandusky, OH 44870
Tel: (419) 625-5000
Area of charter: Lake Erie

Allied Yacht Charters
326 First St.
Suite 28
Annapolis, MD 21403
Tel: (410) 269-6772
Fax: (410) 263-2964
Area of charter: Chesapeake Bay

Anacortes Yacht Charters
P.O. Box 69
Anacortes, WA 98221
Tel: (800) 233-3004
  or (206) 293-4555
Area of charter: Pacific Northwest

Annapolis Bay Charters
P.O. Box 4604
Annapolis, MD 21403
Tel: (301) 261-1815
Area of charter: Chesapeake Bay

Annapolis Sailing School
P.O. Box 3334
601 6th St.
Annapolis, MD 21403
Tel: (800) 638-9192
Area of charter: St. Croix, Florida and Keys, Chesapeake

Associated Mystic Yacht Charters
22R Holmes St.
Mystic, CT 06353
Tel: (203) 536-1949
Area of charter: Atlantic coast

ATM Yachts USA
2280 University Dr.
Suite 102
Newport Beach, CA 92660
Tel: (800) 634-8822
  or (714) 650-0889
Fax: (714) 642-1318
Area of charter: Grenadines, Tahiti

Aventura Sailing Association
24650 Dana Point Harbor Dr.
Dana Point, CA 92629
Tel: (714)-493-9493
Area of charter: Southern California

Avery's Marine, Inc.
Box 5248
St. Thomas, USVI 00803
Tel: (809) 776-0113
Area of charter: Virgin Islands

AYS Charters
7416 Edgewood Rd.
Annapolis, MD 21403
Tel: (410) 267-8181
Area of charter: Chesapeake

Bahia Mar Marine Charters
801 Seabreeze Blvd.
Ft. Lauderdale, FL 33316
Tel: (800) 327-8154
Area of charter: South Florida, Bahamas

Barefoot Yacht Charters
P.O. Box 41127
St. Petersburg, FL 33743
Tel: (800) 677-3195
Fax: (813) 360-0032
Area of charter: St. Vincent

Bay Breeze Yacht Charters
12935 W. Bay Shore Dr.
Traverse City, MI 49684
Tel: (616) 941-0535
Area of charter: Lake Michigan

Bay Island Yacht Charters Co.
P.O. Box 639
Camden, ME 04843
Tel: (800) 421-2492
  or (207) 236-2776
Area of charter: Maine

Bellhaven Charters
9 Squalicum Mall
Bellingham, WA 98225
Tel: (206) 733-6636
Area of charter: Pacific Northwest

Bight Services, Inc.
P.O. Box 4249
Annapolis, MD 21403
Tel: (410) 263-2838
Area of charter: Chesapeake

Bitter End Yacht Club
875 N. Michigan Ave.
Chicago, IL 60611
Tel: (800) 872-2392
  or (312) 944-5855
Area of charter: Virgin Islands

Blue Goose Enterprises
P.O. Box 433
Severn, MD 21144
Tel: (800) 874-6673
Area of charter: Chesapeake, Florida, Bahamas

Blue Water Yacht Charters
1414 S. Andrews Ave.
Ft. Lauderdale, FL 33316
Tel: (800) 522-2992
  or (305) 768-0695
Fax: (305) 768-0695
Area of charter: East coast Florida

Bosun's Charters
P.O. Box 2464
Sydney, British Columbia V8L 3Y3
CANADA
Tel: (604) 656-6644
Area of charter: Pacific Northwest

BVI Bareboats Ltd.
Box 3018
Road Town, BVI
Tel: (809) 494-4289
Fax: (809) 494-6552
Area of charter: Windward and Leeward Islands

C & C Charters
1717 Bay Ave.
Point Pleasant, NJ 08742
Tel: (800) 626-0426
  or (908) 295-3450
Area of charter: East coast United States, Bahamas, Virgin Islands

C & C Charters Maryland
506 Kent Narrows Way N.
Grasonville, MD 2163
Tel: (800) 733-7245
  or (410) 827-7888
Area of charter: East coast United States, Bahamas, Virgin Islands

Canadian Yacht Charters
R.R. 2
Minesing, Ontario L0L 1YO
CANADA
Area of charter: Lake Huron

Cape Yacht Charters
419 Sippewisset Rd.
Falmouth, MA 02540
Tel: (800) 345-5395
  or (508) 540-5395
Area of charter: Cape Cod, Buzzards Bay

Caribbean Adventures
P.O. Box 9997
St. Thomas, USVI 00801
Tel: (800) 626-4517
  or (809) 776-7245
Fax: (809) 774-2283
Area of charter: Virgin Islands

**Caribbean Sailing
Charters, Inc.**
3883 Andrews Crossing
Roswell, GA 30075
Tel: (800) 824-1331
  or (404) 641-9640
Area of charter: Virgin Islands

Caribbean Yacht Charters
P.O. Box 583
Marblehead, MA 01945
Tel: (800) 225-2520
  or (617) 599-7990
Fax: (617) 639-0216
Area of charter: Virgin Islands

**Caribbean Yacht Owners
Association**
5300 Long Bay Rd.
Yacht Haven Marina
St. Thomas, USVI 00802
Tel: (800) 944-2962
  or (809) 774-3677
Fax: (809) 774-6910
Area of charter: Virgin Islands

**Carolina Wind Yachting
Center, Inc.**
P.O. Box 967
Washington, NC 27889
Tel: (800) 334-7671
  or (919) 946-4653
Fax: (919) 946-8841
*Area of charter: Chesapeake
Bay*

Cedar Mills Marina
Rt. 1, Box 37
Gordonville, TX 76245
Tel: (903) 523-4222
Area of charter: Lake Texoma

The Charter Locker
74-425 Kealakohe Pkwy. #16
Kailua-Kona, HI 96740
Tel: (800) 247-1484
  or (808) 326-32553
Area of charter: Hawaii

Chitwood Charters
P.O. Box 4075
Sarasota, FL 34230
Tel: (813) 957-1530
*Area of charter: West Florida
coast*

Classic Charters
RR4, Box 395
Wiscasset, ME 04578
Tel: (207) 882-5448
Area of charter: Maine

Club Nautique
1150 Ballena Blvd.
Suite 161
Alameda, CA 94501
Tel: (800) 343-7245
  or (415) 865-4700
*Area of charter: San Francisco
Bay*

**Coastline Sailing School &
Yacht Charters**
Eldridge Yard
Marsh Rd.
Noank, CT 06340
Tel: (800) 749-7245
  or (203) 536-2689
*Area of charter: Eastern Long
Island Sound*

Conch Charters
19 Donegani Ave.
Suite 207
Pt. Claire, Quebec H9R 2V6
CANADA
Tel: (514) 630-4802
Fax: (514) 694-7892
Area of charter: Tortola

Coral Bay Cruises
17 Ft. Royal Isle
Ft. Lauderdale, FL 33308
Tel: (800) 433-7262
  or (305) 563-1711
*Area of charter: W. Florida
coast*

CSA Charter & Sail
1525 Bayville St.
Norfolk, VA 23503
Tel: (800) 296-7245
  or (804) 588-2022
Area of charter: Chesapeake

Cruzan Yacht Charters
2270 S.W. 27th Way
Coconut Grove, FL 33133
Tel: (305) 858-2822
Area of charter: South Florida

Discovery Yacht Charter
15 Water St. E.
Little Current, Ontario POP
1KO
CANADA
Tel: (800) 268-8222
  or (705) 368-3744
Area of charter: Virgin Islands

Dodson Boat Sales
194 Water St.
Stonington, CT 06378
Tel: (203) 536-1507
*Area of charter: East coast
United States*

East Passage Sailing
One Lagoon Rd.
Portsmouth, RI 02871
Tel: (800) 922-2930
  or (401) 683-5930
*Area of charter: Narraganset
Bay and Islands*

Eastern Shore Yacht Charters
P.O. Box 589
Oxford, MD 21654
Tel: (800) 854-0061
  or (301) 226-5000
Area of charter: Chesapeake

Eleuthera-Bahamas Charters
190 Widgeon Dr.
Eastham, MA 02642
Tel: (800) 548-9684
  or in Massachusetts (508) 255-8930
Fax: (508) 255-8971
Area of charter: Bahamas

Fantasy Cruises
3101 Ocean Park Blvd.
Suite 302
Santa Monica, CA 90405
Tel: (310) 392-8054
Area of charter: Worldwide

First Class Yachting
c/o Le Boat
P.O. Box E
Maywood, NJ 07607
Tel: (800) 922-0291
  or (201) 342-1838
Fax: (201) 342-7498
Area of Charter: Leeward Islands

Florida Sailing & Cruising School
3444 Marinatown Ln., N.W.
North Fort Myers, FL 33903
Tel: (800) 262-7939
  or (813) 656-1339
Fax: (813) 656-BOAT
Area of charter: Southwest Florida and Keys

Florida West Coast Charter Service
12022 Gandy Blvd.
St. Petersburg, Fl 33702
Tel: (813) 576-3801
Area of charter: West Florida coast

Florida Yacht Charters and Sales, Inc.
1290 5th St.
Miami Beach Marina
Miami Beach, FL 33139
Tel: (800) 537-0050
  or (305) 532-8600
Fax: (305) 672-2039
Area of charter: Florida Keys

Freedom Yacht Charters
305 Oliphant Ln.
Middletown, RI 02840
Tel: (800) 999-2909
  or (401) 848-2900
Fax: (401) 848-2904
Area of charter: Virgin Islands, New England

Fun in the Sun Charters
320 N. Federal Hwy.
Dania, FL 33004
Tel: (800) 327-0228
  or (305) 923-2808
Area of charter: South Florida, Bahamas

Hinkley Yacht Charters
P.O. Box 10
Bass Harbor, ME 04653
Tel: (207) 244-5008
Area of charter: Maine

Horizon Yachts
669 St. Andrews Blvd.
Naples, FL 33962
Tel: (800) 833-0618
  or (813) 732-0997
Area of charter: Southwest Florida and Keys

Island Yachts
6807 Estate Smith Bay
18-B Red Hook Quarter
Charlotte Amalie
St. Thomas, USVI 00802-3201
Tel: (800) 524-2019
  or (809) 775-6666
Fax: (809) 779-8557
Area of charter: Virgin Islands

Jetsea
1650 S.E. 17th St.
Suite 204
Ft. Lauderdale, FL 33316
Tel: (305) 467-0528
Fax: (305) 467-6661
Area of charter: Grenadines, Bahamas

Landfall Charter Services
P.O. Box 030402
Ft. Lauderdale, FL 33301
Tel: (800) 225-1840
  or (305) 763-8464
Area of charter: Bahamas

Latitude 18
Box 88
Red Hook Quarter
St. Thomas, USVI 00802
Tel: (800) 925-0315
  or (809) 775-9964
Area of charter: Virgin Islands

Leeward Islands Yacht Charters
43 N. Pleasant Ave.
Ridgewood, NJ 07450
Tel: (201) 444-5560
Area of charter: Leeward Islands

Ledger Marine Charters
1500 Westlake Ave. N.
Seattle, WA 98109
Tel: (206) 283-6160
Area of charter: Pacific Northwest

Long Reach Charters
RR 1 Box 348
Orr's Island, ME 04066
Tel: (207) 833-665
Area of charter: Maine

Marina Sailing
746 Washington Blvd.
Marina del Rey, CA 90292
Tel: (800) 262-7245
  or (310) 822-6617
Area of charter: California coast

Manset Yacht Service
P.O. Box 681
Southwest Harbor, ME 04679
Tel: (207) 244-4040
Area of charter: Maine

McKibben Sailing Vacations
176 Battery St.
Burlington, VT 05401
Tel: (800) 845-0028
  or (802) 864-7733
Area of charter: Lake Champlain

Morris Yachts
P.O. Box 58
Southwest Harbor, ME 04670
Tel: (207) 244-5509
Area of charter: Maine

Misty Isle Yacht Charters
P.O. Box 1118
Virgin Gorda Yacht Harbor, BVI
Tel: (809) 495-5643
Fax: (809) 495-5300
Area of charter: Virgin Islands

The Moorings
Suite 402
19345 U.S. 19 N.
Clearwater, FL 34624
Tel: (800) 535-7289
  or (813) 535-1446
  or Outside US and Canada
(813) 530-5651
Fax: (813) 530-9747
Area of charter: Bahamas, Virgin, Leeward, and Windard Islands, South Pacific

Mystic Yacht Charters
P.O. Box 237
Mystic, CT 06355
Tel: (800) 873-2692
  or (203) 536-1949
Area of charter: East coast United States, Bay Islands, Belize

Nautors Swan Charters
55 America's Cup Ave.
Newport, RI 02840
Tel: (800) 356-7926
  or (401) 848-7181
Area of charter: Leeward Islands

Neptune Charters
Compass Point Marina
St. Thomas, USVI 00802
Tel: (800) 637-6402
  or (809) 775-7174
Area of charter: Virgins Islands

Nordic Tugs Charter
Box 020006
Juneau, AK 99802
Tel: (907) 586-2844
Area of charter: Alaska

NorthEast Wind Yacht Charter
306 Second St.
Annapolis, MD 21403
Tel: (800) 638-5139
  or (301) 267-6333
Area of charter: Chesapeake Bay

North-South Vacations
655 Dixon Rd. Unit 18
Toronto, Ontario M9W 1J4
CANADA
Tel: (800) 387-4964
  or (416) 242-7462
Fax: (416) 242-7426
Area of charter: Virgin Islands, St. Martin

Northwest Marine Charters
2400 Westlake Ave. N.
Seattle, WA 98109
Tel: (800) 659-3048
  or (206) 283-3040
Area of charter: Pacific Northwest, Alaska

Ocean Incentives
American Yacht Harbor
Red Hook
St. Thomas, USVI 00802
Tel: (800) 344-5762
  or (809) 775-6406
Fax: (809) 775-6712
Area of charter: Virgin Islands

Offshore Sail and Motor Yachts
Nanny Cay
Tortola, BVI
Tel: (800) 582-0175
  or (809) 494-4726
Fax: (809) 494-0132
Area of charter: Virgin Islands

Pacific Destination Center
3471 Via Lido
Suite 206
Newport Beach, CA 92663
Tel: (800) 227-5317
Area of charter: Pacific, Australia, New Zealan

Pacific Quest Yacht Charters
1523 Foreshore Walk
Vancouver, British Columbia
V6H 3X3
CANADA
Area of charter: Pacific Northwest

Pearl Yacht Line
800 East Broward Blvd.
Suite 510
Ft Lauderdale, FL 33301
Tel: (800) GO-PEARL
  or (305) 463- 4400
Fax: (305) 463-4831
Area of charter: Leeward Islands, Mediterranean

Penmar Marine Co.
2011 Skyline Way
Anacortes, WA 98221
Tel: (800) 828-7337
  or (206) 293-4839
Area of charter: Pacific Northwest

Prevailing Winds
Waites Wharf
Newport, RI 02840
Tel: (401) 864-6096
Area of charter: Narragansett Bay and Islands

Privilege Charters,
1650 S.E. 17th St.
Suite 204
Ft. Lauderdale, FL 33316
Tel: (800) 262-0308
  or (305) 462-6506
Fax: (305) 462-6104
Area of charter: Bahamas, Virgin, Leeward and Windward Islands, Mediterranean, South Pacific, and Galapagos

Proper Yacht
P.O. Box 70
Cruz Bay
St. John, USVI 00830
Tel: (809) 776-6256
Fax: (809) 776-7406
Area of charter: Virigin Islands

Rainbow Yacht Charters International
80 W. Fiesta Green
Port Hueneme, CA 93041
Tel: (805) 985-2170
Area of charter: South Pacific, New Zealand

Regency Yacht Vacations
P.O. Box 9997
St. Thomas, USVI 00802
Tel: (800) 524-7676
  or (809) 776-5950
Fax: (809) 776-7631
Area of charter: Virgin Islands

Sailboats, Inc.
250 Marina Dr.
Superior, WI 54880
Tel: (800) 826-7010
  or (715) 392-7131
Area of charter: West Florida coast, Great Lakes

Sailing Center of Santa Barbara
The Breakwater
Santa Barbara, CA 93109
Tel: (805) 962-2826
Area of charter: Southern California

San Diego Yacht Charters
1880 Harbor Island Dr.
San Diego, CA 92101
Tel: (800) 456-0222
  or (619) 297-4300
Area of charter: Southern California

San Juan Sailing
15 Harbor Esplanade
Bellingham, WA 98225
Tel: (800) 677-7245
  or (206) 671-4300
Area of charter: Pacific Northwest

Sassafras Charters
P.O. Box 267
Galena, MD 21635
Tel: (800) 548-1358
  or (301) 648-5827
Area of charter: Florida Keys

Seabreeze Yacht Charters
150 Consumer's Rd.
Suite 307
Willowdale, Ontario M2J 1P9
CANADA
Tel: (800) 388-6224
  or in Canada (416)
499-3102
Fax: (416) 499-3113
Area of charter: Virgin Islands

Set Sail Yacht Charters
2131 Shelter Island Dr.
San Diego, CA 92106
Tel: (619) 224-3791
*Area of charter: Southern
California*

Signature Yacht Charters
164 Eglington Ave. E.
Suite 200
Toronto, Ontario M4P 1G4
CANADA
Tel: (800) 388-1368
  or in Canada (800)
561-8975
  or (416) 489-7245
Fax: (416) 322-6757
*Area of charter: Virgin Islands,
Puerto Rico*

Southernmost Sailing
P.O. Box 369
Key West, FL 33040
Tel: (305) 745-2430
Area of charter: Florida Keys

Southwest Florida Yachts
3444 Marinatown Ln. N.W
N. Ft. Myers, FL 33903
Tel: (800) 262-7939
  or (813) 656-1339
Fax: (813) 656-BOAT
*Area of charter: West coast of
Florida*

St. Augustine Sailing, Inc.
A-1-A at ICW
Camachee Island
St. Augustine, FL 32095
Tel: (800) 683-7245
  or (904) 829-2294
*Area of charter: West coast of
Florida*

**St. Petersburg Yacht
Charters**
Municipal Marina
500 1st Ave. S.E.
St. Petersburg, FL 33701
Tel: (813) 823-2555
*Area of charter: West coast of
Florida*

Star Voyage
c/o Le Boat
P.O. Box E
Maywood, NJ 07607
Tel: (800) 922-0291
  or (201) 342-1838
Fax: (201) 342-7498
Area of charter: Caribbean

Sunsail USA
2 Prospect Park
3347 NW 55th St.
Ft. Lauderdale, FL 33309
Tel: (800) 327-2276
Fax: (305) 485-5072
*Area of charter: Virgin,
Leeward, and Windward
Islands, Mediterranean,
Thailand*

Trade Wind Yachts
P.O. Box 1186
Court Circle
Gloucester, VA 23061
Tel: (800) 825-7245
  or (804) 694-0881
Fax: (804 693-7245
*Area of charter: Grenadines,
Windward and Leeward
Islands*

Thomas Sailing
Nanny Cay Marina
Tortola, BVI
Tel: (800) 258-8753
  or (809) 494-0333
Fax: (809) 494-0334
Area of charter: Virgin Islands

**Tortola Marine
Management**
P.O. Box 3042
Road Town
Tortola, BVI
Tel: (800) 633-0155
  or (203) 854-5131
Area of charter: Virgin Islands

Treasure Harbor Marine
200 Treasure Harbor Dr.
Islamorada, FL 33036
Tel: (800) 352-2628
  or (305) 852-2458
Area of charter: Bahamas

**Tropical Diversions Yacht
Service**
1126 S. Federal Hwy.
Suite 242
Ft. Lauderdale, FL 33316
Tel: (305) 921-9084
Area of charter: Bahamas

Tropic Island Yacht
Management Ltd.
P.O. Box 532
Maya Cove
Tortola, BVI
Tel: (809) 494-2450
Fax: (809) 495-2155
Area of charter: Virgin Islands

Tropic Island Yacht
Management Ltd.
2 Thorncliffe Park Dr. Unit 20
Toronto, Ontario M4H 1H2
CANADA
Tel: (416) 696-9711
Fax: (809) 495-2155
Area of charter: Virgin Islands

Tumbaco/Quasar Nautica
7855 NW 12th St.
Suite 115
Miami, FL 33126
Tel: (800) 247-2925
 or (305) 599-9008
Fax: (305) 592-7060
*Area of charter: Galapagos
Islands*

Via Caribe Yacht Charters
65 De Castelnau West
Suite 102
Montreal, Quebec H2R 2W3
CANADA
Tel: (514) 274-0011
Fax: (514) 274-3432
*Area of charter: Leeward
Islands*

V.I.P. Yacht Charters
Box 6760
St. Thomas, USVI 00804
Tel: (800) 524-2015
Area of charter: Virgin Islands

Virgin Island Sailing Ltd.
Tel: (800) 233-7936
Fax: (809) 494-6774
Area of charter: Virgin Islands

Yachting Vacations
3162 Matecumbe Key Rd.
Punta Gorda, FL 33955
Tel: (800) 447-0080
 or (813) 637-6634
*Area of charter: West Florida
coast*

Yacht Services
International
P.O. Box 703
Green Brook, NJ 08812
Tel: (908) 752-1463
Area of charter: Mid Atlantic

Yacht Charter Brokers and Agents

Alden Yacht Brokerage
89 Commercial Wharf
Boston, MA 02110
Tel: (617) 227-9480
Fax: (617) 523-5465

Ann-Wallis White
P.O. Box 4100
Annapolis, MD 21403
Tel: (800) 732-3861
Fax: (410) 263-6366

Ardell Yacht and Ship
Brokers
2101 West Coast Hwy.
Newport Beach, CA 92663
Tel: (714) 642-9884
Fax: (714) 642-5735

Ardell Yacht and Ship
Brokers
1550 S.E. 17th St.
Ft. Lauderdale, FL 33316
Tel: (305) 527-1292
Fax: (305) 527-7637

Bartram & Brakenhoff
2 Marina Plaza
Goat Island
Newport, RI 02840-1560
Tel: (401) 846-7355
Fax: (401) 837-6329

Bass Harbor Marine
Bass Harbor, ME 04653
Tel: (207) 244-7534
Fax: (207) 244-7535

Blue Water Cruises
P.O. Box 3980
St. Thomas, VI 00803
Tel: (800) 524-2020

Brewer Yacht Charters
37 Pratt St.
Essex, CT 06426
Tel: (203) 767-7655
Fax: (203) 767-3074

Burr Yacht Charters
32575 S. River Rd.
Harrison Turnpike, MI 48045
Tel: (800) 445-6592
Fax: (313) 463-7842

Luke Brown & Assoc.
1500 Cordova Rd.
Suite 200
Ft. Lauderdale, FL 33316
Tel: (305) 525-6617
Fax: (305) 525-6626

Camper & Nicholsons
450 Royal Palm Way
Palm Beach, FL 33480
Tel: (407) 655-2121
Fax: (407) 655-2202

Caribbean Yacht Cruises
7310 Blanco
San Antonio, TX 78216
Tel: (800) 835-6666
  or   (210) 340-4444
Fax: (210) 349-7735

**Castlemain International
Yacht Brokers**
New River Ct.
Suite 4
300 S.W. 2nd St.
Ft. Lauderdale, FL 33312
Tel: (305) 760-4730
Fax: (305) 760-4737

**Charters Unlimited
International**
506 S.W. 19th St.
Ft. Lauderdale, FL 33315
Tel: (305) 779-1817

**Tom Collins Yachts
Worldwide, Inc.**
400 S. Hibiscus Dr.
Miami Beach, FL 33139
Tel: (800) 637-5407
  or   (305) 673-5400
Fax: (305) 673-0220

Rikki Davis, Inc.
1323 S.E. 17th St.
Suite 209
Ft. Lauderdale, FL 33316
Tel: (305) 761-3237
Fax: (305) 764-0497

Driftaway Charters
P.O. Box 421
N. Scituate, MA 02060-0421
Tel: (800) 423-5701
Fax: (617) 545-7983

Emerald Yacht and Ship
3300 Irvine Ave.
Suite 308
Newport Beach, CA 92660
Tel: (714) 553-0695
Fax: (714) 752-0462

Emerald Yacht and Ship
801 Seabreeze Blvd.
Bahia Mar Yachting Center
Ft. Lauderdale, FL 33316
Tel: (800) 938-9938
  or   (305) 522-0556
Fax: (305) 522-3194

**Florida Yacht Charter and
Sales**
Miami Beach Marina
1290 5th St.
Miami Beach, FL 33139
Tel: (800) 537-0050
  or   (305) 532-7600
Fax: (305) 672-2039

Gilman Yachts
1212-A U.S. Hwy. 1
N.Palm Beach, FL 33480
Tel: (407) 626-1790
Fax: (407) 626-5870

GPSC Charters Ltd.
600 St Andrews Rd.
Philadelphia, PA 19118
Tel: (800) 732-6786
  or   (215) 247-3903
Fax: (215) 247-1505

Ed Hamilton & Co.
Yacht Charter Agents
Box 430
N. Whitfield, ME 04353
Tel: (800) 621-7855
  or   (207) 549-7855
Fax: (207) 549-7822

Hinckley Yacht Brokerage
Shore Rd.
South West Harbor, ME 04679
Tel: (207) 244-5531
Fax: (207) 244-9833

The Hinckley Co.
49 America's Cup Ave.
Newport, RI 02840
Tel: (401) 849-0120

**International Charter
Connection**
51 West 84th Ave., # 330
Denver, CO 80221
Tel: (303) 426-0914
Fax: (303) 426-0915

Interpac Yachts, Inc.
1050 Anchorage Ln.
San Diego, CA 92106
Tel: (619) 222-0327
Fax: (619) 222-0326

Chas. P. Irwin Yacht Brokerage
Bahia Mar Yachting Center
801 Seabreeze Blvd.
Ft. Lauderdale, FL 33316
Tel: (305) 463-6302
Fax: (305) 523-0056

Sam Israeloff
711 N.E. 205 Terr.
N. Miami Beach, FL 33179

Lynn Jachney Charters
P.O. Box 302
Marblehead, MA 01945
Tel: (800) 223-2050
Fax: (617) 639-0216

Jet Sea Yacht Brokers
1650 SE 17th St.
204
Ft. Lauderdale, FL 33316
Tel: (305) 766-2600
Fax: (305) 766-2611

Jody Lexow Yacht Charters
Box 573
Jamestwon, RI 02835
Tel: (800) 662-2628
 or (401) 423-3730
Fax: (401) 423- 3740

Jubilee Yacht Charters
1051 Boston Post Rd.
Darien, CT 06820
Tel: (800) 992-4871
Fax: (203) 655-7240

Le Boat, Inc.
P.O. Box E
Maywood, NJ 07607
Tel: (800) 922-0291
Fax: (201)342-1838

Liberty Yacht Sales and Charter, Inc.
Royal Palm Yacht Basin
629 N.E. 3rd St.
Dania, FL 33004
Tel: (305) 920-0117
Fax: (305) 920-1122

Meridian Charters, Inc.
348 W. Front St.
Perrysburg, OH 43551
Tel: (800) 448-4405
Fax: (419) 385-8835

Nicholson Yacht Charters
432 Columbia St.
Cambridge, MA 02141
Tel: (800) 662-6066
Fax: (617) 225-0555

Northrop & Johnson Yachts-Ships, Inc.
3575 N.E. 207th St.
Suite B16
Aventura, FL 33180
Tel: (305) 933-3344
 or (305) 522-3344
Fax: (305) 933-3523

Northrup & Johnson Sales Corp. of Mass.
256 Marginal St.
E. Boston, MA 02128
Tel: (617) 569-6900
Fax: (617) 569-9247

Northrup & Johnson
19 Brown and Howard Wharf
Newport, RI 02840
Tel: (401) 848-5500
Fax: (401) 848-0120

Ocean Charters, Inc.
41 Galloping Hill
Holmdel, NJ 07733
Tel: (800) 922-4833
Fax: (908) 222-5001

Rex Yacht Sales
2152 S.E. 17th St.
Ft. Lauderdale, FL 3316
Tel: (305) 463-8810
Fax: (305) 462-3640

Russell Yacht Charters
2750 Black Rock Tpk.
Suite 75
Fairfield, CT 06430
Tel: (800) 635-8895
 or (203) 372-6633

The Sacks Group
1650 S.E. 17th St.
Suite 200
Ft. Lauderdale, FL 33316
Tel: (305) 764-7742
Fax: (305) 523-3769

Sailaway Yachts
5006 Dauphin Island Pky.
Mobile, AL 36605
Tel: (800) 476-9295
Fax: (205) 476-2132

Sailaway Yachts
400-D N. Flagler Dr.
West Palm Beach, FL 33401
Tel: (800) 369-2445
Fax: (407) 655-2669

Sailing Vacations
270 Borman Ave.
Merrit Island, FL 32953
Tel: (800) 922-4880
Fax: (407) 459-3028

Bob Saxon Associates
1500 Cordova Rd.
Suite 214
Ft. Lauderdale, FL 33316
Tel: (305) 467-8876
Fax: (305) 467-8909

Seven Seas Yacht Charters
2216 Lake Shore Dr.
Nokomis, FL 34275
Tel: (800) 346-5355
Fax: (813) 966-6017

Sparkman & Stephens
79 Madison Ave.
New York, NY 10016
Tel: (212) 689-3880
 or (212) 689-9292
Fax: (212) 689-3884

Spinnaker Key Yacht Sales & Charters
1500 Cordova Rd.
Suite 300
Ft. Lauderdale, FL 3316
Tel: (305) 525-6379
Fax: (305) 525-6385

Sun Yacht Charters
P.O. Box 737
Camden, ME 04843
Tel: (800) 772-3500
 or in Maine (207) 236-9611
Fax: (207) 236-3972

Thomas Cook Travel
100 Cambridge Park Dr.
Cambridge, MA 02140
Tel: (800) 234 9959
 or (617) 854-5131

Tobi Marine & Charter, Inc.
1323 S.E. 17th St.
Suite 606
Ft. Lauderdale, FL 33316
Tel: (305) 525-0860
Fax: (305) 525-0951

Tom Collins Worldwide
400 S. Hibiscus Dr.
Miami Beach, FL 33139
Tel: (800) 637-5407
Fax: (305) 673-0220

Tropic Island Yacht Management Ltd.
2 Thorncliffe Park Dr.
Unit 20
Toronto, Ontario M4H 1H2
CANADA
Tel: (416) 696-9711
Fax: (809) 495-2155

Worldwide Travel & Cruise Associates
400 S.E. 12th St.
Suite E
Ft. Lauderdale, FL 33316
Tel: (305) 463-1922

European Charterers

Emerald Yacht and Ship
8 Vine Yard
London SE1 1QN
ENGLAND
Tel: (+44) 71 378-0014
Fax: (+44) 71 357-6070

Kiriacoulis Caribe
51 Posidonos Ave.
Palean Faliron
175-62 Athens
GREECE
Tel: (+30) 1 981-8979

Kiriacoulis Mediterranean
51 Posidonos Ave.
Palean Faliron
175-62 Athens
GREECE
Tel: (+30) 1 981-8979

Yachting Charters International
28/29 Richmond Place
Brighton BN2 2NA
ENGLAND
Tel: in US (800) 626-0019
 or in UK (+44) 273 571722
Fax: (+44) 273 571720

Yachting Charters International
Residence du Port Vauban 17
Avenue du 11 Novembre
06600
Antibes
FRANCE
Tel: (+33) 93 34 01 00
Fax: (+33) 93 34 20 40

Figure 1: Boats like this Little Harbor 36 can often be chartered from a reputable broker.

Yacht Transportation

By Steve Justus

Steve Justus is the Operations Manager of Justus Boat Transport, Inc., a family owned company and a fully licensed and bonded carrier that has been moving boats for more than 20 years all over the United States and Canada.

Suppose your company has promoted you and you have to move to another state. If your boat is not higher than 13 feet 6 inches sitting on a trailer, you can get it transported across country easily. If it is higher than 13 feet 6 inches, it can still be transported, but special permits will be needed, plus the job will take longer because a route that avoids low bridges must be planned. In many states, larger boats need a police escort and can travel only during certain hours of the day or night. If the boat has to pass under or over an obstruction, such as a narrow bridge, the police often have to hold up traffic to allow its progress. Even if the police do not escort your boat, a good trucking company will have an escort vehicle both leading and following an oversize load, which adds expense. All this takes time, so if you intend to truck a large vessel across country, allow up to 4 to 6 weeks for the truck to make the journey.

You should be concerned about insurance if you are having your boat transported. If the carrier is licensed by the Interstate Commerce Commision (the ICC is the federal regulatory body for the trucking industry), it must have insurance, and be bonded. The insurance must be renewed every year and a copy of the documentation filed with the ICC. If your carrier is not insured and is in an accident, you could lose your boat. Should your boat be crossing Canada, the carrier should have Canadian authority under the Interstate Transport Act. Canadian carriers must also be bonded and insured.

Even if the boat transport company you are using is insured, it is often a good idea for the boat owner to purchase insurance as well. Although few boat policies cover the tranportation of boats overland, your insurer will often write a special policy. Having your own coverage means that should your boat be in an accident and damaged or written off, you will be compensated quickly by your own insurer and your insurer will negotiate with the trucker or other party at fault. Without your own insurance, it might take a while longer for the trucker's or other party's insurance company to pay you, and you would miss time on the water.

If your boat is going to be shipped abroad, make sure all your customs permits and other documents are in order. Rather than attempting to do this yourself, work with a customs broker or freight forwarder who works with the shipping company, as well as the trucking company. Allow plenty of time for the trucker to get your boat to the wharf where it will be loaded on the ship. At the other end, make sure the shipper or somebody else, with all the needed documentation, will be there for the customs inspection. Quite often, if the boat is in good order, it can be launched at the port of entry and sailed to its ultimate destination. You should check with your shipper to see what is possible. Check also that the carrier is familiar with the destination. You don't want your valuable boat meandering around the countryside while the truck driver tries to find the marina.

To get your boat ready for moving, we have developed a prep sheet based upon our twenty years of experience.

FOR BOTH POWERBOATS AND SAILBOATS:

1. Stow everything below deck and secure it properly. While a boat usually travels smoothly on the road, some sudden stops are inevitable, and a heavy anchor or other piece of gear loose inside the boat can create a large amount of damage on a long trip.

2. Remove all canvas and stow it away carefully. If your boat is shrink-wrapped for shipping, you should know that shrink wrap is not designed for road travel and can tear off. We assume no liability for damage if the wrap comes loose.

3. Remove every loose piece of gear from the deck and stow it. Ideally, the anchor should be in its well or wrapped with padding and stowed below deck.

4. All hatches and companionways should be secured and locked.

5. If the boat is to travel through cold weather areas, it should be fully winterized. Heavy snow can delay transit in very cold regions, and without winterizing, damage can result.

6. Usually we inspect the job before shipping, and suggest items that can be removed to reduce height. Please make sure that these removals are done before the truck arrives.

7. Try to get all liquid levels as low as possible. The bilges should be dry, fresh water pumped out, and all holding tanks empty. If possible, draw down the fuel tanks until they are empty. On large heavy boats where weight is a concern, this is essential.

FOR SAILBOATS ONLY:

1. Remove the mast before the truck arrives. Either strip the mast and remove the shrouds and spreaders, or make sure they are tightly secured (either wrapped around the mast or firmly taped or tied to it). Note, however, that shrouds wrapped or tied to the mast can mark it as they vibrate on the trip. A piece of carpet or padding can prevent this.

2. Remove turnbuckles or tape them tightly together. They can vibrate undone and drop off.

3. Let the moving co-ordinator know how many masts, booms, spinnaker poles, or wishbones will be moved, and how long they are.

FOR POWERBOATS ONLY:

1. A flybridge must have its windscreens removed. Sometimes the frame holding the windscreen will also need to be removed to reduce height.
2. Some boats will ride easier if the props, shafts, and rudders are removed before moving. Your co-ordinator will tell you what is needed.

In general, common sense is your best help when getting your boat ready. If a crane or lift is needed, try to co-ordinate its arrival with that of the truck. If a piece of gear looks like it may come adrift, secure it. A boat transported along an interstate highway faces a wind pressure equal to a severe gale. If you think an item would tear off in a gale, remove it before the boat is moved. While we do our best to carry your boat in a professional and courteous manner, our drivers are not sailors or boaters, and cannot be expected to work on your boat.

Yacht and Boat Transportation Companies

Yacht and Boat Movers

A&B Marine Trucking, Inc.
7310 Edgewood Rd.
Annapolis, MD 21403
Tel: (800) 843-5265
 or (410) 269-1720
Fax: (410) 623-6215

J.A. Ambrose, Inc.
658 North Shore
Gloversville, NY 12078
Tel: (800) 448-5477
East of the Missippi transport

Associated Boat Transport, Inc.
13930 N.E. 190 St.
Woodinsville, WA 98072
Tel: (800) 247-1198
 or (206) 487-6700
Fax: (206) 485 4480

Brownell Hyd. Trailers, Inc
7 Industrial Dr.
P.O. Box 61
Mattapoisett, MA 02739-0061
Tel: (508) 758-3774
Fax: (508) 758-9762

Dock Express
1535 S.E. 17th St.
Ft. Lauderdale, FL 33316
Tel: (305) 525-8707
Fax: (305) 525-8781

Dock Express
P.O. Box 1035
3160 AE Rhoon
NETHERLANDS
Tel: (+ 31) 1890-31100
Fax: (+31) 1890-12765

Dock Express
5, Avenue Victor Hugo
Domaine le Grand Duc
06216 Mandelieu
FRANCE
Tel: (+33) 93 93 1856
Fax: (+33) 93 93 1856
Overseas shipping

East Coast Trailers
Box 331, Route One
Westbrook, CT 06498
Tel: (203) 399-6120

Hostar Marine Transport Systems, Inc.
1 William Gould Way
Kingston, MA 02634
Tel: (617) 585-9300
Fax: (617) 585-6131

Jordan Marine Transport
P.O. Box 674
Mystic, CT 06355
Tel: (800) 232-0317
Fax: (203) 536-6572

Justus Boat Transport
18580 E. Colonial Dr.
Orlando, FL 32820
Tel: (800) 597-5878
 or (407) 568-0019
Fax: (407) 568-0034
Boat transport to all of North America; fully licensed

L & M Transportation Services, Inc.
2925 Huntleigh Dr.
Raleigh, NC 27604
Tel: (800) 851-9540
  or (919) 850-9540
Fax: (919) 850-3351
A network of over 200 trucking companies

Marine Distibutors, Inc.
339 Market St.
Warren, RI 02885
Tel: (800) 242-2266
  or (401) 247-0200

Mariner Marine
1429 US 1
Riviera Beach, FL 33404
Tel: (407) 687-9904

Marine Transport, Inc.
2115 E. Huron Rd.
Au Gres, MI 48703
Tel: (800) 343-0988
Fax: (517) 876-6617

Marine Travelift, Inc.
P.O. Box 66
49 E. Yew St.
Sturgeon Bay, WI 54235
Tel: (414) 743-6202
Fax: (414) 743-1522

Monaco International Forwarders, Inc.
Suite 8
2550 Eisenhower Blvd.
Ft. Lauderdale, FL 33316
Tel: (305) 463-6910
  or (305) 940-5109
Overseas shipping agents

Overland, Inc.
Annapolis, MD
Tel: (800) 447-0258
  or (410) 263-1312
Fax: (410) 267-6373

Seariders International, Inc.
1800 Eller Dr.
Suite 210
Port Everglades, FL 33316
Tel: (800) 275-2678
  or (305) 764-0616
  or (305) 948-6652
Fax: (305) 764-0855
Licensed, Bonded, Customs Broker

Top Line Express
P.O. Box 342
Grosse Ile, MI 48138
Tel: (800) 622-1744
Fax: (313) 692-2520

US Boat Transport
952 Nentmore Circle
Deltona Beach, FL 32728
Tel: (800) 535-6082
  or (407) 860-3521

Western Marine Trucking
Box 72B, Rt. 1
La Center, WA 98629
Tel: (206) 263-4125

World Marine Transport, Inc.
9798 Normandy Blvd.
Jacksonville, FL 32221
Tel: (800) 332-6287

Wyskochil Marine
2061 Whitfield Park Ave.
Sarasota, FL 34243
Tel: (813) 758-0223
Fax: (813) 758-4196
Licensed, bonded, insured

Boat Stands

Brownell Boat Stands
P.O. Box 744
5 Boat Rock Rd.
Mattapoisen, MA 02739
Tel: (508) 758-3671
Fax: (508) 758-3574
Boat stands

Con-O-Lift Hydraulic Trailers
R.R. 2
Parry Sound, Ontario P2A 2W8
CANADA
Tel: (705) 366-2210
Fax: (705) 378-3814
Boat stands

DOC Boat Stands
115 Hale St.
Haverhill, MA 01830
Tel: (508) 373-9181
Fax: (508) 373-3868
DOC boat stands

Hostar Marine Transport Systems, Inc.
1 William Gould Way
Kingston, MA 02634
Tel: (617) 585-9300
Fax: (617) 585-6131
Hydraulic jacks and boat stands

Price Designs
Box 87, Rt. 1
Grifton, NC 28530
Tel: (919) 524-5790
Jowi boat stands

Waco Boat Shores
5251 W 130th St.
Cleveland, OH 44130
Tel: (800) 321-3150
Fax: (216) 267-5983

Slings

Cambridge Wire Cloth Co.
P.O. Box 399
Cambridge, MD 21613
Tel: (800) 638-9560
Fax: (301) 228-6752

Murray Marine, Inc.
P.O. Box 2092
Darien, CT 06820
Tel: (203) 655-3201
Fax: (203) 655-1669

Figure 1: This Bertram sportfisherman is about to be hauled by Justus Boat Transport. Note the tight tiedowns and chafe preventative padding. Justus Boat Transport specializes in moving boats all over North America.

Keeping Up to Date

Marshall's Monthly Review is a monthly newsletter with the latest information on new products, independent testing of new products, new faces, new addresses, and new developments in the marine industry. It accepts no advertising, company-written promo blurbs, or self-congratulatory statements by manufacturers.

A print edition, in water-resistant, looseleaf format with a handy reference binder for storage, is printed by Xerox Corporation's Docutech electronic publishing system on DuPont Tyvek sheets, designed for long life and durability in the marine environment. Over time, *Marshall's Monthly Review* binders will become your standard reference source.

The electronic edition uses the latest in computer technology, to enable you:

- to read, annotate, and mark the monthly newsletters;
- to print out part or all of a newsletter;
- to search through one, several, or all editions for a name, product, subject, source, or word and to review the results of searches on screen or on printed reports;
- to automatically scan each issue for items of special concern;
- to build personalized research files on areas of your own personal interests or needs;

- to access manufacturer's information and even order literature equipment by sending a fax or electronic mail directly to a manufacturer or supplier; and
- to see and hear multimedia reports and demonstrations.

An enhanced industry electronic edition will provide access to world-wide boat brokerage listings, images of manufacturers' catalogs, and regulatory information. This added functionality is available on the full range of i386 or higher IBM-compatible or MacIntosh computers and on computers using the PowerPC processor or AIX or Unix operating systems. *Marshall's Monthly Review* electronic editions comply with international, U.S. Department of Defense, and other information exchange standards and are completely compatible with mil-spec, GPO, and OCLC electronic information systems.

Here's how it works. Suppose you are reading a review on sail technology and want to know more about a particular sail or sailmaker. You click on the name of the sailmaker, which brings up information, including, for example, a complete up-to-date list of the sails made by that manufacturer, information on sail cloths, contact persons, diagrams, photographic images, prices, and other data.) You find the sail info you want, then click on it. A sail plan is displayed. You enter the dimensions of your sail plan and, if you want, you can send the sail plan by fax to the sailmaker for a quote, or you can enter your credit card number and order the sail direct.

HOW CAN YOU GET A COPY?

Single copies of our premier edition (April 1994) are available for $5.00. Just send us your name and address and five dollars and tell us if you want the print version or the electronic one. (Sorry, The print version will not contain manufacturer's catalogs.) Indicate if you want an IBM compatible disk or an Apple disk for the electronic version. (IBM edition requires Windows 3.1 or OS/2.)

WANT TO SUBSCRIBE?

Send us a check for the introductory price of $60 per year for the printed version. The electronic version is $77 per year and includes a binder and copies of print editions. (Introductory offer valid until December 31, 1994.)

Computer network users may arrange for electronic distribution of *Marshall's Monthly Review* and to receive additional no-cost cost updates and alert messages. Prodigy, Compuserve, America On-Line, Internet, Bitnet, GEnie, MCI Mail, Delphi, or SprintNet connection and other on-line network users may contact the editor by electronic mail at *news@marshall.org* for further information or may request subscription information by email to *subs@marshall.org*.

Advance summaries of *Marshall's Monthly Review* appear in HOTT, the global Internet magazine; on YACHT-L, the bitnet yachting listserver; on MARINE-L, the international marine sciences listerver; and on FISH-L, the global fisheries listserver. Summaries may also be accessed through the World Wide Web and X-Mosaic platforms. For further information about electronic access to *Marshall's Monthly Review*, use your Prodigy, Compuserve, America On-Line, Internet, Bitnet, GEnie, MCI Mail, Delphi, or SprintNet connection to email *news@marshall.org*.

Mailing address:

Marshall Organization, 44 Fort Wetherill Road, Jamestown, R.I. 02835